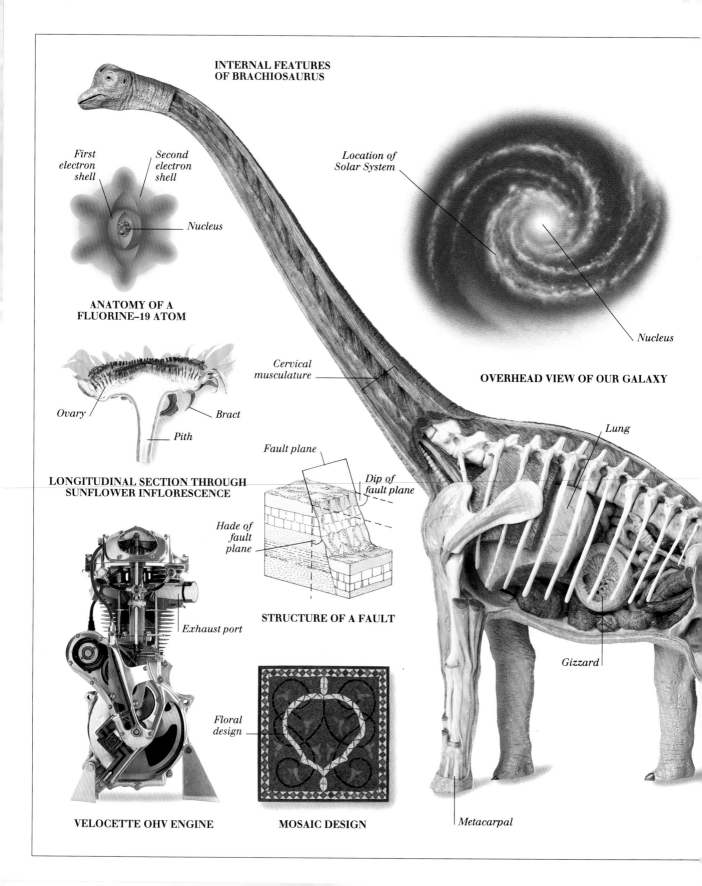

INTERNAL FEATURES OF BRACHIOSAURUS

First electron shell

Second electron shell

Nucleus

ANATOMY OF A FLUORINE–19 ATOM

Location of Solar System

Nucleus

OVERHEAD VIEW OF OUR GALAXY

Ovary

Bract

Pith

LONGITUDINAL SECTION THROUGH SUNFLOWER INFLORESCENCE

Cervical musculature

Lung

Fault plane

Dip of fault plane

Hade of fault plane

STRUCTURE OF A FAULT

Gizzard

Exhaust port

Floral design

VELOCETTE OHV ENGINE

MOSAIC DESIGN

Metacarpal

DORLING KINDERSLEY
ULTIMATE
VISUAL
DICTIONARY

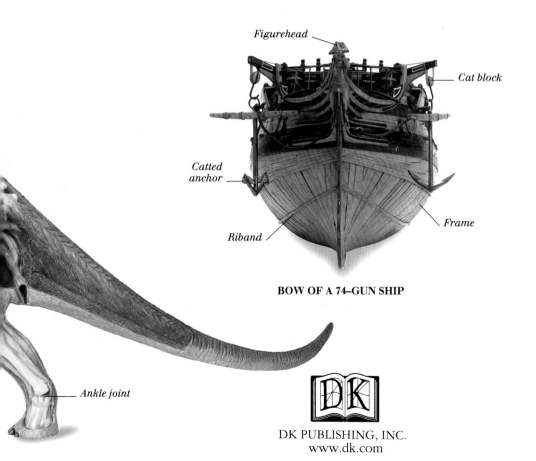

Figurehead

Cat block

Catted anchor

Riband

Frame

BOW OF A 74–GUN SHIP

Ankle joint

DK

DK PUBLISHING, INC.
www.dk.com

A DK PUBLISHING BOOK
www.dk.com

PROJECT ART EDITORS HEATHER MCCARRY, JOHNNY PAU, CHRIS WALKER, KEVIN WILLIAMS
DESIGNER SIMON MURRELL

PROJECT EDITORS LUISA CARUSO, PETER JONES, JANE MASON, GEOFFREY STALKER
EDITOR JO EVANS
U.S. EDITOR JULEE BINDER

DTP DESIGNER ZIRRINIA AUSTIN
PICTURE RESEARCHER CHARLOTTE BUSH

MANAGING ART EDITOR TONI KAY
SENIOR EDITOR ROGER TRITTON
MANAGING EDITOR SEAN MOORE

PRODUCTION MANAGER HILARY STEPHENS

ANATOMICAL AND BOTANICAL MODELS SUPPLIED BY SOMSO MODELLE, COBURG, GERMANY

Sound hole

Hollow body

Bridge

Headstock

ACOUSTIC GUITAR

FIRST AMERICAN EDITION, 1994
10 9

PUBLISHED IN THE UNITED STATES BY
DK PUBLISHING INC., 95 MADISON AVENUE,
NEW YORK, NY 10016

LIBRARY OF CONGRESS CATALOGING-IN-PUBLICATION DATA

DORLING KINDERSLEY ULTIMATE VISUAL DICTIONARY. - -1ST AMERICAN ED.
INCLUDES INDEX

1. PICTURE DICTIONARIES, ENGLISH. I. DORLING KINDERSLEY. INC.
PE 1629.D67 1994   94-11173
423 ' . 1- -dc20   CIP

REPRODUCED BY COLOURSCAN, SINGAPORE
Printed and bound in the United States
by World Color Book Services

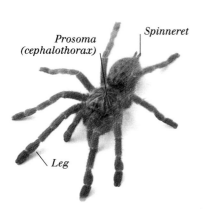

Prosoma
(cephalothorax)

Spinneret

Leg

**EXTERNAL FEATURES
OF A SPIDER**

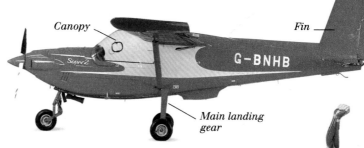

Canopy

Fin

G-BNHB

Main landing
gear

SIDE VIEW OF ARV SUPER 2 AIRPLANE

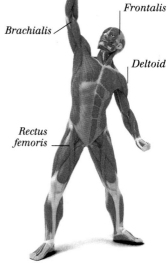

Frontalis

Brachialis

Deltoid

Rectus
femoris

**SUPERFICIAL
SKELETAL MUSCLES**

Barrel

Permanent
black ink

FOUNTAIN PEN AND INK

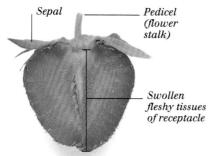

Architrave

Podium

**TEMPLE OF VESTA, TIVOLI,
ITALY, c.80 BC**

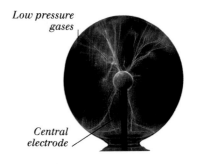

Low pressure
gases

Central
electrode

**BALL CONTAINING HIGH
TEMPERATURE GAS (PLASMA)**

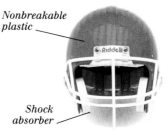

Nonbreakable
plastic

Shock
absorber

FOOTBALL HELMET

CONTENTS

Sepal

Pedicel
(flower
stalk)

Swollen
fleshy tissues
of receptacle

**LONGITUDINAL SECTION
THROUGH A STRAWBERRY**

Introduction

THE ULTIMATE VISUAL DICTIONARY is a completely new kind of reference book. It provides a link between pictures and words in a way that no ordinary dictionary ever has. Most dictionaries simply tell you what a word means, but the *Ultimate Visual Dictionary* shows you —through a combination of detailed annotations, explicit photographs, and illustrations. In the *Ultimate Visual Dictionary*, pictures define the annotations around them. You do not read definitions of the annotated words, you see them. The highly accessible format of the *Ultimate Visual Dictionary*, the thoroughness of its annotations, and the range of its subject matter make it a unique and helpful reference tool.

How to use the Ultimate Visual Dictionary
You will find the *Ultimate Visual Dictionary* simple to use. It is divided by subject into 14 sections— The Universe, Prehistoric Earth, Plants, Animals, The Human Body, etc. Each section begins with a table of contents listing the major entries within that section. For example, The Visual Arts section contains entries on *Drawing, Tempera, Fresco, Oils, Watercolor, Pastels, Acrylics, Calligraphy, Printmaking, Mosaic,* and *Sculpture.* Every entry includes a short introduction explaining the purpose of the photographs and illustrations, and the significance of the annotations.

If you know what something looks like, but don't know its name, turn to the annotations surrounding the pictures; if you know a word, but don't know what it refers to, use the comprehensive index to direct you to the appropriate page.

Suppose you want to know what the bone at the end of your little finger is called. With a standard dictionary, you wouldn't know where to begin. But with the *Ultimate Visual Dictionary* you simply turn to the entry called *Hands*—within The Human Body section—and you will find four fully annotated color photographs showing the skin, muscles, and bones of the human hand. In this entry you will quickly find that the bone you are searching for is called the distal phalanx. In addition, you will discover that it is attached to the middle phalanx by the distal interphalangeal joint.

Perhaps you want to know what a catalytic converter looks like. If you look up "catalytic converter" in an ordinary dictionary, you will be told what it is and possibly what it does—but you will not be able to tell what shape it is or what it is made of. However, if you look up "catalytic converter" in the index of the *Ultimate Visual Dictionary*, you will be directed to the *Modern engines* entry on page 344—where the introduction gives you basic information about what a catalytic converter is—and to page 350—where there is a spectacular exploded-view photograph of the mechanics of a Renault Clio. From these pages you will find out not only what a catalytic converter looks like, but also that it is attached at one end to an exhaust downpipe and at the other to a silencer.

Whatever it is that you want to find a name for, or whatever name you want to find a picture for, you will find it quickly and easily in the *Ultimate Visual Dictionary*. Perhaps you need to know where the vamp on a shoe is; or how to tell obovate and lanceolate leaves apart; or what a spiral galaxy looks like; or whether birds have nostrils. With the *Ultimate Visual Dictionary* close by, the answers to each of these questions, and thousands more, are readily available.

The *Ultimate Visual Dictionary* does not just tell you what the names of the different parts of an object are. The photographs, illustrations, and annotations are all specially arranged to help you understand which parts relate to one another and how objects function.

With the *Ultimate Visual Dictionary*, in seconds you can find the words or pictures that you are looking for; or you can simply browse. The *Ultimate Visual Dictionary* is not intended to replace a standard dictionary or encyclopedia, but is instead a stimulating and valuable companion to ordinary reference volumes. Giving you access to the language that is used by astronomers and architects, musicians and mechanics, pilots and professional athletes, it is the ideal reference book for experts and novices of all ages.

Sections of the ULTIMATE VISUAL DICTIONARY

The 14 sections of the *ULTIMATE VISUAL DICTIONARY* contain a total of more than 30,000 terms, encompassing a wide range of topics:

●In the first section, THE UNIVERSE, spectacular photographs and illustrations are used to show the names of the stars and planets and to explain the structure of solar systems, galaxies, nebulae, comets, and black holes.

●PREHISTORIC EARTH tells the story of how our own planet has evolved since its formation. It includes examples of prehistoric flora and fauna, and fascinating dinosaur models—some with parts of the body stripped away to show anatomical sections.

●PLANTS covers a huge range of species—from the familiar to the exotic. In addition to the color photographs of plants included in this section, there is a series of micrographic photographs illustrating plant details—such as pollen grains, spores, and cross-sections of stems and roots.

●In the ANIMALS section, skeletons, anatomical diagrams, and different parts of animals' bodies have been meticulously annotated. This section provides a comprehensive guide to the vocabulary of zoological classification and animal physiology.

●The structure of the human body, its parts, and its systems are presented in THE HUMAN BODY. The section includes lifelike, three-dimensional models and the latest false-color images. Clear and authoritative annotations indicate the correct anatomical terms.

●GEOLOGY, GEOGRAPHY, AND METEOROLOGY describes the structure of the Earth—from the inner core to the exosphere—and the physical phenomena, such as volcanoes, rivers, glaciers, and climate, that shape its surface.

●PHYSICS AND CHEMISTRY is a visual journey through the fundamental principles underlying the physical universe, that provides the essential vocabulary of these sciences.

●In RAIL AND ROAD, a wide range of trains, trolleys and buses, cars, bicycles, and motorcycles are described. Exploded-view photographs show mechanical details with striking clarity.

●SEA AND AIR illustrates hundreds of parts of ships and airplanes. The section includes civil and fighting craft, both historical and modern.

●THE VISUAL ARTS shows the equipment and materials used by painters, sculptors, printers, and other artists. Well-known compositions have been chosen to illustrate specific artistic techniques and effects.

●ARCHITECTURE includes photographs of exemplary architectural models and illustrates dozens of additional features such as columns, domes, and arches.

●MUSIC provides a visual introduction to the special language of music and musical instruments. It includes clearly annotated photographs of each of the major groups of traditional instruments—brass, woodwind, strings, and percussion—together with modern electronic instruments.

●The SPORTS section is a guide to the playing areas, formations, equipment, and techniques needed for many of today's most popular sports.

●In EVERYDAY THINGS, familiar objects, such as shoes, clocks, and toasters, are taken apart—down to the very last screw or length of thread—to show their inner workings and to give a special insight into the language that is used by their manufacturers.

THE UNIVERSE

Anatomy of the Universe

Fireball of rapidly expanding, extremely hot gas lasting about one million years

THE UNIVERSE CONTAINS EVERYTHING that exists, from the tiniest subatomic particles to galactic superclusters (the largest structures known). Nobody knows how big the Universe is, but astronomers estimate that it contains about 100 billion galaxies, each comprising an average of 100 billion stars. The most widely accepted theory about the origin of the Universe is the Big Bang theory, which states that the Universe came into being in a huge explosion—the Big Bang—that took place between 10 and 20 billion years ago. The Universe initially consisted of a very hot, dense fireball of expanding, cooling gas. After about one million years, the gas probably began to condense into localized clumps called protogalaxies. During the next five billion years, the protogalaxies continued condensing, forming galaxies in which stars were being born. Today, billions of years later, the Universe as a whole is still expanding, although there are localized areas in which objects are held together by gravity; for example, many galaxies are found in clusters. The Big Bang theory is supported by the discovery of faint, cool background radiation coming evenly from all directions. This radiation is believed to be the remnant of the radiation produced by the Big Bang. Small "ripples" in the temperature of the cosmic background radiation are thought to be evidence of slight fluctuations in the density of the early Universe, which resulted in the formation of galaxies. Astronomers do not yet know if the Universe is "closed," which means it will eventually stop expanding and begin to contract, or if it is "open," which means it will continue expanding forever.

COMPUTER-ENHANCED MICROWAVE MAP OF COSMIC BACKGROUND RADIATION

Pink indicates "warm ripples" in background radiation

Pale blue indicates "cool ripples" in background radiation

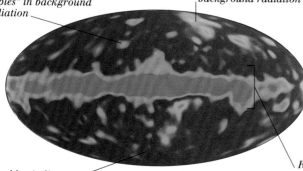

Deep blue indicates background radiation corresponding to -454.5°F (remnant of the Big Bang)

Red and pink band indicates radiation from our galaxy

Low-energy microwave radiation corresponding to about -454°F

High-energy gamma radiation corresponding to about 5,400°F

ORIGIN AND EXPANSION OF THE UNIVERSE

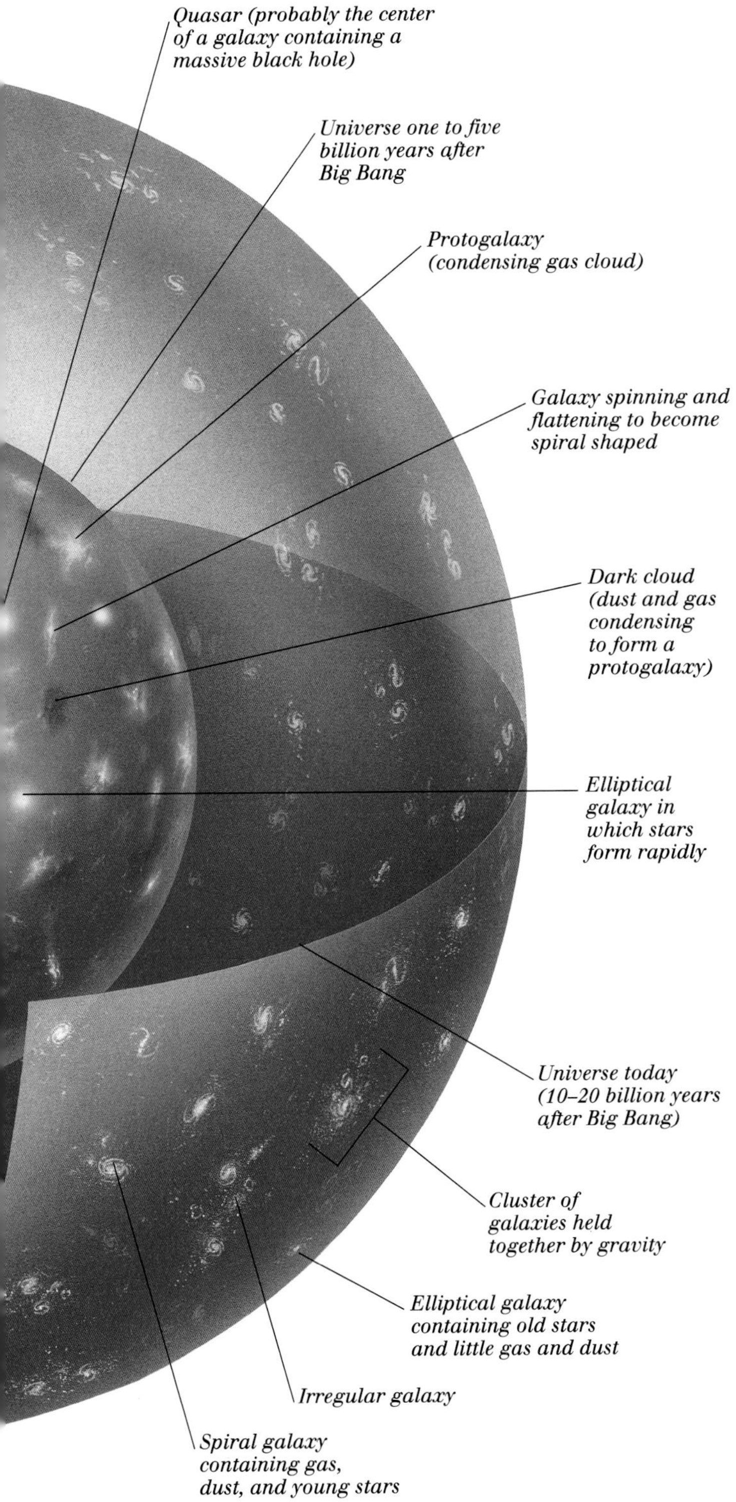

Quasar (probably the center
of a galaxy containing a
massive black hole)

Universe one to five
billion years after
Big Bang

Protogalaxy
(condensing gas cloud)

Galaxy spinning and
flattening to become
spiral shaped

Dark cloud
(dust and gas
condensing
to form a
protogalaxy)

Elliptical
galaxy in
which stars
form rapidly

Universe today
(10–20 billion years
after Big Bang)

Cluster of
galaxies held
together by gravity

Elliptical galaxy
containing old stars
and little gas and dust

Irregular galaxy

Spiral galaxy
containing gas,
dust, and young stars

OBJECTS IN THE UNIVERSE

CLUSTER OF
GALAXIES IN VIRGO

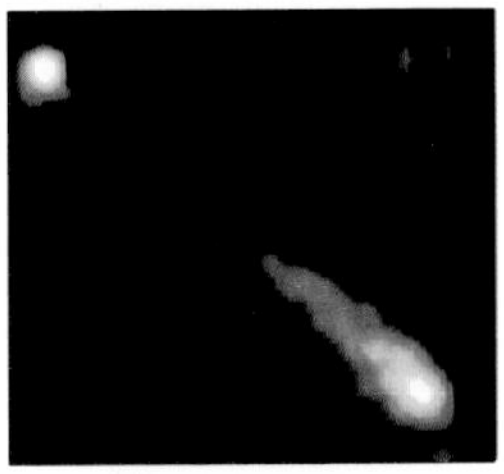

COLOR-ENHANCED IMAGE
OF 3C273 (QUASAR)

NGC 4406
(ELLIPTICAL GALAXY)

NGC 5236
(SPIRAL GALAXY)

NGC 6822
(IRREGULAR GALAXY)

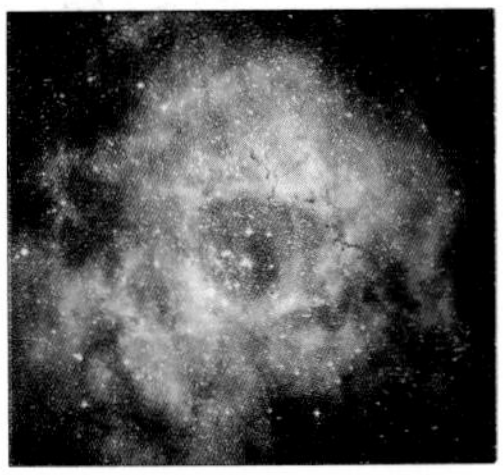

THE ROSETTE NEBULA
(EMISSION NEBULA)

THE JEWEL BOX
(STAR CLUSTER)

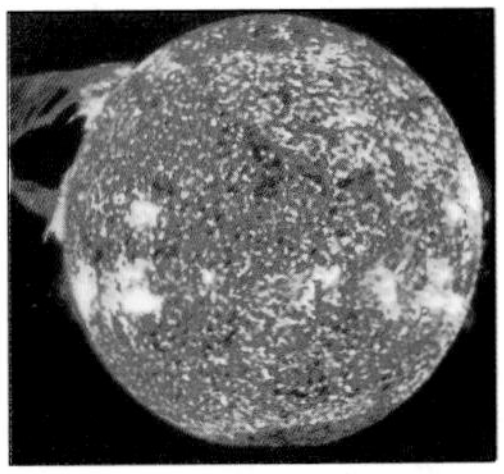

THE SUN
(MAIN SEQUENCE STAR)

EARTH

THE MOON

Galaxies

SOMBRERO,
A SPIRAL GALAXY

A GALAXY IS A HUGE MASS OF STARS, nebulae, and interstellar material. The smallest galaxies contain about 100,000 stars, while the largest contain up to 3,000 billion stars. There are three main types of galaxy, classified according to their shape: elliptical, which are oval shaped; spiral, which have arms spiraling outward from a central bulge; and irregular, which have no obvious shape. Sometimes, the shape of a galaxy is distorted by a collision with another galaxy. Quasars (quasi-stellar objects) are thought to be galactic nuclei but are so far away that their exact nature is still uncertain. They are compact, highly luminous objects in the outer reaches of the known Universe; while the farthest known "ordinary" galaxies are about 10 billion light-years away, the farthest known quasar is about 15 billion light-years away. Active galaxies, such as Seyfert galaxies and radio galaxies, emit intense radiation. In a Seyfert galaxy, this radiation comes from the galactic nucleus; in a radio galaxy, it also comes from huge lobes on either side of the galaxy. The radiation from active galaxies and quasars is thought to be caused by black holes (see pp. 28-29).

OPTICAL IMAGE OF NGC 4486 (ELLIPTICAL GALAXY)

Globular cluster containing very old red giants

Central region containing old red giants

Less densely populated region

Neighboring galaxy

OPTICAL IMAGE OF LARGE MAGELLANIC CLOUD (IRREGULAR GALAXY)

Tarantula Nebula

Dust cloud obscuring light from stars

Emission nebula

Light from stars

OPTICAL IMAGE OF NGC 2997 (SPIRAL GALAXY)

Glowing nebula in spiral arm

Spiral arm containing young stars

Galactic nucleus containing old stars

Dust in spiral arm reflecting blue light from hot young stars

Hot, ionized hydrogen gas emitting red light

Dust lane

OPTICAL IMAGE OF CENTAURUS A
(RADIO GALAXY)

*Dust lane crossing
elliptical galaxy*

*Galactic nucleus
containing
powerful source
of radiation*

*Light from
old stars*

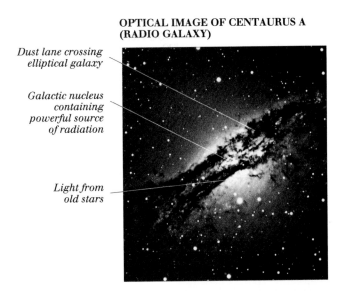

COLOR-ENHANCED RADIO
IMAGE OF CENTAURUS A

*Red indicates
high-intensity
radio waves*

*Blue indicates
low-intensity
radio waves*

*Radio
lobe*

*Radiation from
galactic nucleus*

*Outline of
optical image
of Centaurus A*

*Radio
lobe*

*Yellow indicates
medium-intensity
radio waves*

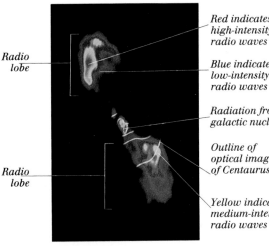

COLOR-ENHANCED RADIO IMAGE OF 3C273 (QUASAR)

*Radiation from jet
of high-energy
particles moving
away from quasar*

Quasar nucleus

*White indicates high-
intensity radio waves*

*Blue indicates
low-intensity
radio waves*

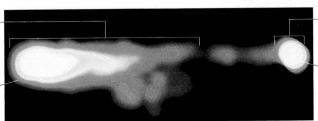

OPTICAL IMAGE OF NGC 1566
(SEYFERT GALAXY)

*Nebula in
spiral arm*

*Compact nucleus
emitting intense
radiation*

Spiral arm

COLOR-ENHANCED OPTICAL IMAGE OF
NGC 5754 (TWO COLLIDING GALAXIES)

*Blue indicates low-
intensity radiation*

*Red indicates
medium-intensity
radiation*

*Spiral arm distorted
by gravitational
influence of smaller
galaxy*

*Large spiral
galaxy*

*Smaller galaxy
colliding with
larger galaxy*

*Yellow indicates
high-intensity
radiation*

The Milky Way

VIEW TOWARD GALACTIC CENTER

THE MILKY WAY IS THE NAME GIVEN TO THE FAINT BAND OF LIGHT that stretches across the night sky. This light comes from stars and nebulae in our galaxy, known as the Milky Way Galaxy or simply as "the Galaxy." The Galaxy is shaped like a spiral, with a dense central bulge that is encircled by four arms spiraling outward and surrounded by a less dense halo. We cannot see the spiral shape because our Solar System is in one of the spiral arms, the Orion Arm (also called the Local Arm). From our position, the center of the Galaxy is completely obscured by dust clouds; as a result, optical maps give only a limited view of the Galaxy. However, a more complete picture can be obtained by studying radio, infrared, and other radiation. The central bulge of the Galaxy is a relatively small, dense sphere that contains mainly older red and yellow stars. The halo is a less dense region in which the oldest stars are situated; some of these stars may be as old as the Galaxy itself (possibly 15 billion years). The spiral arms contain mainly hot, young, blue stars, as well as nebulae (clouds of dust and gas, inside which stars are born). The Galaxy is vast—about 100,000 light-years across (a light-year is about 5,879 billion miles); in comparison, the Solar System seems small, at about 12 light-hours across (about 8 billion miles). The entire Galaxy is rotating in space, although the inner stars travel faster than those further out. The Sun, which is about two-thirds out from the center, completes one lap of the Galaxy about every 220 million years.

PANORAMIC OPTICAL MAP OF OUR GALAXY AND NEARBY GALAXIES

SIDE VIEW OF OUR GALAXY

Disk of spiral arms containing mainly young stars

Central bulge containing mainly older stars

Halo containing oldest stars

Nucleus

100,000 light-years

OVERHEAD VIEW OF OUR GALAXY

Central bulge

Nucleus

Perseus Arm

Crux-Centaurus Arm

Dust in spiral arm reflecting blue light from hot young stars

Location of Solar System

Patch of dust clouds

Orion Arm (Local Arm)

Emission nebula

Sagittarius Arm

Polaris (the Pole Star), a blue-green variable binary star

Light from stars and nebulae in the Perseus Arm

Galactic plane

Milky Way (the band of light that stretches across the night sky)

Pleiades (the Seven Sisters), an open star cluster

Andromeda Galaxy, a spiral galaxy 2.2 million light-years away; the most distant object visible to the naked eye

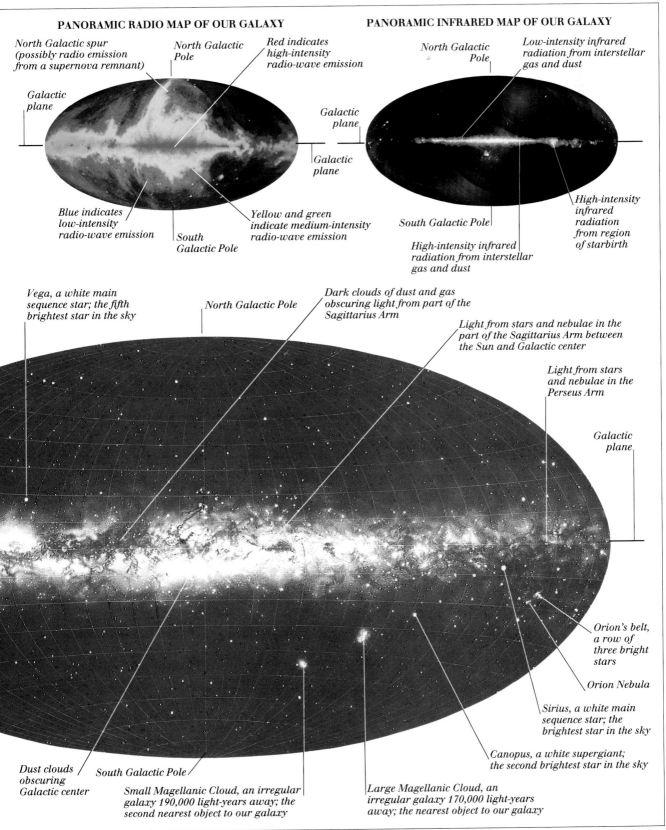

PANORAMIC RADIO MAP OF OUR GALAXY

North Galactic spur
(possibly radio emission
from a supernova remnant)

North Galactic
Pole

Red indicates
high-intensity
radio-wave emission

Galactic
plane

Galactic
plane

Galactic
plane

Blue indicates
low-intensity
radio-wave emission

South
Galactic Pole

Yellow and green
indicate medium-intensity
radio-wave emission

PANORAMIC INFRARED MAP OF OUR GALAXY

North Galactic
Pole

Low-intensity infrared
radiation from interstellar
gas and dust

High-intensity
infrared
radiation
from region
of starbirth

South Galactic Pole

High-intensity infrared
radiation from interstellar
gas and dust

Vega, a white main
sequence star; the fifth
brightest star in the sky

North Galactic Pole

Dark clouds of dust and gas
obscuring light from part of the
Sagittarius Arm

Light from stars and nebulae in the
part of the Sagittarius Arm between
the Sun and Galactic center

Light from stars
and nebulae in the
Perseus Arm

Galactic
plane

Orion's belt,
a row of
three bright
stars

Orion Nebula

Sirius, a white main
sequence star; the
brightest star in the sky

Canopus, a white supergiant;
the second brightest star in the sky

Dust clouds
obscuring
Galactic center

South Galactic Pole

Small Magellanic Cloud, an irregular
galaxy 190,000 light-years away; the
second nearest object to our galaxy

Large Magellanic Cloud, an
irregular galaxy 170,000 light-years
away; the nearest object to our galaxy

Nebulae and star clusters

HODGE 11, A GLOBULAR CLUSTER

A NEBULA IS A CLOUD OF DUST AND GAS inside a galaxy. Nebulae become visible if the gas glows or if the cloud reflects starlight or obscures light from more distant objects. Emission nebulae shine because their gas emits light when it is stimulated by radiation from hot young stars. Reflection nebulae shine because their dust reflects light from stars in or around the nebula. Dark nebulae appear as silhouettes because they block light from shining nebulae or stars behind them. Two types of nebula are associated with dying stars: planetary nebulae and supernova remnants. Both consist of expanding shells of gas that were once the outer layers of a star. A planetary nebula is a gas shell drifting away from a dying stellar core. A supernova remnant is a gas shell moving away from a stellar core at great speed following a violent explosion called a supernova (see pp. 26-27). Stars are often found in groups known as clusters. Open clusters are loose groups of a few thousand young stars that were born in the same cloud and are drifting apart. Globular clusters are densely packed, roughly spherical groups of hundreds of thousands of older stars.

TRIFID NEBULA (EMISSION NEBULA)

Reflection nebula

Emission nebula

Dust lane

Starbirth region (area in which dust and gas combine to form stars)

PLEIADES (OPEN STAR CLUSTER) WITH A REFLECTION NEBULA

Wisps of dust and hydrogen gas remaining from cloud in which stars formed

Young star in an open cluster of 300–500 stars

Reflection nebula

HORSEHEAD NEBULA (DARK NEBULA)

Glowing filament of hot, ionized hydrogen gas

Alnitak (star in Orion's belt)

Dust lane

Emission nebula

Star near southern end of Orion's belt

Emission nebula

Horsehead Nebula

Reflection nebula

Dark nebula obscuring light from distant stars

ORION NEBULA (DIFFUSE EMISSION NEBULA)

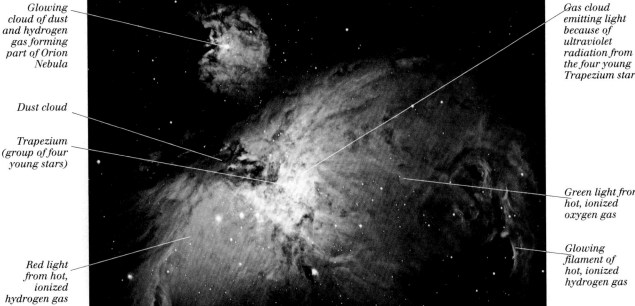

Glowing cloud of dust and hydrogen gas forming part of Orion Nebula

Dust cloud

Trapezium (group of four young stars)

Red light from hot, ionized hydrogen gas

Gas cloud emitting light because of ultraviolet radiation from the four young Trapezium stars

Green light from hot, ionized oxygen gas

Glowing filament of hot, ionized hydrogen gas

VELA SUPERNOVA REMNANT

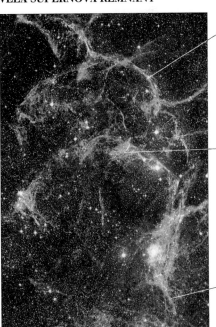

Supernova remnant (gas shell consisting of outer layers of star thrown off in supernova explosion)

Hydrogen gas emitting red light due to being heated by supernova explosion

Glowing filament of hot, ionized hydrogen gas

HELIX NEBULA (PLANETARY NEBULA)

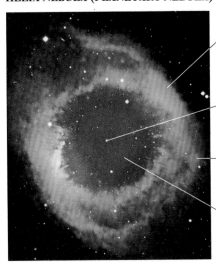

Planetary nebula (gas shell expanding outward from dying stellar core)

Stellar core at a temperature of about 180,000°F

Red light from hot, ionized hydrogen gas

Blue-green light from hot, ionized oxygen and nitrogen gases

Stars of northern skies

WHEN YOU LOOK AT THE NORTHERN SKY, you look away from the densely populated Galactic center, so the northern sky generally appears less bright than the southern sky (see pp. 20-21). Among the best-known sights in the northern sky are the constellations Ursa Major (the Great Bear) and Orion. Some ancient civilizations believed that the stars were fixed to a celestial sphere surrounding the Earth, and modern maps of the sky are based on a similar idea. The North and South Poles of this imaginary celestial sphere are directly above the North and South Poles of the Earth, at the points where the Earth's axis of rotation intersects the sphere. The celestial North Pole is at the center of the map shown here, and Polaris (the Pole Star) lies very close to it. The celestial equator marks a projection of the Earth's equator on the sphere. The ecliptic marks the path of the Sun across the sky as the Earth orbits the Sun. The Moon and planets move against the background of the stars because the stars are much more distant; the nearest star outside the Solar System (Proxima Centauri) is more than 50,000 times farther away than the planet Jupiter.

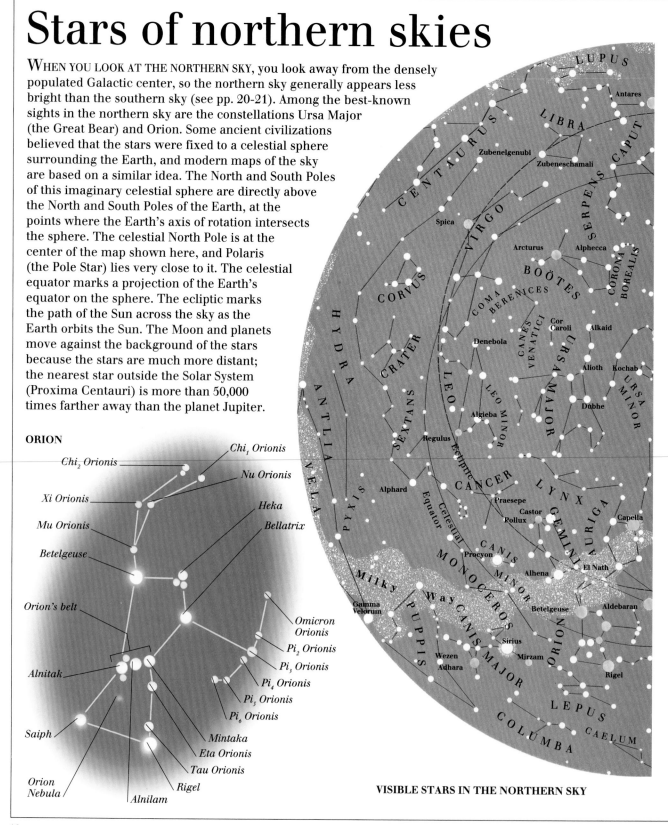

ORION

Chi₂ Orionis

Chi₁ Orionis

Nu Orionis

Xi Orionis

Heka

Mu Orionis

Bellatrix

Betelgeuse

Orion's belt

Omicron Orionis

Pi₂ Orionis

Pi₃ Orionis

Pi₄ Orionis

Pi₅ Orionis

Pi₆ Orionis

Alnitak

Saiph

Mintaka

Eta Orionis

Tau Orionis

Orion Nebula

Rigel

Alnilam

VISIBLE STARS IN THE NORTHERN SKY

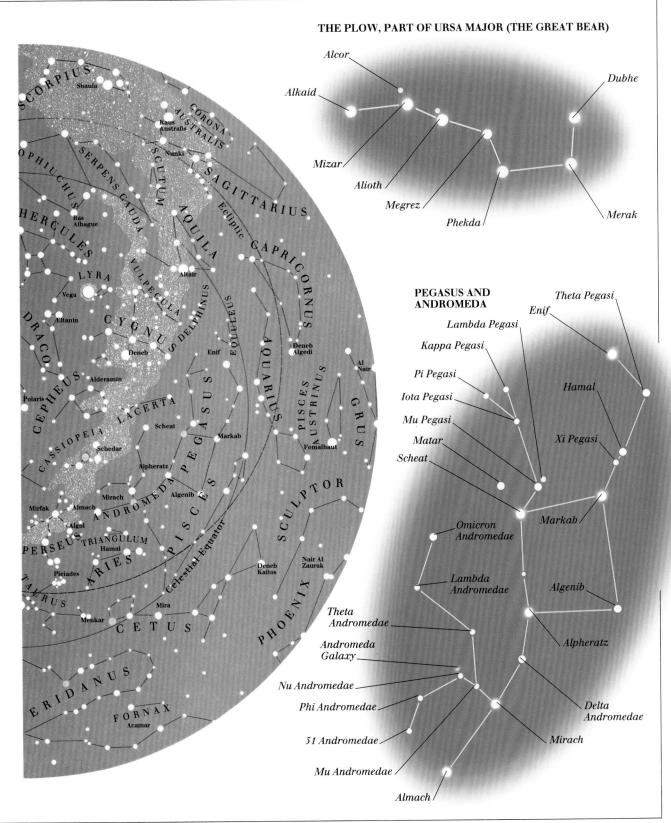

THE PLOW, PART OF URSA MAJOR (THE GREAT BEAR)

Alcor
Alkaid
Dubhe
Mizar
Alioth
Megrez
Phekda
Merak

PEGASUS AND ANDROMEDA

Theta Pegasi
Enif
Lambda Pegasi
Kappa Pegasi
Hamal
Pi Pegasi
Iota Pegasi
Mu Pegasi
Xi Pegasi
Matar
Scheat
Markab
Omicron Andromedae
Lambda Andromedae
Algenib
Theta Andromedae
Alpheratz
Andromeda Galaxy
Nu Andromedae
Phi Andromedae
Delta Andromedae
51 Andromedae
Mirach
Mu Andromedae
Almach

SCORPIUS
Shaula
CORONA AUSTRALIS
Kaus Australis
OPHIUCHUS
SERPENS CAUDA
SCUTUM
Nunki
SAGITTARIUS
Ras Alhague
HERCULES
AQUILA
CAPRICORNUS
Ecliptic
LYRA
VULPECULA
Altair
Vega
Eltanin
CYGNUS
DELPHINUS
EQUULEUS
Deneb Algedi
Al Nair
DRACO
Deneb
Enif
AQUARIUS
PISCES AUSTRINUS
GRUS
CEPHEUS
Alderamin
PEGASUS
Polaris
LACERTA
Scheat
CASSIOPEIA
Schedar
Markab
Fomalhaut
Alpheratz
ANDROMEDA
Algenib
SCULPTOR
Mirfak
Mirach
Almach
Algol
PERSEUS
TRIANGULUM
PISCES
Celestial Equator
Nair Al Zaurak
Hamal
ARIES
Deneb Kaitos
Pleiades
TAURUS
Mira
PHOENIX
Menkar
CETUS
ERIDANUS
FORNAX
Acamar

Stars of southern skies

WHEN YOU LOOK AT THE SOUTHERN SKY, you look toward the Galactic center, which has a huge population of stars. As a result, the Milky Way appears brighter in the southern sky than in the northern sky (see pp. 18-19). The southern sky is rich in nebulae and star clusters. It contains the Large and Small Magellanic Clouds, which are the two nearest galaxies to our own. Stars make fixed patterns in the sky called constellations. The constellations, however, are only apparent groupings of stars, because the distances to the stars in a constellation may vary enormously. The shapes of constellations may change over many thousands of years because of the relative motions of stars. The apparent movement of entire constellations across the sky is due to the Earth's motion in space. The daily rotation of the Earth causes the constellations to move across the sky from east to west, and the orbit of the Earth around the Sun causes different areas of sky to be visible in different seasons. The visibility of areas of sky also depends on the location of the observer. For instance, stars near the celestial equator may be seen from either hemisphere at some time during the year, while stars close to the celestial poles (the celestial South Pole is at the center of the map shown here) can never be seen from the opposite hemisphere.

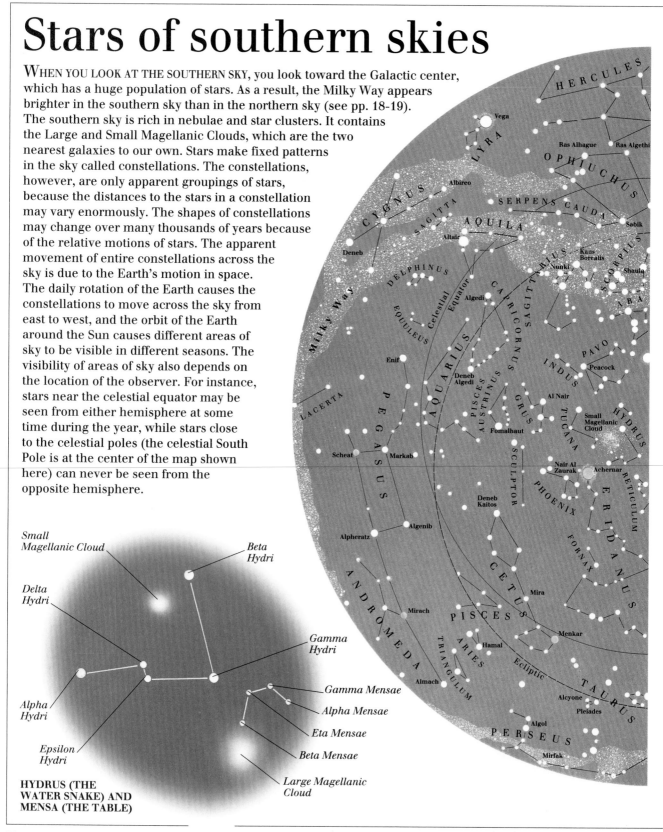

HYDRUS (THE WATER SNAKE) AND MENSA (THE TABLE)

Small Magellanic Cloud

Beta Hydri

Delta Hydri

Gamma Hydri

Gamma Mensae

Alpha Mensae

Eta Mensae

Beta Mensae

Large Magellanic Cloud

Alpha Hydri

Epsilon Hydri

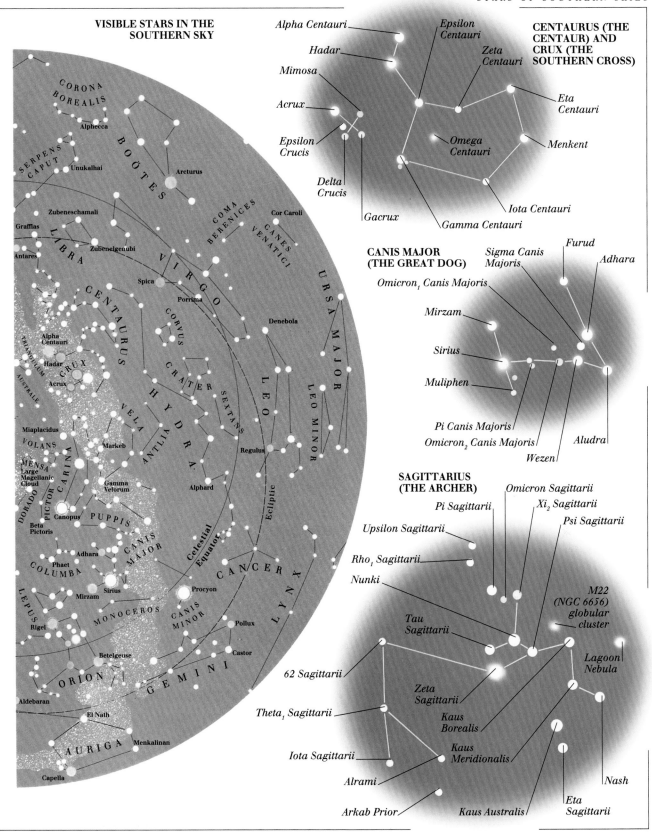

VISIBLE STARS IN THE SOUTHERN SKY

CORONA BOREALIS
Alphecca
BOÖTES
SERPENS CAPUT
Unukalhai
Arcturus
COMA BERENICES
CANES VENATICI
Cor Caroli
Zubeneschamali
Graffias
LIBRA
Zubenelgenubi
Antares
VIRGO
Spica
Porrima
CORVUS
Denebola
CENTAURUS
URSA MAJOR
LEO
LEO MINOR
CRATER
SEXTANS
Triangulum
Australe
Alpha Centauri
Hadar
CRUX
Acrux
HYDRA
VELA
ANTLIA
Regulus
Miaplacidus
VOLANS
MENSA
Large Magellanic Cloud
DORADO
PICTOR
CARINA
Markeb
Gamma Velorum
Alphard
Ecliptic
CANCER
LYNX
Canopus
PUPPIS
Beta Pictoris
Adhara
COLUMBA
Phaet
CANIS MAJOR
Celestial Equator
Mirzam
Sirius
Procyon
Pollux
LEPUS
MONOCEROS
CANIS MINOR
Castor
Rigel
GEMINI
ORION
Betelgeuse
Aldebaran
El Nath
Menkalinan
AURIGA
Capella

CENTAURUS (THE CENTAUR) AND CRUX (THE SOUTHERN CROSS)

Alpha Centauri
Epsilon Centauri
Hadar
Zeta Centauri
Mimosa
Eta Centauri
Acrux
Epsilon Crucis
Omega Centauri
Menkent
Delta Crucis
Gacrux
Iota Centauri
Gamma Centauri

CANIS MAJOR (THE GREAT DOG)

Sigma Canis Majoris
Furud
Adhara
Omicron₁ Canis Majoris
Mirzam
Sirius
Muliphen
Pi Canis Majoris
Omicron₂ Canis Majoris
Wezen
Aludra

SAGITTARIUS (THE ARCHER)

Omicron Sagittarii
Pi Sagittarii
Xi₂ Sagittarii
Upsilon Sagittarii
Psi Sagittarii
Rho₁ Sagittarii
Nunki
M22 (NGC 6656) globular cluster
Tau Sagittarii
Lagoon Nebula
62 Sagittarii
Zeta Sagittarii
Theta₁ Sagittarii
Kaus Borealis
Iota Sagittarii
Kaus Meridionalis
Alrami
Arkab Prior
Kaus Australis
Eta Sagittarii
Nash

21

Stars

OPEN STAR CLUSTER AND DUST CLOUD

STARS ARE BODIES of hot glowing gas that are born in nebulae (see pp. 24-27). They vary enormously in size, mass, and temperature: diameters range from about 450 times smaller to over 1,000 times bigger than that of the Sun; masses range from about a twentieth to over 50 solar masses; and surface temperatures range from about 5,500°F to over 90,000°F. The color of a star is determined by its temperature: the hottest stars are blue and the coolest are red. The Sun, with a surface temperature of 10,000°F, is between these extremes and appears yellow. The energy emitted by a shining star is produced by nuclear fusion in the star's core. The brightness of a star is measured in magnitudes—the brighter the star, the lower its magnitude. There are two types of magnitude: apparent magnitude, which is the brightness seen from Earth, and absolute magnitude, which is the brightness that would be seen from a standard distance of 10 parsecs (32.6 light-years). The light emitted by a star may be split to form a spectrum containing a series of dark lines (absorption lines). The patterns of lines indicate the presence of particular chemical elements, enabling astronomers to deduce the composition of the star's atmosphere. The magnitude and spectral type (color) of stars may be plotted on a graph called a Hertzsprung-Russell diagram, which shows that stars tend to fall into several well-defined groups. The principal groups are main sequence stars (those which are fusing hydrogen to form helium), giants, supergiants, and white dwarfs.

STAR SIZES

Red giant (diameters between about 10 million and 100 million miles)

The Sun (main sequence star with diameter about 870,000 miles)

White dwarf (diameters between about 2,000 and 30,000 miles)

ENERGY EMISSION FROM THE SUN

Nuclear fusion in core produces gamma rays and neutrinos

Neutrinos travel to Earth directly from Sun's core in about 8 minutes

Lower-energy radiation travels to Earth in about 8 minutes

Earth

Sun

Lower-energy radiation (mainly ultraviolet, infrared, and light rays) leaves surface

High-energy radiation (gamma rays) loses energy while traveling to surface over 2 million years

STAR MAGNITUDES

APPARENT MAGNITUDE   **ABSOLUTE MAGNITUDE**

Brighter stars

-9

0

+9

Sirius: apparent magnitude of -1.46

Rigel: apparent magnitude of +0.12

Objects of magnitude higher than about +5.5 cannot be seen by the naked eye

Rigel: absolute magnitude of -7.1

Sirius: absolute magnitude of +1.4

Fainter stars

NUCLEAR FUSION IN MAIN SEQUENCE STARS LIKE THE SUN

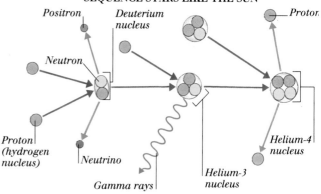

Positron

Deuterium nucleus

Proton

Neutron

Proton (hydrogen nucleus)

Neutrino

Gamma rays

Helium-3 nucleus

Helium-4 nucleus

HERTZSPRUNG-RUSSELL DIAGRAM

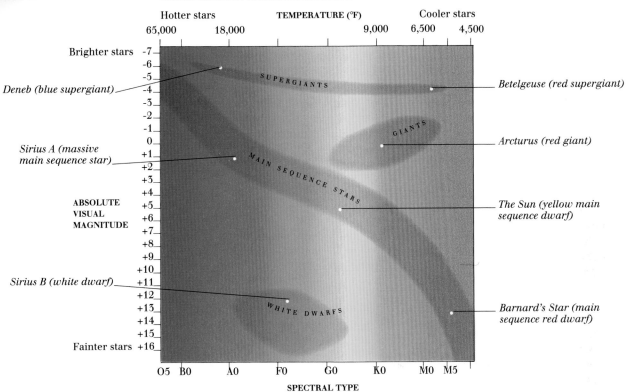

Hotter stars   **TEMPERATURE (°F)**   Cooler stars

65,000   18,000   9,000   6,500   4,500

Brighter stars   -7
-6
-5
-4   SUPERGIANTS
-3
-2
-1
0   GIANTS
+1
+2   MAIN SEQUENCE STARS
+3
+4
+5
+6
+7
+8
+9
+10
+11
+12
+13   WHITE DWARFS
+14
+15
Fainter stars   +16

ABSOLUTE VISUAL MAGNITUDE

Deneb (blue supergiant)

Sirius A (massive main sequence star)

Sirius B (white dwarf)

Betelgeuse (red supergiant)

Arcturus (red giant)

The Sun (yellow main sequence dwarf)

Barnard's Star (main sequence red dwarf)

O5   B0   A0   F0   G0   K0   M0   M5

SPECTRAL TYPE

STELLAR SPECTRAL ABSORPTION LINES

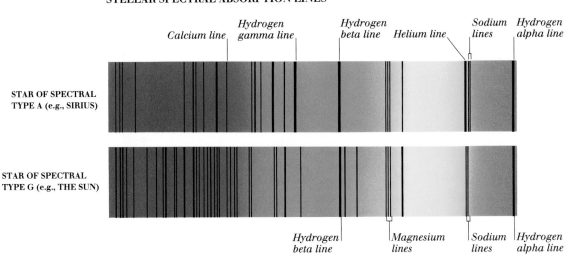

Calcium line   Hydrogen gamma line   Hydrogen beta line   Helium line   Sodium lines   Hydrogen alpha line

STAR OF SPECTRAL TYPE A (e.g., SIRIUS)

STAR OF SPECTRAL TYPE G (e.g., THE SUN)

Hydrogen beta line   Magnesium lines   Sodium lines   Hydrogen alpha line

Small stars

**REGION OF
STAR FORMATION
IN ORION**

SMALL STARS HAVE A MASS of up to about one and a half times that of the Sun. They begin to form when a region of higher density in a nebula condenses into a huge globule of gas and dust that contracts under its own gravity. Within a globule, regions of condensing matter heat up and begin to glow, forming protostars. If a protostar contains enough matter, the central temperature reaches about 27 million °F. At this temperature, nuclear reactions in which hydrogen fuses to form helium can start. This process releases energy, which prevents the star from contracting further, and also causes it to shine; it is now a main sequence star. A star of about one solar mass remains in the main sequence for about 10 billion years, until the hydrogen in the star's core has been converted into helium. The helium core then contracts again, and nuclear reactions continue in a shell around the core. The core becomes hot enough for helium to fuse to form carbon, while the outer layers of the star expand, cool, and shine less brightly. The expanding star is known as a red giant. When the helium in the core runs out, the outer layers of the star may drift off as an expanding gas shell called a planetary nebula. The remaining core (about 80 percent of the original star) is now in its final stages. It becomes a white dwarf star that gradually cools and dims. When it finally stops shining altogether, the dead star will become a black dwarf.

STRUCTURE OF A MAIN SEQUENCE STAR

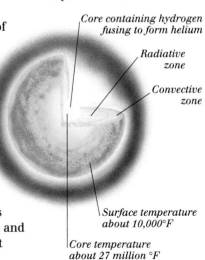

Core containing hydrogen fusing to form helium

Radiative zone

Convective zone

Surface temperature about 10,000°F

Core temperature about 27 million °F

STRUCTURE OF A NEBULA

Young main sequence star

Dense region of dust and gas (mainly hydrogen) condensing under gravity to form globules

Hot, ionized hydrogen gas emitting red light due to stimulation by radiation from hot young stars

Dark globule of dust and gas (mainly hydrogen) contracting to form protostars

LIFE OF A SMALL STAR OF ABOUT ONE SOLAR MASS

Cool cloud of gas (mainly hydrogen) and dust

Dense globule condensing to form protostars

NEBULA

Glowing ball of gas (mainly hydrogen)

Natal cocoon (shell of dust blown away by radiation from protostar)

PROTOSTAR
Duration: 50 million years

About 870,000 miles

Star producing energy by nuclear fusion in core

MAIN SEQUENCE STAR
Duration: 10 billion years

STRUCTURE OF A RED GIANT

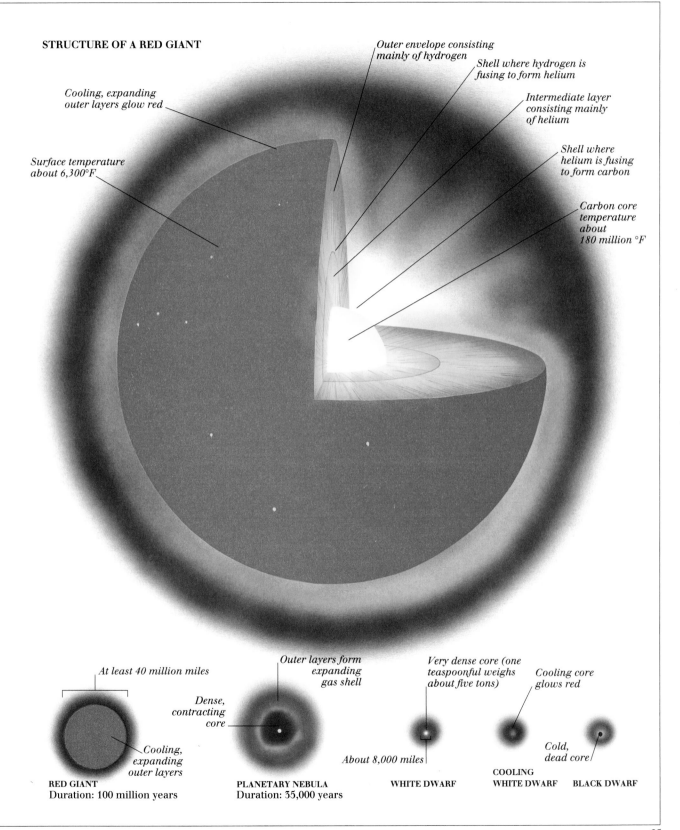

Outer envelope consisting mainly of hydrogen

Shell where hydrogen is fusing to form helium

Intermediate layer consisting mainly of helium

Shell where helium is fusing to form carbon

Carbon core temperature about 180 million °F

Cooling, expanding outer layers glow red

Surface temperature about 6,300°F

At least 40 million miles

Dense, contracting core

Cooling, expanding outer layers

RED GIANT
Duration: 100 million years

Outer layers form expanding gas shell

PLANETARY NEBULA
Duration: 35,000 years

Very dense core (one teaspoonful weighs about five tons)

About 8,000 miles

WHITE DWARF

Cooling core glows red

COOLING WHITE DWARF

Cold, dead core

BLACK DWARF

Massive stars

MASSIVE STARS HAVE A MASS AT LEAST THREE TIMES that of the Sun, and some
stars are as massive as about 50 Suns. A massive star evolves in a similar way to
a small star until it reaches the main sequence stage (see pp. 24-25). During the
main sequence, a star shines steadily until the hydrogen in its core has fused to
form helium. This process takes billions of years in a small star, but only millions
of years in a massive star. A massive star then becomes a red supergiant, which
initially consists of a helium core surrounded by outer layers of cooling, expanding
gas. Over the next few million years, a series of nuclear reactions form different
elements in shells around an iron core. The core eventually collapses in less than
a second, causing a massive explosion called
a supernova, in which a shock wave blows
away the outer layers of the star.
Supernovae shine brighter than
an entire galaxy for a short
time. Sometimes, the core
survives the supernova
explosion. If the surviving
core is between about
one and a half and
three solar masses, it
contracts to become
a tiny, dense neutron
star. If the core is
considerably greater
than three solar
masses, it contracts
to become a black
hole (see pp. 28-29).

SUPERNOVA

**TARANTULA NEBULA BEFORE
SUPERNOVA**

**STRUCTURE
OF A RED SUPERGIANT**

*Outer envelope consisting
mainly of hydrogen*

*Layer consisting
mainly of helium*

*Layer consisting
mainly of carbon*

*Layer consisting
mainly of oxygen*

*Layer consisting
mainly of silicon*

*Shell of hydrogen
fusing to form
helium*

*Shell of helium
fusing to form
carbon*

*Shell of carbon
fusing to form
oxygen*

*Shell of oxygen fusing
to form silicon*

*Shell of silicon fusing
to form iron core*

*Surface temperature
about 5,500°F*

*Cooling, expanding
outer layers glow red*

*Core of mainly iron at a
temperature of 5.4–9 billion °F*

**LIFE OF A MASSIVE STAR OF
ABOUT 10 SOLAR MASSES**

*Dense globule
condensing to
form protostars*

*Cool cloud of gas
(mainly hydrogen)
and dust*

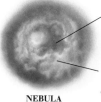

NEBULA

*Glowing
ball of gas
(mainly hydrogen)*

*Natal cocoon (shell
of dust blown away
by radiation from
protostar)*

PROTOSTAR
Duration: a few hundred
thousand years

*About
2 million miles*

*Star producing
energy by nuclear
fusion in
core*

MAIN SEQUENCE STAR
Duration: 10 million years

FEATURES OF A SUPERNOVA

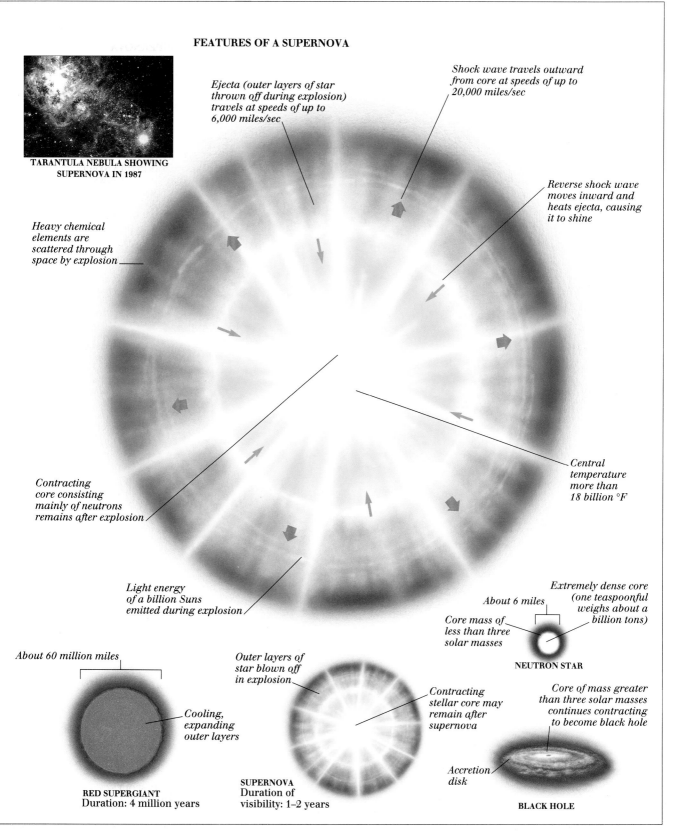

**TARANTULA NEBULA SHOWING
SUPERNOVA IN 1987**

Ejecta (outer layers of star
thrown off during explosion)
travels at speeds of up to
6,000 miles/sec

Shock wave travels outward
from core at speeds of up to
20,000 miles/sec

Reverse shock wave
moves inward and
heats ejecta, causing
it to shine

Heavy chemical
elements are
scattered through
space by explosion

Contracting
core consisting
mainly of neutrons
remains after explosion

Central
temperature
more than
18 billion °F

Light energy
of a billion Suns
emitted during explosion

Extremely dense core
(one teaspoonful
weighs about a
billion tons)

About 6 miles

Core mass of
less than three
solar masses

NEUTRON STAR

About 60 million miles

Outer layers of
star blown off
in explosion

Contracting
stellar core may
remain after
supernova

Core of mass greater
than three solar masses
continues contracting
to become black hole

Cooling,
expanding
outer layers

Accretion
disk

RED SUPERGIANT
Duration: 4 million years

SUPERNOVA
Duration of
visibility: 1–2 years

BLACK HOLE

Neutron stars and black holes

NEUTRON STARS AND BLACK HOLES form from the stellar cores that remain after stars have exploded as supernovae (see pp. 26-27). If the remaining core is between about one and a half and three solar masses, it contracts to form a neutron star. If the remaining core is considerably greater than about three solar masses, it contracts to form a black hole. Neutron stars are typically only about six miles in diameter and consist almost entirely of subatomic particles called neutrons. These stars are so dense that a teaspoonful would weigh about a billion tons. Neutron stars are observed as pulsars, so-called because they rotate rapidly and emit two beams of radio waves, which sweep across the sky and are detected as short pulses. Black holes are characterized by their extremely strong gravity, which is so powerful that not even light can escape; as a result, black holes are invisible. However, they may be detected if they have a close companion star. The gravity of the black hole pulls gas from the other star, forming an accretion disk that spirals around the black hole at high speed, heating up and emitting radiation. Eventually, the matter spirals in to cross the event horizon (the boundary of the black hole), finally disappearing from the visible Universe.

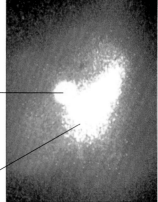

X-ray emission from pulsar (neutron star rotating 30 times each second)

X-ray emission from center of nebula

X-RAY IMAGE OF THE CRAB NEBULA (SUPERNOVA REMNANT)

PULSAR (ROTATING NEUTRON STAR)

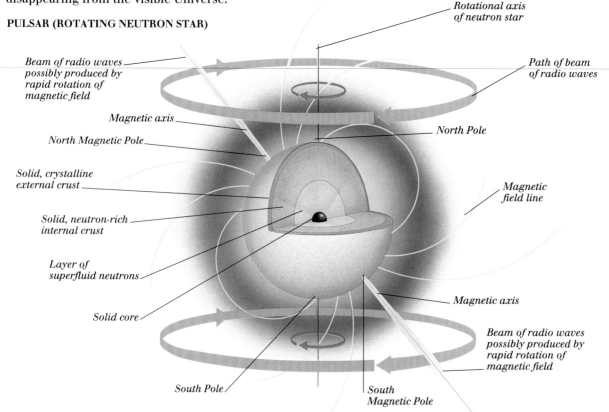

Rotational axis of neutron star

Beam of radio waves possibly produced by rapid rotation of magnetic field

Path of beam of radio waves

Magnetic axis

North Magnetic Pole

North Pole

Solid, crystalline external crust

Magnetic field line

Solid, neutron-rich internal crust

Layer of superfluid neutrons

Solid core

Magnetic axis

Beam of radio waves possibly produced by rapid rotation of magnetic field

South Pole

South Magnetic Pole

STELLAR BLACK HOLE

Blue supergiant star

Gas current (outer layers of nearby blue supergiant pulled toward black hole by gravity)

Singularity (theoretical region of infinite density, pressure, and temperature)

Hot spot (region of intense friction where gas current joins accretion disk)

Gas in outer part of accretion disk emitting low-energy radiation

Event horizon (boundary of black hole)

Hot gas in inner part of accretion disk emitting high-energy X-rays

Accretion disk (matter spiraling around black hole)

Black hole

Gas at temperatures of millions °F spiraling at close to the speed of light

FORMATION OF A BLACK HOLE

Stellar core remains after supernova explosion

Light rays increasingly bent by gravity as core collapses

Core shrinks beyond its event horizon to become a black hole

Light rays cannot escape because gravity is so strong

Density, pressure, and temperature of core increase as core collapses

Core greater than three solar masses collapses under its own gravity

Event horizon

Outer layers of massive star thrown off in explosion

Singularity (theoretical region of infinite density, pressure, and temperature)

SUPERNOVA

COLLAPSING STELLAR CORE

BLACK HOLE

The Solar System

THE SUN

THE SOLAR SYSTEM consists of a central star (the Sun) and the bodies that orbit it. These bodies include nine planets and their 61 known moons, asteroids, comets, and meteoroids. The Solar System also contains interplanetary gas and dust. Most of the planets fall into two groups: four small rocky planets near the Sun (Mercury, Venus, Earth, and Mars), and four planets farther out, the gas giants (Jupiter, Saturn, Uranus, and Neptune). Pluto belongs to neither group—it is very small, solid, and icy. Pluto is the outermost planet, except when it passes briefly inside Neptune's orbit. Between the rocky planets and gas giants is the asteroid belt, which contains thousands of chunks of rock orbiting the Sun. Most of the bodies in the Solar System move around the Sun in elliptical orbits located in a thin disk around the Sun's equator. All the planets orbit the Sun in the same direction (counterclockwise when viewed from above) and all but Venus, Uranus, and Pluto also spin around their axes in this direction. Moons also spin as they, in turn, orbit their planets. The entire Solar System orbits the center of our galaxy, the Milky Way (see pp. 14-15).

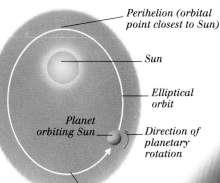

Perihelion (orbital point closest to Sun)

Sun

Elliptical orbit

Planet orbiting Sun

Direction of planetary rotation

Aphelion (orbital point farthest from Sun)

Aphelion of Neptune: 2,819 million miles

ORBITS OF INNER PLANETS

Average orbital speed of Venus: 21.8 miles/sec
Average orbital speed of Mercury: 29.8 miles/sec
Average orbital speed of Earth: 18.5 miles/sec
Average orbital speed of Mars: 15 miles/sec

Mercury

Perihelion of Mercury: 28.5 million miles
Perihelion of Venus: 66.7 million miles
Perihelion of Earth: 91.4 million miles

Mars

Perihelion of Mars: 128.4 million miles

Earth

Venus

Sun

Asteroid belt

Aphelion of Mercury: 43.3 million miles
Aphelion of Venus: 67.7 million miles
Aphelion of Earth: 94.5 million miles
Aphelion of Mars: 154.8 million miles

Aphelion of Pluto: 4,583 million miles

MERCURY
Year: 87.97 Earth days
Mass: 0.055 Earth masses
Diameter: 3,031 miles

VENUS
Year: 224.7 Earth days
Mass: 0.81 Earth masses
Diameter: 7,521 miles

EARTH
Year: 365.26 days
Mass: 1 Earth mass
Diameter: 7,926 miles

MARS
Year: 1.88 Earth years
Mass: 0.11 Earth masses
Diameter: 4,217 miles

JUPITER
Year: 11.86 Earth years
Mass: 318 Earth masses
Diameter: 88,850 miles

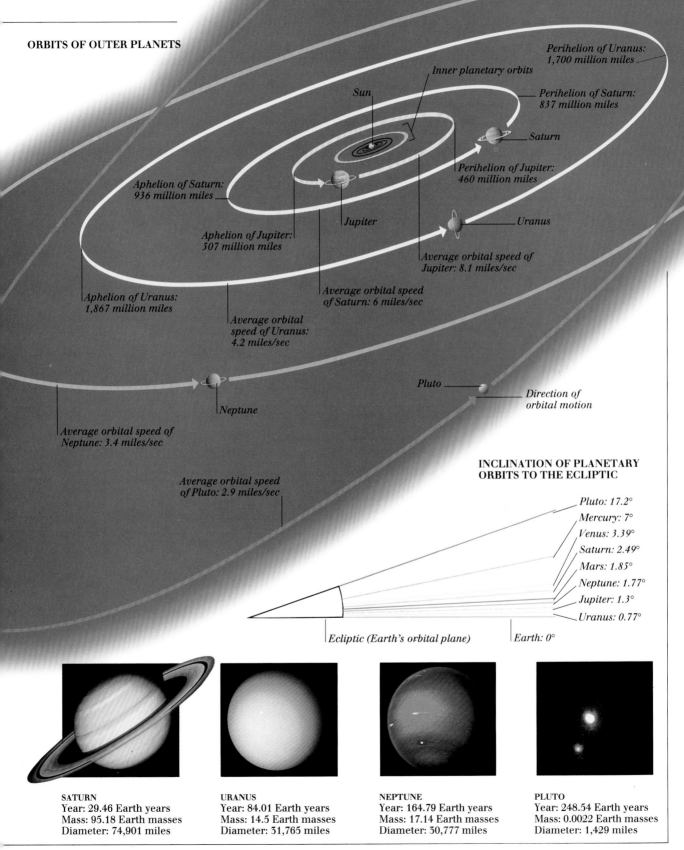

ORBITS OF OUTER PLANETS

Perihelion of Uranus:
1,700 million miles

Inner planetary orbits

Perihelion of Saturn:
837 million miles

Sun

Saturn

Perihelion of Jupiter:
460 million miles

Aphelion of Saturn:
936 million miles

Jupiter

Average orbital speed of
Jupiter: 8.1 miles/sec

Uranus

Aphelion of Jupiter:
507 million miles

Aphelion of Uranus:
1,867 million miles

Average orbital speed
of Saturn: 6 miles/sec

Average orbital
speed of Uranus:
4.2 miles/sec

Pluto

Direction of
orbital motion

Neptune

Average orbital speed of
Neptune: 3.4 miles/sec

Average orbital speed
of Pluto: 2.9 miles/sec

**INCLINATION OF PLANETARY
ORBITS TO THE ECLIPTIC**

Pluto: 17.2°

Mercury: 7°

Venus: 3.39°

Saturn: 2.49°

Mars: 1.85°

Neptune: 1.77°

Jupiter: 1.3°

Uranus: 0.77°

Ecliptic (Earth's orbital plane)

Earth: 0°

SATURN
Year: 29.46 Earth years
Mass: 95.18 Earth masses
Diameter: 74,901 miles

URANUS
Year: 84.01 Earth years
Mass: 14.5 Earth masses
Diameter: 31,765 miles

NEPTUNE
Year: 164.79 Earth years
Mass: 17.14 Earth masses
Diameter: 30,777 miles

PLUTO
Year: 248.54 Earth years
Mass: 0.0022 Earth masses
Diameter: 1,429 miles

The Sun

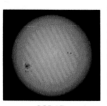

SOLAR PHOTOSPHERE

THE SUN IS THE STAR AT THE CENTER of our Solar System. It is about five billion years old and will probably continue to shine as it does now for about another five billion years. The Sun is a yellow main sequence star (see pp. 22-23) about 870,000 miles in diameter. It consists almost entirely of hydrogen and helium. In the Sun's core, hydrogen is converted to helium by nuclear fusion, releasing energy in the process. The energy travels from the core through the radiative and convective zones to the photosphere (visible surface), where it leaves the Sun in the form of heat and light. On the photosphere there are often dark, relatively cool areas called sunspots. These usually appear in pairs or groups and are thought to be caused by magnetic fields. Other types of solar activity are flares, which are usually associated with sunspots, and prominences. Flares are sudden discharges of high-energy radiation and atomic particles. Prominences are huge loops or filaments of gas extending into the solar atmosphere; some last for hours, others for months. Beyond the photosphere is the chromosphere (inner atmosphere) and the extremely rarified corona (outer atmosphere), which extends millions of miles into space. Tiny particles that escape from the corona give rise to the solar wind, which streams through space at hundreds of miles per second. The chromosphere and corona can be seen from Earth when the Sun is totally eclipsed by the Moon.

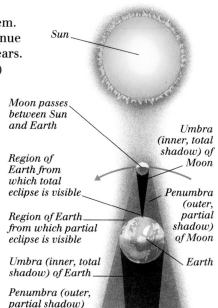

Sun

Moon passes between Sun and Earth

Umbra (inner, total shadow) of Moon

Region of Earth from which total eclipse is visible

Penumbra (outer, partial shadow) of Moon

Region of Earth from which partial eclipse is visible

Earth

Umbra (inner, total shadow) of Earth

Penumbra (outer, partial shadow) of Earth

SURFACE FEATURES

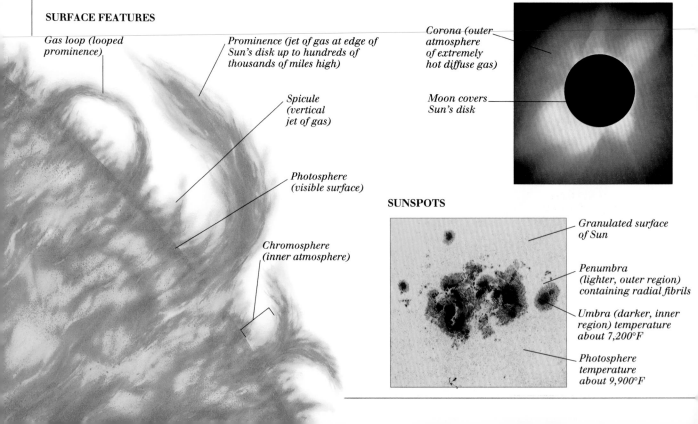

Gas loop (looped prominence)

Prominence (jet of gas at edge of Sun's disk up to hundreds of thousands of miles high)

Spicule (vertical jet of gas)

Photosphere (visible surface)

Chromosphere (inner atmosphere)

TOTAL SOLAR ECLIPSE

Corona (outer atmosphere of extremely hot diffuse gas)

Moon covers Sun's disk

SUNSPOTS

Granulated surface of Sun

Penumbra (lighter, outer region) containing radial fibrils

Umbra (darker, inner region) temperature about 7,200°F

Photosphere temperature about 9,900°F

**EXTERNAL FEATURES AND
INTERNAL STRUCTURE OF THE SUN**

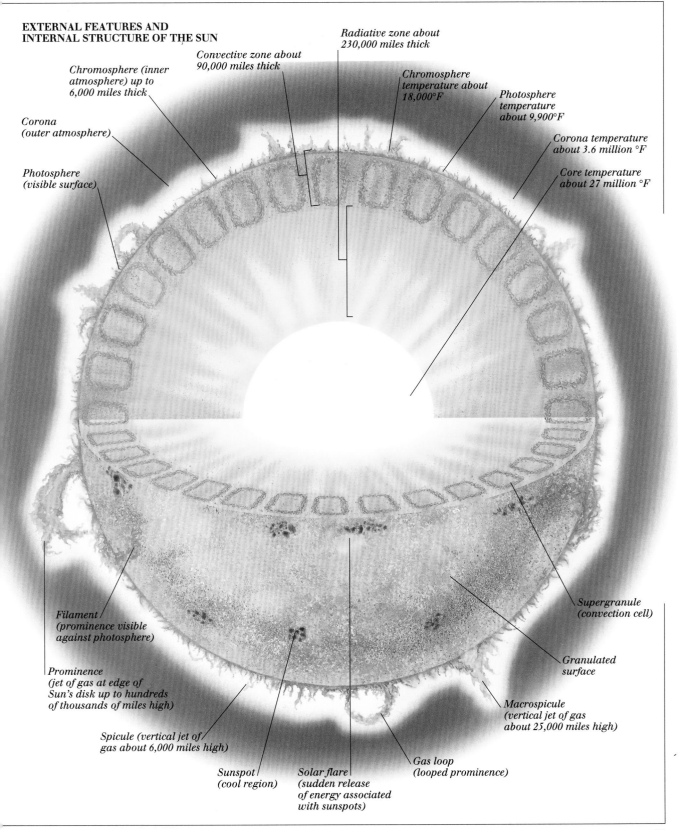

*Chromosphere (inner
atmosphere) up to
6,000 miles thick*

*Convective zone about
90,000 miles thick*

*Radiative zone about
230,000 miles thick*

*Chromosphere
temperature about
18,000°F*

*Photosphere
temperature
about 9,900°F*

*Corona
(outer atmosphere)*

*Corona temperature
about 3.6 million °F*

*Core temperature
about 27 million °F*

*Photosphere
(visible surface)*

*Supergranule
(convection cell)*

*Filament
(prominence visible
against photosphere)*

*Granulated
surface*

*Prominence
(jet of gas at edge of
Sun's disk up to hundreds
of thousands of miles high)*

*Macrospicule
(vertical jet of gas
about 25,000 miles high)*

*Spicule (vertical jet of
gas about 6,000 miles high)*

*Sunspot
(cool region)*

*Solar flare
(sudden release
of energy associated
with sunspots)*

*Gas loop
(looped prominence)*

Mercury

MERCURY

MERCURY IS THE NEAREST PLANET to the Sun, orbiting at an average distance of about 36 million miles. Because Mercury is the closest planet to the Sun, it moves faster than any other planet, traveling at an average speed of nearly 30 miles per second and completing an orbit in just under 88 days. Mercury is very small (only Pluto is smaller) and rocky. Most of the surface has been heavily cratered by the impact of meteorites, although there are also smooth, sparsely cratered plains. The Caloris Basin is the largest crater, measuring about 800 miles across. It is thought to have been formed when a rock the size of an asteroid hit the planet and is surrounded by concentric rings of mountains thrown up by the impact. The surface also has many ridges, called rupes, that are thought to have been formed when the hot core of the young planet cooled and shrank about four billion years ago, buckling the planet's surface in the process. The planet rotates about its axis very slowly, taking nearly 59 Earth days to complete one rotation. As a result, a solar day (sunrise to sunrise) on Mercury is about 176 Earth days—twice as long as the 88-day Mercurian year. Mercury has extreme surface temperatures, ranging from a maximum of 800°F on the sunlit side to -270°F on the dark side. At nightfall, the temperature drops very quickly because the planet's atmosphere is almost nonexistent. It consists only of minute amounts of helium and hydrogen captured from the solar wind, plus traces of other gases.

TILT AND ROTATION OF MERCURY

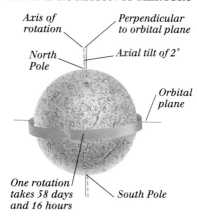

Axis of rotation

Perpendicular to orbital plane

North Pole

Axial tilt of 2°

Orbital plane

One rotation takes 58 days and 16 hours

South Pole

DEGAS AND BRONTË (RAY CRATERS)

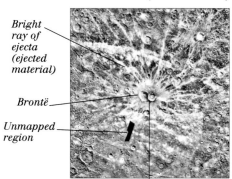

Bright ray of ejecta (ejected material)

Brontë

Unmapped region

Degas with central peak

FORMATION OF A RAY CRATER

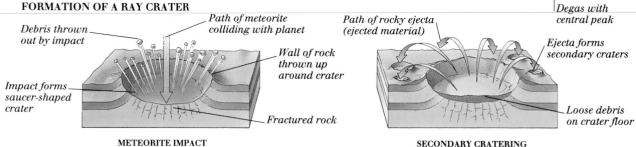

Debris thrown out by impact

Path of meteorite colliding with planet

Wall of rock thrown up around crater

Impact forms saucer-shaped crater

Fractured rock

METEORITE IMPACT

Path of rocky ejecta (ejected material)

Ejecta forms secondary craters

Loose debris on crater floor

SECONDARY CRATERING

Wall of rock forms ring of mountains

Ray of ejecta (ejected material)

Small secondary crater

Loose ejected rock

Central mountain rings form if floor of large crater recoils from meteorite impact

Falling debris forms ridges on side of wall

RAY CRATER

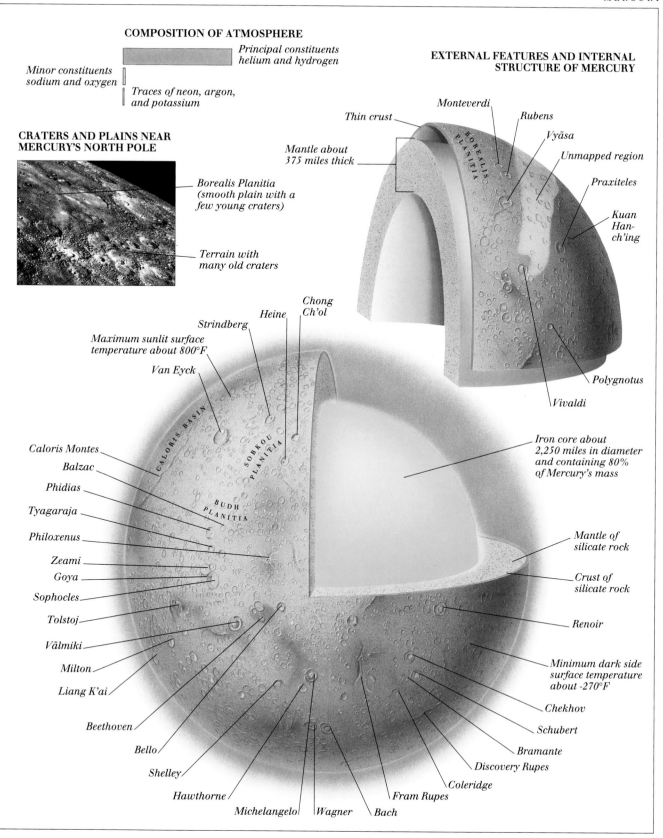

COMPOSITION OF ATMOSPHERE

Principal constituents
helium and hydrogen

Minor constituents
sodium and oxygen

Traces of neon, argon,
and potassium

**CRATERS AND PLAINS NEAR
MERCURY'S NORTH POLE**

Borealis Planitia
(smooth plain with a
few young craters)

Terrain with
many old craters

**EXTERNAL FEATURES AND INTERNAL
STRUCTURE OF MERCURY**

Thin crust

Mantle about
375 miles thick

Monteverdi

Rubens

Vyāsa

Unmapped region

Praxiteles

Kuan
Han-
ch'ing

BOREALIS PLANITIA

Polygnotus

Vivaldi

Chong
Ch'ol

Heine

Strindberg

Maximum sunlit surface
temperature about 800°F

Van Eyck

Caloris Montes

Balzac

Phidias

Tyagaraja

Philoxenus

Zeami

Goya

Sophocles

Tolstoj

Vālmiki

Milton

Liang K'ai

Beethoven

Bello

Shelley

Hawthorne

Michelangelo

Wagner

Bach

Fram Rupes

Coleridge

Discovery Rupes

Bramante

Schubert

Chekhov

CALORIS BASIN

SOBKOU PLANITIA

BUDH PLANITIA

Iron core about
2,250 miles in diameter
and containing 80%
of Mercury's mass

Mantle of
silicate rock

Crust of
silicate rock

Renoir

Minimum dark side
surface temperature
about -270°F

35

Venus

RADAR IMAGE OF VENUS

VENUS IS A ROCKY PLANET and the second planet from the Sun. Venus spins slowly backward as it orbits the Sun, causing its rotational period to be the longest in the Solar System, at about 243 Earth days. It is slightly smaller than Earth and probably has a similar internal structure, consisting of a semisolid metal core surrounded by a rocky mantle and crust. Venus is the brightest object in the sky after the Sun and Moon because its atmosphere reflects sunlight strongly. The main component of the atmosphere is carbon dioxide, which traps heat in a greenhouse effect far stronger than that on Earth. As a result, Venus is the hottest planet, with a maximum surface temperature of about 900°F. The thick cloud layers contain droplets of sulfuric acid and are driven around the planet by winds at speeds of up to 220 miles per hour. Although the planet takes 243 Earth days to rotate once, the high-speed winds cause the clouds to circle the planet in only four Earth days. The high temperature, acidic clouds, and enormous atmospheric pressure (about 90 times greater at the surface than that on Earth) make the environment extremely hostile. However, orbiting satellites have managed to land on Venus and photograph its dry, dusty surface. The Venusian surface has also been mapped by probes with radar equipment that can "see" through the cloud layers. Such radar maps reveal a terrain with craters, mountains, volcanoes, and areas where craters have been covered by plains of solidified volcanic lava. There are two large highland regions called Aphrodite Terra and Ishtar Terra.

TILT AND ROTATION OF VENUS

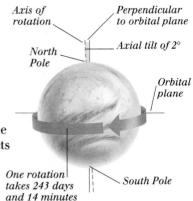

Axis of rotation

Perpendicular to orbital plane

North Pole

Axial tilt of 2°

Orbital plane

One rotation takes 243 days and 14 minutes

South Pole

CLOUD FEATURES

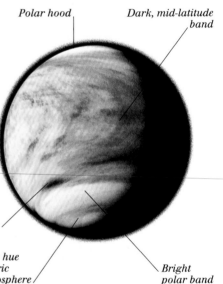

Polar hood

Dark, mid-latitude band

Cloud features swept around planet by winds of up to 220 mph

Dirty yellow hue due to sulfuric acid in atmosphere

Bright polar band

VENUSIAN CRATERS

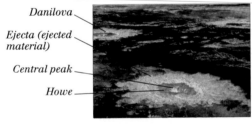

Danilova

Ejecta (ejected material)

Central peak

Howe

COMPUTER-ENHANCED RADAR MAP OF THE SURFACE OF VENUS

Metis Regio

Maxwell Montes

Bell Regio

Tethus Regio

Atalanta Planitia

Sedna Planitia

Leda Planitia

Eisila Regio

Tellus Regio

Guinevere Planitia

Niobe Planitia

Phoebe Regio

Alpha Regio

Ovda Regio

Themis Regio

Thetis Regio

Lavinia Planitia

Aino Planitia

Helen Planitia

Lada Terra

ISHTAR TERRA

APHRODITE TERRA

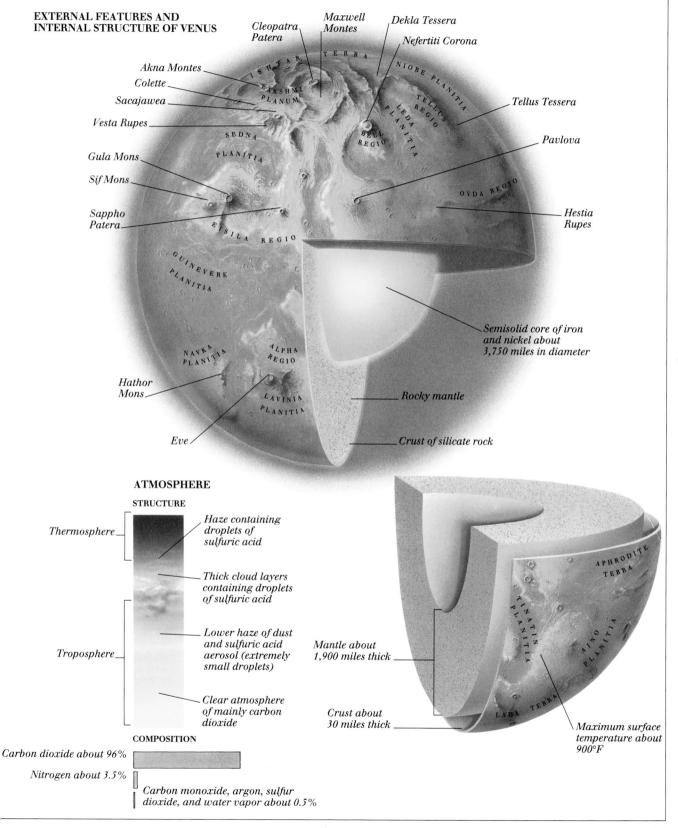

EXTERNAL FEATURES AND INTERNAL STRUCTURE OF VENUS

Cleopatra Patera

Maxwell Montes

Dekla Tessera

Nefertiti Corona

Akna Montes

Colette

Sacajawea

Vesta Rupes

Gula Mons

Sif Mons

Sappho Patera

Hathor Mons

Eve

ISHTAR TERRA

NIOBE PLANITIA

LAKSHMI PLANUM

TELLUS REGIO

LEDA PLANITIA

BELL REGIO

SEDNA PLANITIA

OVDA REGIO

EISILA REGIO

GUINEVERE PLANITIA

NAVKA PLANITIA

ALPHA REGIO

LAVINIA PLANITIA

Tellus Tessera

Pavlova

Hestia Rupes

Semisolid core of iron and nickel about 3,750 miles in diameter

Rocky mantle

Crust of silicate rock

ATMOSPHERE

STRUCTURE

Thermosphere

Troposphere

Haze containing droplets of sulfuric acid

Thick cloud layers containing droplets of sulfuric acid

Lower haze of dust and sulfuric acid aerosol (extremely small droplets)

Clear atmosphere of mainly carbon dioxide

Mantle about 1,900 miles thick

Crust about 30 miles thick

APHRODITE TERRA

TINATIN PLANITIA

AINO PLANITIA

LADA TERRA

Maximum surface temperature about 900°F

COMPOSITION

Carbon dioxide about 96%

Nitrogen about 3.5%

Carbon monoxide, argon, sulfur dioxide, and water vapor about 0.5%

37

The Earth

THE EARTH

THE EARTH IS THE THIRD of the nine planets that orbit the Sun. It is the largest and densest rocky planet, and the only one known to support life. About 70 percent of the Earth's surface is covered by water, which is not found in liquid form on the surface of any other planet. There are four main layers: the inner core, the outer core, the mantle, and the crust. At the heart of the planet the solid inner core has a temperature of about 7,230°F. The heat from this inner core causes material in the molten outer core and mantle to circulate in convection currents. It is thought that these convection currents generate the Earth's magnetic field, which extends into space as the magnetosphere. The Earth's atmosphere helps screen out some of the harmful radiation from the Sun, stops meteorites from reaching the planet's surface, and traps enough heat to prevent extremes of cold. The Earth has one natural satellite, the Moon, which is large enough for both bodies to be considered a double-planet system.

TILT AND ROTATION OF THE EARTH

Axis of rotation

Axial tilt of 23.4°

North Pole

Orbital plane

South Pole

One rotation takes 23 hours and 56 minutes

Perpendicular to orbital plane

THE FORMATION OF THE EARTH

The heat of the collisions caused the planet to glow red

The cloud broke up into particles of ice and rock, which stuck together to form planets

Microorganisms began to photosynthesize, creating a supply of oxygen

4,600 MILLION YEARS AGO, THE SOLAR SYSTEM FORMED FROM A CLOUD OF GAS AND DUST

THE EARTH WAS FORMED FROM COLLIDING ROCKS

4,500 MILLION YEARS AGO THE SURFACE COOLED TO FORM THE CRUST

THE CONTINENTS BROKE UP AND REFORMED, GRADUALLY TAKING THEIR PRESENT POSITIONS

Solar wind enters atmosphere and produces aurora

Magnetosphere (magnetic field)

Solar wind (stream of electrically charged particles)

THE EARTH'S MAGNETOSPHERE

Van Allen radiation belt

Earth

Axis of geographic poles

Axis of magnetic poles

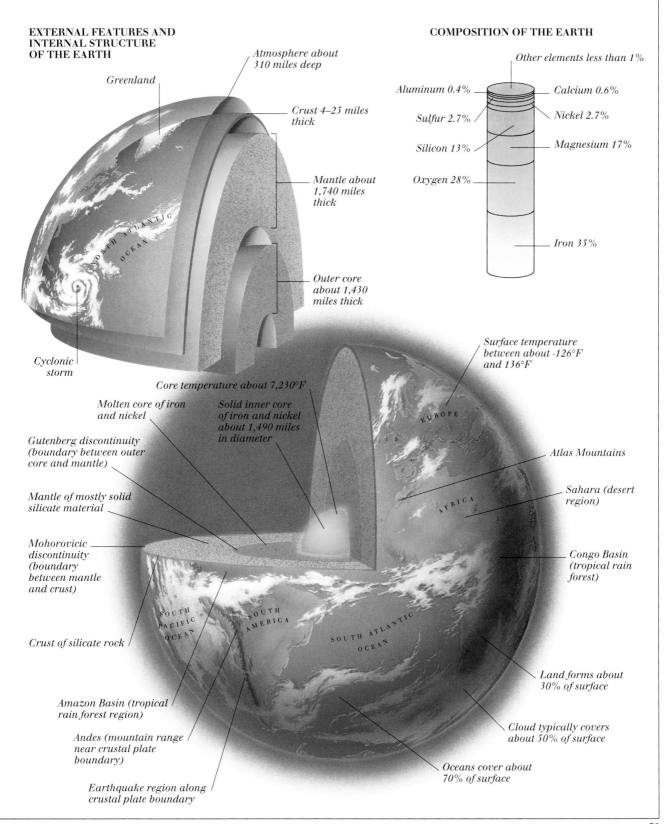

**EXTERNAL FEATURES AND
INTERNAL STRUCTURE
OF THE EARTH**

Greenland

Atmosphere about
310 miles deep

Crust 4–25 miles
thick

Mantle about
1,740 miles
thick

NORTH ATLANTIC OCEAN

Outer core
about 1,430
miles thick

Cyclonic
storm

COMPOSITION OF THE EARTH

Other elements less than 1%

Aluminum 0.4%

Calcium 0.6%

Sulfur 2.7%

Nickel 2.7%

Silicon 13%

Magnesium 17%

Oxygen 28%

Iron 35%

Core temperature about 7,230°F

Molten core of iron
and nickel

Solid inner core
of iron and nickel
about 1,490 miles
in diameter

Gutenberg discontinuity
(boundary between outer
core and mantle)

Mantle of mostly solid
silicate material

Mohorovicic
discontinuity
(boundary
between mantle
and crust)

Crust of silicate rock

Amazon Basin (tropical
rain forest region)

Andes (mountain range
near crustal plate
boundary)

Earthquake region along
crustal plate boundary

Surface temperature
between about -126°F
and 136°F

EUROPE

Atlas Mountains

AFRICA

Sahara (desert
region)

Congo Basin
(tropical rain
forest)

SOUTH
PACIFIC
OCEAN

SOUTH
AMERICA

SOUTH ATLANTIC
OCEAN

Land forms about
30% of surface

Cloud typically covers
about 50% of surface

Oceans cover about
70% of surface

39

Mars

MARS

MARS, KNOWN AS THE RED PLANET, is the fourth planet from the Sun and the outermost rocky planet. In the 19th century, astronomers first observed what were thought to be signs of life on Mars. These signs included apparent canal-like markings on the surface, and dark patches that were thought to be vegetation. It is now known that the canals are an optical illusion and the dark patches are areas where the red dust that covers most of the planet has blown away. The fine dust particles are often whipped up by winds into dust storms that occasionally obscure almost all Mars's surface. Residual dust in the atmosphere gives the Martian sky a pinkish hue. The northern hemisphere of Mars has many large plains formed of solidified volcanic lava, while the southern hemisphere has many craters and large impact basins. There are also several huge, extinct volcanoes, including Olympus Mons, which at 370 miles wide and 15 miles high is the largest known volcano in the Solar System. The surface also has many canyons and branching channels. The canyons were formed by movements of the surface crust, but the channels are thought to have been formed by flowing water that has now vaporized almost completely and escaped from the atmosphere. The Martian atmosphere is much thinner than Earth's, with only a few clouds and morning mists. Mars has two tiny irregularly shaped moons, Phobos and Deimos. Their small size indicates that they may be asteroids that have been captured by the gravity of Mars.

TILT AND ROTATION OF MARS

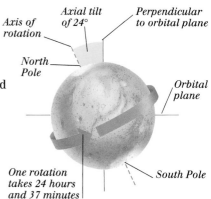

Axis of rotation

Axial tilt of 24°

Perpendicular to orbital plane

North Pole

Orbital plane

One rotation takes 24 hours and 37 minutes

South Pole

SURFACE FEATURES OF MARS

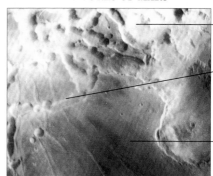

Bright water-ice fog

Fog in canyon about 12 miles wide at end of Valles Marineris

Syria Planum

NOCTIS LABYRINTHUS (CANYON SYSTEM)

Summit caldera consisting of overlapping collapsed volcanic craters

Crater

Gentle slope produced by lava flow

Cloud formation

OLYMPUS MONS (EXTINCT SHIELD VOLCANO)

THE SURFACE OF MARS

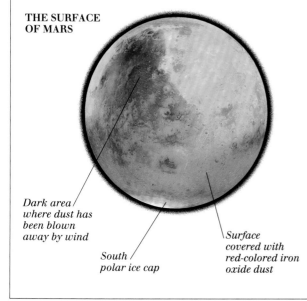

Dark area where dust has been blown away by wind

South polar ice cap

Surface covered with red-colored iron oxide dust

MOONS OF MARS

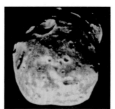

PHOBOS
Average diameter: 14 miles
Average distance from planet: 5,800 miles

DEIMOS
Average diameter: 8 miles
Average distance from planet: 14,600 miles

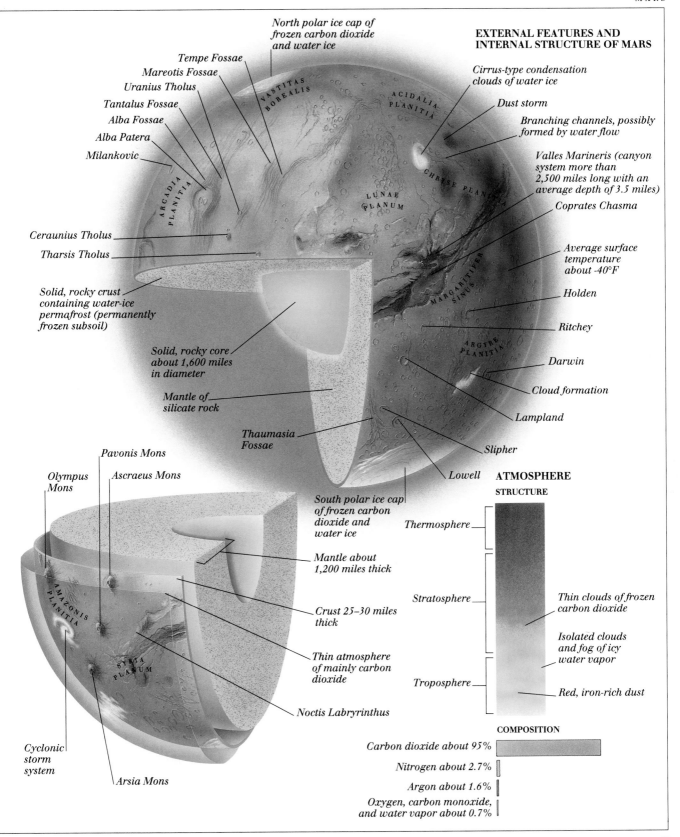

**EXTERNAL FEATURES AND
INTERNAL STRUCTURE OF MARS**

North polar ice cap of
frozen carbon dioxide
and water ice

Tempe Fossae

Mareotis Fossae

Uranius Tholus

Tantalus Fossae

Alba Fossae

Alba Patera

Milankovic

Ceraunius Tholus

Tharsis Tholus

Solid, rocky crust
containing water-ice
permafrost (permanently
frozen subsoil)

Solid, rocky core
about 1,600 miles
in diameter

Mantle of
silicate rock

Thaumasia
Fossae

VASTITAS BOREALIS

ACIDALIA PLANITIA

ARCADIA PLANITIA

CHRYSE PLANITIA

LUNAE PLANUM

MARGARITIFER SINUS

ARGYRE PLANITIA

Cirrus-type condensation
clouds of water ice

Dust storm

Branching channels, possibly
formed by water flow

Valles Marineris (canyon
system more than
2,500 miles long with an
average depth of 3.5 miles)

Coprates Chasma

Average surface
temperature
about -40°F

Holden

Ritchey

Darwin

Cloud formation

Lampland

Slipher

Lowell

South polar ice cap
of frozen carbon
dioxide and
water ice

Olympus
Mons

Pavonis Mons

Ascraeus Mons

AMAZONIS PLANITIA

SYRIA PLANUM

Cyclonic
storm
system

Arsia Mons

Noctis Labryrinthus

Mantle about
1,200 miles thick

Crust 25–30 miles
thick

Thin atmosphere
of mainly carbon
dioxide

ATMOSPHERE

STRUCTURE

Thermosphere

Stratosphere

Troposphere

Thin clouds of frozen
carbon dioxide

Isolated clouds
and fog of icy
water vapor

Red, iron-rich dust

COMPOSITION

Carbon dioxide about 95%

Nitrogen about 2.7%

Argon about 1.6%

Oxygen, carbon monoxide,
and water vapor about 0.7%

Saturn

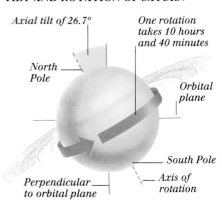

Axial tilt of 26.7°

One rotation takes 10 hours and 40 minutes

North Pole

Orbital plane

South Pole

Axis of rotation

Perpendicular to orbital plane

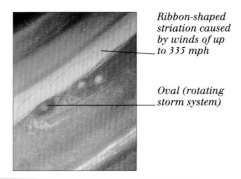

COLOR-ENHANCED IMAGE OF SATURN

SATURN IS THE SIXTH PLANET from the Sun. It is a gas giant almost as big as Jupiter, with an equatorial diameter of about 74,900 miles. Saturn is thought to consist of a small core of rock and ice surrounded by an inner mantle of metallic hydrogen (liquid hydrogen that acts like a metal). Outside the inner mantle is an outer mantle of liquid hydrogen that merges into a gaseous atmosphere. Saturn's clouds form belts and zones similar to those on Jupiter, but obscured by overlying haze. Storms and eddies, seen as red or white ovals, occur in the clouds. Saturn has an extremely thin but wide system of rings that is less than one mile thick but extends outward to about 260,000 miles from the planet's surface. The main rings comprise thousands of narrow ringlets, each made of icy lumps that range in size from tiny particles to chunks several yards across. The D, E, and G rings are very faint, the F ring is brighter, and the A, B, and C rings are bright enough to be seen from Earth with binoculars. Saturn has 18 known moons, some of which orbit inside the rings and are thought to exert a gravitational influence on the shapes of the rings. Unusually, seven of the moons are co-orbital—they share an orbit with another moon. Astronomers believe that such co-orbital moons may have originated from a single satellite that broke up.

COLOR-ENHANCED IMAGE OF SATURN'S CLOUD FEATURES

Ribbon-shaped striation caused by winds of up to 335 mph

Oval (rotating storm system)

INNER RINGS OF SATURN

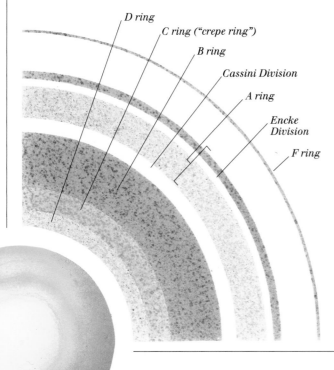

D ring

C ring ("crepe ring")

B ring

Cassini Division

A ring

Encke Division

F ring

MOONS OF SATURN

ENCELADUS
Diameter: 309 miles
Average distance from
planet: 148,000 miles

TETHYS
Diameter: 652 miles
Average distance from
planet: 183,000 miles

DIONE
Diameter: 695 miles
Average distance from
planet: 234,000 miles

MIMAS
Diameter: 247 miles
Average distance from
planet: 115,600 miles

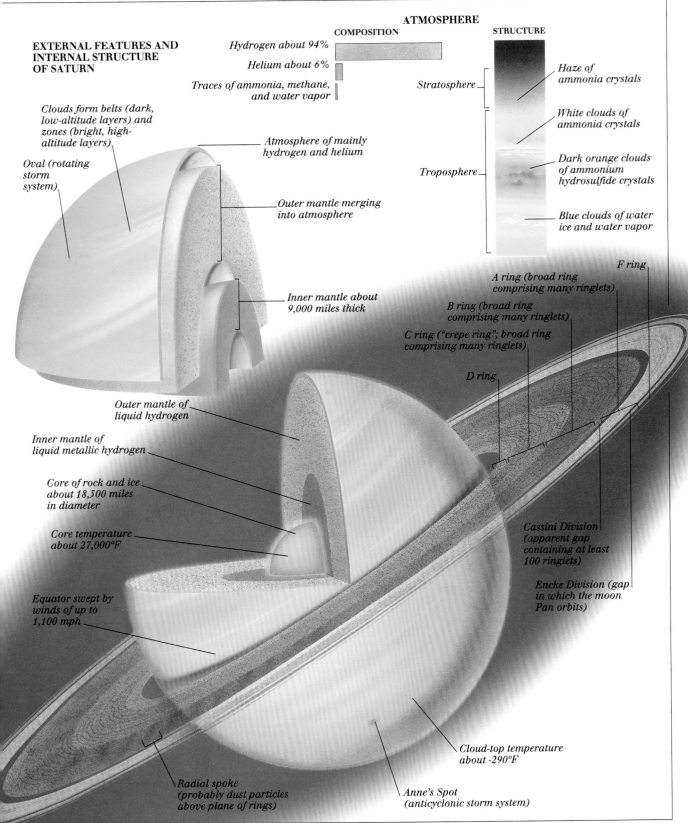

ATMOSPHERE

EXTERNAL FEATURES AND
INTERNAL STRUCTURE
OF SATURN

COMPOSITION

Hydrogen about 94%

Helium about 6%

Traces of ammonia, methane,
and water vapor

STRUCTURE

Stratosphere

Troposphere

Haze of
ammonia crystals

White clouds of
ammonia crystals

Dark orange clouds
of ammonium
hydrosulfide crystals

Blue clouds of water
ice and water vapor

Clouds form belts (dark,
low-altitude layers) and
zones (bright, high-
altitude layers)

Oval (rotating
storm
system)

Atmosphere of mainly
hydrogen and helium

Outer mantle merging
into atmosphere

Inner mantle about
9,000 miles thick

Outer mantle of
liquid hydrogen

Inner mantle of
liquid metallic hydrogen

Core of rock and ice
about 18,500 miles
in diameter

Core temperature
about 27,000°F

Equator swept by
winds of up to
1,100 mph

F ring

A ring (broad ring
comprising many ringlets)

B ring (broad ring
comprising many ringlets)

C ring ("crepe ring"; broad ring
comprising many ringlets)

D ring

Cassini Division
(apparent gap
containing at least
100 ringlets)

Encke Division (gap
in which the moon
Pan orbits)

Cloud-top temperature
about -290°F

Radial spoke
(probably dust particles
above plane of rings)

Anne's Spot
(anticyclonic storm system)

Uranus

COLOR-ENHANCED IMAGE OF URANUS

URANUS IS THE SEVENTH PLANET from the Sun and the third largest, with a diameter of about 32,000 miles. It is thought to consist of a dense mixture of different types of ice and gas around a solid core. Its atmosphere contains traces of methane, giving the planet a blue-green hue, and the temperature at the cloud tops is about -350°F. Uranus is the most featureless planet to have been closely observed: only a few icy clouds of methane have been seen so far. Uranus is unique among the planets in that its axis of rotation lies close to its orbital plane. As a result of its strongly tilted rotational axis, Uranus rolls on its side along its orbital path around the Sun, while other planets spin more or less upright. Uranus is encircled by 11 rings that consist of rocks interspersed with dust lanes. The rings contain some of the darkest matter in the Solar System. They are extremely narrow, making them difficult to detect: nine of them are less than six miles wide, whereas most of Saturn's rings are thousands of miles in width. There are 15 known Uranian moons, all of which are icy and most of which are farther out than the rings. The 10 inner moons are small and dark, with diameters of less than 100 miles, and the five outer moons are between about 290 and 1,000 miles in diameter. The outer moons have a wide variety of surface features. Miranda has the most varied surface, with cratered areas broken up by huge ridges and cliffs 12 miles high.

TILT AND ROTATION OF URANUS

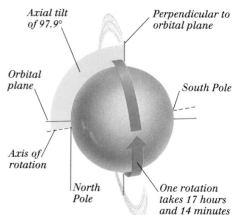

Axial tilt of 97.9°

Perpendicular to orbital plane

Orbital plane

South Pole

Axis of rotation

North Pole

One rotation takes 17 hours and 14 minutes

OUTER MOONS

MIRANDA
Diameter: 293 miles
Average distance from planet: 80,700 miles

RINGS OF URANUS

Epsilon ring

Ring 1986 U1R

Delta ring

Gamma ring

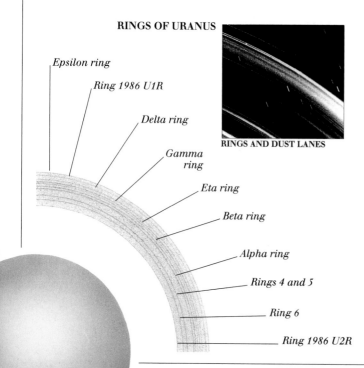

RINGS AND DUST LANES

Eta ring

Beta ring

Alpha ring

Rings 4 and 5

Ring 6

Ring 1986 U2R

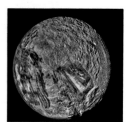

ARIEL
Diameter: 720 miles
Average distance from planet: 118,800 miles

TITANIA
Diameter: 981 miles
Average distance from planet: 270,900 miles

UMBRIEL
Diameter: 726 miles
Average distance from planet: 165,300 miles

OBERON
Diameter: 946 miles
Average distance from planet: 362,000 miles

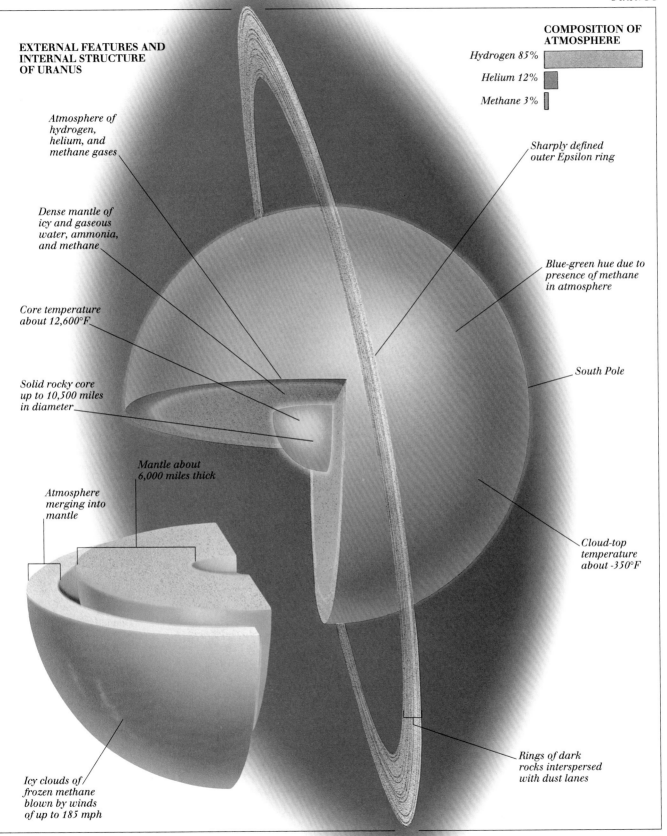

**EXTERNAL FEATURES AND
INTERNAL STRUCTURE
OF URANUS**

**COMPOSITION OF
ATMOSPHERE**

Hydrogen 85%

Helium 12%

Methane 3%

Atmosphere of
hydrogen,
helium, and
methane gases

Dense mantle of
icy and gaseous
water, ammonia,
and methane

Core temperature
about 12,600°F

Solid rocky core
up to 10,500 miles
in diameter

Mantle about
6,000 miles thick

Atmosphere
merging into
mantle

Icy clouds of
frozen methane
blown by winds
of up to 185 mph

Sharply defined
outer Epsilon ring

Blue-green hue due to
presence of methane
in atmosphere

South Pole

Cloud-top
temperature
about -350°F

Rings of dark
rocks interspersed
with dust lanes

Neptune and Pluto

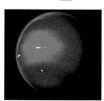

COLOR-ENHANCED
IMAGE OF NEPTUNE

NEPTUNE AND PLUTO are the two farthest planets from the Sun, at an average distance of about 2,800 million miles and 3,700 million miles, respectively. Neptune is a gas giant and is thought to consist of a small rocky core surrounded by a mixture of liquids and gases. The atmosphere contains several prominent cloud features. The largest of these are the Great Dark Spot, which is as wide as the Earth, the Small Dark Spot, and the Scooter. The Great and Small Dark Spots are huge storms that are swept around the planet by winds of about 1,200 miles per hour. The Scooter is a large area of cirrus cloud. Neptune has four tenuous rings and eight known moons. Triton is the largest Neptunian moon and the coldest object in the Solar System, with a temperature of -391°F. Unlike most moons in the Solar System, Triton orbits its mother planet in the opposite direction to the planet's rotation. Pluto is usually the outermost planet, but its elliptical orbit causes it to pass inside the orbit of Neptune for 20 years of its 248-year orbit. Pluto is so small and distant that little is known about it. It is a rocky planet, probably covered with ice and frozen methane. Pluto's only known moon, Charon, is large for a moon, at half the size of its parent planet. Because of the small difference in their sizes, Pluto and Charon are sometimes considered to be a double-planet system.

TILT AND ROTATION OF NEPTUNE

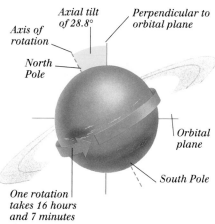

Axis of rotation

Axial tilt of 28.8°

Perpendicular to orbital plane

North Pole

Orbital plane

South Pole

One rotation takes 16 hours and 7 minutes

CLOUD FEATURES OF NEPTUNE

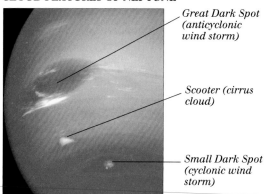

Great Dark Spot (anticyclonic wind storm)

Scooter (cirrus cloud)

Small Dark Spot (cyclonic wind storm)

RINGS OF NEPTUNE

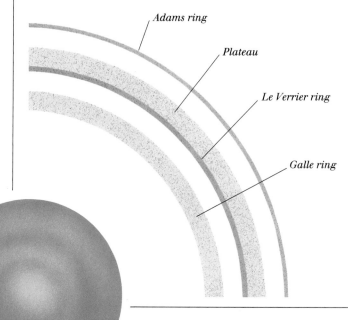

Adams ring

Plateau

Le Verrier ring

Galle ring

HIGH-ALTITUDE CLOUDS

Methane cirrus clouds 25 miles above main cloud deck

Cloud shadow

Main cloud deck blown by winds at speeds of about 1,200 mph

MOONS OF NEPTUNE

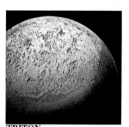

TRITON
Diameter: 1,681 miles
Average distance from planet: 220,500 miles

PROTEUS
Diameter: 259 miles
Average distance from planet: 73,100 miles

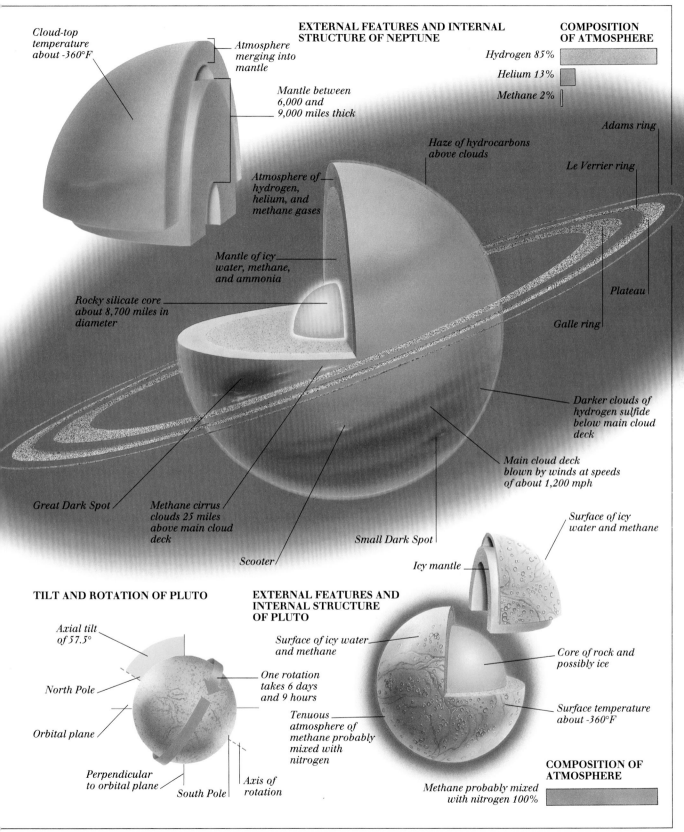

EXTERNAL FEATURES AND INTERNAL STRUCTURE OF NEPTUNE

COMPOSITION OF ATMOSPHERE

Hydrogen 85%

Helium 13%

Methane 2%

Cloud-top temperature about -360°F

Atmosphere merging into mantle

Mantle between 6,000 and 9,000 miles thick

Haze of hydrocarbons above clouds

Adams ring

Le Verrier ring

Atmosphere of hydrogen, helium, and methane gases

Mantle of icy water, methane, and ammonia

Rocky silicate core about 8,700 miles in diameter

Plateau

Galle ring

Darker clouds of hydrogen sulfide below main cloud deck

Main cloud deck blown by winds at speeds of about 1,200 mph

Great Dark Spot

Methane cirrus clouds 25 miles above main cloud deck

Scooter

Small Dark Spot

Surface of icy water and methane

Icy mantle

TILT AND ROTATION OF PLUTO

EXTERNAL FEATURES AND INTERNAL STRUCTURE OF PLUTO

Axial tilt of 57.5°

North Pole

Orbital plane

Perpendicular to orbital plane

South Pole

Axis of rotation

Surface of icy water and methane

One rotation takes 6 days and 9 hours

Tenuous atmosphere of methane probably mixed with nitrogen

Core of rock and possibly ice

Surface temperature about -360°F

COMPOSITION OF ATMOSPHERE

Methane probably mixed with nitrogen 100%

51

Asteroids, comets, and meteoroids

ASTEROIDS, COMETS, AND METEOROIDS are all debris remaining from the nebula in which the Solar System formed 4.6 billion years ago. Asteroids are rocky bodies up to several hundred miles in diameter, although most are much smaller. Most of them orbit the Sun in the asteroid belt, which lies between the orbits of Mars and Jupiter. Comets may originate in a huge cloud, called the Oort Cloud, that is thought to surround the Solar System. They are made of frozen gases and dust, and are a few miles in diameter. Occasionally, a comet is deflected from the Oort Cloud to orbit the Sun in a long, elliptical path. As the comet approaches the Sun, the comet's surface starts to vaporize in the heat, producing a brightly shining coma (a huge sphere of gas and dust around the nucleus), a gas tail, and a dust tail. Meteoroids are small chunks of stone or stone and iron, some of which are fragments of asteroids or comets. Meteoroids range in size from tiny dust particles to objects tens of yards across. If a meteoroid enters the Earth's atmosphere, it is heated by friction and appears as a glowing streak of light called a meteor (also known as a shooting star). Meteor showers occur when the Earth passes through the trail of dust particles left by a comet. Most meteors burn up in the atmosphere. The few that are large enough to reach the Earth's surface are termed meteorites.

ASTEROID 951 GASPRA

OPTICAL IMAGE OF HALLEY'S COMET

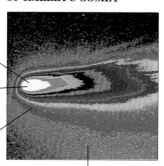

COLOR-ENHANCED IMAGE OF HALLEY'S COMET

High-intensity light emission

Nucleus

Medium-intensity light emission

Low-intensity light emission

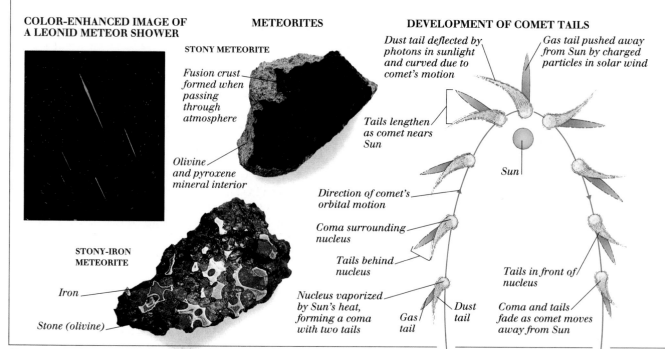

COLOR-ENHANCED IMAGE OF A LEONID METEOR SHOWER

METEORITES

STONY METEORITE

Fusion crust formed when passing through atmosphere

Olivine and pyroxene mineral interior

STONY-IRON METEORITE

Iron

Stone (olivine)

DEVELOPMENT OF COMET TAILS

Dust tail deflected by photons in sunlight and curved due to comet's motion

Gas tail pushed away from Sun by charged particles in solar wind

Tails lengthen as comet nears Sun

Sun

Direction of comet's orbital motion

Coma surrounding nucleus

Tails behind nucleus

Tails in front of nucleus

Nucleus vaporized by Sun's heat, forming a coma with two tails

Gas tail

Dust tail

Coma and tails fade as comet moves away from Sun

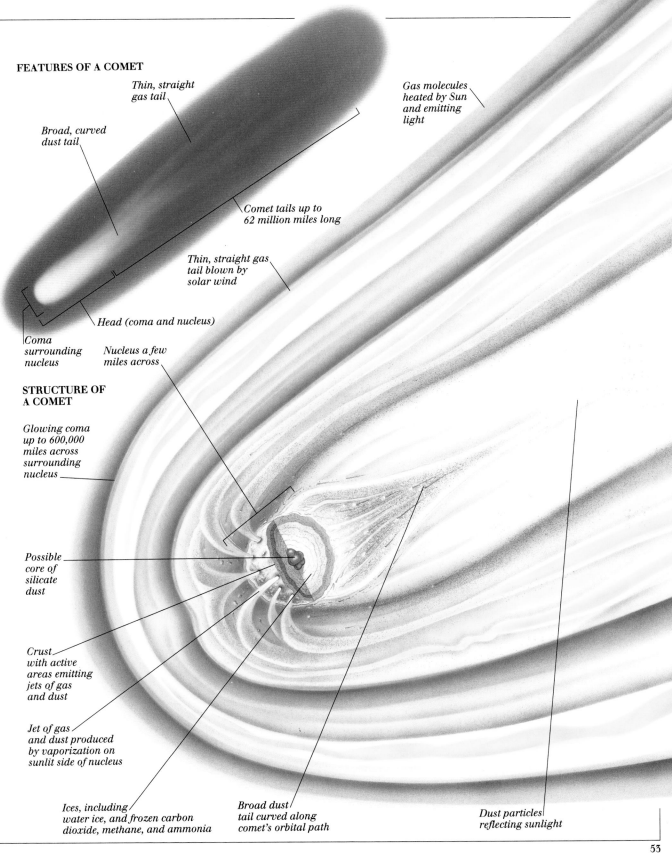

FEATURES OF A COMET

Thin, straight
gas tail

Broad, curved
dust tail

Gas molecules
heated by Sun
and emitting
light

Comet tails up to
62 million miles long

Thin, straight gas
tail blown by
solar wind

Head (coma and nucleus)

Coma
surrounding
nucleus

Nucleus a few
miles across

**STRUCTURE OF
A COMET**

Glowing coma
up to 600,000
miles across
surrounding
nucleus

Possible
core of
silicate
dust

Crust
with active
areas emitting
jets of gas
and dust

Jet of gas
and dust produced
by vaporization on
sunlit side of nucleus

Ices, including
water ice, and frozen carbon
dioxide, methane, and ammonia

Broad dust
tail curved along
comet's orbital path

Dust particles
reflecting sunlight

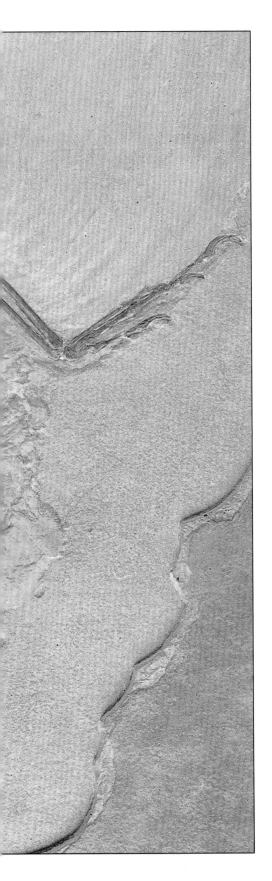

PREHISTORIC EARTH

The Earth's crust

THE EARTH'S CRUST IS THE SOLID outer shell of the Earth. It includes
continental crust (about 25 miles thick) and oceanic crust (about
four miles thick). The crust and the topmost layer of the mantle
form the lithosphere. The lithosphere consists of semi-rigid plates
that move relative to each other on the underlying asthenosphere
(a partly molten layer of the mantle). This movement is known as
plate tectonics and helps explain continental drift. Where two plates
move apart, there are rifts in the crust. In mid-ocean, this movement
results in seafloor spreading and the formation of ocean ridges; on continents,
crustal spreading can form rift valleys. When plates move toward each other,
one may be subducted beneath (forced under) the other. In mid-ocean, this causes
ocean trenches, seismic activity, and arcs of volcanic islands. Where oceanic crust
is subducted beneath continental crust or where continents collide, land may be
uplifted and mountains formed (see pp. 62–63). Plates may also slide past each
other—along the San Andreas fault, for example. Crustal movement on continents
may result in earthquakes, while movement under the seabed can lead to tidal waves.

ELEMENTS IN THE EARTH'S CRUST

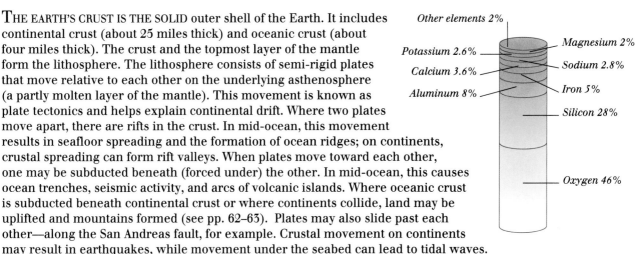

Other elements 2%
Potassium 2.6%
Calcium 3.6%
Aluminum 8%
Magnesium 2%
Sodium 2.8%
Iron 5%
Silicon 28%
Oxygen 46%

FEATURES OF PLATE MOVEMENTS

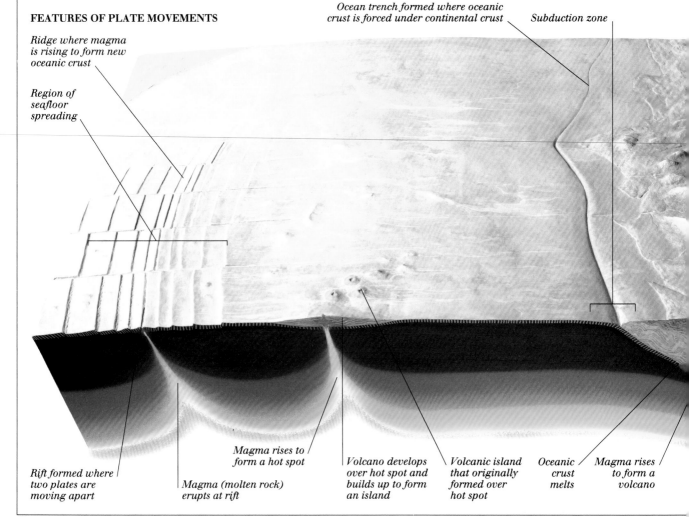

Ocean trench formed where oceanic
crust is forced under continental crust

Subduction zone

Ridge where magma
is rising to form new
oceanic crust

Region of
seafloor
spreading

Magma rises to
form a hot spot

Volcano develops
over hot spot and
builds up to form
an island

Volcanic island
that originally
formed over
hot spot

Oceanic
crust
melts

Magma rises
to form a
volcano

Rift formed where
two plates are
moving apart

Magma (molten rock)
erupts at rift

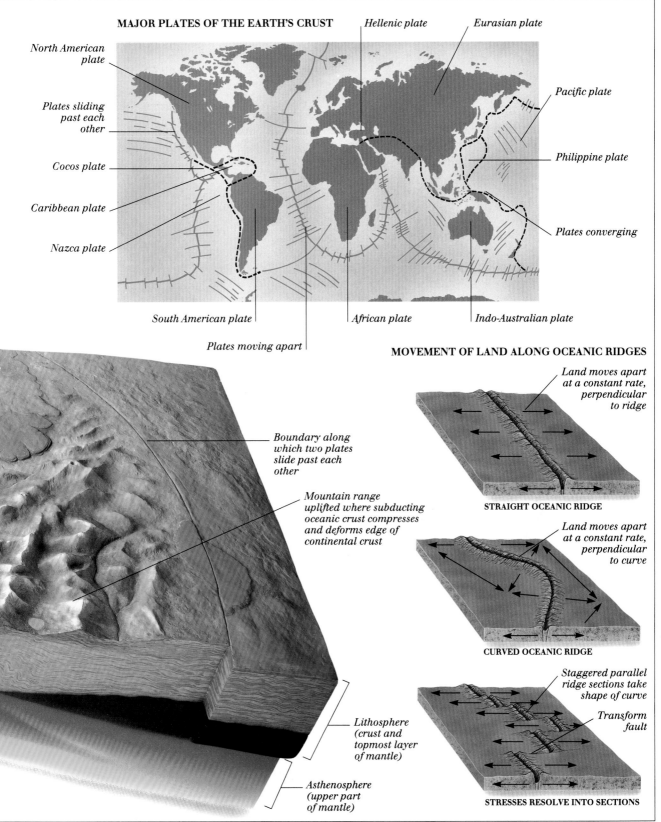

MAJOR PLATES OF THE EARTH'S CRUST

North American plate

Hellenic plate

Eurasian plate

Plates sliding past each other

Pacific plate

Cocos plate

Philippine plate

Caribbean plate

Plates converging

Nazca plate

South American plate

African plate

Indo-Australian plate

Plates moving apart

Boundary along which two plates slide past each other

Mountain range uplifted where subducting oceanic crust compresses and deforms edge of continental crust

Lithosphere (crust and topmost layer of mantle)

Asthenosphere (upper part of mantle)

MOVEMENT OF LAND ALONG OCEANIC RIDGES

Land moves apart at a constant rate, perpendicular to ridge

STRAIGHT OCEANIC RIDGE

Land moves apart at a constant rate, perpendicular to curve

CURVED OCEANIC RIDGE

Staggered parallel ridge sections take shape of curve

Transform fault

STRESSES RESOLVE INTO SECTIONS

Faults and folds

THE CONTINUOUS MOVEMENT of the Earth's crustal plates (see pp. 58–59) can squeeze, stretch, or break rock strata, deforming them and producing faults and folds. A fault is a fracture in a rock along which there is movement of one side relative to the other. The movement can be vertical, horizontal, or oblique (vertical and horizontal). Faults develop when rocks are subjected to compression or tension. They tend to occur in hard, rigid rocks, which are more likely to break than bend. The smallest faults occur in single mineral crystals and are microscopically small, while the largest —the Great Rift Valley in Africa, which formed between 5 million and 100,000 years ago—is more than 6,000 miles long. A fold is a bend in a rock layer caused by compression. Folds occur in elastic rocks, which tend to bend rather than break. The two main types of fold are anticlines (upfolds) and synclines (downfolds). Folds vary in size from a few millimeters long to folded mountain ranges hundreds of miles long, such as the Himalayas (see pp. 62–63) and the Alps, which are repeatedly folding. In addition to faults and folds, other features associated with rock deformations include boudins, mullions, and *en échelon* fractures.

STRUCTURE OF A FOLD

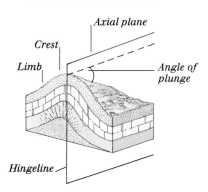

Axial plane
Crest
Limb
Angle of plunge
Hingeline

STRUCTURE OF A FAULT

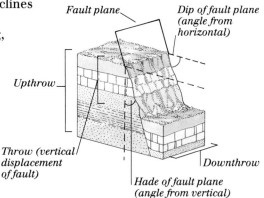

Fault plane
Dip of fault plane (angle from horizontal)
Upthrow
Throw (vertical displacement of fault)
Hade of fault plane (angle from vertical)
Downthrow

STRUCTURE OF A SLOPE

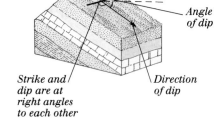

Strike
Angle of dip
Strike and dip are at right angles to each other
Direction of dip

FOLDED ROCK

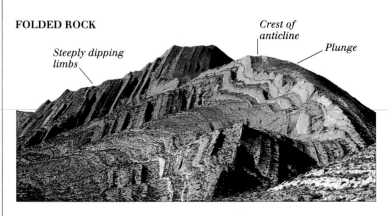

Steeply dipping limbs
Crest of anticline
Plunge

SECTION THROUGH FOLDED ROCK STRATA THAT HAVE BEEN ERODED

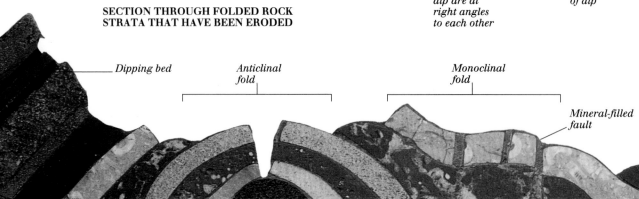

Dipping bed
Anticlinal fold
Monoclinal fold
Mineral-filled fault
Upper Carboniferous Millstone Grit
Lower Carboniferous Limestone

EXAMPLES OF FOLDS

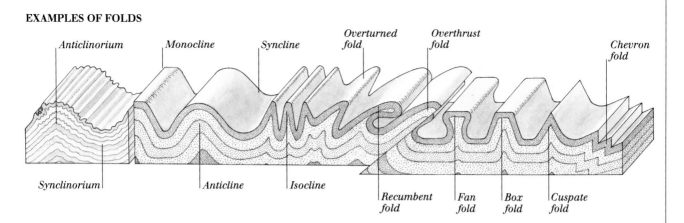

Anticlinorium · Monocline · Syncline · Overturned fold · Overthrust fold · Chevron fold

Synclinorium · Anticline · Isocline · Recumbent fold · Fan fold · Box fold · Cuspate fold

EXAMPLES OF FAULTS

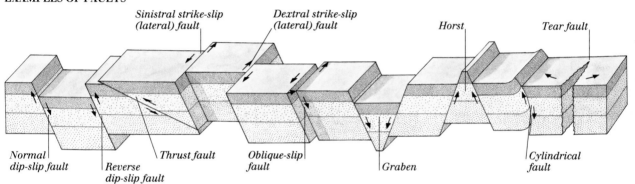

Sinistral strike-slip (lateral) fault · Dextral strike-slip (lateral) fault · Horst · Tear fault

Normal dip-slip fault · Reverse dip-slip fault · Thrust fault · Oblique-slip fault · Graben · Cylindrical fault

SMALL-SCALE ROCK DEFORMATIONS

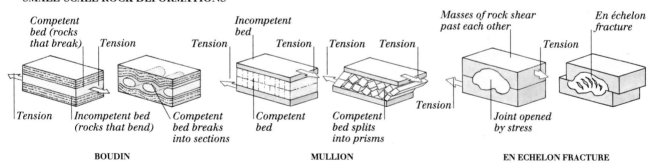

Competent bed (rocks that break) · Tension · Tension · Incompetent bed · Tension · Tension · Tension · Masses of rock shear past each other · En échelon fracture · Tension

Tension · Incompetent bed (rocks that bend) · Competent bed breaks into sections · Competent bed · Competent bed splits into prisms · Tension · Joint opened by stress

BOUDIN · **MULLION** · **EN ECHELON FRACTURE**

Mineral-filled fault · Dipping bed · Gently folded bed · Horizontal bed · Mineral-filled fault · Dipping bed

Upper Carboniferous Millstone Grit · Upper Carboniferous Coal Measures

Mountain building

THE PROCESSES INVOLVED in mountain building—termed orogenesis—occur as a result of the movement of the Earth's crustal plates (see pp. 58-59). There are three main types of mountains: volcanic mountains, fold mountains, and block mountains. Most volcanic mountains have been formed along plate boundaries where plates have come together or moved apart and lava and other debris have been ejected onto the Earth's surface. The lava and debris may have built up to form a dome around the vent of a volcano. Fold mountains are formed where plates push together and cause the rock to buckle upward. Where oceanic crust meets less dense continental crust, the oceanic crust is forced under the continental crust. The continental crust is buckled by the impact. This is how folded mountain ranges, such as the Appalachian Mountains in North America, were formed. Fold mountains are also formed where two areas of continental crust meet. The Himalayas, for example, began to form when India collided with Asia, buckling the sediments and parts of the oceanic crust between them. Block mountains are formed when a block of land is uplifted between two faults as a result of compression or tension in the Earth's crust (see pp. 60-61). Often, the movement along faults has taken place gradually over millions of years. However, two plates may cause an earthquake by suddenly sliding past each other along a faultline.

BHAGIRATHI PARBAT,
HIMALAYAS

Asia

Himalayas formed by buckling of sediment and part of the oceanic crust between two colliding continents

India moves north

India collides with Asia about 40 million years ago

EXAMPLES OF MOUNTAINS

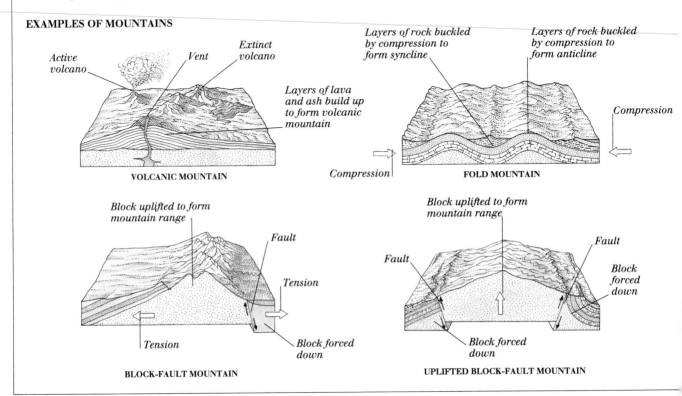

Active volcano

Vent

Extinct volcano

Layers of lava and ash build up to form volcanic mountain

VOLCANIC MOUNTAIN

Layers of rock buckled by compression to form syncline

Layers of rock buckled by compression to form anticline

Compression

Compression

FOLD MOUNTAIN

Block uplifted to form mountain range

Fault

Tension

Tension

Block forced down

BLOCK-FAULT MOUNTAIN

Block uplifted to form mountain range

Fault

Fault

Block forced down

Block forced down

UPLIFTED BLOCK-FAULT MOUNTAIN

STAGES IN THE FORMATION OF THE HIMALAYAS

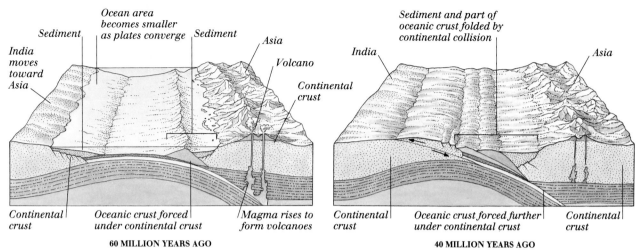

Sediment

Ocean area becomes smaller as plates converge

Sediment

Asia

Volcano

Continental crust

India moves toward Asia

Continental crust

Oceanic crust forced under continental crust

Magma rises to form volcanoes

60 MILLION YEARS AGO

Sediment and part of oceanic crust folded by continental collision

India

Asia

Continental crust

Oceanic crust forced further under continental crust

Continental crust

40 MILLION YEARS AGO

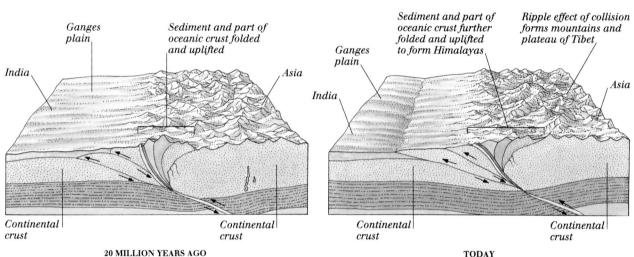

Ganges plain

Sediment and part of oceanic crust folded and uplifted

India

Asia

Continental crust

Continental crust

20 MILLION YEARS AGO

Sediment and part of oceanic crust further folded and uplifted to form Himalayas

Ripple effect of collision forms mountains and plateau of Tibet

Ganges plain

India

Asia

Continental crust

Continental crust

TODAY

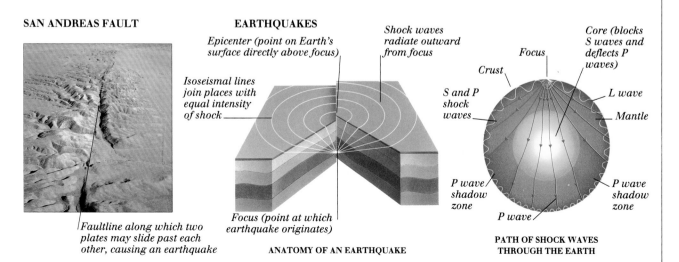

SAN ANDREAS FAULT

Faultline along which two plates may slide past each other, causing an earthquake

EARTHQUAKES

Epicenter (point on Earth's surface directly above focus)

Shock waves radiate outward from focus

Isoseismal lines join places with equal intensity of shock

Focus (point at which earthquake originates)

ANATOMY OF AN EARTHQUAKE

Core (blocks S waves and deflects P waves)

Focus

Crust

L wave

S and P shock waves

Mantle

P wave shadow zone

P wave shadow zone

P wave

PATH OF SHOCK WAVES THROUGH THE EARTH

Precambrian to Devonian periods

WHEN THE EARTH FORMED about 4,600 million years ago, its atmosphere consisted of volcanic gases with little oxygen, making it hostile to most forms of life. One large supercontinent, Gondwanaland, was situated over the southern polar region, while other smaller continents were spread over the rest of the world. Constant movement of the earth's crustal plates carried continents across the earth's surface. The first primitive life-forms emerged around 3,400 million years ago in shallow, warm seas. The build up of oxygen began to form a shield of ozone around the earth, protecting living organisms from the sun's harmful rays and helping to establish an atmosphere in which life could sustain itself. The first vertebrates appeared about 470 million years ago, during the Ordovician period (510–439 million years ago), the first land plants appeared around 400 million years ago during the Devonian period (409–363 million years ago), and the first land animals about 30 million years later.

MIDDLE ORDOVICIAN POSITIONS OF PRESENT-DAY LANDMASSES

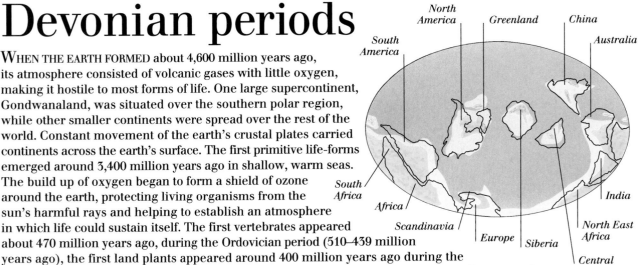

North America · Greenland · China · South America · Australia · South Africa · Africa · India · Scandinavia · Europe · Siberia · North East Africa · Central Asia

EXAMPLES OF PRECAMBRIAN TO DEVONIAN PLANT GROUPS

A PRESENT-DAY CLUBMOSS
(Lycopodium sp.)

A PRESENT-DAY LAND PLANT
(Asparagus setaceous)

FOSSIL OF AN EXTINCT LAND PLANT
(Cooksonia hemisphaerica)

FOSSIL OF AN EXTINCT SWAMP PLANT
(Zosterophyllum llanoveranum)

EXAMPLES OF PRECAMBRIAN TO DEVONIAN TRILOBITES

ACADAGNOSTUS
Family: Agnostidae
Length: $^1/_3$ in (8 mm)

PHACOPS
Family: Phacopidae
Length: $1^3/_4$ in (4.5 cm)

OLENELLUS
Family: Olenellidae
Length: $2^1/_2$ in (6 cm)

ELRATHIA
Family: Ptychopariidae
Length: $^3/_4$ in (2 cm)

THE EARTH DURING THE MIDDLE ORDOVICIAN PERIOD

Siberia

Laurentia

China

Kazakstania

Gondwanaland

Baltica

EXAMPLES OF EARLY MARINE INVERTEBRATES

FOSSIL NAUTILOID
(*Estonioceras perforatum*)

FOSSIL BRACHIOPOD
(*Dicoelosia bilobata*)

TRACE FOSSIL
(*Mawsonites spriggi*)

FOSSIL GRAPTOLITE
(*Monograptus convolutus*)

EXAMPLES OF DEVONIAN FISH

RHAMPHODOPSIS
Family: Ptyctodontidae
Length: 6 in (15 cm)

PTERASPIS
Family: Pteraspidae
Length: 10 in (25 cm)

COCCOSTEUS
Family: Coccosteidae
Length: 14 in (35 cm)

BOTHRIOLEPIS
Family: Bothriolepidae
Length: 16 in (40 cm)

CHEIRACANTHUS
Family: Acanthodidae
Length: 12 in (30 cm)

PTERICHTHYODES
Family: Asterolepidae
Length: 6 in (15 cm)

CHEIROLEPIS
Family: Cheirolepidae
Length: 6¾ in (17 cm)

CEPHALASPIS
Family: Cephalaspidae
Length: 8¾ in (22 cm)

Carboniferous to Permian periods

LATE CARBONIFEROUS POSITIONS OF PRESENT-DAY LANDMASSES

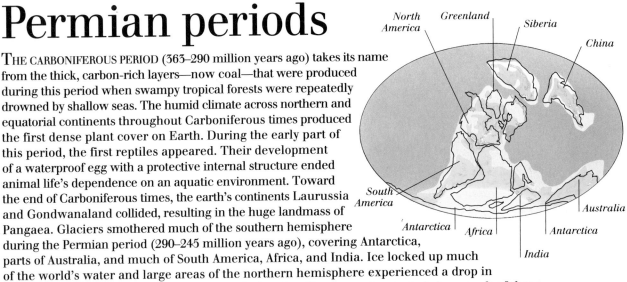

North America · Greenland · Siberia · China · South America · Antarctica · Africa · India · Australia · Antarctica

THE CARBONIFEROUS PERIOD (363–290 million years ago) takes its name from the thick, carbon-rich layers—now coal—that were produced during this period when swampy tropical forests were repeatedly drowned by shallow seas. The humid climate across northern and equatorial continents throughout Carboniferous times produced the first dense plant cover on Earth. During the early part of this period, the first reptiles appeared. Their development of a waterproof egg with a protective internal structure ended animal life's dependence on an aquatic environment. Toward the end of Carboniferous times, the earth's continents Laurussia and Gondwanaland collided, resulting in the huge landmass of Pangaea. Glaciers smothered much of the southern hemisphere during the Permian period (290–245 million years ago), covering Antarctica, parts of Australia, and much of South America, Africa, and India. Ice locked up much of the world's water and large areas of the northern hemisphere experienced a drop in sea-level. Away from the poles, deserts and a hot dry climate predominated. As a result of these conditions, the Permian period ended with the greatest mass extinction of life on earth ever.

EXAMPLES OF CARBONIFEROUS AND PERMIAN PLANT GROUPS

A PRESENT-DAY FIR
(Abies concolor)

FOSSIL OF AN EXTINCT FERN
(Zeilleria frenzlii)

FOSSIL OF AN EXTINCT HORSETAIL
(Equisetites sp.)

FOSSIL OF AN EXTINCT CLUBMOSS
(Lepidodendron sp.)

EXAMPLES OF CARBONIFEROUS AND PERMIAN TREES

PECOPTERIS
Family: Marattiaceae
Height: 13 ft (4 m)

PARIPTERIS
Family: Medullosaceae
Height: 16 ft 6 in (5 m)

MARIOPTERIS
Family: Unclassified
Height: 16 ft 6 in (5 m)

MEDULLOSA
Family: Medullosaceae
Height: 16 ft 6 in (5 m)

THE EARTH DURING THE LATE CARBONIFEROUS PERIOD

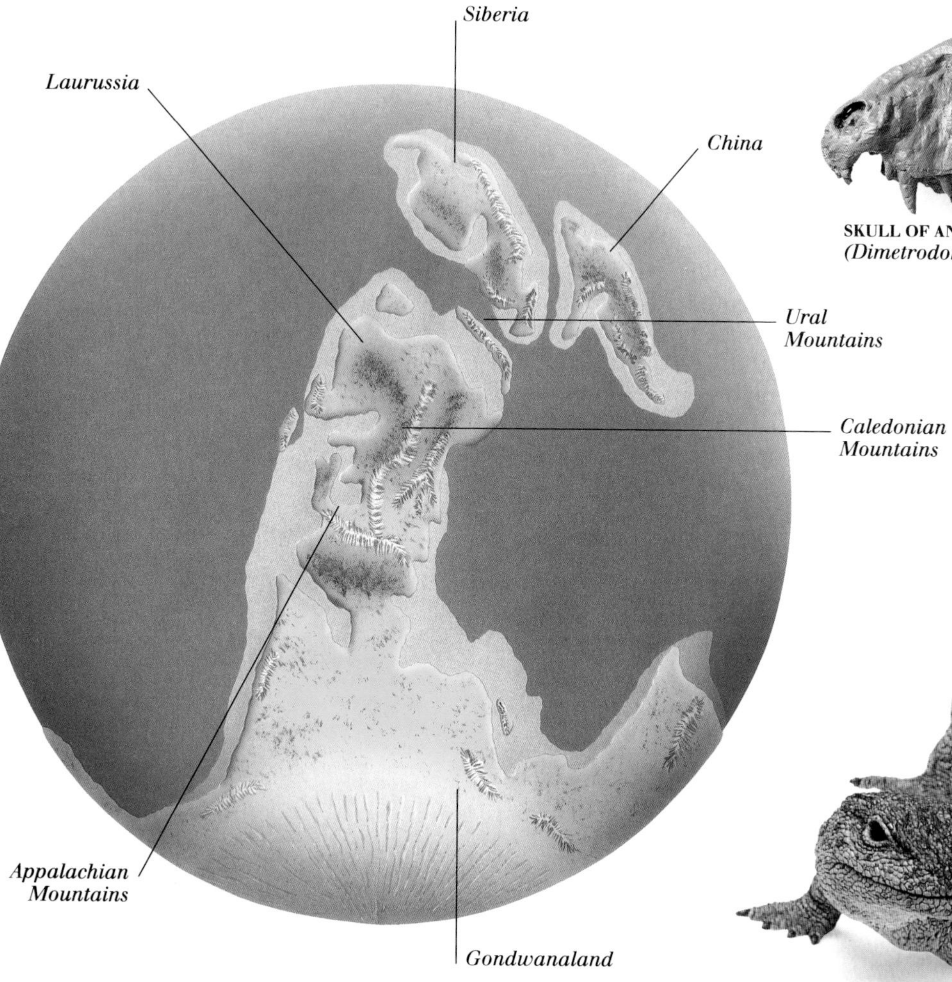

Siberia

Laurussia

China

Ural
Mountains

Caledonian
Mountains

Appalachian
Mountains

Gondwanaland

EXAMPLES OF CARBONIFEROUS AND PERMIAN ANIMALS

SKULL OF AN EXTINCT SYNAPSID REPTILE
(*Dimetrodon loomisi*)

**FOSSIL TEETH OF
AN EXTINCT SHARK**
(*Helicoprion bessonowi*)

**MODEL OF AN EXTINCT
CARBONIFEROUS REPTILE**
(*Westlothiana lizziae*)

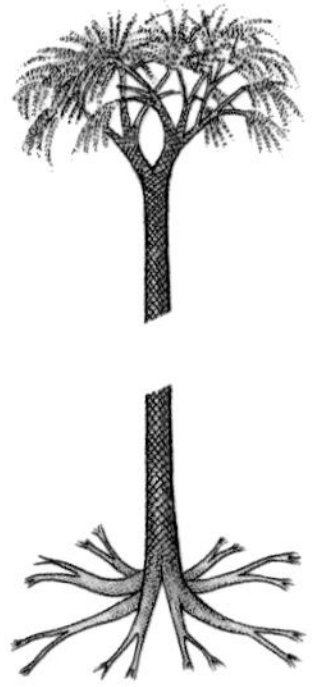

LEPIDODENDRON
Family: Lepidodendraceae
Height: 100 ft (30 m)

CORDAITES
Family: Cordaitacea
Height: 33 ft (10 m)

GLOSSOPTERIS
Family: Glossopteridaceae
Height: 26 ft (8 m)

ALETHOPTERIS
Family Medullosaceae
Height: 16 ft 6 in (5 m)

Jurassic period

THE JURASSIC PERIOD, the middle part of the Mesozoic era, lasted from 208 to 146 million years ago. During the Jurassic period, the landmass of Pangaea broke up into the continents of Gondwanaland and Laurasia, and sea-levels rose, flooding areas of lower land. The Jurassic climate was warm and moist. Plants such as ginkgos, horsetails, and conifers thrived, and giant redwood trees appeared, as did the first flowering plants. The abundance of plant food coincided with the proliferation of herbivorous (plant-eating) dinosaurs, such as the large sauropods (e.g., *Diplodocus*) and stegosaurs (e.g., *Stegosaurus*). Carnivorous (flesh-eating) dinosaurs, such as *Compsognathus* and *Allosaurus*, also flourished by hunting the many animals that existed—among them other dinosaurs. Further Jurassic animals included shrewlike mammals, and pterosaurs (flying reptiles), as well as plesiosaurs and ichthyosaurs (both marine reptiles).

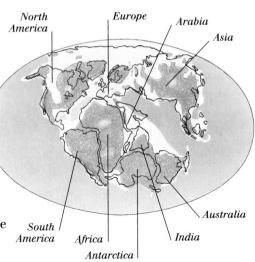

North America Europe Arabia Asia South America Africa Antarctica India Australia

EXAMPLES OF JURASSIC PLANT GROUPS

A PRESENT-DAY FERN
(Dicksonia antarctica)

A PRESENT-DAY HORSETAIL
(Equisetum arvense)

A PRESENT-DAY CONIFER
(Taxus baccata)

FOSSIL LEAF OF AN EXTINCT CONIFER
(Taxus sp.)

FOSSIL LEAF OF AN EXTINCT REDWOOD
(Sequoiadendron affinis)

EXAMPLES OF JURASSIC DINOSAURS

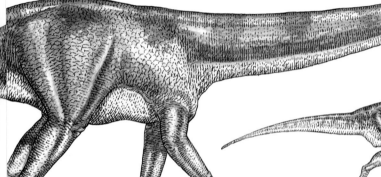
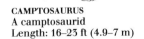

DIPLODOCUS
A diplodocid
Length: 88 ft (26.8 m)

CAMPTOSAURUS
A camptosaurid
Length: 16–23 ft (4.9–7 m)

DRYOSAURUS
A dryosaurid
Length: 10–13 ft (3–4 m)

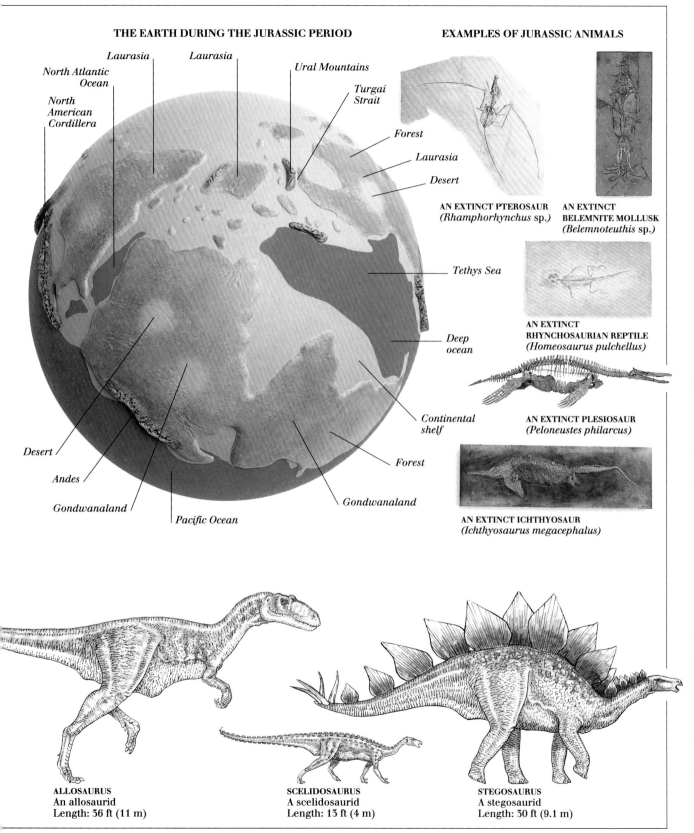

THE EARTH DURING THE JURASSIC PERIOD

Laurasia

Laurasia

North Atlantic Ocean

Ural Mountains

Turgai Strait

North American Cordillera

Forest

Laurasia

Desert

Tethys Sea

Deep ocean

Continental shelf

Desert

Andes

Forest

Gondwanaland

Gondwanaland

Pacific Ocean

EXAMPLES OF JURASSIC ANIMALS

AN EXTINCT PTEROSAUR
(*Rhamphorhynchus* sp.)

AN EXTINCT BELEMNITE MOLLUSK
(*Belemnoteuthis* sp.)

AN EXTINCT RHYNCHOSAURIAN REPTILE
(*Homeosaurus pulchellus*)

AN EXTINCT PLESIOSAUR
(*Peloneustes philarcus*)

AN EXTINCT ICHTHYOSAUR
(*Ichthyosaurus megacephalus*)

ALLOSAURUS
An allosaurid
Length: 36 ft (11 m)

SCELIDOSAURUS
A scelidosaurid
Length: 13 ft (4 m)

STEGOSAURUS
A stegosaurid
Length: 30 ft (9.1 m)

Cretaceous period

THE MESOZOIC ERA ENDED WITH the Cretaceous period, which lasted from 146 to 65 million years ago. During this period, Gondwanaland and Laurasia were breaking up into smaller landmasses that more closely resembled those of the modern continents. The climate remained mild and moist, but the seasons became more marked. Flowering plants, including deciduous trees, replaced many cycads, seed ferns, and conifers. Animal species became more varied, with the evolution of new mammals, insects, fish, crustaceans, and turtles. Dinosaurs evolved into a wide variety of species during Cretaceous times; more than half of all known dinosaurs—including *Iguanodon, Deinonychus, Tyrannosaurus,* and *Hypsilophodon* —lived during this period. At the end of the Cretaceous period, however, large dinosaurs became extinct. The reason for this mass extinction is unknown but it is thought to have been caused by climatic changes due to either a catastrophic meteor impact with the Earth or extensive volcanic eruptions.

CRETACEOUS POSITIONS OF PRESENT-DAY LANDMASSES

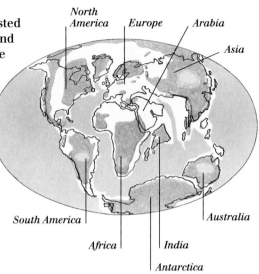

North America
Europe
Arabia
Asia
South America
Africa
India
Antarctica
Australia

EXAMPLES OF CRETACEOUS PLANT GROUPS

A PRESENT-DAY CONIFER
(*Pinus muricata*)

A PRESENT-DAY DECIDUOUS TREE
(*Magnolia* sp.)

FOSSIL OF AN EXTINCT FERN
(*Sphenopteris latiloba*)

FOSSIL OF AN EXTINCT GINKGO
(*Ginkgo pluripartita*)

FOSSIL LEAVES OF AN EXTINCT DECIDUOUS TREE
(*Cercidyphyllum* sp.)

EXAMPLES OF CRETACEOUS DINOSAURS

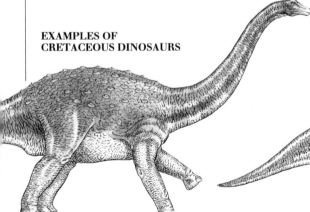

SALTASAURUS
A titanosaurid
Length: 40 ft (12.2 m)

TOROSAURUS
A ceratopsid
Length: 25 ft (7.6 m)

HYPSILOPHODON
A hypsilophodontid
Length: 4 ft 6 in–7 ft 6 in (1.4–2.3 m)

THE EARTH DURING THE CRETACEOUS PERIOD

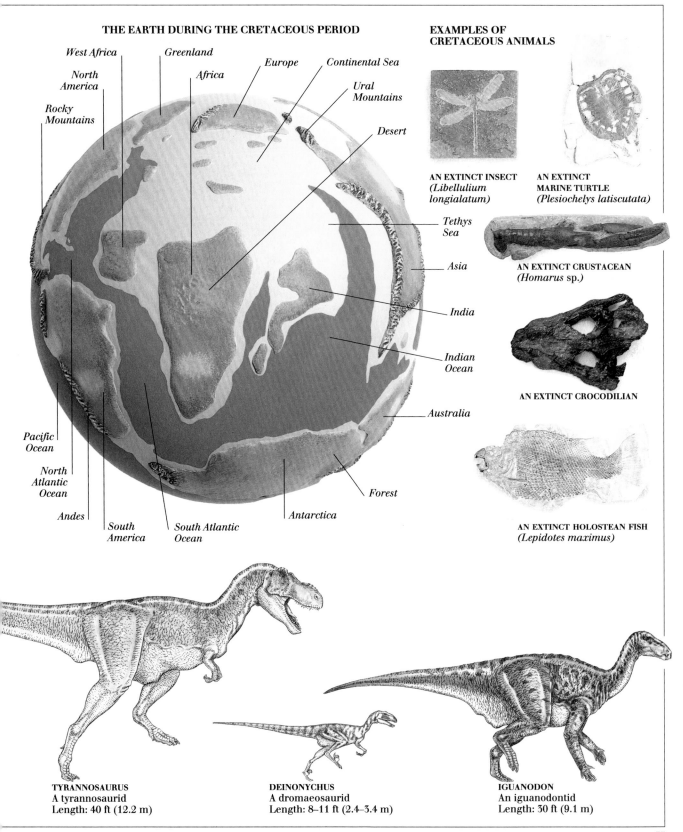

West Africa

North America

Rocky Mountains

Greenland

Africa

Europe

Continental Sea

Ural Mountains

Desert

Tethys Sea

Asia

India

Indian Ocean

Australia

Forest

Antarctica

South Atlantic Ocean

South America

Andes

North Atlantic Ocean

Pacific Ocean

EXAMPLES OF CRETACEOUS ANIMALS

AN EXTINCT INSECT
(Libellulium longialatum)

AN EXTINCT MARINE TURTLE
(Plesiochelys latiscutata)

AN EXTINCT CRUSTACEAN
(Homarus sp.)

AN EXTINCT CROCODILIAN

AN EXTINCT HOLOSTEAN FISH
(Lepidotes maximus)

TYRANNOSAURUS
A tyrannosaurid
Length: 40 ft (12.2 m)

DEINONYCHUS
A dromaeosaurid
Length: 8–11 ft (2.4–3.4 m)

IGUANODON
An iguanodontid
Length: 30 ft (9.1 m)

Tertiary period

TERTIARY POSITIONS OF
PRESENT-DAY LANDMASSES

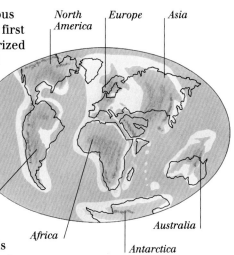

*North
America*   *Europe*   *Asia*

*South
America*

Africa

Australia

Antarctica

FOLLOWING THE DEMISE OF THE DINOSAURS at the end of the Cretaceous period, the Tertiary period (65–1.6 million years ago), which formed the first part of the Cenozoic era (65 million years ago–present), was characterized by a huge expansion of mammal life. Placental mammals nourish and maintain their young in the mother's uterus; only three orders of placental mammals existed during Cretaceous times, compared with 25 orders during the Tertiary period. One of these 25 included the first hominid (see pp.108–109), *Australopithecus*, which appeared in Africa. By the beginning of the Tertiary period, the continents had almost reached their present position. The Tethys Sea, which had separated the northern continents from Africa and India, began to close up, forming the Mediterranean Sea and allowing the migration of terrestrial animals between Africa and western Europe. India's collision with Asia led to the formation of the Himalayas. During the middle part of the Tertiary period, the forest-dwelling and browsing mammals were replaced by mammals such as the horse, better suited to grazing the open savannahs that began to dominate. Repeated cool periods throughout the Tertiary period established the Antarctic as an icy island continent.

EXAMPLES OF TERTIARY PLANT GROUPS

A PRESENT-DAY OAK
(Quercus palustris)

A PRESENT-DAY BIRCH
(Betula grossa)

**FOSSIL LEAF OF AN
EXTINCT BIRCH**
(Betulites sp.)

**FOSSIL STEM OF AN
EXTINCT PALM**
(Palmoxylon)

**EXAMPLES OF TERTIARY
ANIMAL GROUPS**

HYAENODON
An hyaenodontid
Length: 6 ft 6 in (2 m)

TITANOHYRAX
A pliohyracid
Length: 6 ft 6 in (2 m)

PHORUSRHACUS
A phorusrhacid
Length: 5 ft (1.5 m)

SAMOTHERIUM
A giraffid
Length: 10 ft (3 m)

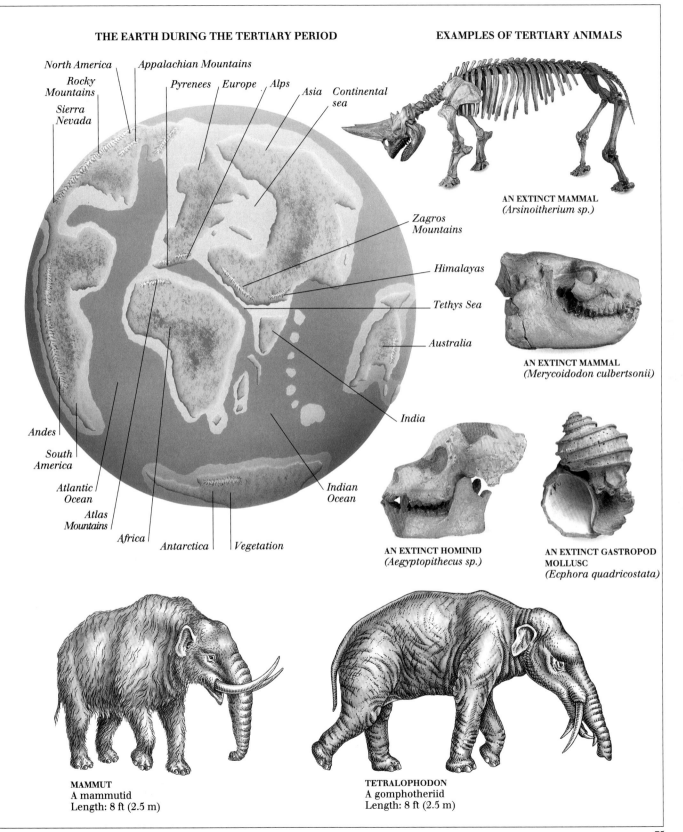

THE EARTH DURING THE TERTIARY PERIOD

North America
Appalachian Mountains
Rocky Mountains
Pyrenees
Europe
Alps
Asia
Continental sea
Sierra Nevada
Zagros Mountains
Himalayas
Tethys Sea
Australia
India
Andes
South America
Atlantic Ocean
Atlas Mountains
Africa
Antarctica
Vegetation
Indian Ocean

EXAMPLES OF TERTIARY ANIMALS

AN EXTINCT MAMMAL
(Arsinoitherium sp.)

AN EXTINCT MAMMAL
(Merycoidodon culbertsonii)

AN EXTINCT HOMINID
(Aegyptopithecus sp.)

AN EXTINCT GASTROPOD MOLLUSC
(Ecphora quadricostata)

MAMMUT
A mammutid
Length: 8 ft (2.5 m)

TETRALOPHODON
A gomphotheriid
Length: 8 ft (2.5 m)

Quaternary period

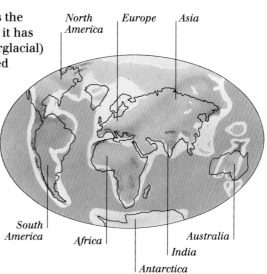

North
America

Europe

Asia

South
America

Africa

Antarctica

Australia

India

THE QUATERNARY PERIOD (1.6 million years ago–present) forms the
second part of the Cenozoic era (65 million years ago–present): it has
been characterized by alternating cold (glacial) and warm (interglacial)
periods. During cold periods, ice sheets and glaciers have formed
repeatedly on northern and southern continents. The cold
environments in North America and Eurasia, and to a lesser
extent in southern South America and parts of Australia, have
caused the migration of many life forms toward the Equator.
Only the specialized ice-age mammals such as *Mammuthus*
and *Coelodonta*, with their thick wool and fat insulation,
were suited to life in very cold climates. Humans developed
throughout the Pleistocene period (1.6 million–10,000 years
ago) in Africa and migrated northward into Europe and Asia.
Modern humans, *Homo sapiens*, lived on the cold European
continent 30,000 years ago and hunted mammals. The end of
the last ice age and the climatic changes that occurred about
10,000 years ago brought extinction to many Pleistocene
mammals, but enabled humans to flourish.

EXAMPLES OF QUATERNARY PLANT GROUPS

A PRESENT-DAY BIRCH
(*Betula lenta*)

A PRESENT-DAY SWEEETGUM
(*Liquidambar styraciflua*)

FOSSIL LEAF OF A SWEETGUM
(*Liquidambar europeanum*)

FOSSIL LEAF OF A BIRCH
(*Betula sp.*)

EXAMPLES OF QUATERNARY ANIMAL GROUPS

PROCOPTODON
A macropodid
Length: 10 ft (3 m)

DIPROTODON
A diprotodontid
Length: 10 ft (3 m)

TOXODON
A toxodontid
Length: 10 ft (3 m)

MAMMUTHUS
An elephantid
Length: 10 ft (3 m)

THE EARTH DURING THE QUATERNARY PERIOD

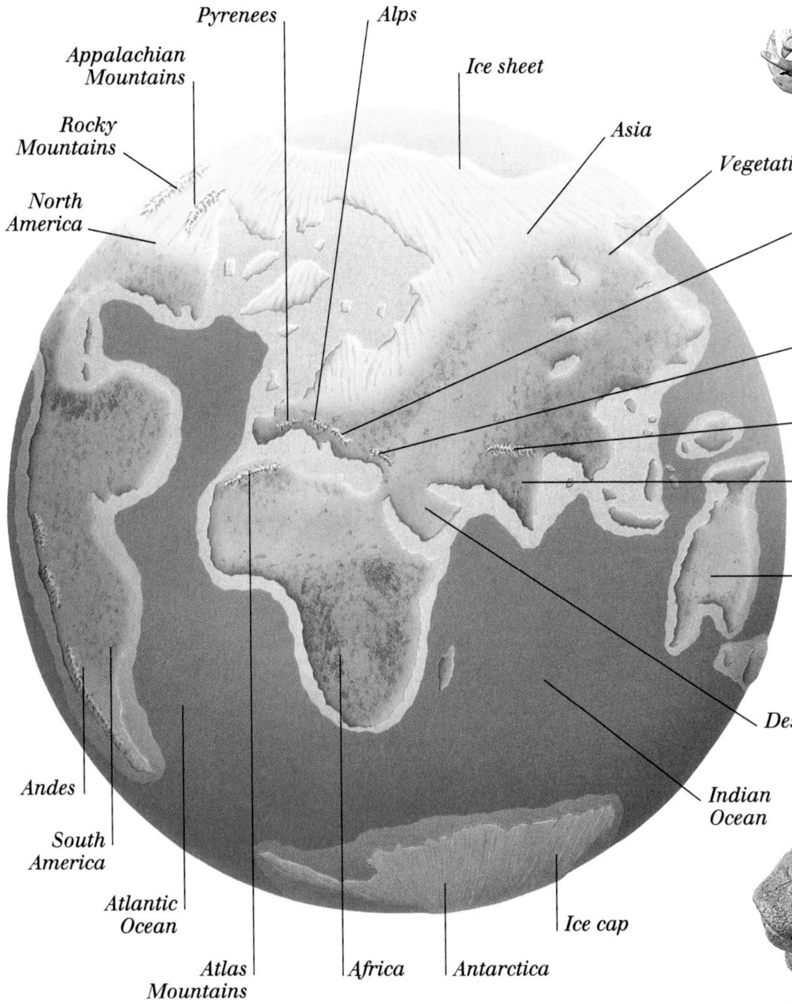

Pyrenees
Alps
Appalachian Mountains
Ice sheet
Rocky Mountains
Asia
North America
Vegetation
Carpathian Mountains
Taurus Mountains
Himalayas
India
Australia
Desert
Indian Ocean
Andes
South America
Atlantic Ocean
Ice cap
Atlas Mountains
Africa
Antarctica

EXAMPLES OF QUATERNARY ANIMALS

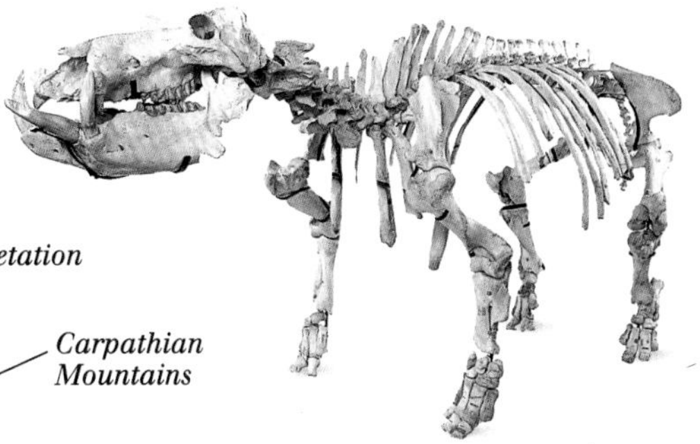

A MAMMAL SKELETON
(Hippopotamus amphibius)

SKULL OF AN EXTINCT CAVE BEAR
(Ursus spelaeus)

SKULL OF AN EXTINCT TORTOISE
(Meiolania platyceps)

A MAMMOTH TOOTH
(Mammuthus primigenius)

DEINOTHERIUM
A deinotheriid
Length: 13 ft (4 m)

COELODONTA
A rhinocerotid
Length: 13 ft (4 m)

AUSTRALOPITHECUS
A hominid
Length: 4 ft (1.2 m)

Early signs of life

STROMATOLITIC LIMESTONE

For ALMOST A THOUSAND MILLION YEARS after its formation, there was no known life on Earth. The first simple, sea-dwelling organic structures appeared about 3,400 years ago; they may have formed when certain chemical molecules joined together. Prokaryotes, single-celled micro-organisms such as blue-green algae, were able to photosynthesize (see pp. 138–139), and thus produce oxygen. A thousand million years later, sufficient oxygen had built up in the earth's atmosphere to allow multicellular organisms to proliferate in the Precambrian seas (before 570 million years ago). Soft-bodied jellyfish, corals, and seaworms flourished about 700 million years ago. Trilobites, the first animals with hard body frames, developed during the Cambrian period (570–510 million years ago). However, it was not until the beginning of the Devonian period (409–363 million years ago) that early land plants, such as *Asteroxylon*, formed a water-retaining cuticle, which ended their dependence on an aquatic environment. About 363 million years ago, the first amphibians (see pp. 80–81) crawled onto the land, although they still returned to the water to lay their soft eggs. Not until the emergence of the first reptiles would animals appear that were not dependent on water in this way.

Alternate layers of mud and sand

Layers bound by algae

Layered structure

Limestone

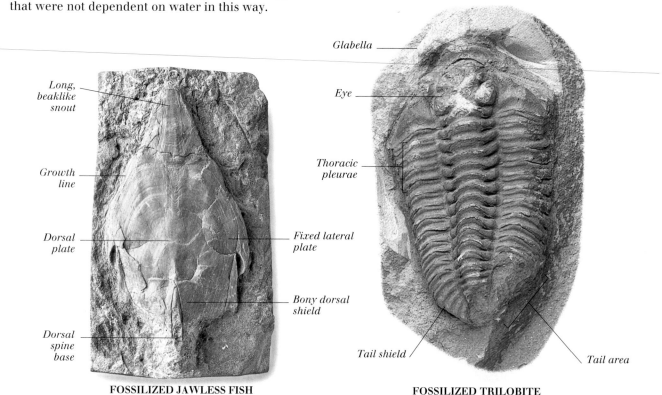

Long, beaklike snout

Growth line

Dorsal plate

Dorsal spine base

Glabella

Eye

Thoracic pleurae

Fixed lateral plate

Bony dorsal shield

Tail shield

Tail area

FOSSILIZED JAWLESS FISH

FOSSILIZED TRILOBITE

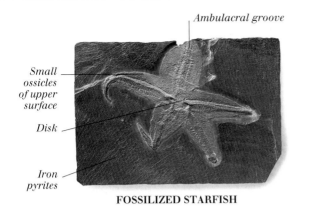

Ambulacral groove

Small ossicles of upper surface

Disk

Iron pyrites

FOSSILIZED STARFISH

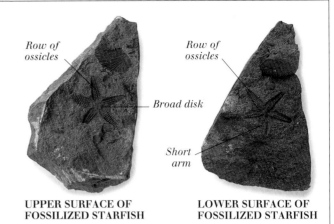

Row of ossicles

Broad disk

Row of ossicles

Short arm

UPPER SURFACE OF FOSSILIZED STARFISH

LOWER SURFACE OF FOSSILIZED STARFISH

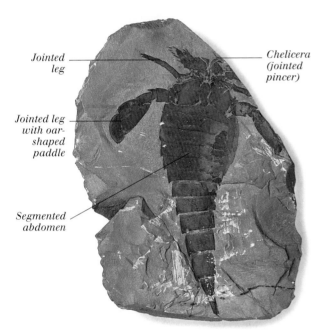

Jointed leg

Chelicera (jointed pincer)

Jointed leg with oar-shaped paddle

Segmented abdomen

UNDERSIDE OF FOSSILIZED EURYPTERID

Growing tip

Disk-shaped sporangium (spore-case)

Leaflike scale

Stem

RECONSTRUCTION OF ASTEROXYLON

Telson (tail spine)

Abdominal segments

Shell contains eight somites (thoracic segments)

Hingeless, bivalved shell

FOSSIL OF AN EXTINCT SHRIMP

Amphibians and reptiles

THE EARLIEST KNOWN AMPHIBIANS, such as *Acanthostega*
and *Ichthyostega*, lived about 363 million years ago
at the end of the Devonian period (409–363 million
years ago). Their limbs may have evolved from the
muscular fins of lungfish. These fish can use their
fins to push themselves along the bottom of lakes
and some can breathe at the water's surface. While
amphibians (see pp. 182–183) can exist on land, they
are dependent on a wet environment because their
skin does not retain moisture and they must return to
the water to lay their eggs. Evolving from amphibians,
reptiles (see pp. 184–187) first appeared during the
Carboniferous period (363–290 million years ago):
Westlothiana, the earliest known reptile, lived on
land 338 million years ago. The development of the
amniotic egg, with an embryo enclosed in its own wet
environment (the amnion) and protected by a waterproof
shell, freed reptiles from the amphibian's dependence on
a wet habitat. A scaly skin protected the reptile from
desiccation on land and enabled it to exploit ways of life
closed to its amphibian ancestors. Reptiles include the
dinosaurs, which came to dominate life on land during
the Mesozoic era (245–65 million years ago).

Orbit

Sculpted or pitted
bone surface

Spiracle
to draw
in water

Pocket
enclosing
nostril

Mandible

Small tooth

FOSSIL SKULL OF ACANTHOSTEGA

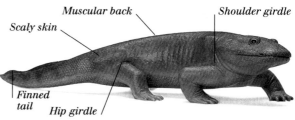

Muscular back

Scaly skin

Shoulder girdle

Finned
tail

Hip girdle

MODEL OF ICHTHYOSTEGA

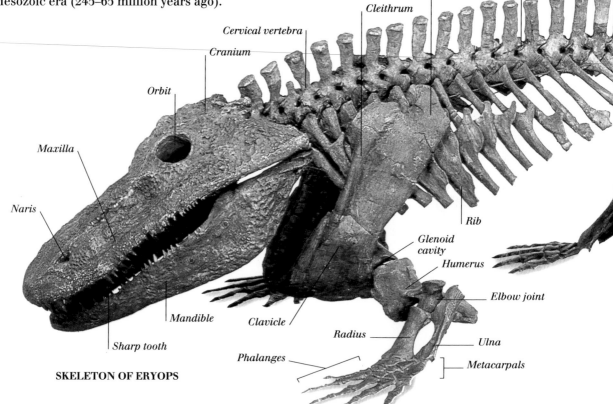

Dorsal vertebra

Scapula

Cleithrum

Cervical vertebra

Cranium

Orbit

Maxilla

Naris

Mandible

Sharp tooth

Clavicle

Radius

Phalanges

Rib

Glenoid
cavity

Humerus

Elbow joint

Ulna

Metacarpals

SKELETON OF ERYOPS

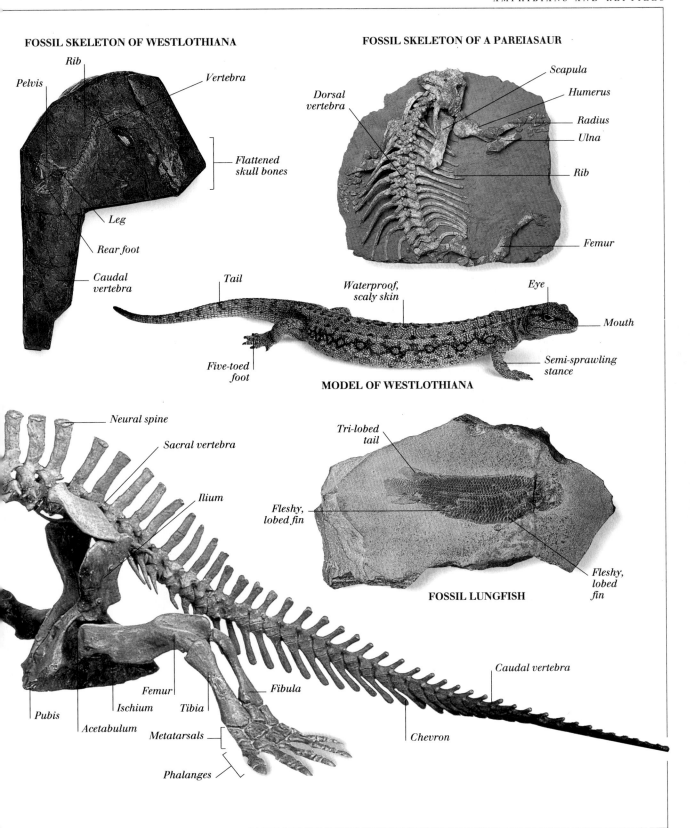

FOSSIL SKELETON OF WESTLOTHIANA

Rib

Pelvis

Vertebra

Flattened
skull bones

Leg

Rear foot

Caudal
vertebra

FOSSIL SKELETON OF A PAREIASAUR

Scapula

Humerus

Dorsal
vertebra

Radius

Ulna

Rib

Femur

Tail

Waterproof,
scaly skin

Eye

Mouth

Semi-sprawling
stance

Five-toed
foot

MODEL OF WESTLOTHIANA

Neural spine

Sacral vertebra

Ilium

Tri-lobed
tail

Fleshy,
lobed fin

Fleshy,
lobed
fin

FOSSIL LUNGFISH

Pubis

Femur

Fibula

Caudal vertebra

Ischium

Tibia

Acetabulum

Metatarsals

Chevron

Phalanges

The dinosaurs

THE DINOSAURS WERE A LARGE GROUP of reptiles that were the dominant land vertebrates (animals with backbones) for most of the Mesozoic era (245–65 million years ago). They appeared some 230 million years ago and were distinguished from other scaly, egg-laying reptiles by an important feature: dinosaurs had an erect limb stance. This enabled them to keep their bodies well above the ground, unlike the sprawling and semi-sprawling stance of other reptiles. The head of the dinosaur's femur (thighbone) fits into a socket in its pelvis (hipbone), producing efficient and mobile locomotion. Dinosaurs are categorized into two groups according to the structure of their pelvis: saurischian (lizard-hipped) and ornithischian (bird-hipped) dinosaurs. In the case of most saurischians, the pubis (part of the pelvis) jutted forward, while in ornithischians it slanted back, parallel to the ischium (another part of the pelvis). The enormous variety of dinosaur species equals that of mammals. The Dinosauria were the most successful land vertebrates ever, and survived for 165 million years, until their extinction 65 million years ago.

STRUCTURE OF SAURISCHIAN PELVIS

Ilium

Postacetabular process

Ilio-ischial joint

Ischium

Hook of preacetabular process

Ilio-pubic joint

Acetabulum

Pubis

Pubic foot

GALLIMIMUS
A saurischian dinosaur

POSITION OF PELVIS IN A SAURISCHIAN DINOSAUR

STRUCTURE OF ORNITHISCHIAN PELVIS

Ilium

Postacetabular process

Ilio-ischial joint

Preacetabular process

Ilio-pubic joint

Prepubis

Acetabulum

Pubis

Ischium

HYPSILOPHODON
An ornithischian dinosaur

POSITION OF PELVIS IN AN ORNITHISCHIAN DINOSAUR

BAROSAURUS
A saurischian dinosaur

COMPARISON OF ANIMAL STANCES

SPRAWLING STANCE
The thighs and upper arms project straight out from the body so that the knees and elbows are bent at right angles.

SEMI-SPRAWLING STANCE
The thighs and upper arms project downward and outward so that the knees and elbows are slightly bent.

ERECT STANCE
The thighs and upper arms project straight down from the body so that the knees and elbows are straight.

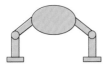

COMMON IGUANA
(*Iguana iguana*)
A present-day reptile

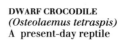

DWARF CROCODILE
(*Osteolaemus tetraspis*)
A present-day reptile

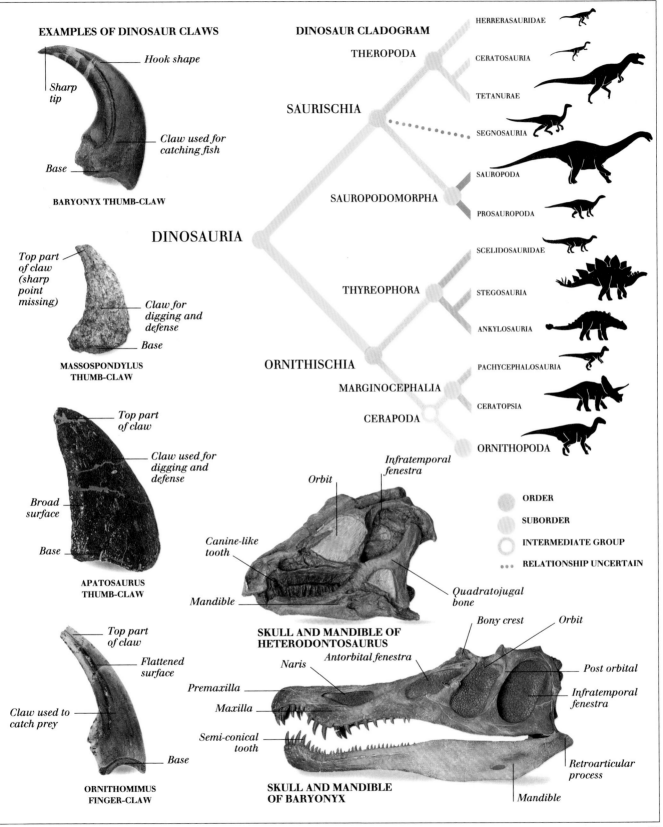

EXAMPLES OF DINOSAUR CLAWS

Hook shape

Sharp tip

Claw used for catching fish

Base

BARYONYX THUMB-CLAW

Top part of claw (sharp point missing)

Claw for digging and defense

Base

MASSOSPONDYLUS THUMB-CLAW

Top part of claw

Claw used for digging and defense

Broad surface

Base

APATOSAURUS THUMB-CLAW

Top part of claw

Flattened surface

Claw used to catch prey

Base

ORNITHOMIMUS FINGER-CLAW

DINOSAUR CLADOGRAM

THEROPODA

HERRERASAURIDAE

CERATOSAURIA

TETANURAE

SAURISCHIA

SEGNOSAURIA

SAUROPODA

SAUROPODOMORPHA

PROSAUROPODA

DINOSAURIA

SCELIDOSAURIDAE

THYREOPHORA

STEGOSAURIA

ANKYLOSAURIA

PACHYCEPHALOSAURIA

ORNITHISCHIA

MARGINOCEPHALIA

CERATOPSIA

CERAPODA

ORNITHOPODA

⬤ **ORDER**

⬤ **SUBORDER**

◯ **INTERMEDIATE GROUP**

•• **RELATIONSHIP UNCERTAIN**

Orbit

Infratemporal fenestra

Canine-like tooth

Quadratojugal bone

Mandible

SKULL AND MANDIBLE OF HETERODONTOSAURUS

Bony crest

Orbit

Naris

Antorbital fenestra

Premaxilla

Post orbital

Maxilla

Infratemporal fenestra

Semi-conical tooth

Retroarticular process

SKULL AND MANDIBLE OF BARYONYX

Mandible

Theropods 1

AN ENORMOUSLY SUCCESSFUL SUBORDER of the Saurischia, the bipedal (two-footed) theropods ("beast feet") emerged 230 million years ago in Late Triassic times; the oldest known example comes from South America. Theropods spanned the whole of the Age of the Dinosaurs (230–65 million years ago) and included most known predatory dinosaurs. The typical theropod had small arms with sharp, clawed fingers; powerful jaws lined with sharp teeth; an S-shaped neck; long, muscular hind limbs; and clawed, usually four-toed feet. Many theropods may have been warm-blooded; most were exclusively carnivorous. Theropods ranged from animals no larger than a chicken to huge creatures, such as *Tyrannosaurus* and *Baryonyx*. The group also included ostrichlike omnivores and herbivores with toothless beaks, such as *Struthiomimus* and *Gallimimus*. Many scientists believe that birds are the closest living relatives to the dinosaurs, and share a common ancestor with the theropods. *Archaeopteryx*, small and feathered, was the first known bird and lived alongside its dinosaur relatives.

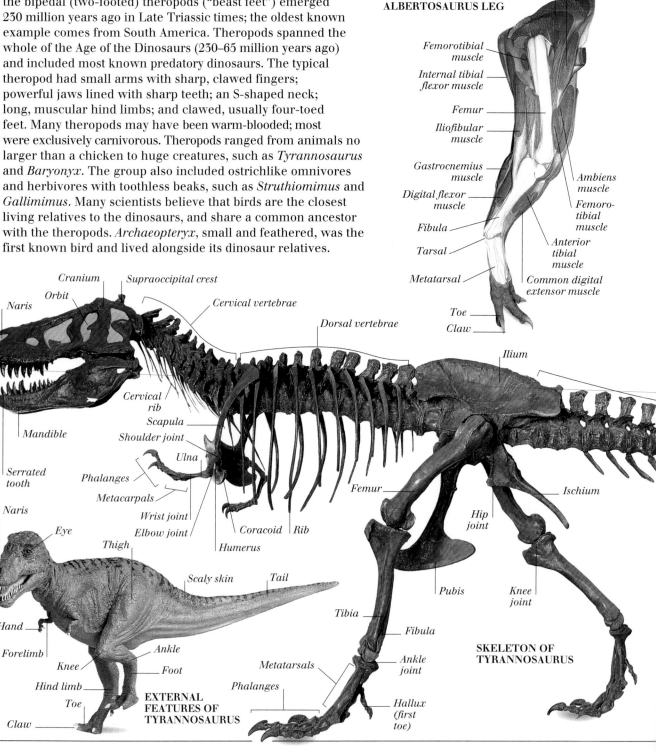

INTERNAL ANATOMY OF ALBERTOSAURUS LEG

Iliotibial muscle
Iliofemoral muscle
Femorotibial muscle
Internal tibial flexor muscle
Femur
Iliofibular muscle
Gastrocnemius muscle
Digital flexor muscle
Fibula
Tarsal
Metatarsal
Ambiens muscle
Femoro-tibial muscle
Anterior tibial muscle
Common digital extensor muscle
Toe
Claw

Cranium
Orbit
Naris
Supraoccipital crest
Cervical vertebrae
Dorsal vertebrae
Ilium
Cervical rib
Scapula
Shoulder joint
Ulna
Mandible
Phalanges
Metacarpals
Wrist joint
Elbow joint
Serrated tooth
Coracoid
Rib
Femur
Ischium
Hip joint
Humerus
Naris
Eye
Thigh
Scaly skin
Tail
Pubis
Knee joint
Hand
Tibia
Fibula
Forelimb
Knee
Ankle
Foot
Hind limb
Toe
Claw
Metatarsals
Phalanges
Ankle joint
Hallux (first toe)

EXTERNAL FEATURES OF TYRANNOSAURUS

SKELETON OF TYRANNOSAURUS

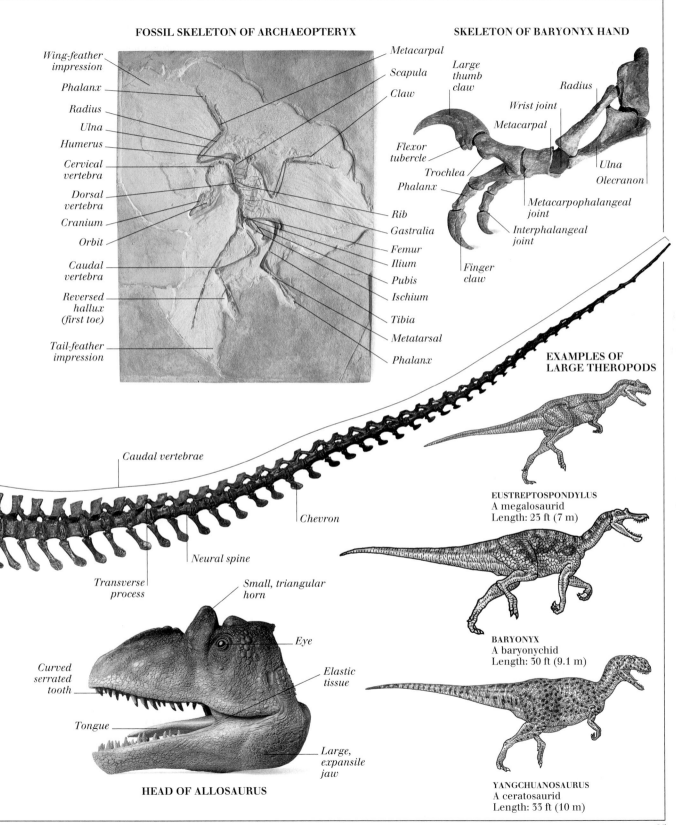

FOSSIL SKELETON OF ARCHAEOPTERYX

Wing-feather impression

Phalanx

Radius

Ulna

Humerus

Cervical vertebra

Dorsal vertebra

Cranium

Orbit

Caudal vertebra

Reversed hallux (first toe)

Tail-feather impression

Metacarpal

Scapula

Claw

Rib

Gastralia

Femur

Ilium

Pubis

Ischium

Tibia

Metatarsal

Phalanx

SKELETON OF BARYONYX HAND

Large thumb claw

Flexor tubercle

Trochlea

Phalanx

Finger claw

Wrist joint

Metacarpal

Radius

Ulna

Olecranon

Metacarpophalangeal joint

Interphalangeal joint

Caudal vertebrae

Chevron

Neural spine

Transverse process

Small, triangular horn

Eye

Elastic tissue

Curved serrated tooth

Tongue

Large, expansile jaw

HEAD OF ALLOSAURUS

EXAMPLES OF LARGE THEROPODS

EUSTREPTOSPONDYLUS
A megalosaurid
Length: 23 ft (7 m)

BARYONYX
A baryonychid
Length: 30 ft (9.1 m)

YANGCHUANOSAURUS
A ceratosaurid
Length: 33 ft (10 m)

Theropods 2

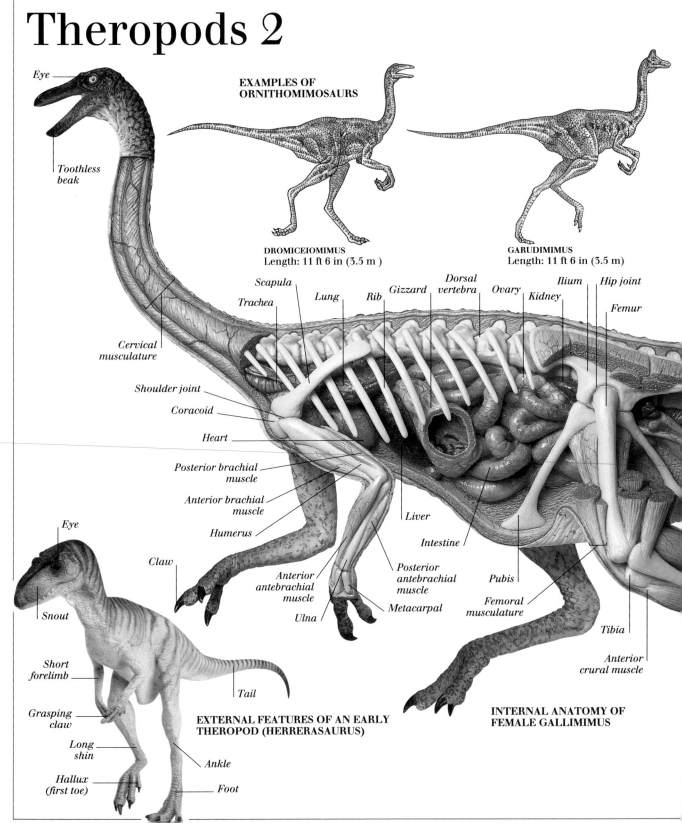

Eye

Toothless
beak

Cervical
musculature

**EXAMPLES OF
ORNITHOMIMOSAURS**

DROMICEIOMIMUS
Length: 11 ft 6 in (3.5 m)

GARUDIMIMUS
Length: 11 ft 6 in (3.5 m)

Scapula

Trachea

Lung

Rib

Gizzard

Dorsal
vertebra

Ovary

Kidney

Ilium

Hip joint

Femur

Shoulder joint

Coracoid

Heart

Posterior brachial
muscle

Anterior brachial
muscle

Humerus

Liver

Intestine

Anterior
antebrachial
muscle

Ulna

Posterior
antebrachial
muscle

Metacarpal

Pubis

Femoral
musculature

Tibia

Anterior
crural muscle

Eye

Snout

Short
forelimb

Grasping
claw

Long
shin

Hallux
(first toe)

Claw

Tail

Foot

Ankle

**EXTERNAL FEATURES OF AN EARLY
THEROPOD (HERRERASAURUS)**

**INTERNAL ANATOMY OF
FEMALE GALLIMIMUS**

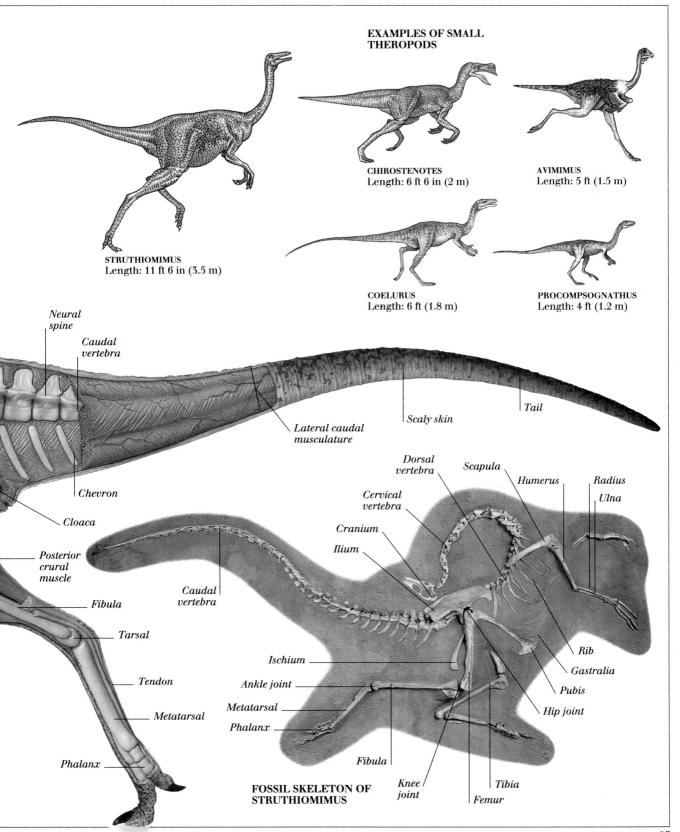

EXAMPLES OF SMALL THEROPODS

CHIROSTENOTES
Length: 6 ft 6 in (2 m)

AVIMIMUS
Length: 5 ft (1.5 m)

STRUTHIOMIMUS
Length: 11 ft 6 in (3.5 m)

COELURUS
Length: 6 ft (1.8 m)

PROCOMPSOGNATHUS
Length: 4 ft (1.2 m)

Neural spine

Caudal vertebra

Lateral caudal musculature

Scaly skin

Tail

Chevron

Cloaca

Dorsal vertebra

Scapula

Humerus

Radius

Ulna

Cervical vertebra

Cranium

Ilium

Posterior crural muscle

Caudal vertebra

Fibula

Tarsal

Tendon

Rib

Gastralia

Pubis

Hip joint

Ischium

Metatarsal

Ankle joint

Metatarsal

Phalanx

Phalanx

Fibula

Knee joint

Tibia

Femur

FOSSIL SKELETON OF STRUTHIOMIMUS

Sauropodomorphs 1

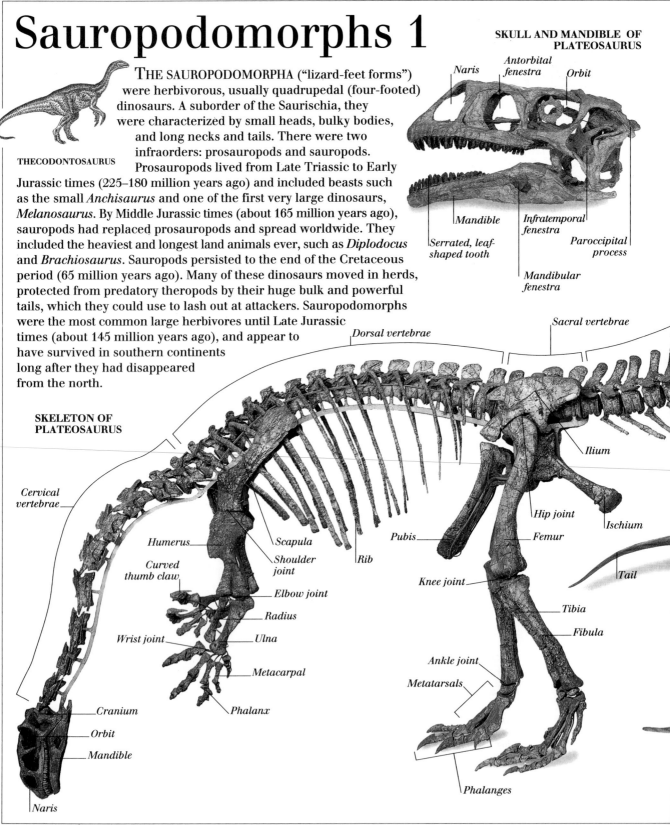

THE SAUROPODOMORPHA ("lizard-feet forms") were herbivorous, usually quadrupedal (four-footed) dinosaurs. A suborder of the Saurischia, they were characterized by small heads, bulky bodies, and long necks and tails. There were two infraorders: prosauropods and sauropods. Prosauropods lived from Late Triassic to Early Jurassic times (225–180 million years ago) and included beasts such as the small *Anchisaurus* and one of the first very large dinosaurs, *Melanosaurus*. By Middle Jurassic times (about 165 million years ago), sauropods had replaced prosauropods and spread worldwide. They included the heaviest and longest land animals ever, such as *Diplodocus* and *Brachiosaurus*. Sauropods persisted to the end of the Cretaceous period (65 million years ago). Many of these dinosaurs moved in herds, protected from predatory theropods by their huge bulk and powerful tails, which they could use to lash out at attackers. Sauropodomorphs were the most common large herbivores until Late Jurassic times (about 145 million years ago), and appear to have survived in southern continents long after they had disappeared from the north.

THECODONTOSAURUS

SKULL AND MANDIBLE OF PLATEOSAURUS

Naris

Antorbital fenestra

Orbit

Mandible

Infratemporal fenestra

Paroccipital process

Serrated, leaf-shaped tooth

Mandibular fenestra

SKELETON OF PLATEOSAURUS

Dorsal vertebrae

Sacral vertebrae

Ilium

Cervical vertebrae

Hip joint

Ischium

Humerus

Scapula

Pubis

Femur

Curved thumb claw

Shoulder joint

Rib

Tail

Elbow joint

Knee joint

Wrist joint

Radius

Tibia

Ulna

Fibula

Metacarpal

Ankle joint

Cranium

Phalanx

Metatarsals

Orbit

Mandible

Phalanges

Naris

88

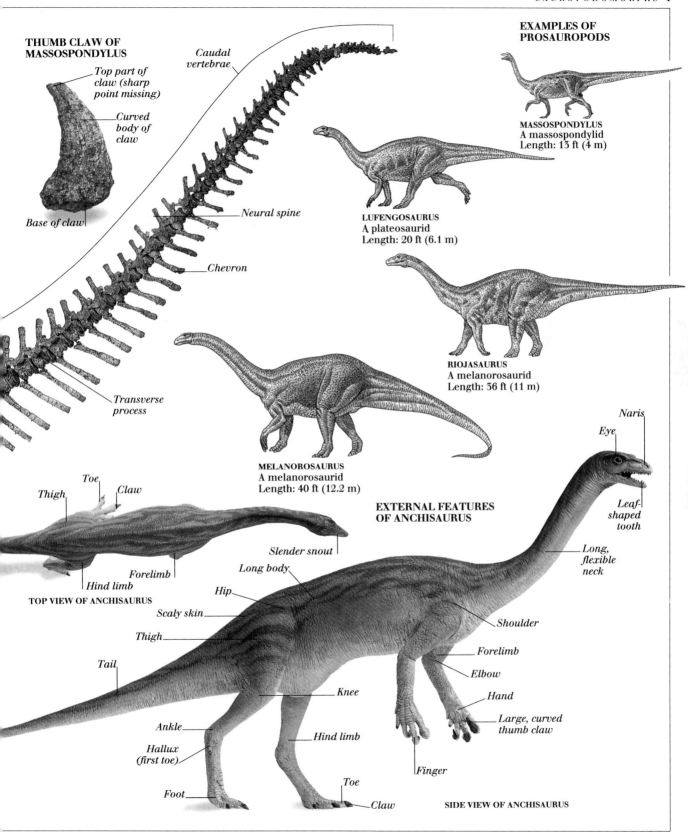

THUMB CLAW OF MASSOSPONDYLUS

Top part of claw (sharp point missing)

Curved body of claw

Base of claw

Caudal vertebrae

Neural spine

Chevron

Transverse process

EXAMPLES OF PROSAUROPODS

MASSOSPONDYLUS
A massospondylid
Length: 13 ft (4 m)

LUFENGOSAURUS
A plateosaurid
Length: 20 ft (6.1 m)

RIOJASAURUS
A melanorosaurid
Length: 36 ft (11 m)

MELANOROSAURUS
A melanorosaurid
Length: 40 ft (12.2 m)

EXTERNAL FEATURES OF ANCHISAURUS

Naris

Eye

Leaf-shaped tooth

Long, flexible neck

Shoulder

Forelimb

Elbow

Hand

Large, curved thumb claw

Finger

Slender snout

Long body

Hip

Scaly skin

Thigh

Knee

Hind limb

Toe

Claw

Tail

Ankle

Hallux (first toe)

Foot

Toe

Claw

Thigh

Hind limb

Forelimb

TOP VIEW OF ANCHISAURUS

SIDE VIEW OF ANCHISAURUS

Sauropodomorphs 2

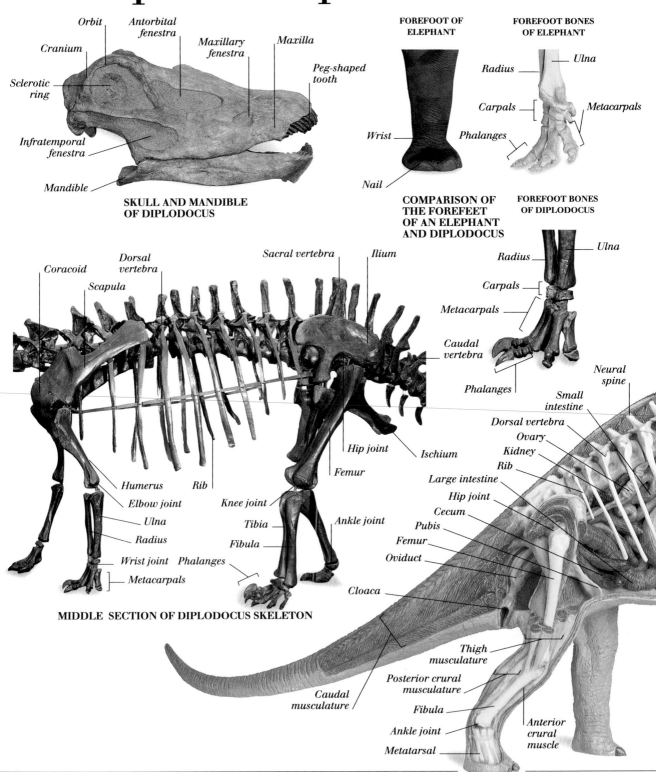

Orbit

Antorbital
fenestra

Maxillary
fenestra

Maxilla

Cranium

Peg-shaped
tooth

Sclerotic
ring

Infratemporal
fenestra

Mandible

**SKULL AND MANDIBLE
OF DIPLODOCUS**

**FOREFOOT OF
ELEPHANT**

**FOREFOOT BONES
OF ELEPHANT**

Radius

Ulna

Carpals

Metacarpals

Phalanges

Wrist

Nail

**COMPARISON OF
THE FOREFEET
OF AN ELEPHANT
AND DIPLODOCUS**

**FOREFOOT BONES
OF DIPLODOCUS**

Radius

Ulna

Carpals

Metacarpals

Phalanges

Coracoid

Dorsal
vertebra

Scapula

Sacral vertebra

Ilium

Caudal
vertebra

Neural
spine

Small
intestine

Dorsal vertebra

Ovary

Kidney

Rib

Large intestine

Hip joint

Cecum

Pubis

Femur

Oviduct

Cloaca

Hip joint

Ischium

Femur

Humerus

Rib

Elbow joint

Knee joint

Ankle joint

Ulna

Tibia

Radius

Fibula

Wrist joint

Phalanges

Metacarpals

MIDDLE SECTION OF DIPLODOCUS SKELETON

Thigh
musculature

Posterior crural
musculature

Caudal
musculature

Fibula

Ankle joint

Anterior
crural
muscle

Metatarsal

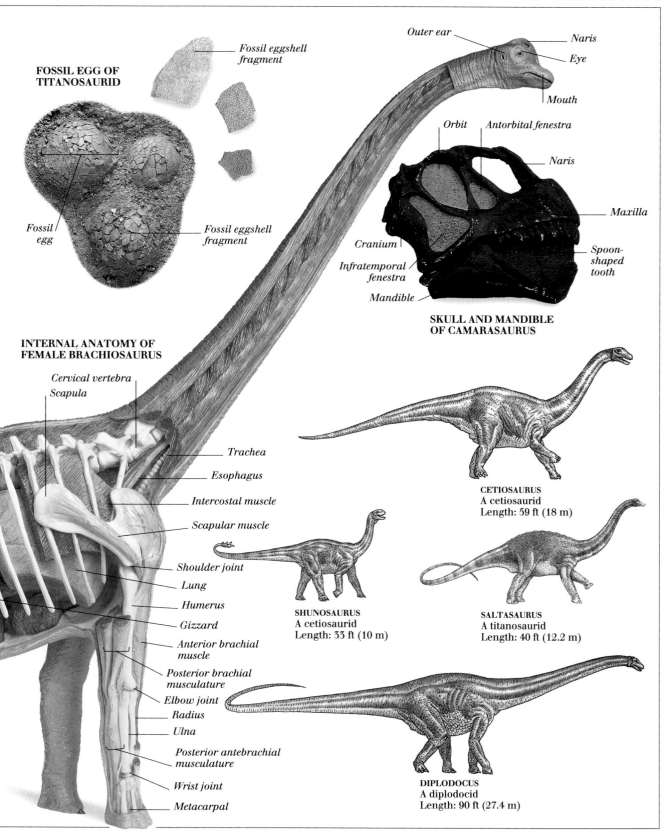

FOSSIL EGG OF TITANOSAURID

Fossil eggshell fragment

Fossil egg

Fossil eggshell fragment

Outer ear

Naris

Eye

Mouth

Orbit

Antorbital fenestra

Naris

Maxilla

Cranium

Spoon-shaped tooth

Infratemporal fenestra

Mandible

SKULL AND MANDIBLE OF CAMARASAURUS

INTERNAL ANATOMY OF FEMALE BRACHIOSAURUS

Cervical vertebra

Scapula

Trachea

Esophagus

Intercostal muscle

Scapular muscle

Shoulder joint

Lung

Humerus

Gizzard

Anterior brachial muscle

Posterior brachial musculature

Elbow joint

Radius

Ulna

Posterior antebrachial musculature

Wrist joint

Metacarpal

CETIOSAURUS
A cetiosaurid
Length: 59 ft (18 m)

SHUNOSAURUS
A cetiosaurid
Length: 33 ft (10 m)

SALTASAURUS
A titanosaurid
Length: 40 ft (12.2 m)

DIPLODOCUS
A diplodocid
Length: 90 ft (27.4 m)

Thyreophorans 1

THYREOPHORANS ("SHIELD BEARERS") were a group
of quadrupedal armored dinosaurs. A suborder of the
Ornithischia (bird-hipped dinosaurs), they were characterized
by rows of bony studs, plates, or spikes along the back, which
protected some from predators and may have helped others regulate
body temperature. Up to 30ft (9m) long, with a small head and small cheek
teeth, Thyreophorans had shorter forelimbs than hind limbs and probably
browsed on low-level vegetation. The earliest thyreophorans were
small and lived in Early Jurassic times (about 200 million
years ago) in Europe, North America, and
China. Stegosaurs, such as *Stegosaurus*
and *Kentrosaurus*, replaced these older
forms. The earliest stegosaur remains
come from England and China. Several genera
of stegosaurs survived into the Early Cretaceous period
(146–100 million years ago), but only in India did they persist
into Late Cretaceous times (97–65 million years ago).
Ankylosaurs, with their toothless beaks and cheek
teeth adapted for cropping vegetation,
appeared later than stegosaurs.
They originated in the Late
Jurassic period (155 million
years ago) and in North
America survived until the
extinction of the dinosaurs,
65 million years ago.

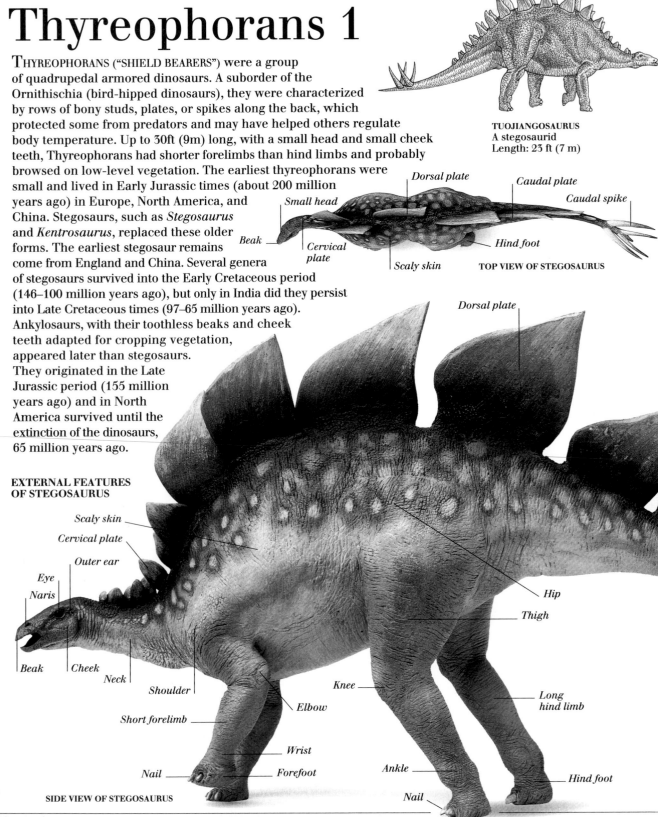

TUOJIANGOSAURUS
A stegosaurid
Length: 23 ft (7 m)

TOP VIEW OF STEGOSAURUS

Dorsal plate

Caudal plate

Caudal spike

Small head

Beak

Cervical
plate

Hind foot

Scaly skin

**EXTERNAL FEATURES
OF STEGOSAURUS**

Dorsal plate

Scaly skin

Cervical plate

Outer ear

Eye

Naris

Beak

Cheek

Neck

Shoulder

Elbow

Short forelimb

Wrist

Nail

Forefoot

Knee

Hip

Thigh

Long
hind limb

Ankle

Hind foot

Nail

SIDE VIEW OF STEGOSAURUS

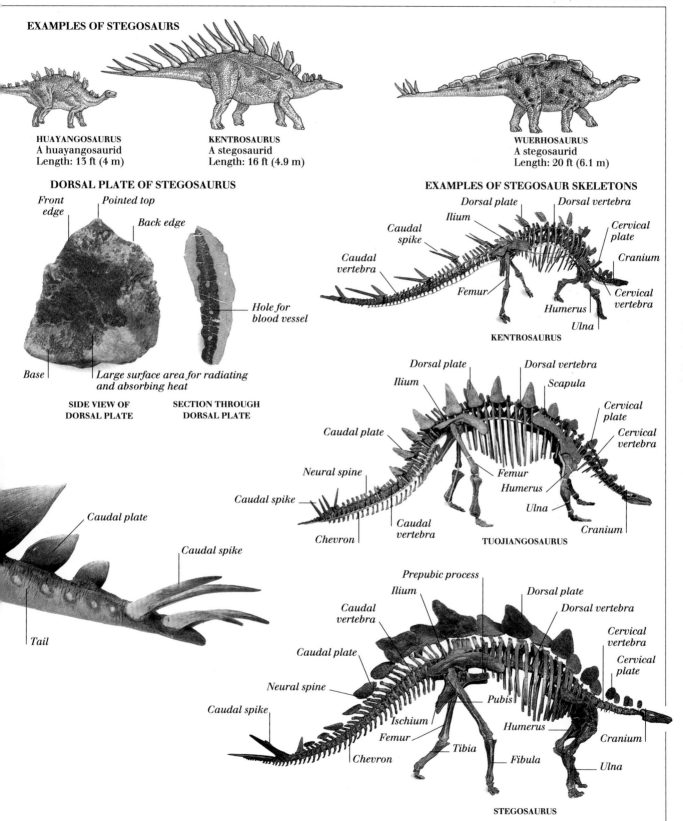

EXAMPLES OF STEGOSAURS

HUAYANGOSAURUS
A huayangosaurid
Length: 13 ft (4 m)

KENTROSAURUS
A stegosaurid
Length: 16 ft (4.9 m)

WUERHOSAURUS
A stegosaurid
Length: 20 ft (6.1 m)

DORSAL PLATE OF STEGOSAURUS

Front edge
Pointed top
Back edge

Hole for blood vessel

Base
Large surface area for radiating and absorbing heat

SIDE VIEW OF DORSAL PLATE

SECTION THROUGH DORSAL PLATE

EXAMPLES OF STEGOSAUR SKELETONS

Dorsal plate
Ilium
Dorsal vertebra
Cervical plate
Caudal spike
Cranium
Caudal vertebra
Femur
Cervical vertebra
Humerus
Ulna

KENTROSAURUS

Dorsal plate
Ilium
Dorsal vertebra
Scapula
Cervical plate
Caudal plate
Cervical vertebra
Neural spine
Caudal spike
Femur
Humerus
Chevron
Caudal vertebra
Ulna
Cranium

TUOJIANGOSAURUS

Caudal plate
Caudal spike
Tail

Prepubic process
Ilium
Dorsal plate
Caudal vertebra
Dorsal vertebra
Cervical vertebra
Caudal plate
Cervical plate
Neural spine
Pubis
Caudal spike
Ischium
Femur
Humerus
Tibia
Cranium
Chevron
Fibula
Ulna

STEGOSAURUS

Thyreophorans 2

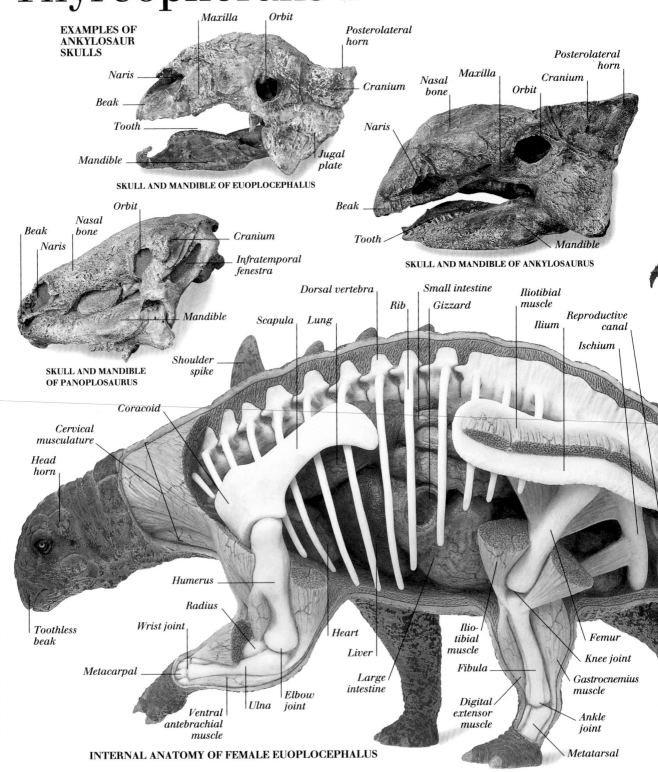

EXAMPLES OF ANKYLOSAUR SKULLS

Maxilla

Orbit

Posterolateral horn

Naris

Cranium

Beak

Tooth

Mandible

Jugal plate

SKULL AND MANDIBLE OF EUOPLOCEPHALUS

Posterolateral horn

Nasal bone

Maxilla

Cranium

Orbit

Naris

Beak

Tooth

Mandible

SKULL AND MANDIBLE OF ANKYLOSAURUS

Beak

Orbit

Nasal bone

Naris

Cranium

Infratemporal fenestra

Mandible

SKULL AND MANDIBLE OF PANOPLOSAURUS

Dorsal vertebra

Small intestine

Rib

Gizzard

Iliotibial muscle

Ilium

Reproductive canal

Scapula

Lung

Ischium

Shoulder spike

Coracoid

Cervical musculature

Head horn

Toothless beak

Humerus

Radius

Wrist joint

Metacarpal

Ventral antebrachial muscle

Ulna

Elbow joint

Heart

Liver

Large intestine

Ilio-tibial muscle

Fibula

Digital extensor muscle

Femur

Knee joint

Gastrocnemius muscle

Ankle joint

Metatarsal

INTERNAL ANATOMY OF FEMALE EUOPLOCEPHALUS

94

EXTERNAL FEATURES OF EDMONTONIA

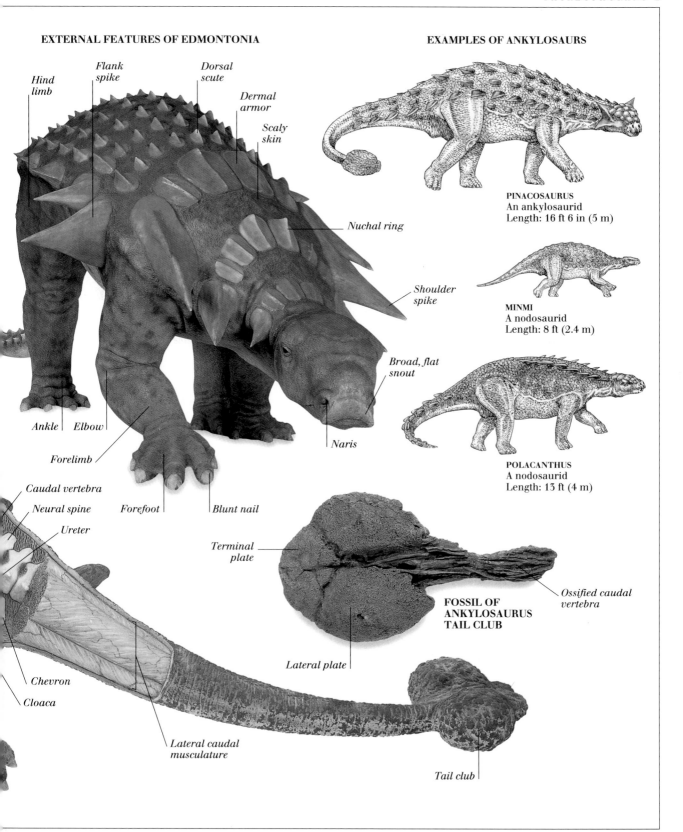

Hind limb

Flank spike

Dorsal scute

Dermal armor

Scaly skin

Nuchal ring

Shoulder spike

Broad, flat snout

Naris

Ankle

Elbow

Forelimb

Forefoot

Blunt nail

Caudal vertebra

Neural spine

Ureter

Terminal plate

Chevron

Cloaca

Lateral caudal musculature

Lateral plate

EXAMPLES OF ANKYLOSAURS

PINACOSAURUS
An ankylosaurid
Length: 16 ft 6 in (5 m)

MINMI
A nodosaurid
Length: 8 ft (2.4 m)

POLACANTHUS
A nodosaurid
Length: 13 ft (4 m)

FOSSIL OF ANKYLOSAURUS TAIL CLUB

Ossified caudal vertebra

Tail club

Ornithopods 1

IGUANODON TOOTH

ORNITHOPODS ("BIRD FEET") were a group of ornithischian ("bird-hipped") dinosaurs. These bipedal and quadrupedal herbivores had a horny beak, plant-cutting or grinding cheek teeth, and a pelvic and tail region stiffened by bony tendons. They evolved teeth and jaws adapted to pulping vegetation and flourished from the Middle Jurassic to the Late Cretaceous period (165–65 million years ago) in North America, Europe, Africa, China, Australia, and Antarctica. Some ornithopods were no larger than a dog, while others were immense creatures up to 49 ft (15 m) long. Iguanodonts, an ornithopod group, had a broad, toothless beak at the end of a long snout, large jaws with long rows of ridged, closely packed teeth for grinding vegetation, a bulky body, and a heavy tail. *Iguanodon* and some other iguanodonts had large thumb-spikes that were strong enough to stab attackers. Another group, the hadrosaurs, such as *Gryposaurus* and *Hadrosaurus*, lived in Late Cretaceous times (97–65 million years ago) and with their broad beaks are sometimes known as "duckbills." They were characterized by their deep skulls and closely packed rows of teeth, while some, such as *Corythosaurus* and *Lambeosaurus*, had tall, hollow, bony head crests.

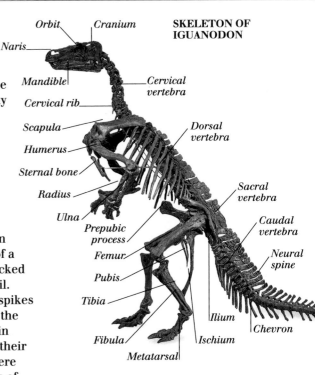

SKELETON OF IGUANODON

Orbit
Cranium
Naris
Mandible
Cervical rib
Cervical vertebra
Scapula
Humerus
Dorsal vertebra
Sternal bone
Radius
Sacral vertebra
Ulna
Caudal vertebra
Prepubic process
Femur
Neural spine
Pubis
Tibia
Ilium
Chevron
Fibula
Ischium
Metatarsal

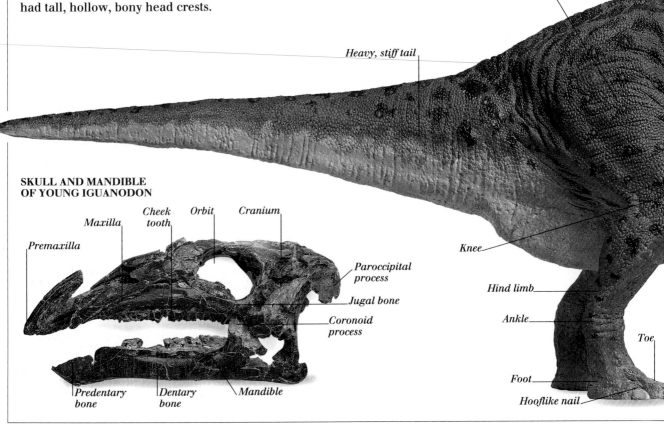

Thigh
Heavy, stiff tail
Knee
Hind limb
Ankle
Toe
Foot
Hooflike nail

SKULL AND MANDIBLE OF YOUNG IGUANODON

Maxilla
Cheek tooth
Orbit
Cranium
Premaxilla
Paroccipital process
Jugal bone
Coronoid process
Predentary bone
Dentary bone
Mandible

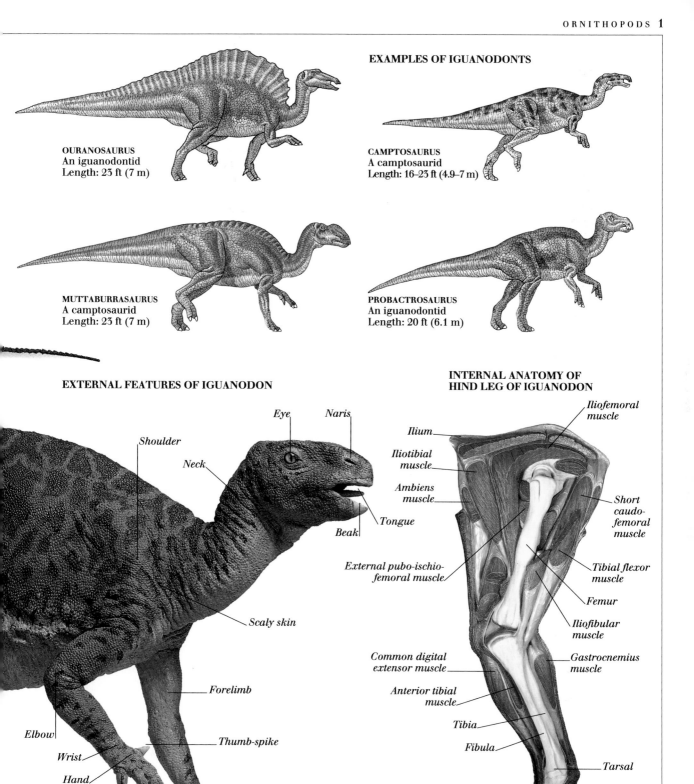

EXAMPLES OF IGUANODONTS

OURANOSAURUS
An iguanodontid
Length: 23 ft (7 m)

CAMPTOSAURUS
A camptosaurid
Length: 16–23 ft (4.9–7 m)

MUTTABURRASAURUS
A camptosaurid
Length: 23 ft (7 m)

PROBACTROSAURUS
An iguanodontid
Length: 20 ft (6.1 m)

EXTERNAL FEATURES OF IGUANODON

Eye

Naris

Shoulder

Neck

Tongue

Beak

Scaly skin

Forelimb

Thumb-spike

Elbow

Wrist

Hand

Finger

Hooflike nail

**INTERNAL ANATOMY OF
HIND LEG OF IGUANODON**

Iliofemoral
muscle

Ilium

Iliotibial
muscle

Ambiens
muscle

Short
caudo-
femoral
muscle

External pubo-ischio-
femoral muscle

Tibial flexor
muscle

Femur

Iliofibular
muscle

Common digital
extensor muscle

Gastrocnemius
muscle

Anterior tibial
muscle

Tibia

Fibula

Tarsal

Toe

Metatarsal

Hooflike nail

Ornithopods 2

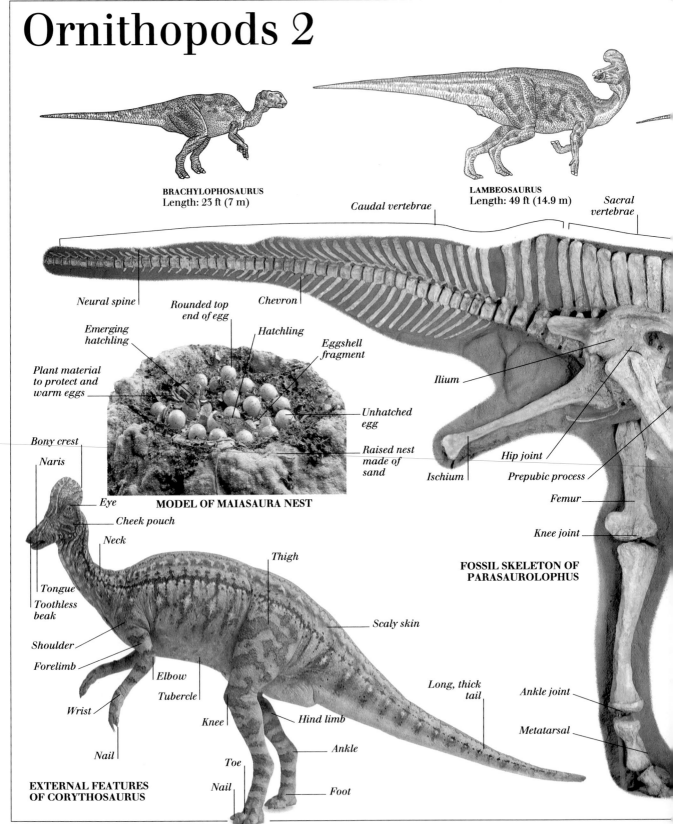

BRACHYLOPHOSAURUS
Length: 23 ft (7 m)

LAMBEOSAURUS
Length: 49 ft (14.9 m)

Caudal vertebrae

Sacral vertebrae

Neural spine

Rounded top end of egg

Chevron

Emerging hatchling

Hatchling

Eggshell fragment

Plant material to protect and warm eggs

Ilium

Unhatched egg

Bony crest

Raised nest made of sand

Hip joint

Naris

Ischium

Prepubic process

MODEL OF MAIASAURA NEST

Eye

Femur

Cheek pouch

Neck

Thigh

Knee joint

Tongue

FOSSIL SKELETON OF PARASAUROLOPHUS

Toothless beak

Scaly skin

Shoulder

Forelimb

Elbow

Long, thick tail

Ankle joint

Tubercle

Wrist

Knee

Hind limb

Metatarsal

Nail

Ankle

Toe

EXTERNAL FEATURES OF CORYTHOSAURUS

Nail

Foot

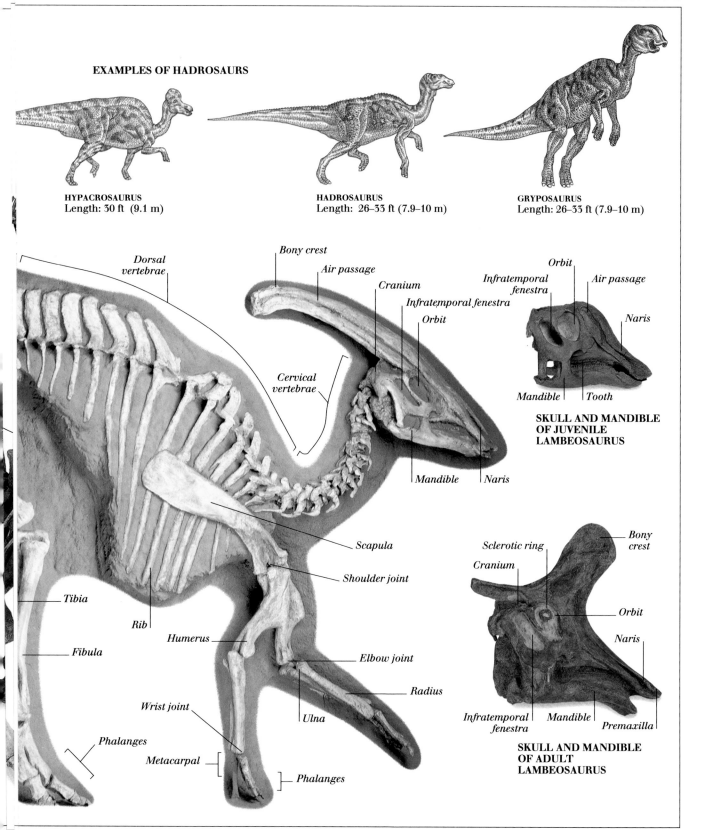

EXAMPLES OF HADROSAURS

HYPACROSAURUS
Length: 30 ft (9.1 m)

HADROSAURUS
Length: 26–33 ft (7.9–10 m)

GRYPOSAURUS
Length: 26–33 ft (7.9–10 m)

Dorsal vertebrae

Bony crest

Air passage

Cranium

Infratemporal fenestra

Orbit

Orbit

Infratemporal fenestra

Air passage

Naris

Cervical vertebrae

Mandible

Tooth

Mandible

Naris

SKULL AND MANDIBLE OF JUVENILE LAMBEOSAURUS

Scapula

Shoulder joint

Sclerotic ring

Bony crest

Cranium

Orbit

Naris

Tibia

Rib

Humerus

Fibula

Elbow joint

Radius

Infratemporal fenestra

Mandible

Premaxilla

Wrist joint

Ulna

Phalanges

Metacarpal

Phalanges

SKULL AND MANDIBLE OF ADULT LAMBEOSAURUS

Mammals 2

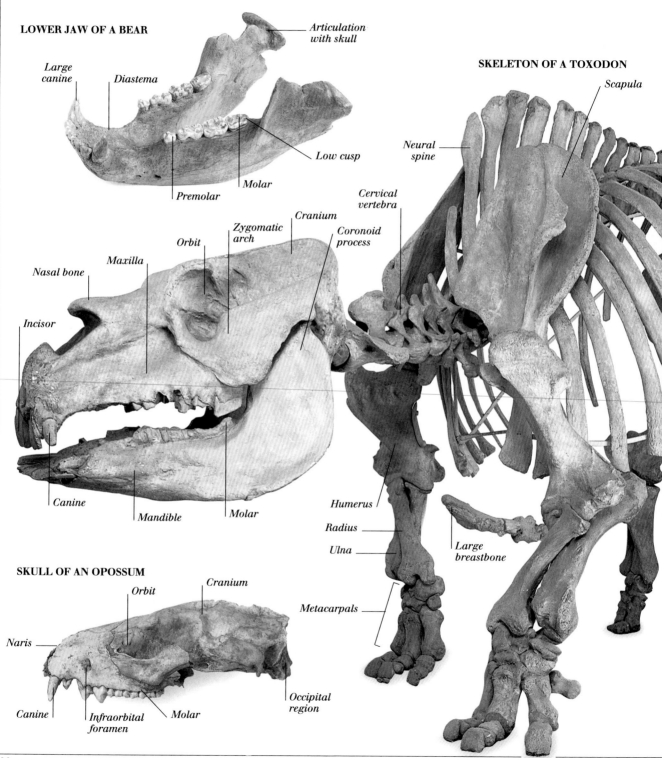

LOWER JAW OF A BEAR

Articulation with skull

Large canine

Diastema

Low cusp

Molar

Premolar

SKELETON OF A TOXODON

Scapula

Neural spine

Cervical vertebra

Cranium

Coronoid process

Zygomatic arch

Orbit

Maxilla

Nasal bone

Incisor

Canine

Mandible

Molar

Humerus

Radius

Ulna

Large breastbone

SKULL OF AN OPOSSUM

Orbit

Cranium

Metacarpals

Naris

Occipital region

Canine

Infraorbital foramen

Molar

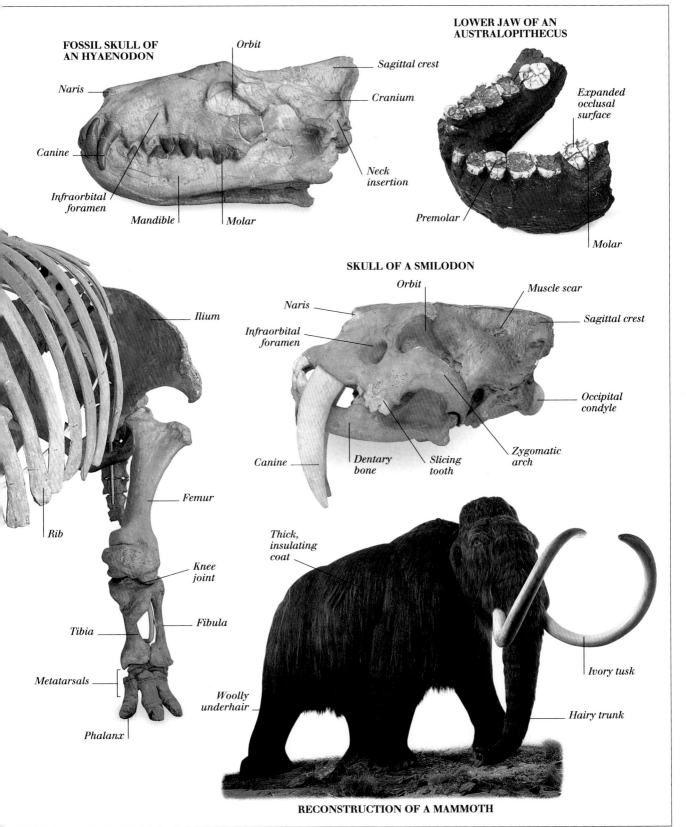

**FOSSIL SKULL OF
AN HYAENODON**

Orbit

Sagittal crest

Cranium

Naris

Canine

Neck
insertion

Infraorbital
foramen

Mandible

Molar

**LOWER JAW OF AN
AUSTRALOPITHECUS**

Expanded
occlusal
surface

Premolar

Molar

SKULL OF A SMILODON

Orbit

Muscle scar

Naris

Sagittal crest

Infraorbital
foramen

Occipital
condyle

Canine

Dentary
bone

Slicing
tooth

Zygomatic
arch

Ilium

Femur

Rib

Knee
joint

Tibia

Fibula

Metatarsals

Phalanx

Thick,
insulating
coat

Woolly
underhair

Ivory tusk

Hairy trunk

RECONSTRUCTION OF A MAMMOTH

The first hominids

MODERN HUMANS BELONG TO THE MAMMALIAN order of primates (see pp. 202–203), which originated about 55 million years ago; they comprise the only extant hominid species. The earliest hominid was *Australopithecus* ("southern ape"), a small-brained intermediate between apes and humans that was capable of standing and walking upright. *Homo habilis*, the first known human appeared at least 2 million years ago. This larger-brained "handy man" began making tools for hunting. *Homo erectus* first appeared in Africa about 1.8 million years ago and spread into Asia about 800,000 years later. Smaller toothed than *Homo habilis*, it developed fire as a tool, which enabled it to cook food. Neanderthals, a near relative of modern humans, originated about 200,000 years ago, and *Homo sapiens* (modern humans) appeared in Africa about 100,000 years later. The two coexisted for thousands of years, but by 30,000 years ago, *Homo sapiens* had become dominant and the Neanderthals had died out. Classification of *Homo sapiens* in relation to its ancestors is enormously problematic: modern humans must be classified not only by bone structure, but also by specific behavior—the ability to plan future action; to follow traditions; and to use symbolic communication, including complex language and the ability to use and recognize symbols.

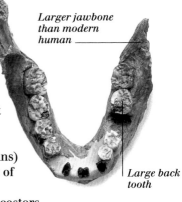

JAWBONE OF AUSTRALOPITHECUS (SOUTHERN APE)

Larger jawbone than modern human

Large back tooth

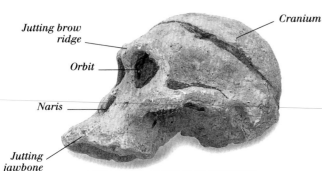

Jutting brow ridge

Cranium

Orbit

Naris

Jutting jawbone

SKULL OF AUSTRALOPITHECUS (SOUTHERN APE)

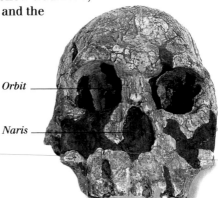

Orbit

Naris

SKULL OF HOMO HABILIS (FIRST KNOWN HUMAN)

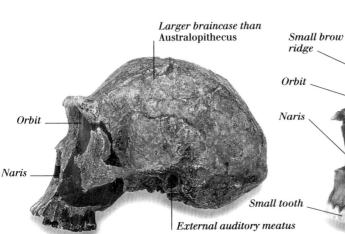

Larger braincase than Australopithecus

Orbit

Naris

External auditory meatus

SKULL OF HOMO ERECTUS (UPRIGHT MAN)

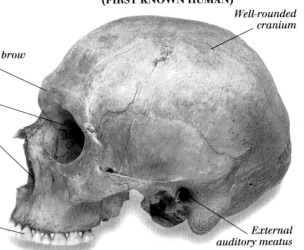

Well-rounded cranium

Small brow ridge

Orbit

Naris

Small tooth

External auditory meatus

SKULL OF HOMO SAPIENS (MODERN HUMAN)

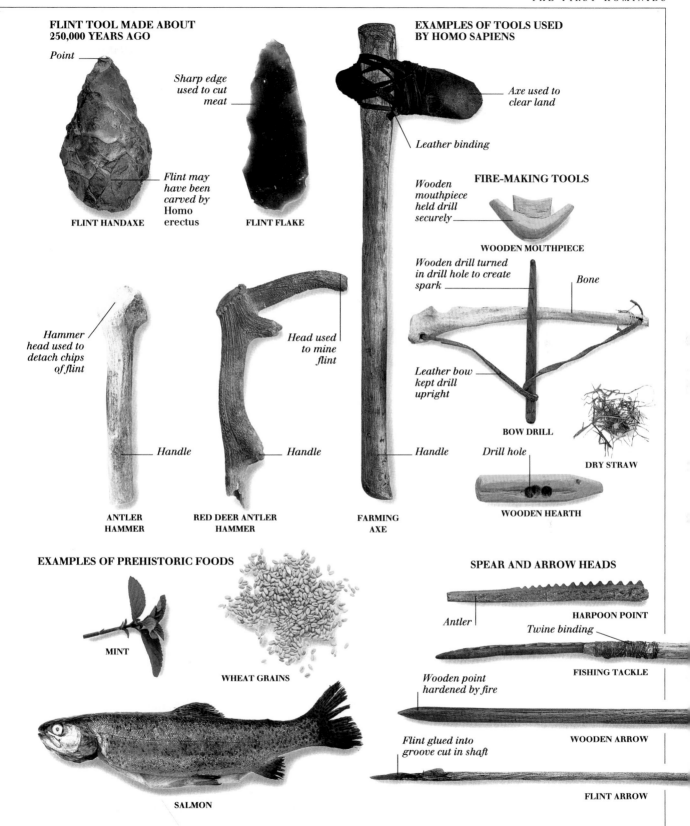

FLINT TOOL MADE ABOUT 250,000 YEARS AGO

Point

Sharp edge used to cut meat

Flint may have been carved by Homo erectus

FLINT HANDAXE

FLINT FLAKE

Hammer head used to detach chips of flint

Head used to mine flint

Handle

Handle

ANTLER HAMMER

RED DEER ANTLER HAMMER

Handle

FARMING AXE

EXAMPLES OF TOOLS USED BY HOMO SAPIENS

Axe used to clear land

Leather binding

FIRE-MAKING TOOLS

Wooden mouthpiece held drill securely

WOODEN MOUTHPIECE

Wooden drill turned in drill hole to create spark

Bone

Leather bow kept drill upright

BOW DRILL

DRY STRAW

Drill hole

Handle

WOODEN HEARTH

EXAMPLES OF PREHISTORIC FOODS

MINT

WHEAT GRAINS

SALMON

SPEAR AND ARROW HEADS

HARPOON POINT

Antler

Twine binding

FISHING TACKLE

Wooden point hardened by fire

WOODEN ARROW

Flint glued into groove cut in shaft

FLINT ARROW

109

PLANTS

Plant varieties

FLOWERING PLANT
Bromeliad
(*Acanthostachys strobilacea*)

Leaf

THERE ARE MORE THAN 300,000 SPECIES of plants. They
show a wide diversity of forms, ranging from delicate liverworts, adapted for life
in a damp habitat, to cacti, capable of surviving in the desert. The plant kingdom includes
herbaceous plants, such as corn, which completes its life cycle in one year, to the giant redwood tree, which
can live for thousands of years. This diversity reflects the adaptations of plants to survive in a wide range of
habitats. This is seen most clearly in the flowering plants (phylum Angiospermophyta), which are the most
numerous, with over 250,000 species. They are also the most widespread, being found from the tropics to the
arctic. Despite their diversity, plants share certain characteristics. Typically, plants are green, and make their
food by photosynthesis. Most plants live in or on a substrate, such as soil, and do not actively move. Algae
(kingdom Protista) and fungi (kingdom Fungi) have some plantlike characteristics and are
often studied alongside plants, although they are not true plants.

GREEN ALGA
Micrograph of desmid
(*Micrasterias sp.*)

FERN
Tree fern
(*Dicksonia antarctica*)

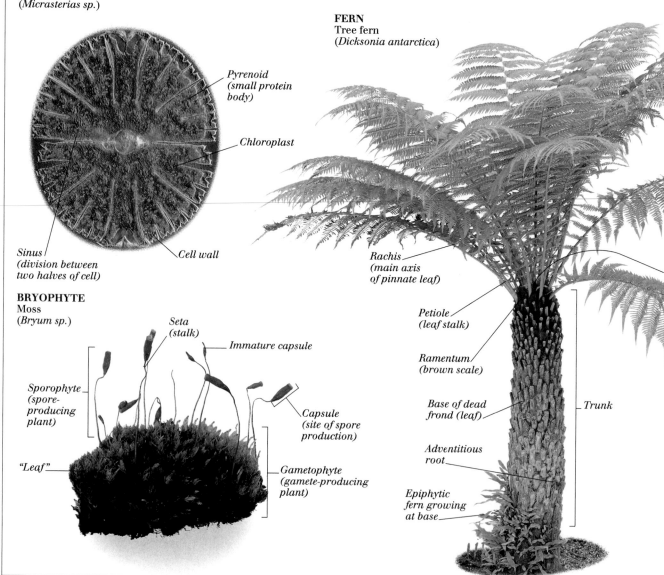

*Pyrenoid
(small protein
body)*

Chloroplast

*Sinus
(division between
two halves of cell)*

Cell wall

*Rachis
(main axis
of pinnate leaf)*

BRYOPHYTE
Moss
(*Bryum sp.*)

*Seta
(stalk)*

Immature capsule

*Petiole
(leaf stalk)*

*Ramentum
(brown scale)*

*Sporophyte
(spore-
producing
plant)*

*Capsule
(site of spore
production)*

*Base of dead
frond (leaf)*

Trunk

*Adventitious
root*

"Leaf"

*Gametophyte
(gamete-producing
plant)*

*Epiphytic
fern growing
at base*

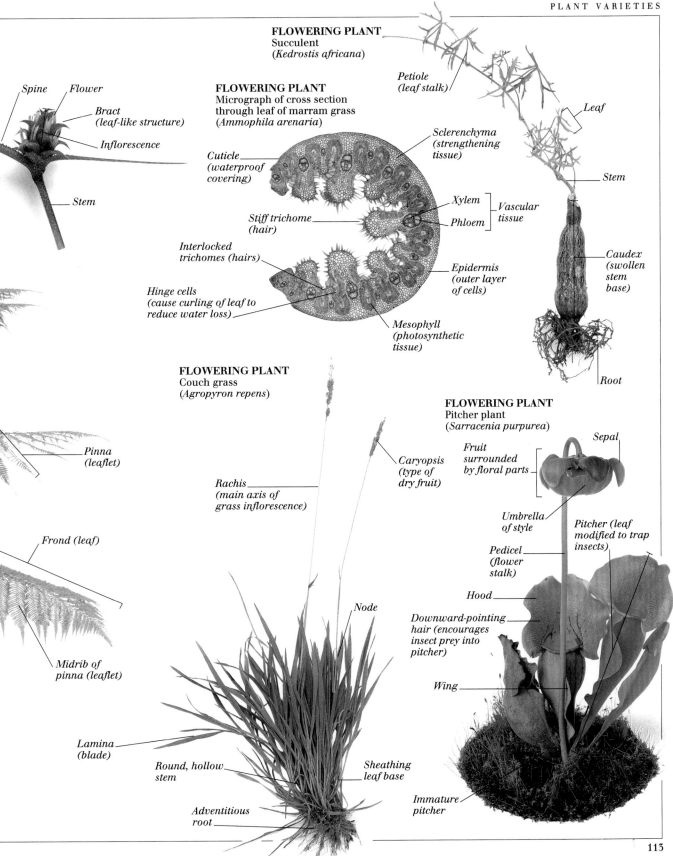

FLOWERING PLANT
Succulent
(*Kedrostis africana*)

*Petiole
(leaf stalk)*

Leaf

Stem

*Caudex
(swollen
stem
base)*

Root

FLOWERING PLANT
Micrograph of cross section
through leaf of marram grass
(*Ammophila arenaria*)

*Sclerenchyma
(strengthening
tissue)*

*Cuticle
(waterproof
covering)*

Xylem

Phloem

*Vascular
tissue*

*Stiff trichome
(hair)*

*Interlocked
trichomes (hairs)*

*Epidermis
(outer layer
of cells)*

*Hinge cells
(cause curling of leaf to
reduce water loss)*

*Mesophyll
(photosynthetic
tissue)*

Spine *Flower*

*Bract
(leaf-like structure)*

Inflorescence

Stem

FLOWERING PLANT
Couch grass
(*Agropyron repens*)

*Caryopsis
(type of
dry fruit)*

*Rachis
(main axis of
grass inflorescence)*

Node

*Pinna
(leaflet)*

Frond (leaf)

*Midrib of
pinna (leaflet)*

*Lamina
(blade)*

*Round, hollow
stem*

*Sheathing
leaf base*

*Adventitious
root*

FLOWERING PLANT
Pitcher plant
(*Sarracenia purpurea*)

Sepal

*Fruit
surrounded
by floral parts*

*Umbrella
of style*

*Pitcher (leaf
modified to trap
insects)*

*Pedicel
(flower
stalk)*

Hood

*Downward-pointing
hair (encourages
insect prey into
pitcher)*

Wing

*Immature
pitcher*

Fungi and lichens

FUNGI WERE ONCE THOUGHT OF AS PLANTS but are now classified as a separate kingdom. This kingdom includes not only the familiar mushrooms, puffballs, stinkhorns, and molds, but also yeasts, smuts, rusts, and lichens. Most fungi are multicellular, consisting of a mass of thread-like hyphae that together form a mycelium. However, the simpler fungi, like yeasts, are microscopic, single-celled organisms. Typically, fungi reproduce by means of spores. Most fungi feed on dead or decaying matter or on living organisms. A few fungi obtain their food from plants or algae, with which they have a symbiotic (mutually advantageous) relationship. Lichens are a symbiotic partnership between algae and fungi. Of the six types of lichens the three most common are crustose (flat and crusty), foliose (leafy), and fruticose (shrub-like). Some lichens (such as *Cladonia floerkeana*) are a combination of types. Lichens reproduce by means of spores or soredia (powdery vegetative fragments).

EXAMPLES OF FUNGI

Emerging sporophore (spore-bearing structure)

Pileus (cap) continuous with stipe (stalk)

Bark of dead beech tree

Inrolled margin of pileus (cap)

Gill (site of spore production)

Sporophore (spore-bearing structure)

Stipe (stalk)

Hyphae (fungal filaments)

OYSTER FUNGUS
(*Pleurotus pulmonarius*)

EXAMPLES OF LICHENS

Secondary fruticose thallus

Branched, hollow stem

Apothecium (spore-producing body)

FRUTICOSE
Cladonia portentosa

Soredia (powdery vegetative fragments) produced at end of lobe

Tree bark

Foliose thallus

FOLIOSE
Hypogymnia physodes

Soredia (powdery vegetative fragments) released onto surface of squamulose thallus

Apothecium (spore-producing body)

Basal scale of primary squamulose thallus

Podetium (granular stalk) of secondary fruticose thallus

Moss

SQUAMULOSE (SCALY) AND FRUTICOSE THALLUS
Cladonia floerkeana

Gleba (spore-producing tissue found in this type of fungus)

Sporophore (spore-bearing structure)

Porous stipe (stalk)

Volva (remains of universal veil)

STINKHORN
(*Phallus impudicus*)

Toothed branchlet

Branch

Sporophore (spore-bearing structure)

Stipe (stalk)

RAMARIA FORMOSA

SECTION THROUGH FOLIOSE LICHEN SHOWING REPRODUCTION BY SOREDIA

Soredium (powdery vegetative fragment involved in propagation) released from lichen

Algal cell

Fungal hypha

Upper cortex

Algal layer

Medulla of fungal hyphae (mycelium)

Lower cortex

Rhizine (bundle of absorptive hyphae)

Soralium (pore in upper surface of thallus)

Upper surface of thallus

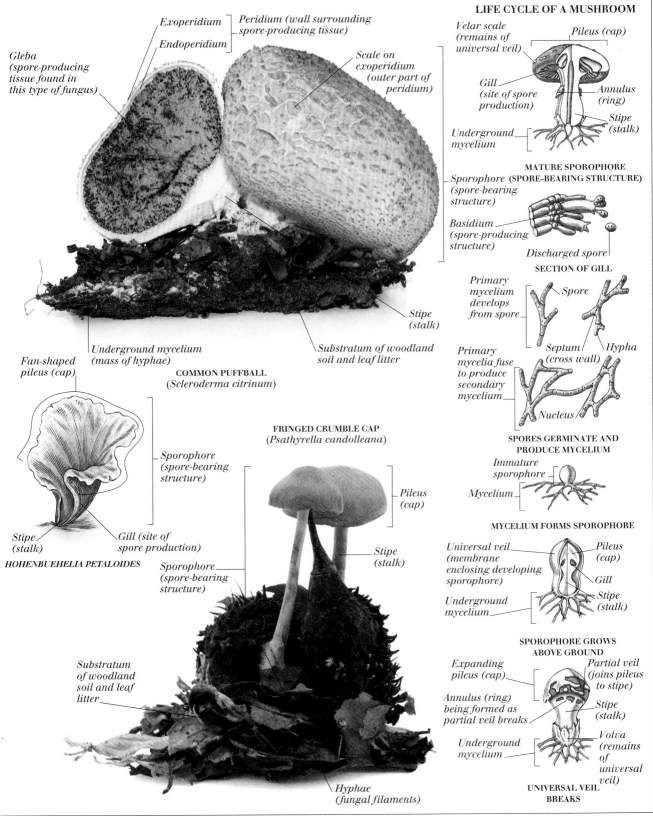

Exoperidium

Endoperidium

Peridium (wall surrounding spore-producing tissue)

Gleba (spore-producing tissue found in this type of fungus)

Scale on exoperidium (outer part of peridium)

Stipe (stalk)

Underground mycelium (mass of hyphae)

Substratum of woodland soil and leaf litter

COMMON PUFFBALL
(Scleroderma citrinum)

Fan-shaped pileus (cap)

Sporophore (spore-bearing structure)

Stipe (stalk)

Gill (site of spore production)

HOHENBUEHELIA PETALOIDES

FRINGED CRUMBLE CAP
(Psathyrella candolleana)

Sporophore (spore-bearing structure)

Pileus (cap)

Stipe (stalk)

Substratum of woodland soil and leaf litter

Hyphae (fungal filaments)

LIFE CYCLE OF A MUSHROOM

Velar scale (remains of universal veil)

Pileus (cap)

Gill (site of spore production)

Annulus (ring)

Stipe (stalk)

Underground mycelium

MATURE SPOROPHORE

Sporophore (spore-bearing structure)

Basidium (spore-producing structure)

Discharged spore

SECTION OF GILL

Primary mycelium develops from spore

Spore

Septum (cross wall)

Hypha

Primary mycelia fuse to produce secondary mycelium

Nucleus

SPORES GERMINATE AND PRODUCE MYCELIUM

Immature sporophore

Mycelium

MYCELIUM FORMS SPOROPHORE

Universal veil (membrane enclosing developing sporophore)

Pileus (cap)

Gill

Stipe (stalk)

Underground mycelium

SPOROPHORE GROWS ABOVE GROUND

Expanding pileus (cap)

Partial veil (joins pileus to stipe)

Annulus (ring) being formed as partial veil breaks

Stipe (stalk)

Underground mycelium

Volva (remains of universal veil)

UNIVERSAL VEIL BREAKS

Algae and seaweed

ALGAE ARE NOT TRUE PLANTS. They form a diverse group of plantlike organisms that belong to the kingdom Protista. Like plants, algae possess the green pigment chlorophyll and make their own food by photosynthesis (see pp. 138-139). Many algae also possess other pigments by which they can be classified. For example, the brown pigment fucoxanthin is found in brown algae. Some of the ten phyla of algae are exclusively unicellular (single-celled); others also contain aggregates of cells in filaments or colonies. Three phyla— the Chlorophyta (green algae), Rhodophyta (red algae), and Phaeophyta (brown algae)—contain larger, multicellular, thalloid (flat), marine organisms commonly known as seaweed. Most algae can reproduce sexually. For example, in brown seaweed *Fucus vesiculosus*, gametes (sex cells) are produced in conceptacles (chambers) in the receptacles (fertile tips of fronds); after their release into the sea, antherozoids (male gametes) and oospheres (female gametes) fuse. The resulting zygote settles on a rock and develops into a new seaweed.

BROWN SEAWEED
Channeled wrack
(*Pelvetia canaliculata*)

Receptacle
(fertile tip
of frond)

Thallus
(plant
body)

Apical
notch

Margin of
lamina (blade)
rolled inwards
to form channel

Hapteron (holdfast)

BROWN SEAWEED
Spiral wrack
(*Fucus spiralis*)

Apical notch

Conceptacle
(chamber)

Receptacle
(fertile tip
of frond)

Lamina
(blade)

Smooth margin

Midrib

Thallus
(plant
body)

Hapteron (holdfast)

EXAMPLES OF ALGAE

Reproductive
chamber

Cap

Sterile whorl

Cell wall

Stalk

Rhizoid

GREEN ALGA
Acetabularia sp.

Flagellum

Eyespot

Contractile
vacuole

Cytoplasm

Nucleus

Cell
wall

Chloroplast

Pyrenoid
(small protein
body)

Starch
grain

GREEN ALGA
Chlamydomonas sp.

Coenobium
(colony of cells)

Daughter
coenobium

Gelatinous
sheath

Biflagellate cell

GREEN ALGA
Volvox sp.

Spine

Cytoplasm

Girdle

Vacuole

Nucleus

Plastid
(photosynthetic
organelle)

DIATOM
Thalassiosira sp.

Apical notch

Receptacle
(fertile tip
of frond)

Conceptacle
(chamber)
containing
reproductive
structures

Lamina
(blade)

Midrib

RECEPTACLE
Spiral wrack
(*Fucus spiralis*)

BROWN SEAWEED
Oarweed
(*Laminaria digitata*)

Thallus (plant body)

Lamina (blade)
palmately
divided

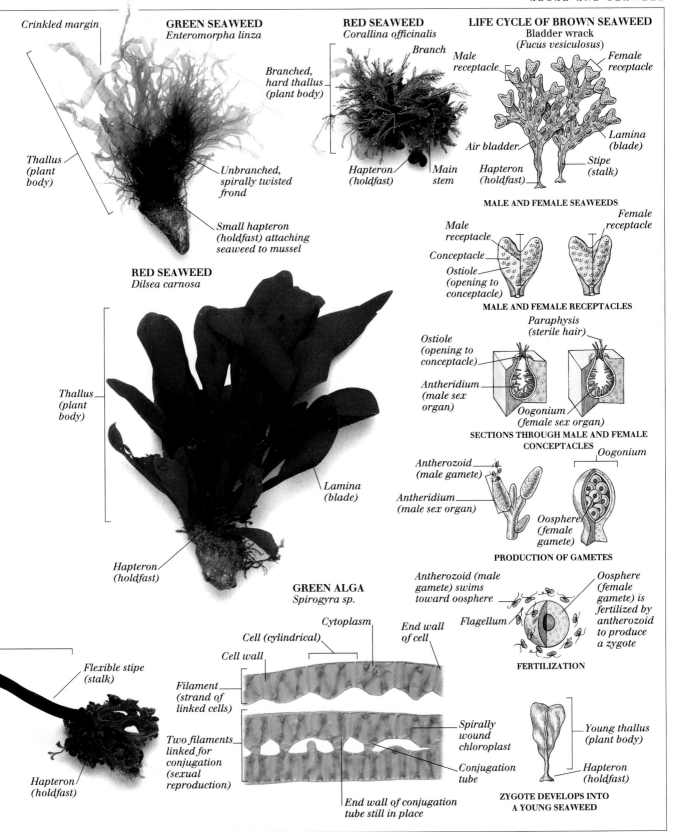

GREEN SEAWEED
Enteromorpha linza

Crinkled margin

Thallus
(plant
body)

Unbranched,
spirally twisted
frond

Small hapteron
(holdfast) attaching
seaweed to mussel

RED SEAWEED
Corallina officinalis

Branch

Branched,
hard thallus
(plant body)

Hapteron
(holdfast)

Main
stem

RED SEAWEED
Dilsea carnosa

Thallus
(plant
body)

Lamina
(blade)

Hapteron
(holdfast)

Flexible stipe
(stalk)

Hapteron
(holdfast)

GREEN ALGA
Spirogyra sp.

Cytoplasm

Cell (cylindrical)

Cell wall

End wall
of cell

Filament
(strand of
linked cells)

Two filaments
linked for
conjugation
(sexual
reproduction)

Spirally
wound
chloroplast

Conjugation
tube

End wall of conjugation
tube still in place

LIFE CYCLE OF BROWN SEAWEED
Bladder wrack
(*Fucus vesiculosus*)

Male
receptacle

Female
receptacle

Air bladder

Lamina
(blade)

Hapteron
(holdfast)

Stipe
(stalk)

MALE AND FEMALE SEAWEEDS

Male
receptacle

Conceptacle

Ostiole
(opening to
conceptacle)

Female
receptacle

MALE AND FEMALE RECEPTACLES

Paraphysis
(sterile hair)

Ostiole
(opening to
conceptacle)

Antheridium
(male sex
organ)

Oogonium
(female sex organ)

**SECTIONS THROUGH MALE AND FEMALE
CONCEPTACLES**

Antherozoid
(male gamete)

Oogonium

Antheridium
(male sex organ)

Oosphere
(female
gamete)

PRODUCTION OF GAMETES

Antherozoid (male
gamete) swims
toward oosphere

Flagellum

Oosphere
(female
gamete) is
fertilized by
antherozoid
to produce
a zygote

FERTILIZATION

Young thallus
(plant body)

Hapteron
(holdfast)

**ZYGOTE DEVELOPS INTO
A YOUNG SEAWEED**

Liverworts and mosses

"Stem"

"Leaf"

Rhizoid

LIVERWORTS AND MOSSES ARE SMALL, LOW-GROWING PLANTS that belong to the phylum Bryophyta. Bryophytes do not have true stems, leaves, or roots (they are anchored to the ground by rhizoids), nor do they have the vascular tissues (xylem and phloem) that transport water and nutrients in higher plants. With no outer, waterproof cuticle, bryophytes are susceptible to dehydration, and most grow in moist habitats. The bryophyte life cycle has two stages. In stage one, the green plant (gametophyte) produces male and female gametes (sex cells), which fuse to form a zygote. In stage two, the zygote develops into a sporophyte that remains attached to the gametophyte. The sporophyte produces spores, which are released and germinate into new green plants. Liverworts (class Hepaticae) grow horizontally and may be thalloid (flat and ribbon-like) or "leafy." Mosses (class Musci) typically have an upright "stem" with spirally arranged "leaves."

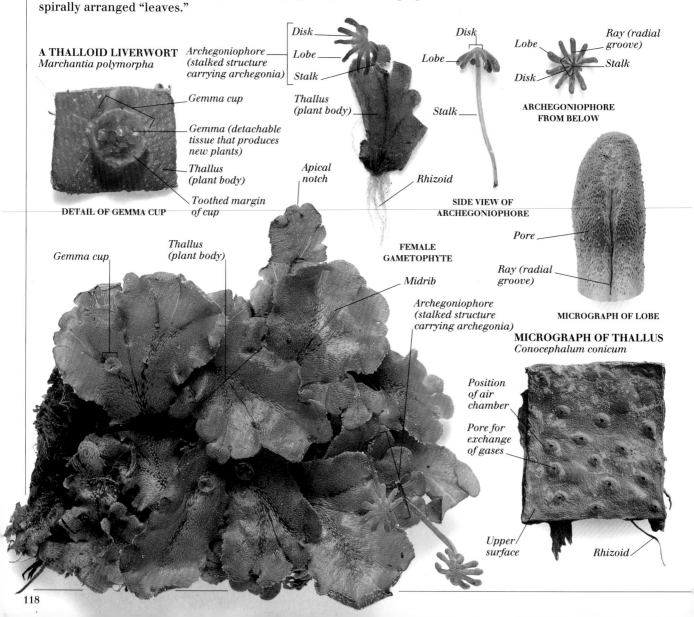

A THALLOID LIVERWORT
Marchantia polymorpha

Archegoniophore (stalked structure carrying archegonia)

Disk

Lobe

Stalk

Gemma cup

Gemma (detachable tissue that produces new plants)

Thallus (plant body)

Thallus (plant body)

Toothed margin of cup

DETAIL OF GEMMA CUP

Apical notch

Rhizoid

Disk

Lobe

Stalk

SIDE VIEW OF ARCHEGONIOPHORE

Lobe

Disk

Ray (radial groove)

Stalk

ARCHEGONIOPHORE FROM BELOW

Pore

Ray (radial groove)

MICROGRAPH OF LOBE

FEMALE GAMETOPHYTE

Gemma cup

Thallus (plant body)

Midrib

Archegoniophore (stalked structure carrying archegonia)

MICROGRAPH OF THALLUS
Conocephalum conicum

Position of air chamber

Pore for exchange of gases

Upper surface

Rhizoid

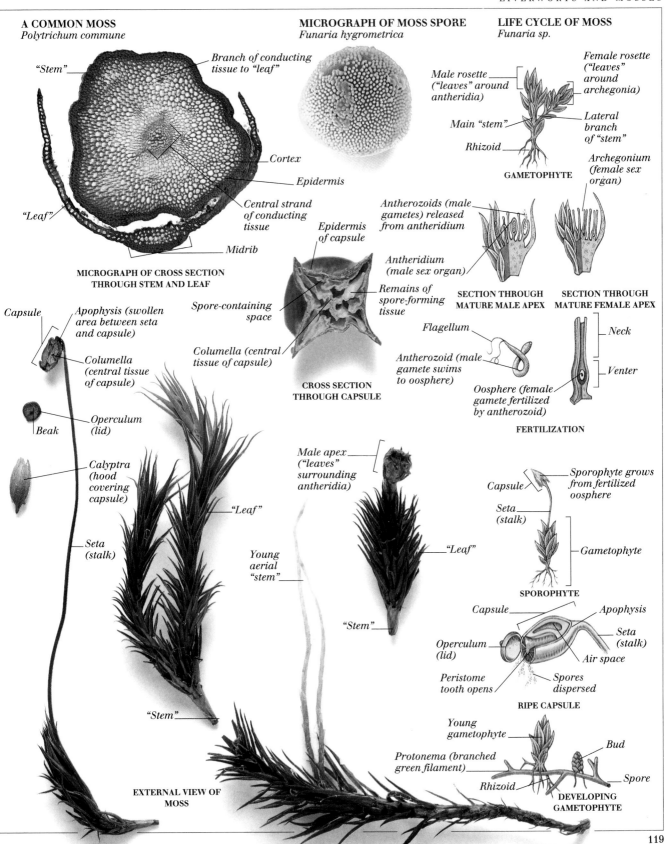

A COMMON MOSS
Polytrichum commune

"Stem"

Branch of conducting
tissue to "leaf"

Cortex

Epidermis

Central strand
of conducting
tissue

"Leaf"

Midrib

**MICROGRAPH OF CROSS SECTION
THROUGH STEM AND LEAF**

MICROGRAPH OF MOSS SPORE
Funaria hygrometrica

LIFE CYCLE OF MOSS
Funaria sp.

Male rosette
("leaves" around
antheridia)

Female rosette
("leaves"
around
archegonia)

Main "stem"

Lateral
branch
of "stem"

Rhizoid

GAMETOPHYTE

Archegonium
(female sex
organ)

Antherozoids (male
gametes) released
from antheridium

Antheridium
(male sex organ)

Epidermis
of capsule

Remains of
spore-forming
tissue

**SECTION THROUGH
MATURE MALE APEX**

**SECTION THROUGH
MATURE FEMALE APEX**

Spore-containing
space

Columella (central
tissue of capsule)

**CROSS SECTION
THROUGH CAPSULE**

Flagellum

Neck

Antherozoid (male
gamete swims
to oosphere)

Venter

Oosphere (female
gamete fertilized
by antherozoid)

FERTILIZATION

Capsule

Apophysis (swollen
area between seta
and capsule)

Columella
(central tissue
of capsule)

Beak

Operculum
(lid)

Calyptra
(hood
covering
capsule)

Seta
(stalk)

"Leaf"

Male apex
("leaves"
surrounding
antheridia)

Young
aerial
"stem"

"Leaf"

"Stem"

Sporophyte grows
from fertilized
oosphere

Capsule

Seta
(stalk)

Gametophyte

SPOROPHYTE

Capsule

Apophysis

Operculum
(lid)

Seta
(stalk)

Air space

Peristome
tooth opens

Spores
dispersed

RIPE CAPSULE

"Stem"

**EXTERNAL VIEW OF
MOSS**

Young
gametophyte

Protonema (branched
green filament)

Bud

Spore

Rhizoid

**DEVELOPING
GAMETOPHYTE**

Horsetails, club mosses, and ferns

CLUB MOSS
Lycopodium sp.

HORSETAILS, CLUB MOSSES, AND FERNS are primitive land plants, which, like higher plants, have stems, roots, leaves, and vascular systems that transport water, minerals, and food. Unlike higher plants, however, they do not produce seeds when reproducing. Their life cycles involve two stages. In stage one, the sporophyte (green plant) produces spores in sporangia. In stage two, the spores germinate, developing into small, short-lived gametophyte plants that produce male and female gametes (sex cells). The gametes fuse to form a zygote from which a new sporophyte plant develops. Horsetails (phylum Sphenophyta) have erect green stems with branches arranged in whorls. Some stems are fertile and have a single spore-producing strobilus (group of sporangia) at the tip. Club mosses (phylum Lycopodophyta) typically have small leaves arranged spirally around the stem, with spore-producing strobili at the tip of some stems. Ferns (phylum Filicinophyta) usually have large, pinnate leaves called fronds. Sporangia, grouped together in sori, develop on the underside of fertile fronds.

FROND
Male fern
(*Dryopteris filix-mas*)

Stem with spirally arranged leaves

Branch

Strobilus
(group of sporangia)

CLUB MOSS
Selaginella sp.

Epidermis
(outer layer of cells)

Cortex (layer between epidermis and vascular tissue)

Shoot apex

Branch

Rhizophore
(leafless branch)

Vascular tissue — Phloem
Xylem

Lacuna
(air space)

Root

Creeping stem with spirally arranged leaves

MICROGRAPH OF CROSS SECTION THROUGH CLUB MOSS STEM

HORSETAIL
Common horsetail
(*Equisetum arvense*)

Apex of sterile shoot

Sporangiophore
(structure carrying sporangia)

Strobilus
(group of sporangia)

Non-photosynthetic fertile stem

Lateral branch

Photosynthetic sterile stem

Node

Internode

Young shoot

Collar of small brown leaves

Node

Tuber

Rhizome

Adventitious root

Endodermis
(inner layer of cortex)

Vascular tissue

Sclerenchyma
(strengthening tissue)

Chlorenchyma
(photosynthetic tissue)

Epidermis
(outer layer of cells)

Cortex
(layer between epidermis and vascular tissue)

Parenchyma
(packing tissue)

Hollow pith cavity

Vallecular canal
(longitudinal channel)

Carinal canal
(longitudinal channel)

MICROGRAPH OF CROSS SECTION THROUGH HORSETAIL STEM

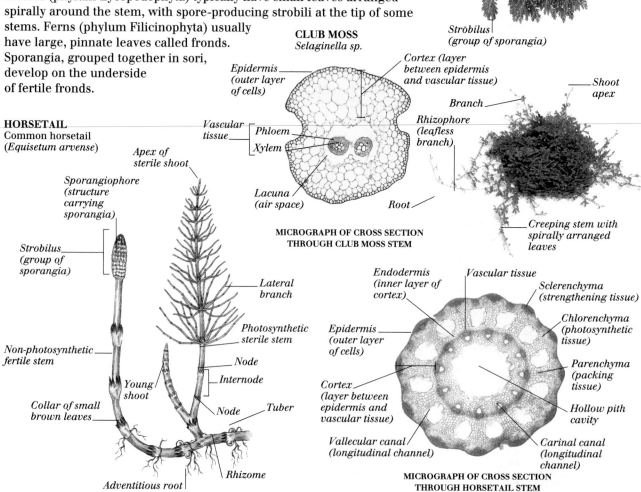

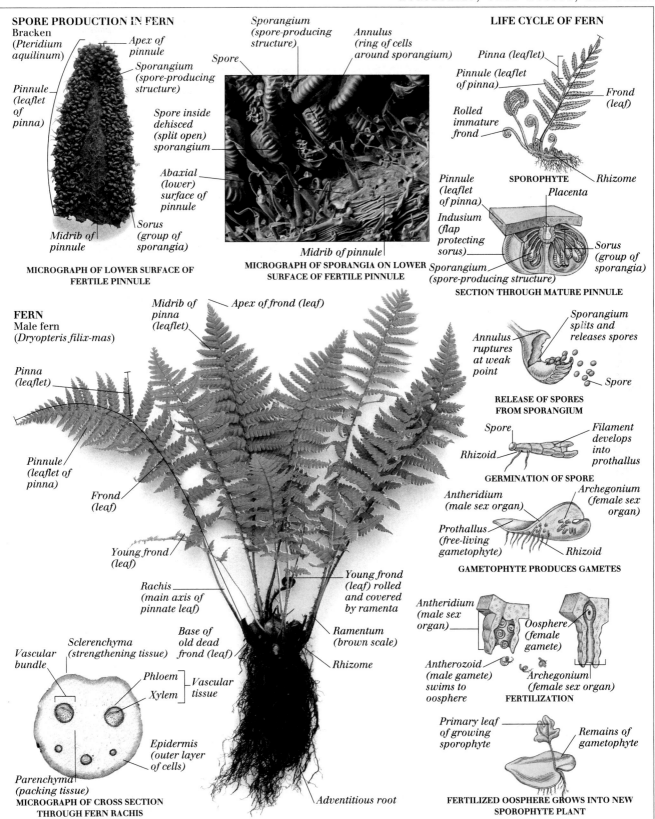

SPORE PRODUCTION IN FERN
Bracken
(*Pteridium aquilinum*)

Apex of pinnule

Sporangium (spore-producing structure)

Pinnule (leaflet of pinna)

Sporangium (spore-producing structure)

Spore inside dehisced (split open) sporangium

Abaxial (lower) surface of pinnule

Midrib of pinnule

Sorus (group of sporangia)

MICROGRAPH OF LOWER SURFACE OF FERTILE PINNULE

Sporangium (spore-producing structure)

Spore

Annulus (ring of cells around sporangium)

Midrib of pinnule

MICROGRAPH OF SPORANGIA ON LOWER SURFACE OF FERTILE PINNULE

LIFE CYCLE OF FERN

Pinna (leaflet)

Pinnule (leaflet of pinna)

Frond (leaf)

Rolled immature frond

SPOROPHYTE

Rhizome

Pinnule (leaflet of pinna)

Placenta

Indusium (flap protecting sorus)

Sporangium (spore-producing structure)

Sorus (group of sporangia)

SECTION THROUGH MATURE PINNULE

FERN
Male fern
(*Dryopteris filix-mas*)

Midrib of pinna (leaflet)

Apex of frond (leaf)

Pinna (leaflet)

Pinnule (leaflet of pinna)

Frond (leaf)

Young frond (leaf)

Rachis (main axis of pinnate leaf)

Base of old dead frond (leaf)

Young frond (leaf) rolled and covered by ramenta

Ramentum (brown scale)

Rhizome

Vascular bundle

Sclerenchyma (strengthening tissue)

Phloem

Xylem

Vascular tissue

Epidermis (outer layer of cells)

Parenchyma (packing tissue)

MICROGRAPH OF CROSS SECTION THROUGH FERN RACHIS

Adventitious root

Sporangium splits and releases spores

Annulus ruptures at weak point

Spore

RELEASE OF SPORES FROM SPORANGIUM

Spore

Filament develops into prothallus

Rhizoid

GERMINATION OF SPORE

Antheridium (male sex organ)

Archegonium (female sex organ)

Prothallus (free-living gametophyte)

Rhizoid

GAMETOPHYTE PRODUCES GAMETES

Antheridium (male sex organ)

Oosphere (female gamete)

Antherozoid (male gamete) swims to oosphere

Archegonium (female sex organ)

FERTILIZATION

Primary leaf of growing sporophyte

Remains of gametophyte

FERTILIZED OOSPHERE GROWS INTO NEW SPOROPHYTE PLANT

121

Gymnosperms 1

THE GYMNOSPERMS ARE FOUR RELATED PHYLA of seed-producing plants: Their seeds, however, lack the protective outer covering which surrounds the seeds of flowering plants. Typically, gymnosperms are woody, perennial shrubs or trees, with stems, leaves, roots, and a well-developed vascular (transport) system. The reproductive structures in most gymnosperms are cones. Male cones produce microspores in which male gametes (sex cells) develop; female cones produce megaspores in which female gametes develop. Microspores are blown by the wind to female cones, male and female gametes fuse during fertilization, and a seed develops. The four gymnosperm phyla are the conifers (phylum Coniferophyta), mostly tall trees; cycads (phylum Cycadophyta), small palm-like trees; the ginkgo or maidenhair tree (phylum Ginkgophyta), a tall tree with bilobed leaves; and gnetophytes (phylum Gnetophyta), a diverse group of plants, mainly shrubs, but also including the horizontally growing welwitschia.

LIFE CYCLE OF SCOTS PINE
(*Pinus sylvestris*)

Needle (foliage leaf)

Cone

Ovuliferous scale (ovule-/seed-bearing structure)

MALE CONES

YOUNG FEMALE CONE

Pollen grain in micropyle (entrance to ovule)

Ovuliferous scale

Pollen grain

Nucleus

Air sac

Ovule (contains female gamete)

POLLINATION

Integument (outer part of ovule)

Pollen tube (carries male gamete from pollen grain to ovum)

Archegonium (containing female gamete)

FERTILIZATION

Seed

Seed

Wing

MATURE FEMALE CONE AND WINGED SEED

SCALE AND SEEDS
Pine
(*Pinus sp.*)

Ovuliferous scale (ovule-/seed-bearing structure)

Wing scar

Wing of seed derived from ovuliferous scale

Seed

Seed

Seed scar

Point of attachment to axis of cone

OVULIFEROUS SCALE FROM THIRD-YEAR FEMALE CONE

Ovuliferous scale (ovule-/seed-bearing structure)

Plumule (embryonic shoot)

Cotyledon (seed leaf)

Root

GERMINATION OF PINE SEEDLING

Microsporangium (structure in which pollen grains are formed)

Microsporophyll (modified leaf carrying microsporangia)

Ovule (contains female gametes)

Bract scale

Axis of cone

Scale leaf

Ovuliferous scale (ovule-/seed-bearing structure)

Axis of cone

MICROGRAPH OF LONGITUDINAL SECTION THROUGH YOUNG MALE CONE

MICROGRAPH OF LONGITUDINAL SECTION THROUGH SECOND-YEAR FEMALE CONE

WELWITSCHIA
(*Welwitschia mirabilis*)

Frayed end of leaf

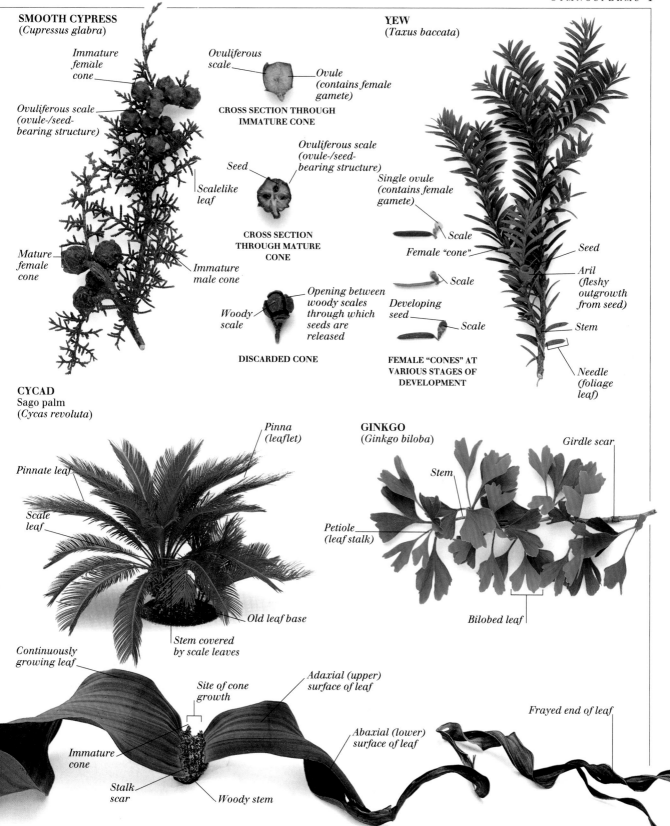

SMOOTH CYPRESS
(*Cupressus glabra*)

Immature female cone

Ovuliferous scale (ovule-/seed-bearing structure)

Mature female cone

Immature male cone

Ovuliferous scale

Ovule (contains female gamete)

CROSS SECTION THROUGH IMMATURE CONE

Ovuliferous scale (ovule-/seed-bearing structure)

Seed

Scalelike leaf

CROSS SECTION THROUGH MATURE CONE

Opening between woody scales through which seeds are released

Woody scale

DISCARDED CONE

YEW
(*Taxus baccata*)

Single ovule (contains female gamete)

Scale

Female "cone"

Scale

Developing seed

Scale

FEMALE "CONES" AT VARIOUS STAGES OF DEVELOPMENT

Seed

Aril (fleshy outgrowth from seed)

Stem

Needle (foliage leaf)

CYCAD
Sago palm
(*Cycas revoluta*)

Pinna (leaflet)

Pinnate leaf

Scale leaf

Mature female cone

Old leaf base

Stem covered by scale leaves

GINKGO
(*Ginkgo biloba*)

Girdle scar

Stem

Petiole (leaf stalk)

Bilobed leaf

Continuously growing leaf

Site of cone growth

Adaxial (upper) surface of leaf

Abaxial (lower) surface of leaf

Frayed end of leaf

Immature cone

Stalk scar

Woody stem

Gymnosperms 2

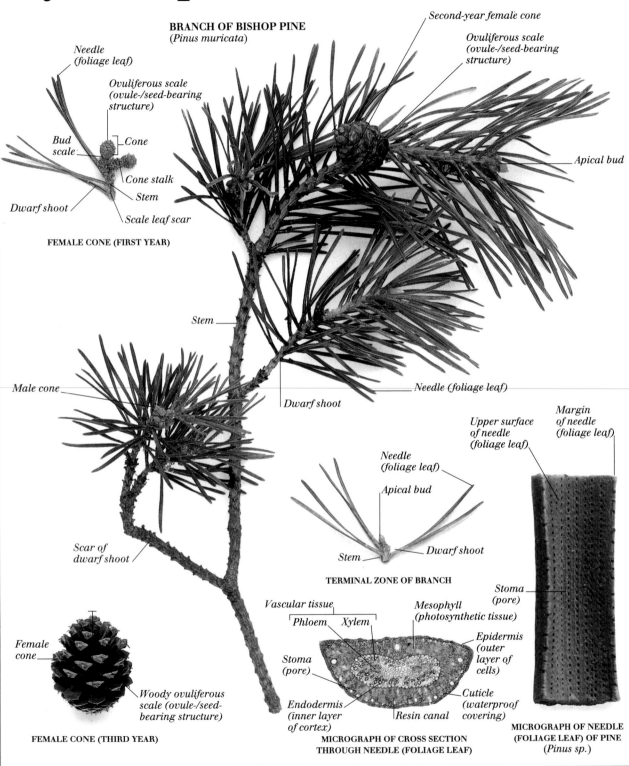

BRANCH OF BISHOP PINE
(*Pinus muricata*)

*Needle
(foliage leaf)*

Second-year female cone

*Ovuliferous scale
(ovule-/seed-bearing
structure)*

*Ovuliferous scale
(ovule-/seed-bearing
structure)*

*Bud
scale*

Cone

Cone stalk

Stem

Dwarf shoot

Scale leaf scar

FEMALE CONE (FIRST YEAR)

Apical bud

Stem

Dwarf shoot

Needle (foliage leaf)

Male cone

*Scar of
dwarf shoot*

*Female
cone*

*Woody ovuliferous
scale (ovule-/seed-
bearing structure)*

FEMALE CONE (THIRD YEAR)

*Upper surface
of needle
(foliage leaf)*

*Margin
of needle
(foliage leaf)*

*Needle
(foliage leaf)*

Apical bud

Stem

Dwarf shoot

TERMINAL ZONE OF BRANCH

Vascular tissue

Phloem *Xylem*

*Mesophyll
(photosynthetic tissue)*

*Stoma
(pore)*

*Epidermis
(outer
layer of
cells)*

*Stoma
(pore)*

*Cuticle
(waterproof
covering)*

*Endodermis
(inner layer
of cortex)*

Resin canal

*Stoma
(pore)*

**MICROGRAPH OF NEEDLE
(FOLIAGE LEAF) OF PINE
(*Pinus sp.*)**

**MICROGRAPH OF CROSS SECTION
THROUGH NEEDLE (FOLIAGE LEAF)**

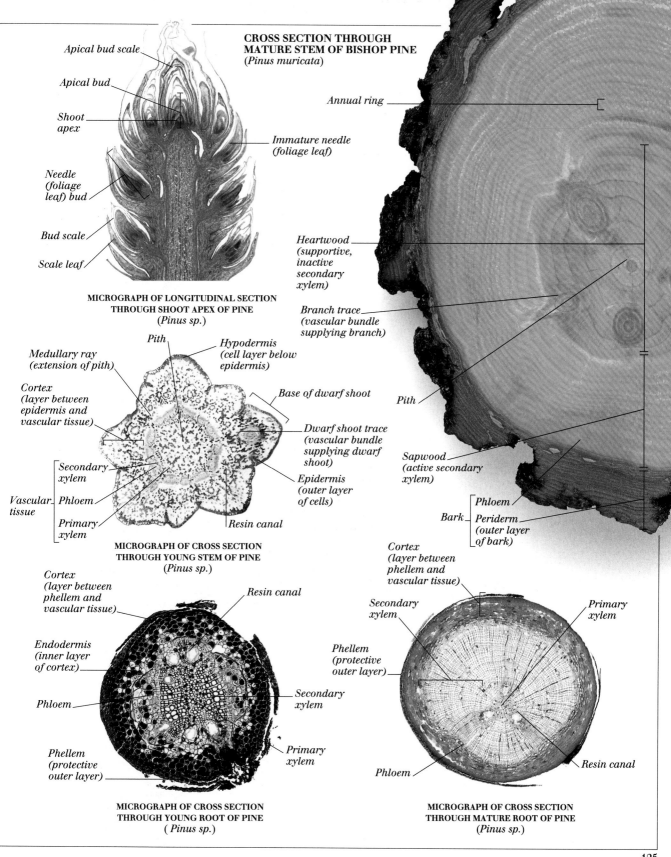

CROSS SECTION THROUGH
MATURE STEM OF BISHOP PINE
(*Pinus muricata*)

Apical bud scale

Apical bud

Shoot apex

Immature needle (foliage leaf)

Needle (foliage leaf) bud

Bud scale

Scale leaf

**MICROGRAPH OF LONGITUDINAL SECTION
THROUGH SHOOT APEX OF PINE
(*Pinus sp.*)**

Annual ring

Heartwood (supportive, inactive secondary xylem)

Branch trace (vascular bundle supplying branch)

Pith

Sapwood (active secondary xylem)

Phloem

Bark

Periderm (outer layer of bark)

Medullary ray (extension of pith)

Pith

Hypodermis (cell layer below epidermis)

Cortex (layer between epidermis and vascular tissue)

Base of dwarf shoot

Dwarf shoot trace (vascular bundle supplying dwarf shoot)

Secondary xylem

Phloem

Vascular tissue

Epidermis (outer layer of cells)

Primary xylem

Resin canal

**MICROGRAPH OF CROSS SECTION
THROUGH YOUNG STEM OF PINE
(*Pinus sp.*)**

Cortex (layer between phellem and vascular tissue)

Resin canal

Cortex (layer between phellem and vascular tissue)

Secondary xylem

Primary xylem

Endodermis (inner layer of cortex)

Phellem (protective outer layer)

Phloem

Secondary xylem

Phloem

Primary xylem

Phellem (protective outer layer)

Resin canal

**MICROGRAPH OF CROSS SECTION
THROUGH YOUNG ROOT OF PINE
(*Pinus sp.*)**

**MICROGRAPH OF CROSS SECTION
THROUGH MATURE ROOT OF PINE
(*Pinus sp.*)**

Monocotyledons and dicotyledons

FLOWERING PLANTS (PHYLUM ANGIOSPERMOPHYTA) are divided into two classes: monocotyledons (class Monocotyledoneae) and dicotyledons (class Dicotyledoneae). Typically, monocotyledons have seeds with one cotyledon (seed leaf); their foliage leaves are narrow with parallel veins; the flower components occur in multiples of three; sepals and petals are indistinguishable and are known as tepals; vascular (transport) tissues are scattered in random bundles throughout the stem; and, because they lack stem cambium (actively dividing cells that produce wood), most monocotyledons are herbaceous (see pp. 128-129). Dicotyledons have seeds with two cotyledons; leaves are broad with a central midrib and branched veins; flower parts occur in multiples of four or five; sepals are generally small and green; petals are large and colorful; vascular bundles are arranged in a ring around the edge of the stem; and, because many dicotyledons possess wood-producing stem cambium, there are woody forms (see pp. 130-131) as well as herbaceous ones.

CROSS SECTION
THROUGH
MONOCOTYLEDONOUS
LEAF BASES

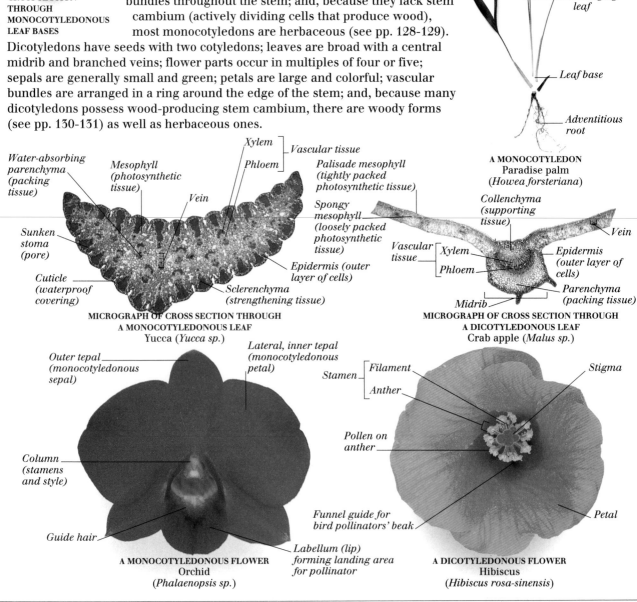

Vein
(parallel
venation)

Leaflet

Petiole
(leaf stalk)

Emerging
leaf

Leaf base

Adventitious
root

A MONOCOTYLEDON
Paradise palm
(*Howea forsteriana*)

Water-absorbing
parenchyma
(packing
tissue)

Mesophyll
(photosynthetic
tissue)

Xylem
Phloem
Vascular tissue

Vein

Sunken
stoma
(pore)

Cuticle
(waterproof
covering)

Epidermis (outer
layer of cells)

Sclerenchyma
(strengthening tissue)

Palisade mesophyll
(tightly packed
photosynthetic tissue)

Spongy
mesophyll
(loosely packed
photosynthetic
tissue)

Vascular
tissue
Xylem
Phloem

Collenchyma
(supporting
tissue)

Vein

Epidermis
(outer layer
of cells)

Parenchyma
(packing tissue)

Midrib

**MICROGRAPH OF CROSS SECTION THROUGH
A MONOCOTYLEDONOUS LEAF**
Yucca (*Yucca sp.*)

**MICROGRAPH OF CROSS SECTION THROUGH
A DICOTYLEDONOUS LEAF**
Crab apple (*Malus sp.*)

Outer tepal
(monocotyledonous
sepal)

Lateral, inner tepal
(monocotyledonous
petal)

Stamen
Filament
Anther

Stigma

Column
(stamens
and style)

Pollen on
anther

Guide hair

Funnel guide for
bird pollinators' beak

Labellum (lip)
forming landing area
for pollinator

Petal

A MONOCOTYLEDONOUS FLOWER
Orchid
(*Phalaenopsis sp.*)

A DICOTYLEDONOUS FLOWER
Hibiscus
(*Hibiscus rosa-sinensis*)

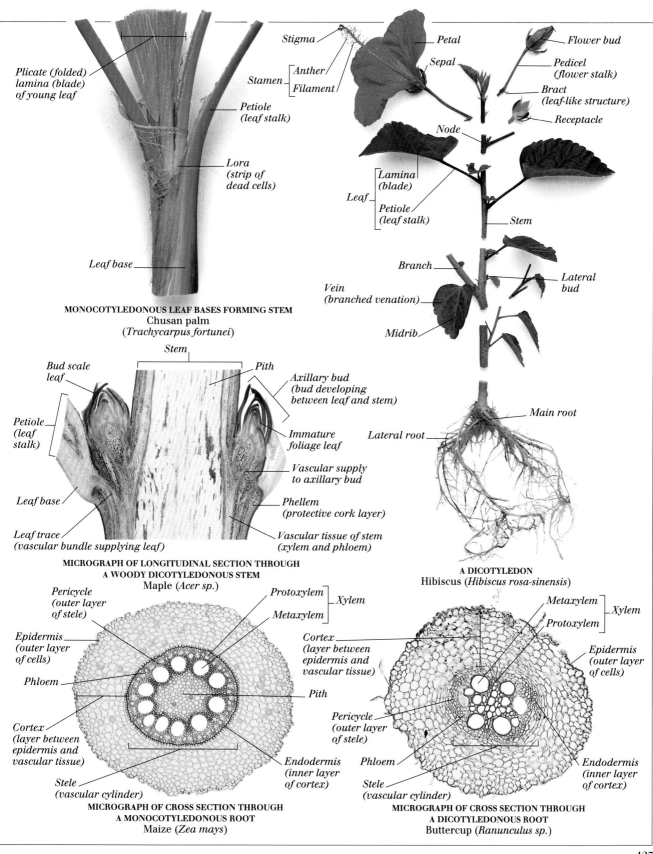

Plicate (folded) lamina (blade) of young leaf

Petiole (leaf stalk)

Lora (strip of dead cells)

Leaf base

MONOCOTYLEDONOUS LEAF BASES FORMING STEM
Chusan palm
(*Trachycarpus fortunei*)

Stigma

Petal

Anther
Filament
Stamen

Sepal

Flower bud

Pedicel (flower stalk)

Bract (leaf-like structure)

Receptacle

Node

Lamina (blade)
Petiole (leaf stalk)
Leaf

Stem

Branch

Vein (branched venation)

Midrib

Lateral bud

Stem

Pith

Bud scale leaf

Axillary bud (bud developing between leaf and stem)

Immature foliage leaf

Petiole (leaf stalk)

Vascular supply to axillary bud

Leaf base

Leaf trace (vascular bundle supplying leaf)

Phellem (protective cork layer)

Vascular tissue of stem (xylem and phloem)

MICROGRAPH OF LONGITUDINAL SECTION THROUGH A WOODY DICOTYLEDONOUS STEM
Maple (*Acer sp.*)

Main root

Lateral root

A DICOTYLEDON
Hibiscus (*Hibiscus rosa-sinensis*)

Pericycle (outer layer of stele)

Protoxylem
Metaxylem
Xylem

Epidermis (outer layer of cells)

Cortex (layer between epidermis and vascular tissue)

Phloem

Pith

Cortex (layer between epidermis and vascular tissue)

Stele (vascular cylinder)

Endodermis (inner layer of cortex)

MICROGRAPH OF CROSS SECTION THROUGH A MONOCOTYLEDONOUS ROOT
Maize (*Zea mays*)

Metaxylem
Protoxylem
Xylem

Epidermis (outer layer of cells)

Pericycle (outer layer of stele)

Phloem

Stele (vascular cylinder)

Endodermis (inner layer of cortex)

MICROGRAPH OF CROSS SECTION THROUGH A DICOTYLEDONOUS ROOT
Buttercup (*Ranunculus sp.*)

Herbaceous flowering plants

HERBACEOUS FLOWERING PLANTS TYPICALLY HAVE GREEN NON-WOODY STEMS, and tend to be relatively short-lived. Many herbaceous plants live for only one or two years. Annuals (such as sweet peas) grow from seed, produce flowers and then seeds, and die within a single year. Biennials (like carrots) have a two-year life cycle. In the first year, seeds grow into plants, which produce leaves and store food in underground storage organs; the stems and foliage then die in winter. In the second year, new stems grow from the storage organs, produce leaves, flowers, and seeds, and then die. Some herbaceous plants (such as potatoes) are perennial. They grow back year after year, producing shoots and flowers in spring, storing food in underground tubers or rhizomes during summer, dying in autumn, and surviving underground during winter.

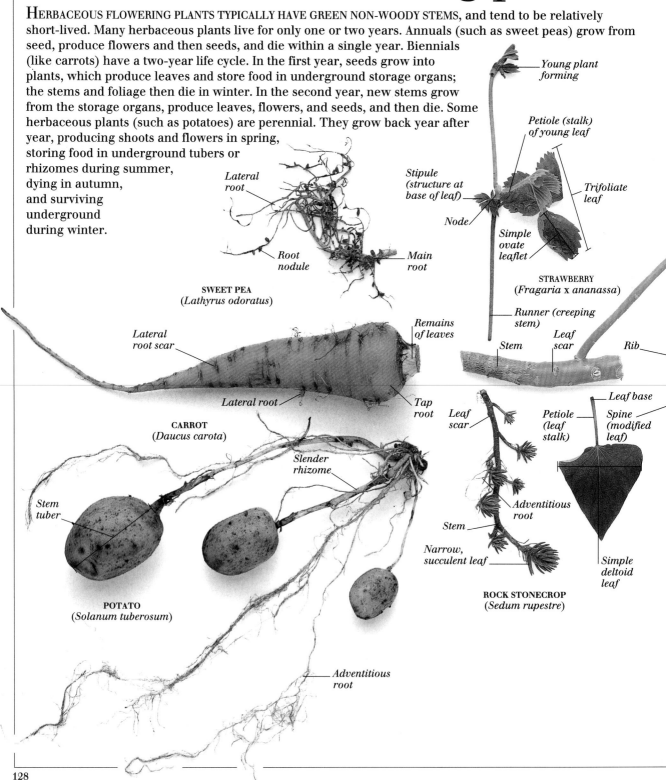

Lateral root

Root nodule

Main root

SWEET PEA
(*Lathyrus odoratus*)

Young plant forming

Petiole (stalk) of young leaf

Stipule (structure at base of leaf)

Node

Trifoliate leaf

Simple ovate leaflet

STRAWBERRY
(*Fragaria* x *ananassa*)

Runner (creeping stem)

Leaf scar

Stem

Rib

Lateral root scar

Remains of leaves

Lateral root

Tap root

CARROT
(*Daucus carota*)

Leaf scar

Leaf base

Petiole (leaf stalk)

Spine (modified leaf)

Slender rhizome

Stem tuber

Adventitious root

Stem

Narrow, succulent leaf

Simple deltoid leaf

POTATO
(*Solanum tuberosum*)

ROCK STONECROP
(*Sedum rupestre*)

Adventitious root

PARTS OF HERBACEOUS FLOWERING PLANTS

Bract
(leaf-like
structure)

Bracteole
(small bract)

Midrib

Cyme (type of
inflorescence)

Succulent,
simple ovate
leaf

Inner, tubular
disk floret

Outer, ligulate
ray floret

Node

Flower bud

Dentate
margin

Peduncle
(inflorescence stalk)

Capitulum (type
of inflorescence)

Internode

Leaf

SHOWY STONECROP
(*Sedum spectabile*)

Simple lobed
leaf

Peduncle
(inflorescence
stalk)

Flower
bud

Succulent
stem

Petiole
(leaf stalk)

Petiole
(leaf
stalk)

Leaf base

Linear
leaf

Leaf
scar

Lateral
bud

Prickle

FLORISTS' CHRYSANTHEMUM
(*Chrysanthemum morifolium*)

Stem

**CEREOID
CACTUS**

BEGONIA
(*Begonia* x
tuberhybrida)

Bract
(leaf-like
structure)

Capitulum (type
of inflorescence)

Hollow
stem

Sheath formed
from leaf base

TOADFLAX
(*Linaria sp.*)

Spinose-dentate
margin

Dentate
margin

Unwinged rachis
(main axis of
pinnate leaf)

Rachis (main
axis of pinnate
leaf)

SLENDER THISTLE
(*Carduus tenuiflorus*)

Peduncle
(inflorescence
stalk)

Winged
stem

Tendril

Winged
rachis
(main
axis of
pinnate
leaf)

Flower bud

Stipule
(structure at
base of leaf)

Stem
segment

Pinna
(leaflet)

HOGWEED
(*Heracleum sphondylium*)

Bract
(leaflike
structure)

Tepal

Petiole
(leaf stalk)

Margin of
cladode

Toothed
notch

PERUVIAN LILY
(*Alstroemeria aurea*)

Peduncle
(inflorescence
stalk)

Cladode
(flattened stem)

Stem
branch

Raceme (type
of inflorescence)

CRAB CACTUS
(*Schlumbergera truncata*)

Petal

Sepal

EVERLASTING PEA
(*Lathyrus latifolius*)

Woody flowering plants

WOODY FLOWERING PLANTS ARE PERENNIAL: They continue to grow and reproduce for many years. They have one or more permanent stems above ground and numerous smaller branches. The stems and branches have a strong woody core that supports the plant and contains vascular tissue for transporting water and nutrients. Outside the woody core is a layer of tough, protective bark, which has lenticels (tiny pores) to allow gases to pass through. Woody flowering plants may be shrubs, which have several stems rising from the soil; bushes, which are shrubs with dense branching and foliage; or trees, which typically have a single upright stem (the trunk) that bears branches. Deciduous woody plants (like roses) shed all their leaves once a year and remain leafless during winter. Evergreen woody plants (such as holly) shed their leaves gradually, so they retain full leaf cover throughout the year.

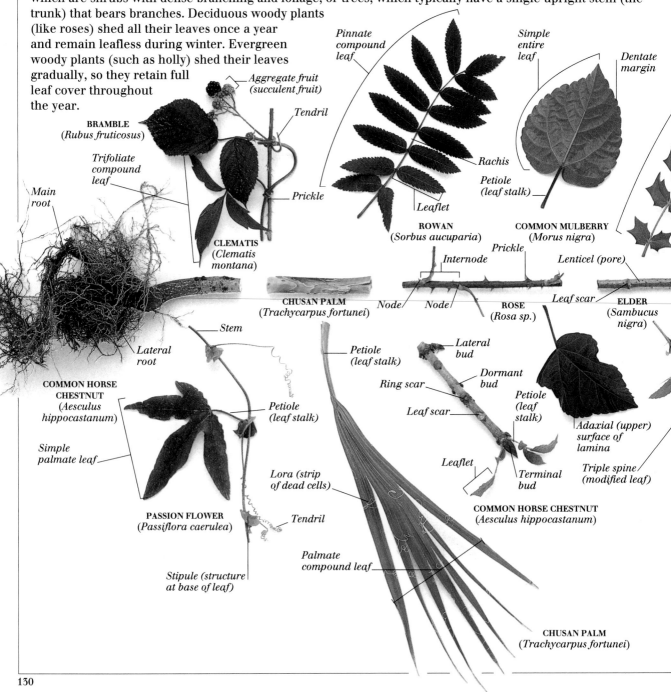

Aggregate fruit (succulent fruit)

BRAMBLE (*Rubus fruticosus*)

Trifoliate compound leaf

Tendril

Prickle

Pinnate compound leaf

Rachis

Petiole (leaf stalk)

Leaflet

ROWAN (*Sorbus aucuparia*)

Simple entire leaf

Dentate margin

COMMON MULBERRY (*Morus nigra*)

CLEMATIS (*Clematis montana*)

Main root

Lateral root

COMMON HORSE CHESTNUT (*Aesculus hippocastanum*)

Simple palmate leaf

Stem

Petiole (leaf stalk)

PASSION FLOWER (*Passiflora caerulea*)

Tendril

Stipule (structure at base of leaf)

CHUSAN PALM (*Trachycarpus fortunei*)

Node

Internode

Node

Prickle

ROSE (*Rosa sp.*)

Lenticel (pore)

Leaf scar

ELDER (*Sambucus nigra*)

Petiole (leaf stalk)

Lora (strip of dead cells)

Palmate compound leaf

Lateral bud

Ring scar

Leaf scar

Dormant bud

Petiole (leaf stalk)

Leaflet

Terminal bud

COMMON HORSE CHESTNUT (*Aesculus hippocastanum*)

Adaxial (upper) surface of lamina

Triple spine (modified leaf)

CHUSAN PALM (*Trachycarpus fortunei*)

PARTS OF WOODY FLOWERING PLANTS

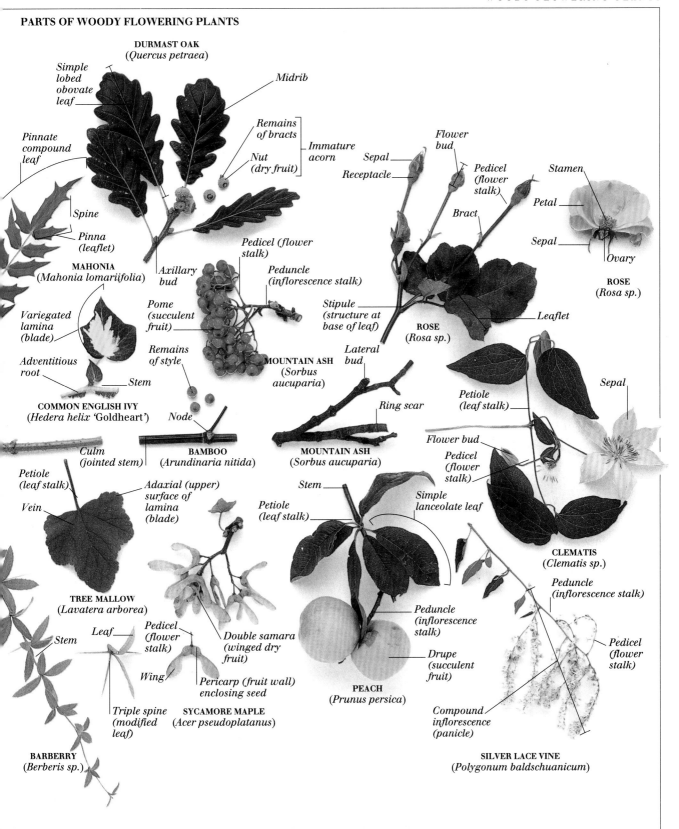

DURMAST OAK
(*Quercus petraea*)

Simple lobed obovate leaf

Midrib

Pinnate compound leaf

Remains of bracts

Nut (dry fruit)

Immature acorn

Spine

Pinna (leaflet)

Sepal

Receptacle

Flower bud

Pedicel (flower stalk)

Stamen

Petal

Bract

Sepal

Ovary

ROSE
(*Rosa sp.*)

MAHONIA
(*Mahonia lomariifolia*)

Axillary bud

Pedicel (flower stalk)

Peduncle (inflorescence stalk)

Variegated lamina (blade)

Pome (succulent fruit)

Adventitious root

Stem

Remains of style

Stipule (structure at base of leaf)

Leaflet

ROSE
(*Rosa sp.*)

COMMON ENGLISH IVY
(*Hedera helix* 'Goldheart')

Node

MOUNTAIN ASH
(*Sorbus aucuparia*)

Lateral bud

Petiole (leaf stalk)

Sepal

Culm (jointed stem)

BAMBOO
(*Arundinaria nitida*)

Ring scar

MOUNTAIN ASH
(*Sorbus aucuparia*)

Flower bud

Pedicel (flower stalk)

Petiole (leaf stalk)

Vein

Adaxial (upper) surface of lamina (blade)

Stem

Petiole (leaf stalk)

Simple lanceolate leaf

CLEMATIS
(*Clematis sp.*)

TREE MALLOW
(*Lavatera arborea*)

Leaf

Pedicel (flower stalk)

Double samara (winged dry fruit)

Peduncle (inflorescence stalk)

Peduncle (inflorescence stalk)

Stem

Wing

Pericarp (fruit wall) enclosing seed

Drupe (succulent fruit)

Pedicel (flower stalk)

Triple spine (modified leaf)

SYCAMORE MAPLE
(*Acer pseudoplatanus*)

PEACH
(*Prunus persica*)

Compound inflorescence (panicle)

BARBERRY
(*Berberis sp.*)

SILVER LACE VINE
(*Polygonum baldschuanicum*)

Roots

ROOTS ARE THE UNDERGROUND PARTS OF PLANTS. They have three main functions. First, they anchor the plant in the soil. Second, they absorb water and minerals from the spaces between soil particles. The roots' absorptive properties are increased by root hairs, which grow behind the root tip, allowing maximum absorption of vital substances. Third, the root is part of the plant's transport system. Xylem carries water and minerals from the roots to the stem and leaves, and phloem carries nutrients from the leaves to all parts of the root system. In addition, some roots (like carrots) are food stores. Roots have an outer epidermis covering a cortex of parenchyma (packing tissue), and a central cylinder of vascular tissue. This arrangement helps the roots resist the forces of compression as they grow through the soil.

CARROT
(*Daucus carota*)

MICROGRAPH OF PRIMARY ROOT DEVELOPMENT
Cabbage (*Brassica sp.*)

Split in testa
as seed
germinates

Cotyledon
(seed leaf)

Primary root

Testa
(seed coat)

Root hair

Root tip
(region of
cell division)

FEATURES OF A TYPICAL ROOT
Buttercup
(*Ranunculus sp.*)

Pericycle
(outer layer
of stele)

Root hair

Air space
(allowing gas
diffusion in
the root)

Stele
(vascular cylinder)

Phloem sieve tube
(through which
nutrients are
transported)

Companion cell
(cell associated
with phloem
sieve tube)

Cortex
(layer between
epidermis and
vascular tissue)

Root hair

Epidermis
(outer layer
of cells)

Xylem vessel
(through which water
and minerals are transported)

Endodermis
(inner layer
of cortex)

Cell wall

Nucleus

Cytoplasm

Parenchyma
(packing) cell

PRIMARY ROOT AND MICROGRAPHS OF SECTIONS THROUGH ROOTS

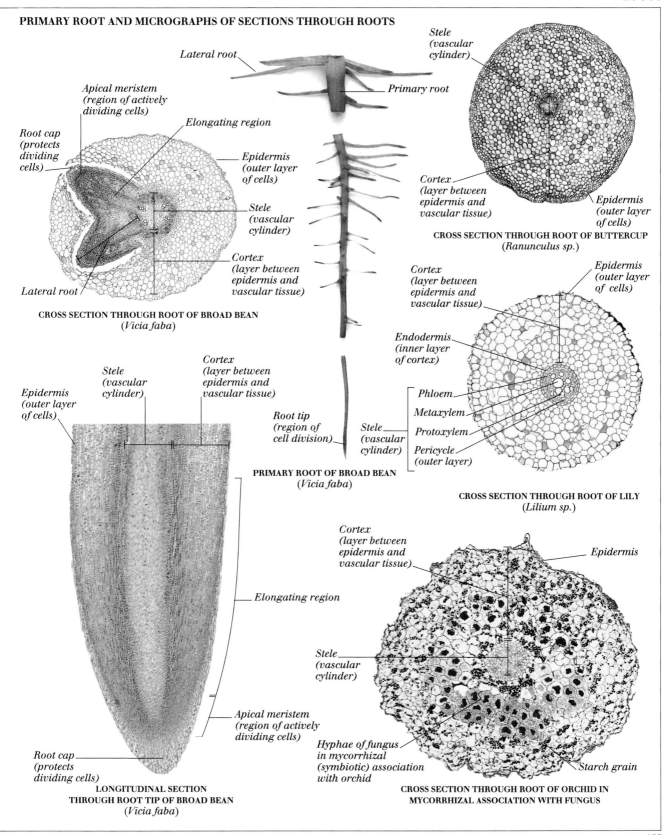

Lateral root

Primary root

Stele
(vascular
cylinder)

Apical meristem
(region of actively
dividing cells)

Elongating region

Root cap
(protects
dividing
cells)

Epidermis
(outer layer
of cells)

Stele
(vascular
cylinder)

Cortex
(layer between
epidermis and
vascular tissue)

Lateral root

CROSS SECTION THROUGH ROOT OF BROAD BEAN
(*Vicia faba*)

Cortex
(layer between
epidermis and
vascular tissue)

Epidermis
(outer layer
of cells)

CROSS SECTION THROUGH ROOT OF BUTTERCUP
(*Ranunculus sp.*)

Cortex
(layer between
epidermis and
vascular tissue)

Epidermis
(outer layer
of cells)

Endodermis
(inner layer
of cortex)

Phloem

Metaxylem

Protoxylem

Pericycle
(outer layer)

Stele
(vascular
cylinder)

CROSS SECTION THROUGH ROOT OF LILY
(*Lilium sp.*)

Epidermis
(outer layer
of cells)

Stele
(vascular
cylinder)

Cortex
(layer between
epidermis and
vascular tissue)

Root tip
(region of
cell division)

Stele
(vascular
cylinder)

PRIMARY ROOT OF BROAD BEAN
(*Vicia faba*)

Elongating region

Apical meristem
(region of actively
dividing cells)

Root cap
(protects
dividing
cells)

**LONGITUDINAL SECTION
THROUGH ROOT TIP OF BROAD BEAN**
(*Vicia faba*)

Cortex
(layer between
epidermis and
vascular tissue)

Epidermis

Stele
(vascular
cylinder)

Hyphae of fungus
in mycorrhizal
(symbiotic) association
with orchid

Starch grain

**CROSS SECTION THROUGH ROOT OF ORCHID IN
MYCORRHIZAL ASSOCIATION WITH FUNGUS**

133

Stems

THE STEM IS THE MAIN SUPPORTIVE PART OF A PLANT that grows above ground. Stems bear leaves (organs of photosynthesis), which grow at nodes; buds (shoots covered by protective scales), which grow at the stem tip (apical or terminal buds) and in the angle between a leaf and the stem (axillary or lateral buds); and flowers (reproductive structures). The stem forms part of the plant's transport system. Xylem tissue in the stem transports water and minerals from the roots to the aerial parts of the plant, and phloem tissue transports nutrients manufactured in the leaves to other parts of the plant. Stem tissues are also used for storing water and food. Herbaceous (nonwoody) stems have an outer protective epidermis covering a cortex that consists mainly of parenchyma (packing tissue) but also has some collenchyma (supporting tissue). The vascular tissue of such stems is arranged in bundles, each of which consists of xylem, phloem, and sclerenchyma (strengthening tissue). Woody stems have an outer protective layer of tough bark, which is perforated with lenticels (pores) to allow gas exchange. Inside the bark is a ring of secondary phloem, which surrounds an inner core of secondary xylem.

MICROGRAPH OF LONGITUDINAL SECTION THROUGH APEX OF STEM
Coleus sp.

Apical meristem (region of actively dividing cells)

Procambial strand (cells that produce vascular tissue)

Leaf primordium (developing leaf)

Developing bud

Cortex (layer between epidermis and vascular tissue)

Vascular tissue

Epidermis (outer layer of cells)

Pith

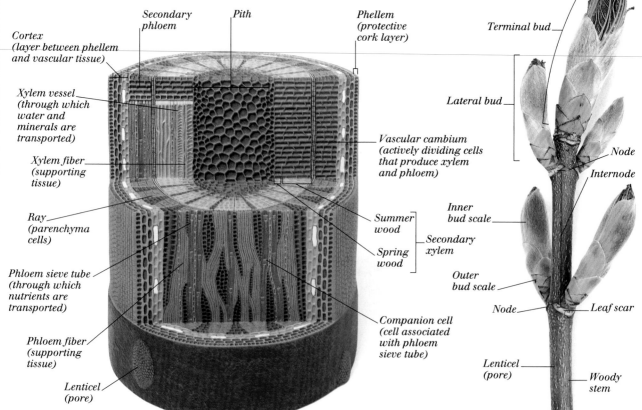

YOUNG WOODY STEM
Linden
(Tilia sp.)

Cortex (layer between phellem and vascular tissue)

Secondary phloem

Pith

Phellem (protective cork layer)

Xylem vessel (through which water and minerals are transported)

Xylem fiber (supporting tissue)

Ray (parenchyma cells)

Phloem sieve tube (through which nutrients are transported)

Phloem fiber (supporting tissue)

Lenticel (pore)

Vascular cambium (actively dividing cells that produce xylem and phloem)

Summer wood

Spring wood

Inner bud scale

Secondary xylem

Outer bud scale

Companion cell (cell associated with phloem sieve tube)

Node

EMERGENT BUDS
Maple
(Acer)

Young leaves emerging

Terminal bud

Lateral bud

Node

Internode

Node

Leaf scar

Lenticel (pore)

Woody stem

MICROGRAPHS OF CROSS SECTIONS THROUGH VARIOUS STEMS

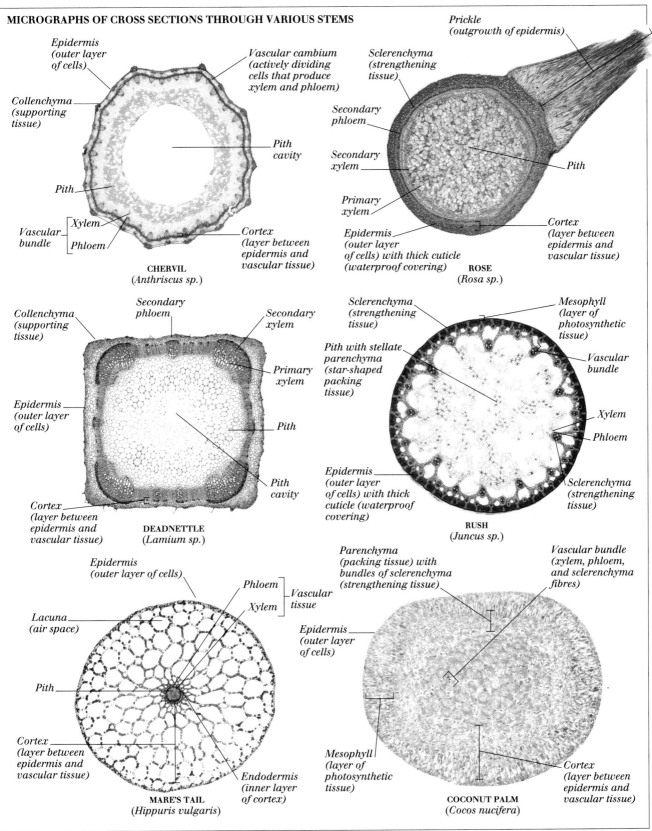

Epidermis (outer layer of cells)

Collenchyma (supporting tissue)

Pith

Vascular bundle
  Xylem
  Phloem

Vascular cambium (actively dividing cells that produce xylem and phloem)

Pith cavity

Cortex (layer between epidermis and vascular tissue)

CHERVIL (*Anthriscus sp.*)

Prickle (outgrowth of epidermis)

Sclerenchyma (strengthening tissue)

Secondary phloem

Secondary xylem

Primary xylem

Epidermis (outer layer of cells) with thick cuticle (waterproof covering)

Pith

Cortex (layer between epidermis and vascular tissue)

ROSE (*Rosa sp.*)

Collenchyma (supporting tissue)

Secondary phloem

Secondary xylem

Primary xylem

Epidermis (outer layer of cells)

Pith

Pith cavity

Cortex (layer between epidermis and vascular tissue)

DEADNETTLE (*Lamium sp.*)

Sclerenchyma (strengthening tissue)

Pith with stellate parenchyma (star-shaped packing tissue)

Epidermis (outer layer of cells) with thick cuticle (waterproof covering)

Mesophyll (layer of photosynthetic tissue)

Vascular bundle

Xylem

Phloem

Sclerenchyma (strengthening tissue)

RUSH (*Juncus sp.*)

Epidermis (outer layer of cells)

Lacuna (air space)

Pith

Cortex (layer between epidermis and vascular tissue)

Phloem
Xylem
Vascular tissue

Endodermis (inner layer of cortex)

MARE'S TAIL (*Hippuris vulgaris*)

Parenchyma (packing tissue) with bundles of sclerenchyma (strengthening tissue)

Epidermis (outer layer of cells)

Mesophyll (layer of photosynthetic tissue)

Vascular bundle (xylem, phloem, and sclerenchyma fibres)

Cortex (layer between epidermis and vascular tissue)

COCONUT PALM (*Cocos nucifera*)

Leaves

LEAVES ARE THE MAIN SITES OF PHOTOSYNTHESIS (see pp. 138-139) and transpiration (water loss by evaporation) in plants. A typical leaf consists of a thin, flat lamina (blade) supported by a network of veins; a petiole (leaf stalk); and a leaf base, where the petiole joins the stem. Leaves can be classified as simple, in which the lamina is a single unit, or compound, in which the lamina is divided into separate leaflets. Compound leaves may be pinnate, with pinnae (leaflets) on both sides of a rachis (main axis), or palmate, with leaflets arising from a single point at the tip of the petiole. Leaves can be classified further by the overall shape of the lamina, and by the shape of the lamina's apex, margin, and base.

CHECKERBLOOM
(*Sidalcea malviflora*)

GENERAL LEAF FEATURES

Apex

Midrib

Lamina (blade)

Margin

Lateral vein

Lamina base

Petiole (leaf stalk)

Leaf base

Spanish chestnut
(*Castanea sativa*)

SIMPLE LEAF SHAPES

Subacute apex

Acuminate apex

Entire margin

Entire margin

Cuneate base

Cordate base

PANDURIFORM
Croton
(*Codiaeum variegatum*)

LANCEOLATE
Sea buckthorn
(*Hippophae rhamnoides*)

COMPOUND LEAF SHAPES

Terminal pinna (leaflet)

Emarginate apex

Rachis (main axis of pinnate leaf)

Pinna (leaflet)

Petiolule (leaflet stalk)

Petiole (leaf stalk)

ODD PINNATE
Black locust
(*Robinia pseudoacacia*)

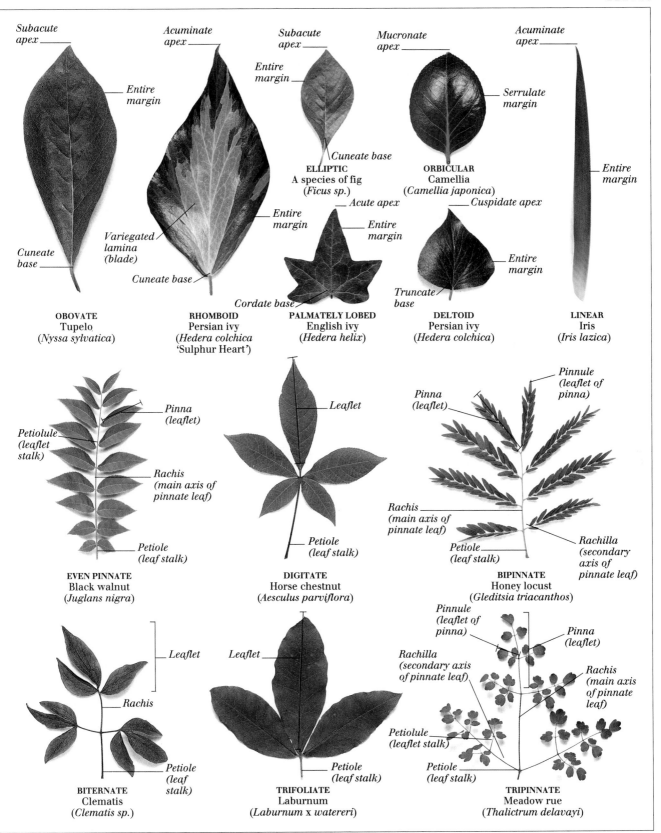

Subacute apex

Acuminate apex

Subacute apex

Mucronate apex

Acuminate apex

Entire margin

Entire margin

Serrulate margin

Entire margin

Cuneate base

ELLIPTIC
A species of fig
(*Ficus sp.*)

ORBICULAR
Camellia
(*Camellia japonica*)

Entire margin

Acute apex

Cuspidate apex

Entire margin

Variegated lamina (blade)

Entire margin

Entire margin

Cuneate base

Cuneate base

Cordate base

Truncate base

OBOVATE
Tupelo
(*Nyssa sylvatica*)

RHOMBOID
Persian ivy
(*Hedera colchica*
'Sulphur Heart')

PALMATELY LOBED
English ivy
(*Hedera helix*)

DELTOID
Persian ivy
(*Hedera colchica*)

LINEAR
Iris
(*Iris lazica*)

Pinna (leaflet)

Leaflet

Pinna (leaflet)

Pinnule (leaflet of pinna)

Petiolule (leaflet stalk)

Rachis (main axis of pinnate leaf)

Rachis (main axis of pinnate leaf)

Rachilla (secondary axis of pinnate leaf)

Petiole (leaf stalk)

Petiole (leaf stalk)

Petiole (leaf stalk)

EVEN PINNATE
Black walnut
(*Juglans nigra*)

DIGITATE
Horse chestnut
(*Aesculus parviflora*)

BIPINNATE
Honey locust
(*Gleditsia triacanthos*)

Pinnule (leaflet of pinna)

Pinna (leaflet)

Leaflet

Rachilla (secondary axis of pinnate leaf)

Rachis (main axis of pinnate leaf)

Leaflet

Rachis

Petiolule (leaflet stalk)

Petiole (leaf stalk)

Petiole (leaf stalk)

Petiole (leaf stalk)

BITERNATE
Clematis
(*Clematis sp.*)

TRIFOLIATE
Laburnum
(*Laburnum x watereri*)

TRIPINNATE
Meadow rue
(*Thalictrum delavayi*)

137

Photosynthesis

PHOTOSYNTHESIS IS THE PROCESS by which plants make their food
using sunlight, water, and carbon dioxide. It takes place inside special
structures in leaf cells called chloroplasts. The chloroplasts contain
chlorophyll, a green pigment that absorbs energy from sunlight.
During photosynthesis, the absorbed energy is used to join together
carbon dioxide and water to form the sugar glucose, which is the
energy source for the whole plant. Oxygen, a waste product, is
released into the air. Leaves are the main sites of photosynthesis and
have various adaptations for that purpose. Flat laminae (blades)
provide a large surface for absorbing sunlight; stomata (pores) in the
lower surface of the laminae allow gases (carbon dioxide and oxygen)
to pass into and out of the leaves; and an extensive network of veins
brings water into the leaves and transports the glucose produced by
photosynthesis to the rest of the plant.

MICROGRAPH OF LEAF
Lily (*Lilium sp.*)

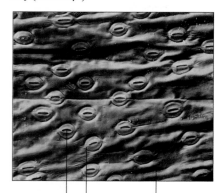

Stoma (pore)

Guard cell (controls opening and closing of stoma)

Lower surface of lamina (blade)

THE PROCESS OF PHOTOSYNTHESIS

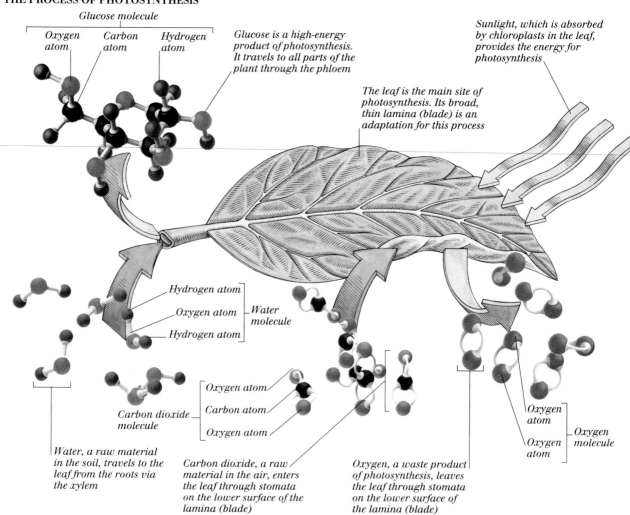

Glucose molecule

Oxygen atom

Carbon atom

Hydrogen atom

Glucose is a high-energy product of photosynthesis. It travels to all parts of the plant through the phloem

Sunlight, which is absorbed by chloroplasts in the leaf, provides the energy for photosynthesis

The leaf is the main site of photosynthesis. Its broad, thin lamina (blade) is an adaptation for this process

Hydrogen atom

Oxygen atom — Water molecule

Hydrogen atom

Oxygen atom

Carbon atom

Oxygen atom

Carbon dioxide molecule

Oxygen atom

Oxygen atom

Oxygen molecule

Water, a raw material in the soil, travels to the leaf from the roots via the xylem

Carbon dioxide, a raw material in the air, enters the leaf through stomata on the lower surface of the lamina (blade)

Oxygen, a waste product of photosynthesis, leaves the leaf through stomata on the lower surface of the lamina (blade)

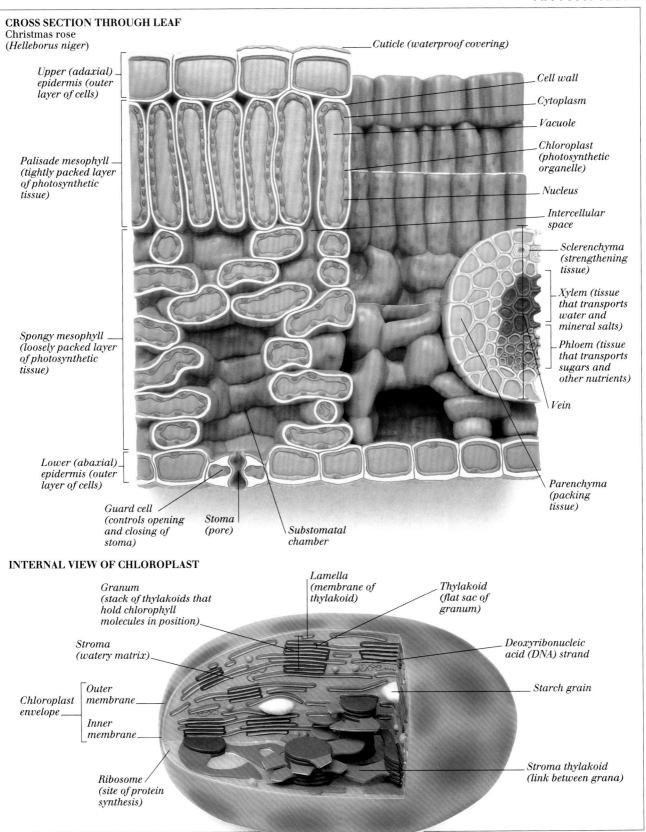

CROSS SECTION THROUGH LEAF
Christmas rose
(*Helleborus niger*)

Cuticle (waterproof covering)

Upper (adaxial) epidermis (outer layer of cells)

Cell wall

Cytoplasm

Vacuole

Chloroplast (photosynthetic organelle)

Palisade mesophyll (tightly packed layer of photosynthetic tissue)

Nucleus

Intercellular space

Sclerenchyma (strengthening tissue)

Xylem (tissue that transports water and mineral salts)

Spongy mesophyll (loosely packed layer of photosynthetic tissue)

Phloem (tissue that transports sugars and other nutrients)

Vein

Lower (abaxial) epidermis (outer layer of cells)

Parenchyma (packing tissue)

Guard cell (controls opening and closing of stoma)

Stoma (pore)

Substomatal chamber

INTERNAL VIEW OF CHLOROPLAST

Granum (stack of thylakoids that hold chlorophyll molecules in position)

Lamella (membrane of thylakoid)

Thylakoid (flat sac of granum)

Stroma (watery matrix)

Deoxyribonucleic acid (DNA) strand

Chloroplast envelope

Outer membrane

Inner membrane

Starch grain

Ribosome (site of protein synthesis)

Stroma thylakoid (link between grana)

Flowers 2

COMPOUND INFLORESCENCE (CAPITULUM)
Sunflower
(*Helianthus annuus*)

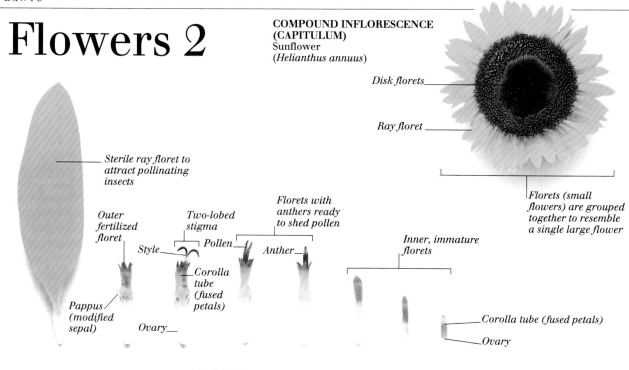

Disk florets

Ray floret

Florets (small flowers) are grouped together to resemble a single large flower

Sterile ray floret to attract pollinating insects

Outer fertilized floret

Two-lobed stigma

Florets with anthers ready to shed pollen

Style

Pollen

Anther

Inner, immature florets

Corolla tube (fused petals)

Pappus (modified sepal)

Ovary

Corolla tube (fused petals)

Ovary

FLORETS FROM SUNFLOWER

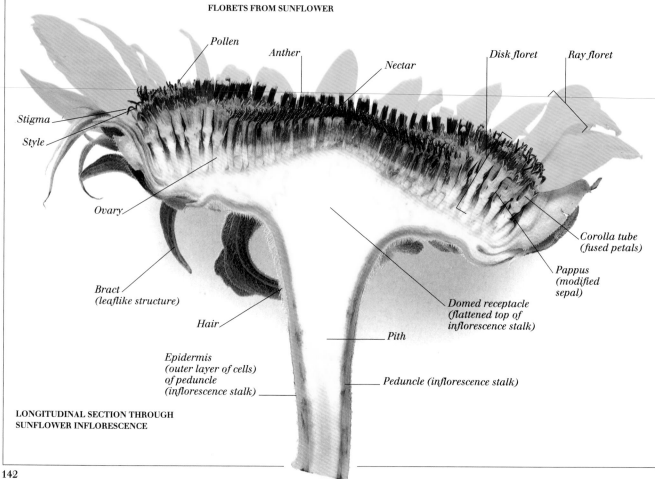

Pollen

Anther

Nectar

Disk floret

Ray floret

Stigma

Style

Ovary

Corolla tube (fused petals)

Pappus (modified sepal)

Bract (leaflike structure)

Hair

Domed receptacle (flattened top of inflorescence stalk)

Pith

Epidermis (outer layer of cells) of peduncle (inflorescence stalk)

Peduncle (inflorescence stalk)

LONGITUDINAL SECTION THROUGH SUNFLOWER INFLORESCENCE

ARRANGEMENT OF FLOWERS ON STEM

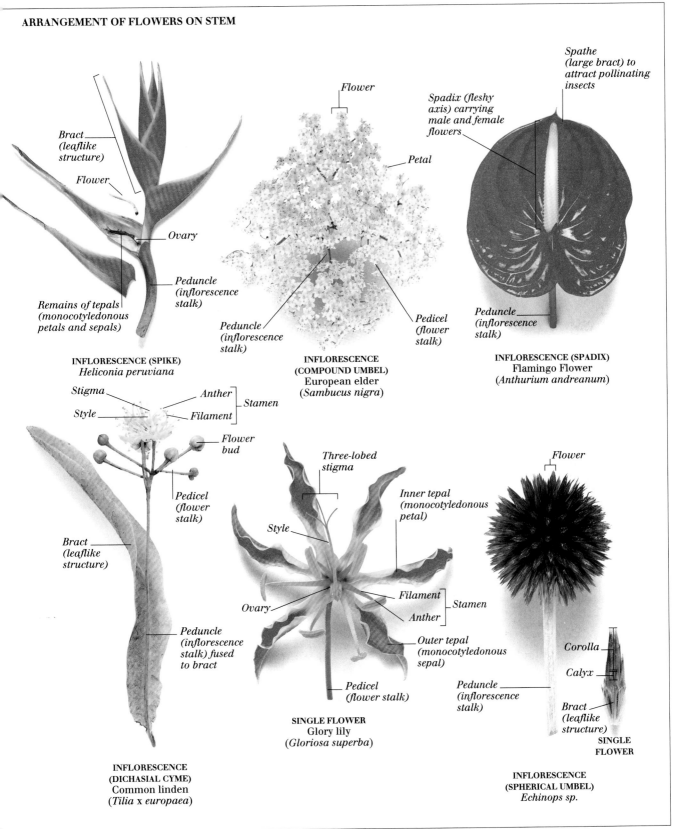

Bract
(leaflike
structure)

Flower

Ovary

Peduncle
(inflorescence
stalk)

Remains of tepals
(monocotyledonous
petals and sepals)

INFLORESCENCE (SPIKE)
Heliconia peruviana

Flower

Petal

Peduncle
(inflorescence
stalk)

Pedicel
(flower
stalk)

**INFLORESCENCE
(COMPOUND UMBEL)**
European elder
(*Sambucus nigra*)

Spathe
(large bract) to
attract pollinating
insects

Spadix (fleshy
axis) carrying
male and female
flowers

Peduncle
(inflorescence
stalk)

INFLORESCENCE (SPADIX)
Flamingo Flower
(*Anthurium andreanum*)

Stigma

Anther

Style

Filament

Stamen

Flower
bud

Pedicel
(flower
stalk)

Bract
(leaflike
structure)

Peduncle
(inflorescence
stalk) fused
to bract

**INFLORESCENCE
(DICHASIAL CYME)**
Common linden
(*Tilia* x *europaea*)

Three-lobed
stigma

Inner tepal
(monocotyledonous
petal)

Style

Filament

Stamen

Anther

Ovary

Outer tepal
(monocotyledonous
sepal)

Pedicel
(flower stalk)

SINGLE FLOWER
Glory lily
(*Gloriosa superba*)

Flower

Peduncle
(inflorescence
stalk)

Corolla

Calyx

Bract
(leaflike
structure)

**SINGLE
FLOWER**

**INFLORESCENCE
(SPHERICAL UMBEL)**
Echinops sp.

Pollination

POLLINATION IS THE TRANSFER OF POLLEN (which contains the male sex cells) from an anther (part of the male reproductive organ) to a stigma (part of the female reproductive organ). This process precedes fertilization (see pp. 146-147). Pollination may occur within the same flower (self-pollination), or between flowers on separate plants of the same species (cross-pollination). In most plants, pollination is carried out either by insects (entomophilous pollination) or by the wind (anemophilous pollination). Less commonly, birds, bats, or water are the agents of pollination. Insect-pollinated flowers are typically scented and brightly colored. They also produce nectar, on which insects feed. Such flowers also tend to have patterns that are visible only in ultraviolet light, which many insects can see but which humans cannot. These features attract insects, which become covered with the sticky pollen grains when they visit one flower, and then transfer the pollen to the next flower they visit. Wind-pollinated flowers are generally small, relatively inconspicuous, and unscented. They produce large quantities of light pollen grains that are easily blown by the wind to other flowers.

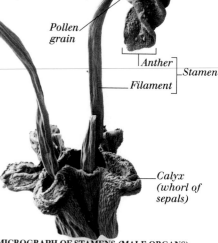

REPRODUCTIVE STRUCTURES IN WIND-POLLINATED PLANT
Sweet chestnut
(*Castanea sativa*)

Flower bud

Prominent stigma protrudes from flower

Female flower

Petiole (leaf stalk)

Bract (leaflike structure)

Peduncle (inflorescence stalk)

FEMALE

Male flower

Part of male catkin (inflorescence adapted for wind pollination)

Peduncle (inflorescence stalk)

Filament

Anther

MALE

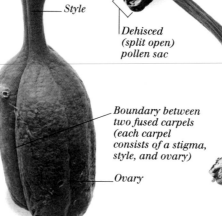

REPRODUCTIVE STRUCTURES IN INSECT-POLLINATED PLANTS

Stigma

Style

Dehisced (split open) pollen sac

Boundary between two fused carpels (each carpel consists of a stigma, style, and ovary)

Ovary

Endothecium (pollen sac wall)

Pollen grain

Anther

Stamen

Filament

Calyx (whorl of sepals)

MICROGRAPHS OF POLLEN GRAINS

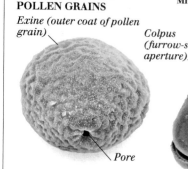

Exine (outer coat of pollen grain)

Pore

EUROPEAN FIELD ELM
(*Ulmus minor*)

Colpus (furrow-shaped aperture)

Exine (outer coat of pollen grain)

JUSTICIA AUREA

MICROGRAPH OF CARPELS (FEMALE ORGANS)
Yellow-wort
(*Blackstonia perfoliata*)

Exine (outer coat of pollen grain)

Pore

Baculum (rod-shaped structure)

MEADOW CRANESBILL
(*Geranium pratense*)

MICROGRAPH OF STAMENS (MALE ORGANS)
Common centaury
(*Centaurium erythraea*)

Colpus (furrow-shaped aperture)

Exine (outer coat of pollen grain)

Equatorial furrow

BOX-LEAVED MILKWORT
(*Polygala chamaebuxus*)

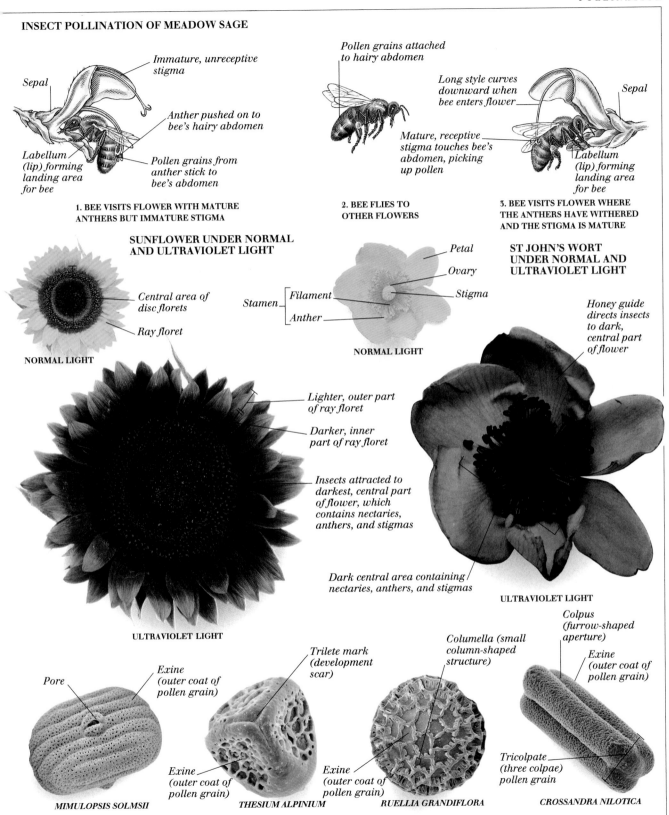

INSECT POLLINATION OF MEADOW SAGE

Sepal

Immature, unreceptive stigma

Anther pushed on to bee's hairy abdomen

Labellum (lip) forming landing area for bee

Pollen grains from anther stick to bee's abdomen

1. BEE VISITS FLOWER WITH MATURE ANTHERS BUT IMMATURE STIGMA

Pollen grains attached to hairy abdomen

Long style curves downward when bee enters flower

Sepal

Mature, receptive stigma touches bee's abdomen, picking up pollen

Labellum (lip) forming landing area for bee

2. BEE FLIES TO OTHER FLOWERS

3. BEE VISITS FLOWER WHERE THE ANTHERS HAVE WITHERED AND THE STIGMA IS MATURE

SUNFLOWER UNDER NORMAL AND ULTRAVIOLET LIGHT

Central area of disc florets

Ray floret

NORMAL LIGHT

Petal

Ovary

Stigma

Stamen { Filament / Anther

NORMAL LIGHT

ST JOHN'S WORT UNDER NORMAL AND ULTRAVIOLET LIGHT

Honey guide directs insects to dark, central part of flower

Lighter, outer part of ray floret

Darker, inner part of ray floret

Insects attracted to darkest, central part of flower, which contains nectaries, anthers, and stigmas

ULTRAVIOLET LIGHT

Dark central area containing nectaries, anthers, and stigmas

ULTRAVIOLET LIGHT

Colpus (furrow-shaped aperture)

Exine (outer coat of pollen grain)

Columella (small column-shaped structure)

Trilete mark (development scar)

Pore

Exine (outer coat of pollen grain)

Exine (outer coat of pollen grain)

Exine (outer coat of pollen grain)

Tricolpate (three colpae) pollen grain

MIMULOPSIS SOLMSII

THESIUM ALPINIUM

RUELLIA GRANDIFLORA

CROSSANDRA NILOTICA

Fertilization

FERTILIZATION IS THE FUSION of male and female gametes (sex cells) to produce a zygote (embryo). Following pollination (see pp. 144-145), the pollen grains that contain the male gametes are on the stigma, some distance from the female gamete (ovum) inside the ovule. To enable the gametes to meet, the pollen grain germinates and produces a pollen tube, which grows down and enters the embryo sac (the inner part of the ovule that contains the ovum). Two male gametes, traveling at the tip of the pollen tube, enter the embryo sac. One gamete fuses with the ovum to produce a zygote that will develop into an embryo plant. The other male gamete fuses with two polar nuclei to produce the endosperm, which acts as a food supply for the developing embryo. Fertilization also initiates other changes: the integument (outer part of ovule) forms a testa (seed coat) around the embryo and endosperm; the petals fall off; the stigma and style wither; and the ovary wall forms a layer (called the pericarp) around the seed. Together, the pericarp and seed form the fruit, which may be succulent (see pp. 148-149) or dry (see pp. 150-151). In some species (such as blackberry), apomixis can occur: The seed develops without fertilization of the ovum by a male gamete, but endosperm formation and fruit development take place as in other species.

BANANA
(*Musa 'Lacatan'*)

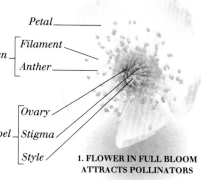

DEVELOPMENT OF A SUCCULENT FRUIT
Blackberry
(*Rubus fruticosus*)

Petal

Stamen — Filament

Anther

Carpel — Ovary

Stigma

Style

1. FLOWER IN FULL BLOOM ATTRACTS POLLINATORS

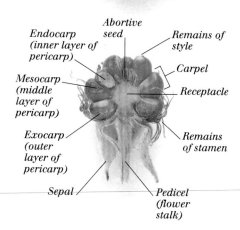

Abortive seed

Endocarp (inner layer of pericarp)

Remains of style

Carpel

Mesocarp (middle layer of pericarp)

Receptacle

Exocarp (outer layer of pericarp)

Remains of stamen

Sepal

Pedicel (flower stalk)

4. PERICARP FORMS FLESH, SKIN, AND A HARD INNER LAYER (SHOWN IN CROSS SECTION)

Exocarp (outer layer of pericarp)

Carpel

Remains of style

Remains of sepal

Remains of stamen

Pedicel (flower stalk)

7. MESOCARP (FLESHY PART OF PERICARP) OF EACH CARPEL STARTS TO CHANGE COLOR

Exocarp (outer layer of pericarp)

Drupelet

Remains of style

Remains of sepal

Remains of stamen

Pedicel (flower stalk)

8. CARPELS MATURE INTO DRUPELETS (SMALL FLESHY FRUITS WITH SINGLE SEEDS SURROUNDED BY HARD ENDOCARP)

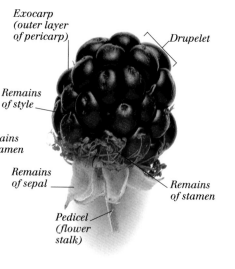

Exocarp (outer layer of pericarp)

Drupelet

Remains of style

Remains of sepal

Remains of stamen

Pedicel (flower stalk)

9. MESOCARP OF DRUPELET BECOMES DARKER AND SWEETER

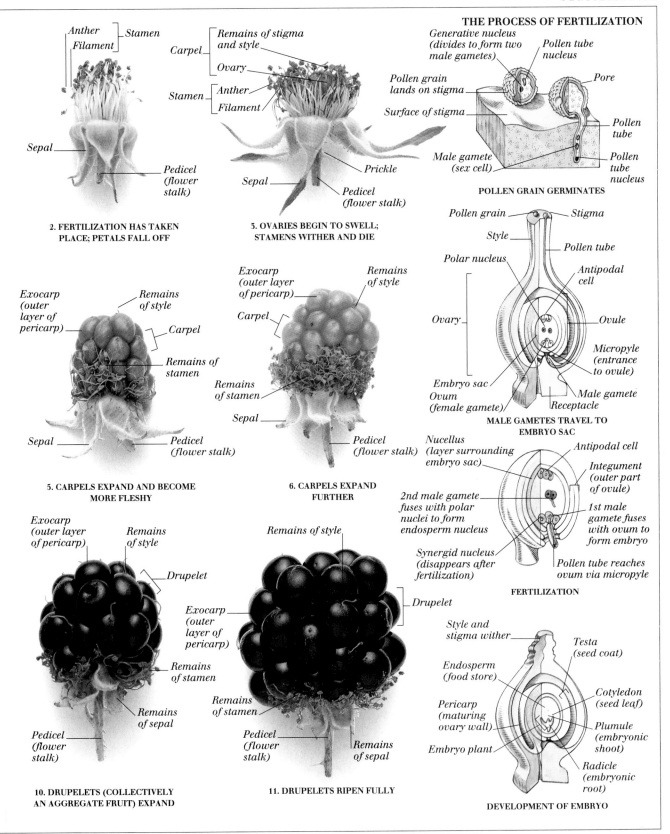

THE PROCESS OF FERTILIZATION

Anther
Filament } Stamen

Sepal

Pedicel
(flower
stalk)

**2. FERTILIZATION HAS TAKEN
PLACE; PETALS FALL OFF**

Carpel {
Remains of stigma
and style

Ovary

Stamen {
Anther
Filament

Sepal

Prickle

Pedicel
(flower stalk)

**3. OVARIES BEGIN TO SWELL;
STAMENS WITHER AND DIE**

Generative nucleus
(divides to form two
male gametes)

Pollen tube
nucleus

Pollen grain
lands on stigma

Pore

Surface of stigma

Pollen
tube

Male gamete
(sex cell)

Pollen
tube
nucleus

POLLEN GRAIN GERMINATES

Exocarp
(outer
layer of
pericarp)

Remains
of style

Carpel

Remains of
stamen

Sepal

Pedicel
(flower stalk)

**5. CARPELS EXPAND AND BECOME
MORE FLESHY**

Exocarp
(outer layer
of pericarp)

Remains
of style

Carpel {

Remains
of stamen

Sepal

Pedicel
(flower stalk)

**6. CARPELS EXPAND
FURTHER**

Pollen grain

Stigma

Style

Pollen tube

Polar nucleus

Antipodal
cell

Ovary

Ovule

Micropyle
(entrance
to ovule)

Embryo sac
Ovum
(female gamete)

Male gamete

Receptacle

**MALE GAMETES TRAVEL TO
EMBRYO SAC**

Nucellus
(layer surrounding
embryo sac)

Antipodal cell

Integument
(outer part
of ovule)

2nd male gamete
fuses with polar
nuclei to form
endosperm nucleus

1st male
gamete fuses
with ovum to
form embryo

Synergid nucleus
(disappears after
fertilization)

Pollen tube reaches
ovum via micropyle

FERTILIZATION

Exocarp
(outer layer
of pericarp)

Remains
of style

Drupelet

Remains
of stamen

Remains
of sepal

Pedicel
(flower
stalk)

**10. DRUPELETS (COLLECTIVELY
AN AGGREGATE FRUIT) EXPAND**

Remains of style

Exocarp
(outer
layer of
pericarp)

Drupelet

Remains
of stamen

Pedicel
(flower
stalk)

Remains
of sepal

11. DRUPELETS RIPEN FULLY

Style and
stigma wither

Testa
(seed coat)

Endosperm
(food store)

Cotyledon
(seed leaf)

Pericarp
(maturing
ovary wall)

Plumule
(embryonic
shoot)

Embryo plant

Radicle
(embryonic
root)

DEVELOPMENT OF EMBRYO

Succulent fruits

A FRUIT IS A FULLY DEVELOPED and ripened ovary—the seed-producing part of a plant's female reproductive organs. Fruits may be succulent or dry (see pp. 150-151). Succulent fruits are fleshy and brightly colored, making them attractive to animals, which eat them and disperse the seeds away from the parent plant. The wall (pericarp) of a succulent fruit has three layers: an outer exocarp, a middle mesocarp, and an inner endocarp. These three layers vary in thickness and texture in different types of fruits and may blend into each other. Succulent fruits can be classed as simple (derived from one ovary) or compound (derived from several ovaries). Simple succulent fruits include berries, which typically have many seeds, and drupes, which typically have a single stone or pit (such as cherry and peach). Compound succulent fruits include aggregate fruits, which are formed from many ovaries in one flower, and multiple fruits, which develop from the ovaries of many flowers. Some fruits, known as false fruits or pseudocarps, develop from parts of the flower in addition to the ovaries. For example, the flesh of the apple is formed from the receptacle (the upper end of the flower stalk).

BERRY
Cocoa
(*Theobroma cacao*)

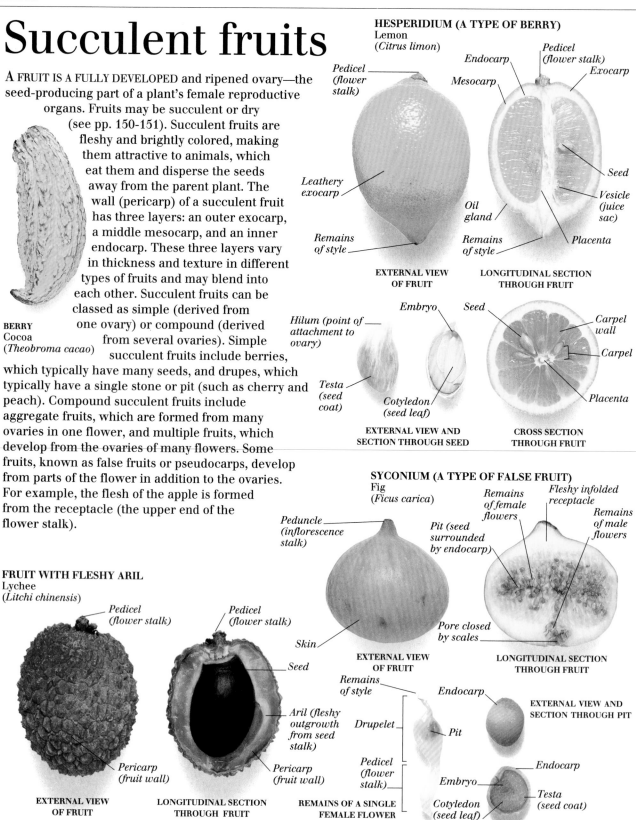

HESPERIDIUM (A TYPE OF BERRY)
Lemon
(*Citrus limon*)

Pedicel (flower stalk)
Leathery exocarp
Remains of style

EXTERNAL VIEW OF FRUIT

Endocarp
Mesocarp
Pedicel (flower stalk)
Exocarp
Seed
Vesicle (juice sac)
Oil gland
Remains of style
Placenta

LONGITUDINAL SECTION THROUGH FRUIT

Hilum (point of attachment to ovary)
Embryo
Seed
Testa (seed coat)
Cotyledon (seed leaf)

EXTERNAL VIEW AND SECTION THROUGH SEED

Carpel wall
Carpel
Placenta

CROSS SECTION THROUGH FRUIT

SYCONIUM (A TYPE OF FALSE FRUIT)
Fig
(*Ficus carica*)

Peduncle (inflorescence stalk)
Skin

EXTERNAL VIEW OF FRUIT

Remains of female flowers
Fleshy infolded receptacle
Remains of male flowers
Pit (seed surrounded by endocarp)
Pore closed by scales

LONGITUDINAL SECTION THROUGH FRUIT

FRUIT WITH FLESHY ARIL
Lychee
(*Litchi chinensis*)

Pedicel (flower stalk)
Pericarp (fruit wall)

EXTERNAL VIEW OF FRUIT

Pedicel (flower stalk)
Seed
Aril (fleshy outgrowth from seed stalk)
Pericarp (fruit wall)

LONGITUDINAL SECTION THROUGH FRUIT

Remains of style
Drupelet
Pedicel (flower stalk)

REMAINS OF A SINGLE FEMALE FLOWER

Endocarp
Pit

EXTERNAL VIEW AND SECTION THROUGH PIT

Embryo
Cotyledon (seed leaf)
Endocarp
Testa (seed coat)

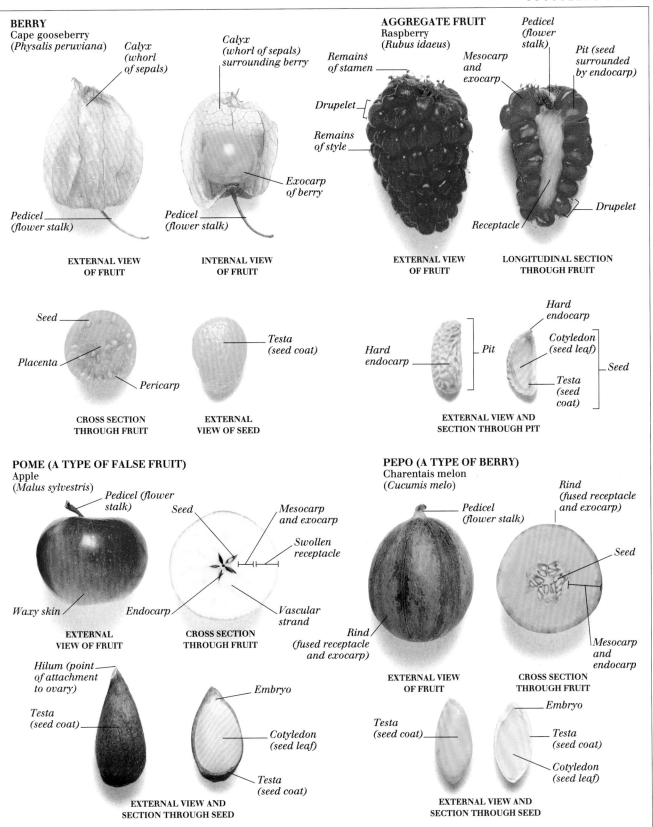

BERRY
Cape gooseberry
(*Physalis peruviana*)

Calyx (whorl of sepals)

Pedicel (flower stalk)

EXTERNAL VIEW OF FRUIT

Calyx (whorl of sepals) surrounding berry

Exocarp of berry

Pedicel (flower stalk)

INTERNAL VIEW OF FRUIT

Seed

Placenta

Pericarp

CROSS SECTION THROUGH FRUIT

Testa (seed coat)

EXTERNAL VIEW OF SEED

AGGREGATE FRUIT
Raspberry
(*Rubus idaeus*)

Remains of stamen

Drupelet

Remains of style

Mesocarp and exocarp

Pedicel (flower stalk)

Pit (seed surrounded by endocarp)

Drupelet

Receptacle

EXTERNAL VIEW OF FRUIT

LONGITUDINAL SECTION THROUGH FRUIT

Hard endocarp

Pit

Hard endocarp

Cotyledon (seed leaf)

Seed

Testa (seed coat)

EXTERNAL VIEW AND SECTION THROUGH PIT

POME (A TYPE OF FALSE FRUIT)
Apple
(*Malus sylvestris*)

Pedicel (flower stalk)

Waxy skin

EXTERNAL VIEW OF FRUIT

Seed

Mesocarp and exocarp

Swollen receptacle

Endocarp

Vascular strand

CROSS SECTION THROUGH FRUIT

Hilum (point of attachment to ovary)

Testa (seed coat)

Embryo

Cotyledon (seed leaf)

Testa (seed coat)

EXTERNAL VIEW AND SECTION THROUGH SEED

PEPO (A TYPE OF BERRY)
Charentais melon
(*Cucumis melo*)

Pedicel (flower stalk)

Rind (fused receptacle and exocarp)

Seed

Rind (fused receptacle and exocarp)

Mesocarp and endocarp

EXTERNAL VIEW OF FRUIT

CROSS SECTION THROUGH FRUIT

Testa (seed coat)

Embryo

Testa (seed coat)

Cotyledon (seed leaf)

EXTERNAL VIEW AND SECTION THROUGH SEED

149

Dry fruits

DRY FRUITS HAVE A HARD, DRY PERICARP (fruit wall) around their seeds, unlike succulent fruits, which have fleshy pericarps (see pp. 148-149). Dry fruits are divided into three types: dehiscent, in which the pericarp splits open to release the seeds; indehiscent, which do not split open; and schizocarpic, in which the fruit splits but the seeds are not exposed. Dehiscent dry fruits include capsules (for example, love-in-a-mist), follicles (delphinium), legumes (pea), and silicles (honesty). Typically, the seeds of dehiscent fruits are dispersed by the wind. Indehiscent dry fruits include nuts (sweet chestnut), nutlets (goose grass), achenes (strawberry), caryopses (wheat), samaras (elm), and cypselas (dandelion). Some indehiscent dry fruits are dispersed by the wind, assisted by "wings" (elm) or "parachutes" (dandelion); others (goose grass) have hooked pericarps to aid dispersal on animals' fur. Schizocarpic dry fruits include cremocarps (hogweed), and double samaras (sycamore maple); these are dispersed by the wind.

NUTLET
Goose grass
(*Galium aparine*)

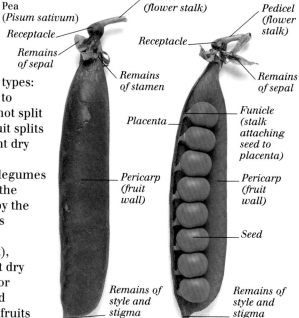

LEGUME
Pea
(*Pisum sativum*)

Pedicel (flower stalk)
Receptacle
Remains of sepal
Remains of stamen
Placenta
Pericarp (fruit wall)
Pedicel (flower stalk)
Receptacle
Remains of sepal
Funicle (stalk attaching seed to placenta)
Pericarp (fruit wall)
Seed
Remains of style and stigma
Remains of style and stigma

EXTERNAL VIEW OF FRUIT

INTERNAL VIEW OF FRUIT

Funicle (stalk attaching seed to placenta)
Micropyle (pore for water absorption)
Testa (seed coat)
Cotyledon (seed leaf)
Radicle (embryonic root)
Testa (seed coat)
Plumule (embryonic shoot)

EXTERIOR VIEW AND SECTION THROUGH SEED

NUT
Spanish chestnut
(*Castanea sativa*)

Line of splitting between valves of cupule

Peduncle (inflorescence stalk)
Remains of male inflorescence
Nut (indehiscent fruit)
Spiky cupule (husk around fruit formed from bracts)

EXTERNAL VIEW OF FRUIT WITH SURROUNDING CUPULE

ACHENE
Strawberry
(*Fragaria* x *ananassa*)
Sepal
Pedicel (flower stalk)
Swollen receptacle
Remains of stigma and style
Achene (one-seeded dry fruit)
Sepal
Pedicel (flower stalk)
Swollen fleshy tissues of receptacle

EXTERNAL VIEW OF FRUIT

LONGITUDINAL SECTION THROUGH FRUIT

Remains of stigma
Remains of style
Remains of stigma
Remains of style
Nut (indehiscent fruit)
Embryo
Cotyledon (seed leaf)
Testa (seed coat)
Woody pericarp (fruit wall)
Woody pericarp (fruit wall)

EXTERNAL VIEW AND SECTION THROUGH FRUIT

Pericarp (fruit wall)
Pericarp (fruit wall)
Cotyledon (seed leaf)
Testa (seed coat)

EXTERNAL VIEW AND SECTION THROUGH SEED

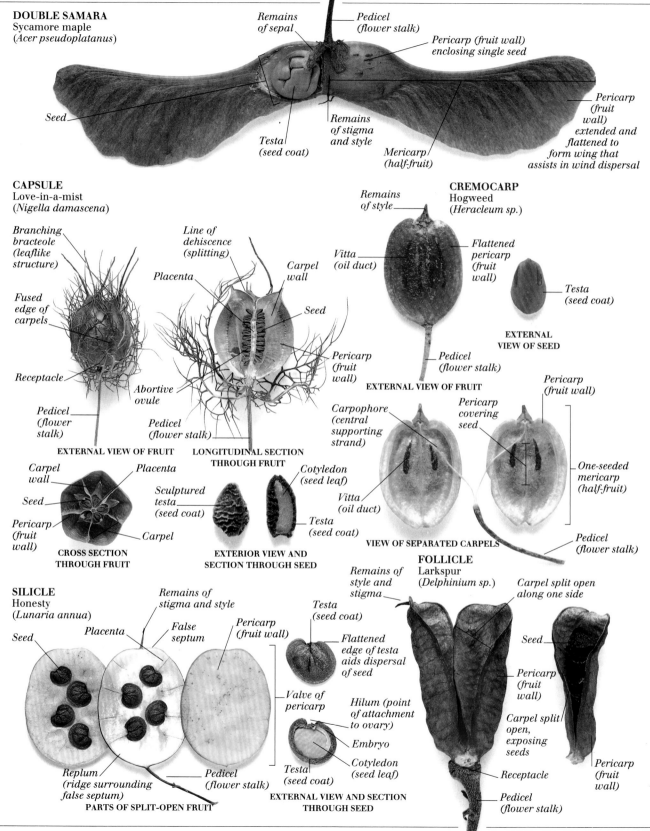

DOUBLE SAMARA
Sycamore maple
(*Acer pseudoplatanus*)

Remains
of sepal

Pedicel
(flower stalk)

Pericarp (fruit wall)
enclosing single seed

Seed

Testa
(seed coat)

Remains
of stigma
and style

Mericarp
(half-fruit)

Pericarp
(fruit
wall)
extended and
flattened to
form wing that
assists in wind dispersal

CAPSULE
Love-in-a-mist
(*Nigella damascena*)

Branching
bracteole
(leaflike
structure)

Fused
edge of
carpels

Receptacle

Pedicel
(flower
stalk)

Line of
dehiscence
(splitting)

Placenta

Carpel
wall

Seed

Pericarp
(fruit
wall)

Abortive
ovule

Pedicel
(flower stalk)

EXTERNAL VIEW OF FRUIT

**LONGITUDINAL SECTION
THROUGH FRUIT**

Carpel
wall

Placenta

Seed

Pericarp
(fruit
wall)

Carpel

**CROSS SECTION
THROUGH FRUIT**

Sculptured
testa
(seed coat)

Cotyledon
(seed leaf)

Testa
(seed coat)

**EXTERIOR VIEW AND
SECTION THROUGH SEED**

CREMOCARP
Hogweed
(*Heracleum sp.*)

Remains
of style

Vitta
(oil duct)

Flattened
pericarp
(fruit
wall)

Testa
(seed coat)

**EXTERNAL
VIEW OF SEED**

Pedicel
(flower stalk)

EXTERNAL VIEW OF FRUIT

Carpophore
(central
supporting
strand)

Pericarp
covering
seed

Pericarp
(fruit wall)

Vitta
(oil duct)

One-seeded
mericarp
(half-fruit)

Pedicel
(flower stalk)

VIEW OF SEPARATED CARPELS

SILICLE
Honesty
(*Lunaria annua*)

Seed

Remains of
stigma and style

Placenta

False
septum

Pericarp
(fruit wall)

Valve of
pericarp

Replum
(ridge surrounding
false septum)

Pedicel
(flower stalk)

PARTS OF SPLIT-OPEN FRUIT

Testa
(seed coat)

Flattened
edge of testa
aids dispersal
of seed

Hilum (point
of attachment
to ovary)

Embryo

Testa
(seed coat)

Cotyledon
(seed leaf)

**EXTERNAL VIEW AND SECTION
THROUGH SEED**

FOLLICLE
Larkspur
(*Delphinium sp.*)

Remains of
style and
stigma

Carpel split open
along one side

Seed

Pericarp
(fruit
wall)

Carpel split
open,
exposing
seeds

Receptacle

Pericarp
(fruit
wall)

Pedicel
(flower stalk)

Vegetative reproduction

MANY PLANTS CAN PROPAGATE THEMSELVES by vegetative reproduction. In this process, part of a plant separates, takes root, and grows into a new plant. Vegetative reproduction is a type of asexual reproduction; it involves only one parent and there is no fusion of gametes (sex cells). Plants use various structures to reproduce vegetatively. Some plants use underground storage organs. Such organs include rhizomes (horizontal, underground stems), the branches of which produce new plants; bulbs (swollen leaf bases) and corms (swollen stems), which produce daughter bulbs or corms that separate from the parent; and stem tubers (thickened underground stems) and root tubers (swollen adventitious roots), which also separate from the parent. Other propagative structures include runners and stolons, creeping horizontal stems that take root and produce new plants; bulbils, small bulbs that develop on the stem or in the place of flowers, and then drop off and grow into new plants; and adventitious buds, miniature plants that form on leaf margins before dropping to the ground and growing into mature plants.

CORM
Gladiolus
(*Gladiolus sp.*)

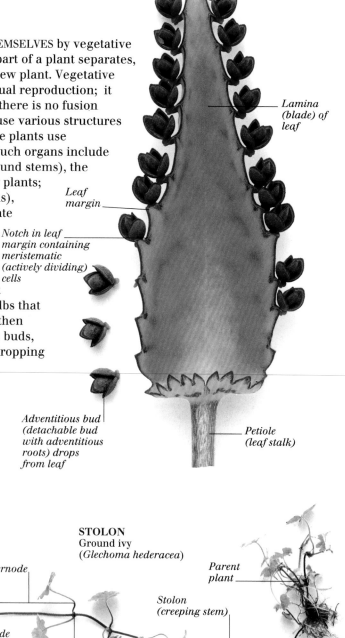

ADVENTITIOUS BUD
Mexican hat plant
(*Kalanchoe daigremontiana*)

Apex of leaf

Lamina (blade) of leaf

Leaf margin

Notch in leaf margin containing meristematic (actively dividing) cells

Adventitious bud (detachable bud with adventitious roots) drops from leaf

Petiole (leaf stalk)

BULBIL IN PLACE OF FLOWER
Orange lily
(*Lilium bulbiferum*)

Scar left by flower

Leaf

Pedicel (flower stalk)

Terminal bud

Detachable bulbil formed in place of flower

Peduncle (inflorescence stalk)

STOLON
Ground ivy
(*Glechoma hederacea*)

Internode

Parent plant

Node

Stolon (creeping stem)

Node

Adventitious root of daughter plant

Daughter plant developed from lateral bud

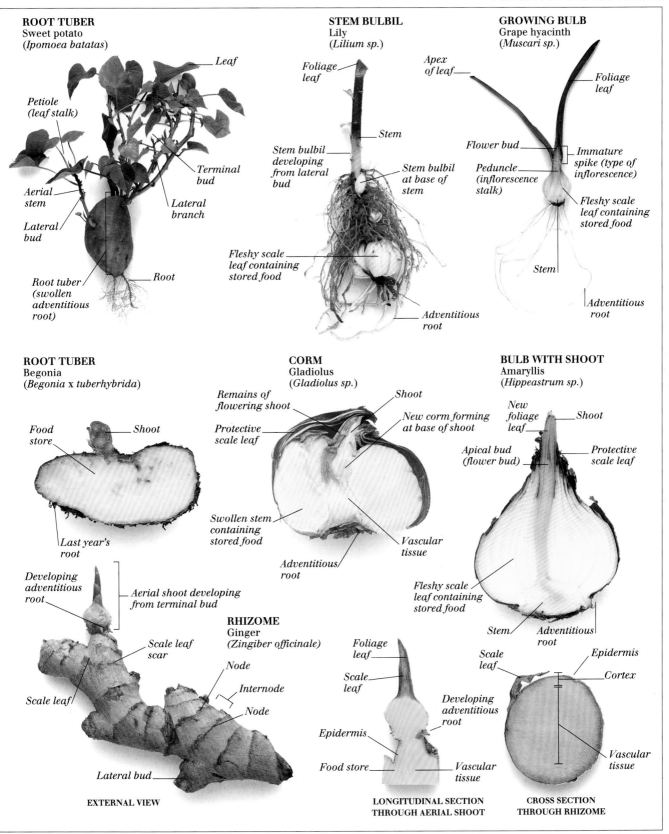

ROOT TUBER
Sweet potato
(*Ipomoea batatas*)

Leaf
Petiole
(leaf stalk)
Terminal bud
Aerial stem
Lateral branch
Lateral bud
Root tuber
(swollen adventitious root)
Root

STEM BULBIL
Lily
(*Lilium sp.*)

Foliage leaf
Stem
Stem bulbil developing from lateral bud
Stem bulbil at base of stem
Fleshy scale leaf containing stored food
Adventitious root

GROWING BULB
Grape hyacinth
(*Muscari sp.*)

Apex of leaf
Foliage leaf
Flower bud
Peduncle (inflorescence stalk)
Immature spike (type of inflorescence)
Fleshy scale leaf containing stored food
Stem
Adventitious root

ROOT TUBER
Begonia
(*Begonia* x *tuberhybrida*)

Food store
Shoot
Last year's root

Developing adventitious root
Aerial shoot developing from terminal bud
Scale leaf scar
Node
Internode
Node
Scale leaf
Lateral bud

EXTERNAL VIEW

CORM
Gladiolus
(*Gladiolus sp.*)

Remains of flowering shoot
Shoot
Protective scale leaf
New corm forming at base of shoot
Swollen stem containing stored food
Adventitious root
Vascular tissue

RHIZOME
Ginger
(*Zingiber officinale*)

Foliage leaf
Scale leaf
Epidermis
Food store
Developing adventitious root
Vascular tissue

**LONGITUDINAL SECTION
THROUGH AERIAL SHOOT**

BULB WITH SHOOT
Amaryllis
(*Hippeastrum sp.*)

New foliage leaf
Shoot
Apical bud (flower bud)
Protective scale leaf
Fleshy scale leaf containing stored food
Stem
Adventitious root

Scale leaf
Epidermis
Cortex
Vascular tissue

**CROSS SECTION
THROUGH RHIZOME**

Dryland plants

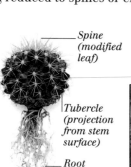

LEAF SUCCULENT
Lithops sp.

DRYLAND PLANTS (XEROPHYTES) are able to survive in unfavorable habitats. All are found in places where little water is available; some live in high temperatures that cause excessive loss of water from the leaves. Xerophytes show a number of adaptations to dry conditions. These include reduced leaf area, rolled leaves, sunken stomata, hairs, spines, and thick cuticles. One group, succulent plants, stores water in specially enlarged spongy tissues found in leaves, roots, or stems. Leaf succulents have enlarged, fleshy, water-storing leaves. Root succulents have a large underground water-storage organ with short-lived stems and leaves above ground. Stem succulents are represented by the cacti (family Cactaceae). Cacti stems are fleshy, green, and photosynthetic. They are typically ribbed or covered by tubercles in rows, with leaves being reduced to spines or entirely absent.

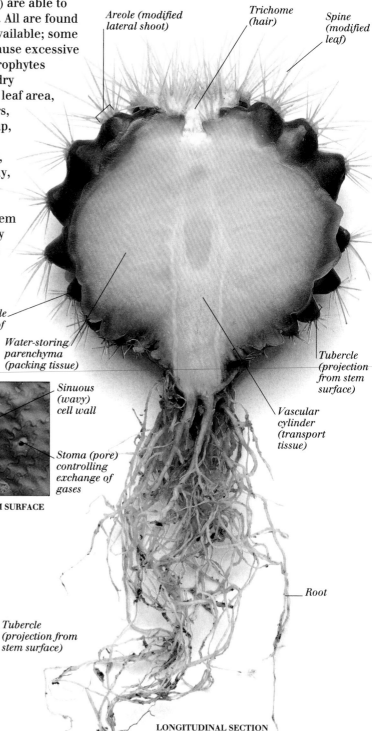

STEM SUCCULENT
Golden barrel cactus
(*Echinocactus grusonii*)

Areole (modified lateral shoot)

Trichome (hair)

Spine (modified leaf)

Waxy cuticle (waterproof covering)

Water-storing parenchyma (packing tissue)

Tubercle (projection from stem surface)

Vascular cylinder (transport tissue)

Root

LONGITUDINAL SECTION THROUGH STEM

Spine (modified leaf)

Tubercle (projection from stem surface)

Root

EXTERNAL VIEW

Sinuous (wavy) cell wall

Stoma (pore) controlling exchange of gases

MICROGRAPH OF STEM SURFACE

Spine (modified leaf)

Areole (modified lateral shoot)

Tubercle (projection from stem surface)

Waxy cuticle (waterproof covering)

DETAIL OF STEM SURFACE

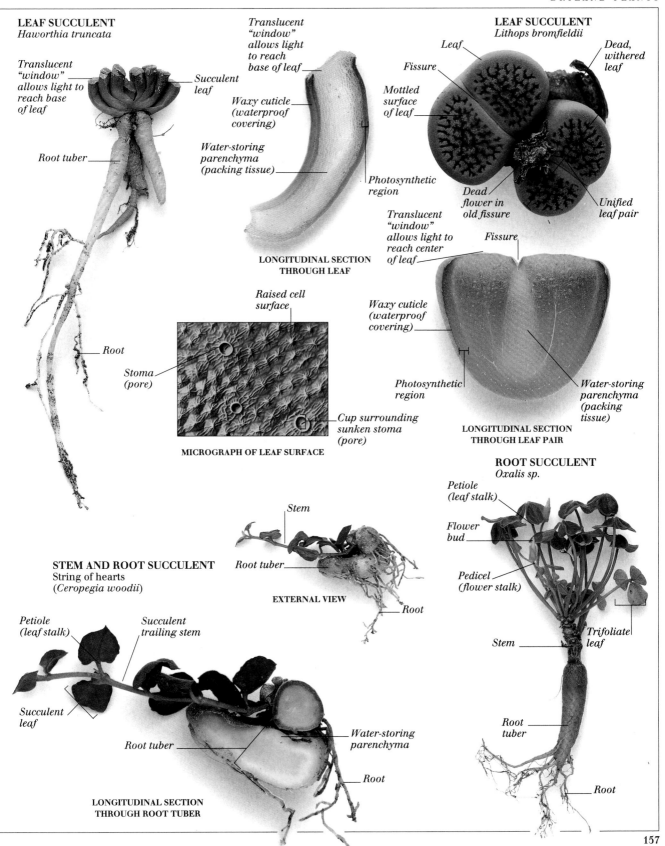

LEAF SUCCULENT
Haworthia truncata

Translucent "window" allows light to reach base of leaf

Succulent leaf

Root tuber

Root

Translucent "window" allows light to reach base of leaf

Waxy cuticle (waterproof covering)

Water-storing parenchyma (packing tissue)

Photosynthetic region

LONGITUDINAL SECTION THROUGH LEAF

Raised cell surface

Stoma (pore)

Cup surrounding sunken stoma (pore)

MICROGRAPH OF LEAF SURFACE

LEAF SUCCULENT
Lithops bromfieldii

Leaf

Fissure

Mottled surface of leaf

Dead, withered leaf

Dead flower in old fissure

Unified leaf pair

Translucent "window" allows light to reach center of leaf

Fissure

Waxy cuticle (waterproof covering)

Photosynthetic region

Water-storing parenchyma (packing tissue)

LONGITUDINAL SECTION THROUGH LEAF PAIR

ROOT SUCCULENT
Oxalis sp.

Petiole (leaf stalk)

Flower bud

Pedicel (flower stalk)

Trifoliate leaf

Stem

Root tuber

Root

STEM AND ROOT SUCCULENT
String of hearts
(*Ceropegia woodii*)

Stem

Root tuber

Root

EXTERNAL VIEW

Petiole (leaf stalk)

Succulent trailing stem

Succulent leaf

Root tuber

Water-storing parenchyma

Root

LONGITUDINAL SECTION THROUGH ROOT TUBER

157

Wetland plants

WETLAND PLANTS GROW SUBMERGED IN WATER, either partially, like the water hyacinth, or completely, like the pondweeds, and show various adaptations to this habitat. Typically, there are numerous air spaces inside the stems, leaves, and roots; these aid gas exchange and buoyancy. Submerged parts generally have no cuticle (waterproof covering), allowing the plants to absorb minerals and gases directly from the water. Also, because they are supported by the water, wetland plants need little of the supportive tissue found in land plants. Stomata, the gas exchange pores, are absent from plants that are completely submerged. In partially submerged plants with floating leaves, such as water lilies, stomata are found on the upper leaf surfaces, where they cannot be flooded.

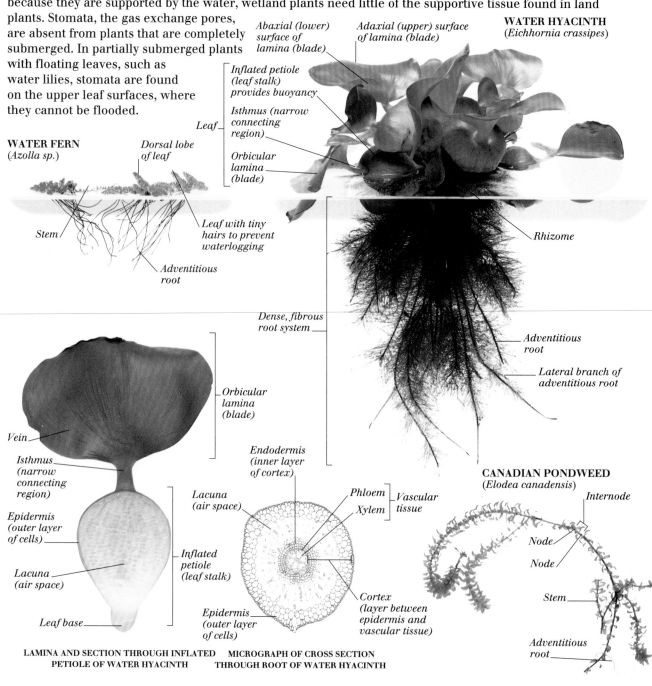

WATER FERN
(*Azolla sp.*)

Dorsal lobe of leaf

Stem

Leaf with tiny hairs to prevent waterlogging

Adventitious root

Abaxial (lower) surface of lamina (blade)

Adaxial (upper) surface of lamina (blade)

WATER HYACINTH
(*Eichhornia crassipes*)

Inflated petiole (leaf stalk) provides buoyancy

Leaf

Isthmus (narrow connecting region)

Orbicular lamina (blade)

Rhizome

Dense, fibrous root system

Adventitious root

Lateral branch of adventitious root

Orbicular lamina (blade)

Vein

Isthmus (narrow connecting region)

Epidermis (outer layer of cells)

Lacuna (air space)

Leaf base

Lacuna (air space)

Inflated petiole (leaf stalk)

Epidermis (outer layer of cells)

Endodermis (inner layer of cortex)

Phloem

Xylem

Vascular tissue

Cortex (layer between epidermis and vascular tissue)

CANADIAN PONDWEED
(*Elodea canadensis*)

Internode

Node

Node

Stem

Adventitious root

LAMINA AND SECTION THROUGH INFLATED PETIOLE OF WATER HYACINTH

MICROGRAPH OF CROSS SECTION THROUGH ROOT OF WATER HYACINTH

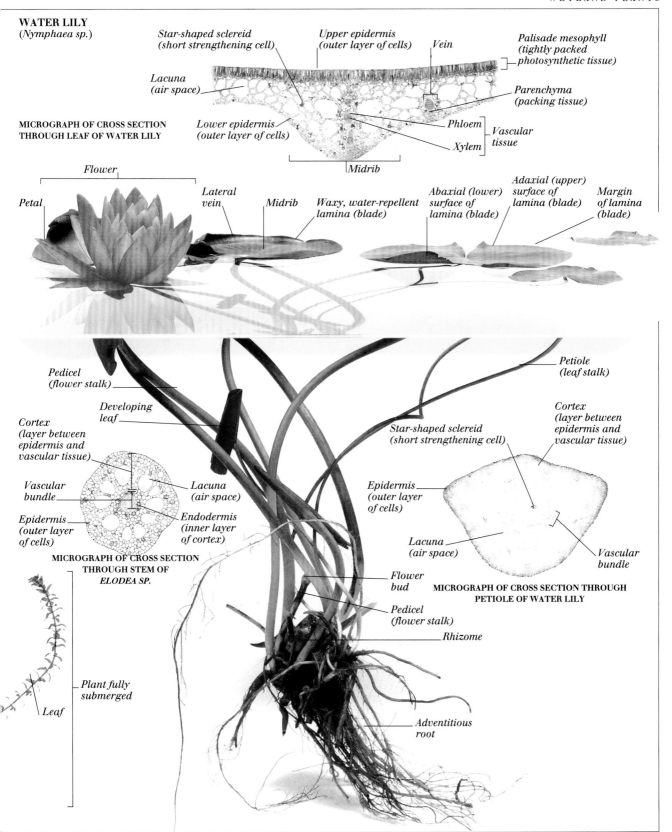

WATER LILY
(*Nymphaea sp.*)

Star-shaped sclereid
(short strengthening cell)

Upper epidermis
(outer layer of cells)

Vein

Palisade mesophyll
(tightly packed
photosynthetic tissue)

Lacuna
(air space)

Parenchyma
(packing tissue)

MICROGRAPH OF CROSS SECTION
THROUGH LEAF OF WATER LILY

Lower epidermis
(outer layer of cells)

Phloem

Xylem

Vascular
tissue

Midrib

Flower

Petal

Lateral
vein

Midrib

Waxy, water-repellent
lamina (blade)

Abaxial (lower)
surface of
lamina (blade)

Adaxial (upper)
surface of
lamina (blade)

Margin
of lamina
(blade)

Pedicel
(flower stalk)

Petiole
(leaf stalk)

Developing
leaf

Cortex
(layer between
epidermis and
vascular tissue)

Star-shaped sclereid
(short strengthening cell)

Cortex
(layer between
epidermis and
vascular tissue)

Vascular
bundle

Lacuna
(air space)

Epidermis
(outer layer
of cells)

Epidermis
(outer layer
of cells)

Endodermis
(inner layer
of cortex)

Lacuna
(air space)

Vascular
bundle

MICROGRAPH OF CROSS SECTION
THROUGH STEM OF
ELODEA SP.

MICROGRAPH OF CROSS SECTION THROUGH
PETIOLE OF WATER LILY

Flower
bud

Pedicel
(flower stalk)

Rhizome

Plant fully
submerged

Leaf

Adventitious
root

Carnivorous plants

CARNIVOROUS (INSECTIVOROUS) PLANTS FEED ON INSECTS and other small animals in addition to producing food in their leaves by photosynthesis. The nutrients absorbed from trapped insects allow carnivorous plants to thrive in acid, boggy soils that lack essential minerals, especially nitrates, where most other plants could not survive.

All carnivorous plants have some leaves modified as traps. Many use bright colors and scented nectar to attract prey, and most use enzymes to digest the prey. There are three types of traps. Pitcher plants, such as the monkey cup and cobra lily, have leaves modified as pitcher-shaped pitfall traps, half-filled with water. Once lured inside the mouth of the trap, insects lose their footing on the slippery surface, fall into the liquid, and either decompose or are digested. Venus fly-traps use a spring-trap mechanism; when an insect touches trigger hairs on the inner surfaces of the leaves, the two lobes of the trap snap shut. Butterworts and sundews entangle prey by sticky droplets on the leaf surface, while the edges of the leaves slowly curl over to envelop and digest the prey.

A PITCHER PLANT
Cobra lily (*Darlingtonia californica*)

Areola ("window" of transparent tissue)

Fishtail nectary

Wing

Hood

Pitcher

Tubular petiole (leaf stalk)

Areola ("window" of transparent tissue)

Smooth surface

Nectar roll

Dome-shaped hood develops

Fishtail nectary appears

Mouth

Immature pitcher

Wing

Downward-pointing hair

DEVELOPMENT OF MODIFIED LEAF IN COBRA LILY

Immature trap

Interlocked teeth

Closed trap

VENUS FLYTRAP
(*Dionaea muscipula*)

Red color of trap attracts insects

Phyllode (flattened petiole)

Summer petiole (leaf stalk)

Nectary zone (glands secrete nectar)

Digestive zone (glands secrete digestive enzymes)

Lobe of trap

Midrib (hinge of trap)

Tooth

Trigger hair

Spring petiole (leaf stalk)

Trap (twin-lobed leaf blade)

Sensory hinge

Trigger hair

Inner surface of trap

Digestive gland

MICROGRAPH OF LOBE OF VENUS FLYTRAP

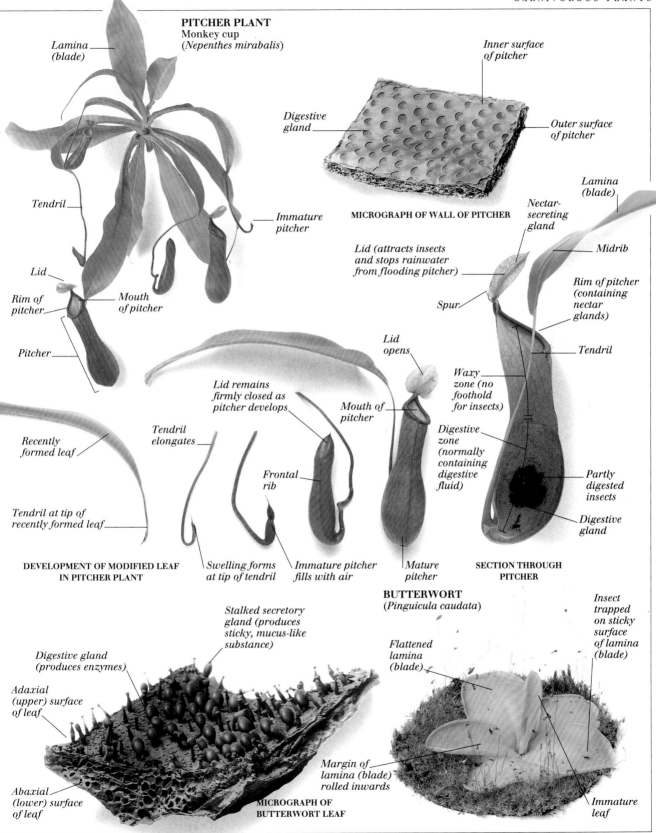

PITCHER PLANT
Monkey cup
(*Nepenthes mirabalis*)

Lamina
(blade)

Tendril

Immature
pitcher

Lid

Rim of
pitcher

Mouth
of pitcher

Pitcher

*Inner surface
of pitcher*

*Digestive
gland*

*Outer surface
of pitcher*

MICROGRAPH OF WALL OF PITCHER

*Nectar-
secreting
gland*

*Lamina
(blade)*

Midrib

*Lid (attracts insects
and stops rainwater
from flooding pitcher)*

*Rim of pitcher
(containing
nectar
glands)*

Spur

Tendril

*Waxy
zone (no
foothold
for insects)*

*Digestive
zone
(normally
containing
digestive
fluid)*

*Partly
digested
insects*

*Digestive
gland*

*Recently
formed leaf*

*Tendril
elongates*

*Lid remains
firmly closed as
pitcher develops*

*Lid
opens*

*Mouth of
pitcher*

*Tendril at tip of
recently formed leaf*

*Frontal
rib*

*Swelling forms
at tip of tendril*

*Immature pitcher
fills with air*

*Mature
pitcher*

**SECTION THROUGH
PITCHER**

**DEVELOPMENT OF MODIFIED LEAF
IN PITCHER PLANT**

BUTTERWORT
(*Pinguicula caudata*)

*Insect
trapped
on sticky
surface
of lamina
(blade)*

*Stalked secretory
gland (produces
sticky, mucus-like
substance)*

*Flattened
lamina
(blade)*

*Digestive gland
(produces enzymes)*

*Adaxial
(upper) surface
of leaf*

*Abaxial
(lower) surface
of leaf*

*Margin of
lamina (blade)
rolled inwards*

**MICROGRAPH OF
BUTTERWORT LEAF**

*Immature
leaf*

161

Epiphytic and parasitic plants

EPIPHYTIC AND PARASITIC PLANTS GROW ON OTHER LIVING PLANTS. Typically, epiphytic plants are not rooted in the soil. Instead, they live above ground level on the stems and branches of other plants. Epiphytes obtain water from trapped rainwater and from moisture in the air. They obtain minerals from organic matter that has accumulated on the surface of the plant on which they are growing. Like other green plants, epiphytes produce their food by photosynthesis. Epiphytes include tropical orchids and bromeliads (air plants) and some mosses that live in temperate regions. Parasitic plants obtain all their nutrient requirements from the host plants on which they grow. The parasites produce haustoria, root-like organs that penetrate the stem or roots of the host and grow inward to merge with the host's vascular tissue. These extract water, minerals, and manufactured nutrients. Because they have no need to produce their own food, parasitic plants lack chlorophyll, the green photosynthetic pigment, and they have no foliage leaves. Partial parasitic plants, like mistletoe, obtain water and minerals from the host plant but have green leaves and stems and are therefore able to produce their own food by photosynthesis.

EPIPHYTIC BROMELIAD
Aechmea miniata

Inflorescence
(spike)

Peduncle
(inflorescence
stalk)

Flower
bud

Strap-shaped
arching leaf
(part of rosette
of leaves)

Leaf margin
with spines

Overlapping leaf
bases in which
rainwater is trapped

Mass of
adventitious roots

Stem

Bark of tree to
which epiphyte
is attached

EPIPHYTIC ORCHID
Brassavola nodosa

Peduncle
(inflorescence
stalk)

Pedicel
(flower
stalk)

Flower

Scale
leaf

Leaf

Velamen
(multilayered epidermis
capable of absorbing
water from rain or
condensation)

Exodermis
(outer layer
of cortex)

Cortex
(layer between
epidermis and
vascular tissue)

Cortex cell
containing
chloroplasts

Pith

Aerial
root

Node

Stem

Vascular
tissue

Xylem

Phloem

Endodermis
(inner layer
of cortex)

Bark of tree to
which epiphyte
is attached

**MICROGRAPH OF CROSS SECTION THROUGH
AERIAL ROOT OF EPIPHYTIC ORCHID**

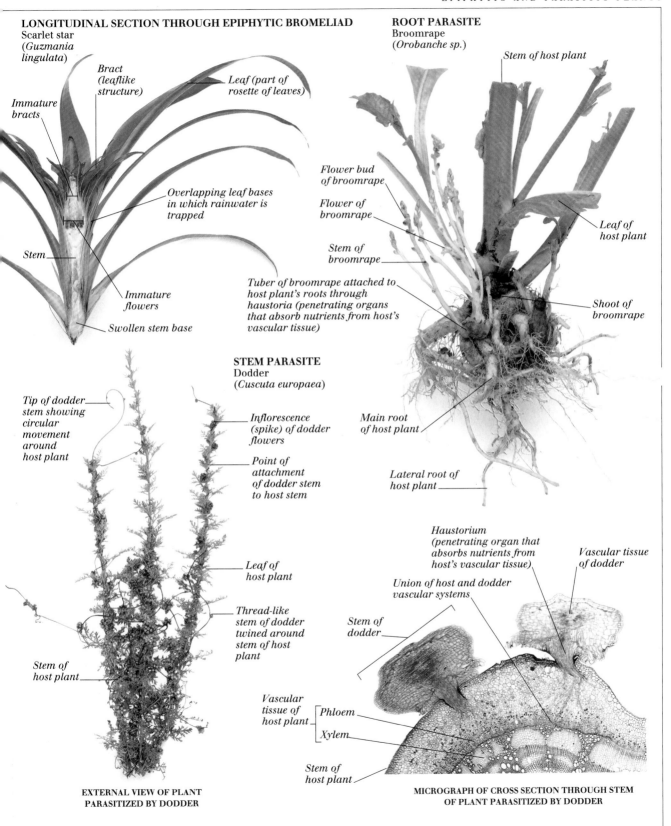

LONGITUDINAL SECTION THROUGH EPIPHYTIC BROMELIAD
Scarlet star (*Guzmania lingulata*)

Bract (leaflike structure)

Leaf (part of rosette of leaves)

Immature bracts

Overlapping leaf bases in which rainwater is trapped

Stem

Immature flowers

Swollen stem base

ROOT PARASITE
Broomrape (*Orobanche sp.*)

Stem of host plant

Flower bud of broomrape

Flower of broomrape

Leaf of host plant

Stem of broomrape

Tuber of broomrape attached to host plant's roots through haustoria (penetrating organs that absorb nutrients from host's vascular tissue)

Shoot of broomrape

Main root of host plant

Lateral root of host plant

STEM PARASITE
Dodder (*Cuscuta europaea*)

Tip of dodder stem showing circular movement around host plant

Inflorescence (spike) of dodder flowers

Point of attachment of dodder stem to host stem

Leaf of host plant

Thread-like stem of dodder twined around stem of host plant

Stem of host plant

EXTERNAL VIEW OF PLANT PARASITIZED BY DODDER

Haustorium (penetrating organ that absorbs nutrients from host's vascular tissue)

Vascular tissue of dodder

Union of host and dodder vascular systems

Stem of dodder

Vascular tissue of host plant

Phloem

Xylem

Stem of host plant

MICROGRAPH OF CROSS SECTION THROUGH STEM OF PLANT PARASITIZED BY DODDER

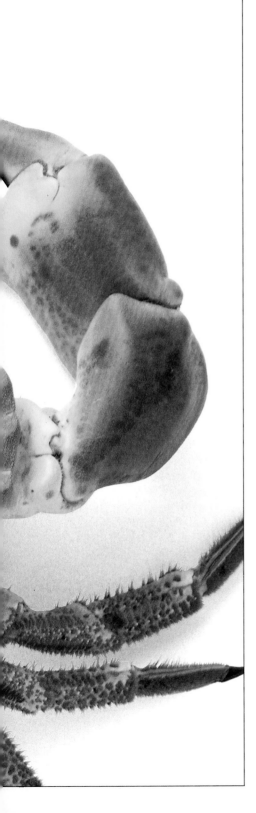

ANIMALS

Sponges, jellyfish, and sea anemones

SPONGES ARE MAINLY MARINE animals that make up the phylum Porifera. They are among the simplest of all animals, having no tissues or organs. Their bodies consist of two layers of cells separated by a jelly-like layer (mesohyal) that is strengthened by mineral spicules or protein fibers. The body is perforated by a system of pores and water channels called the aquiferous system. Special cells (choanocytes) with whip-like structures (flagella) draw water through the aquiferous system, thereby bringing tiny food particles to the sponge's cells. Jellyfish (class Scyphozoa), sea anemones (class Anthozoa), and corals (also class Anthozoa) belong to the phylum Cnidaria, also known as Coelenterata. More complex than sponges, coelenterates have simple tissues, such as nervous tissue; a radially symmetrical body; and a mouth surrounded by tentacles with unique stinging cells (cnidocytes).

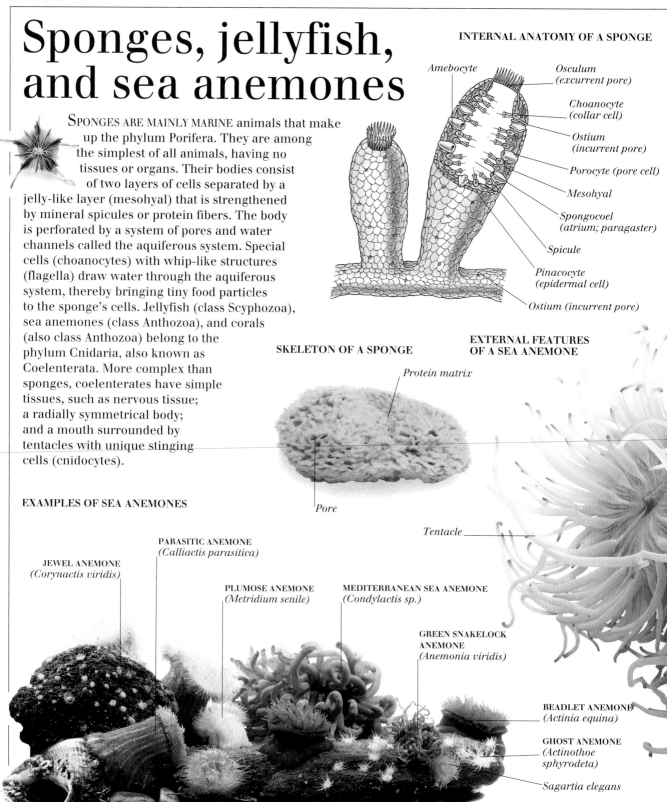

INTERNAL ANATOMY OF A SPONGE

Amebocyte
Osculum (excurrent pore)
Choanocyte (collar cell)
Ostium (incurrent pore)
Porocyte (pore cell)
Mesohyal
Spongocoel (atrium; paragaster)
Spicule
Pinacocyte (epidermal cell)
Ostium (incurrent pore)

SKELETON OF A SPONGE

Protein matrix

Pore

EXTERNAL FEATURES OF A SEA ANEMONE

Tentacle

EXAMPLES OF SEA ANEMONES

PARASITIC ANEMONE
(Calliactis parasitica)

JEWEL ANEMONE
(Corynactis viridis)

PLUMOSE ANEMONE
(Metridium senile)

MEDITERRANEAN SEA ANEMONE
(Condylactis sp.)

GREEN SNAKELOCK ANEMONE
(Anemonia viridis)

BEADLET ANEMONE
(Actinia equina)

GHOST ANEMONE
(Actinothoe sphyrodeta)

Sagartia elegans

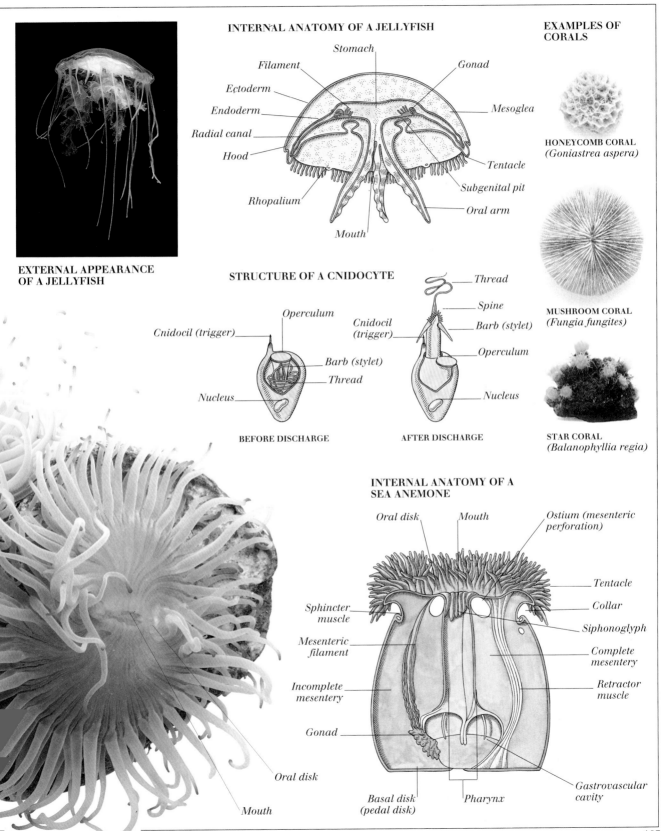

**EXTERNAL APPEARANCE
OF A JELLYFISH**

INTERNAL ANATOMY OF A JELLYFISH

Stomach

Filament

Gonad

Ectoderm

Endoderm

Mesoglea

Radial canal

Hood

Tentacle

Subgenital pit

Rhopalium

Oral arm

Mouth

**EXAMPLES OF
CORALS**

HONEYCOMB CORAL
(Goniastrea aspera)

MUSHROOM CORAL
(Fungia fungites)

STAR CORAL
(Balanophyllia regia)

STRUCTURE OF A CNIDOCYTE

Operculum

Cnidocil (trigger)

Barb (stylet)

Thread

Nucleus

BEFORE DISCHARGE

Thread

Spine

Cnidocil
(trigger)

Barb (stylet)

Operculum

Nucleus

AFTER DISCHARGE

**INTERNAL ANATOMY OF A
SEA ANEMONE**

Oral disk

Mouth

Ostium (mesenteric
perforation)

Tentacle

Sphincter
muscle

Collar

Siphonoglyph

Mesenteric
filament

Complete
mesentery

Incomplete
mesentery

Retractor
muscle

Gonad

Oral disk

Mouth

Basal disk
(pedal disk)

Pharynx

Gastrovascular
cavity

Insects

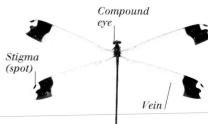

PUPA (CHRYSALIS)

THE WORD INSECT REFERS to small invertebrate creatures, especially those with bodies divided into sections. Insects, including beetles, ants, bees, butterflies, and moths, belong to various orders in the class Insecta, which is a division of the phylum Arthropoda. Features common to all insects are an exoskeleton (external skeleton); three pairs of jointed legs; three body sections (head, thorax, and abdomen); and one pair of sensory antennae. Beetles (order Coleoptera) are the biggest group of insects, with about 300,000 species (about 30 percent of all known insects). They have a pair of hard elytra (wing cases), which are modified front wings. The principal function of the elytra is to protect the hind wings, which are used for flying. Ants, together with bees and wasps, form the order Hymenoptera, which contains about 200,000 species. This group is characterized by a marked narrowing between the thorax and abdomen. Butterflies and moths form the order Lepidoptera, which has about 150,000 species. They have wings covered with tiny scales, hence the name of their order (Lepidoptera means "scale wings"). The separation of lepidopterans into butterflies and moths is largely artificial as there are no features that categorically distinguish one group from the other. In general, however, most butterflies fly by day, whereas most moths are night flyers. Some insects, including butterflies and moths, undergo complete metamorphosis (transformation) during their life cycle. A butterfly metamorphoses from an egg to a larva (caterpillar), then to a pupa (chrysalis), and finally to an imago (adult).

EXAMPLES OF INSECTS

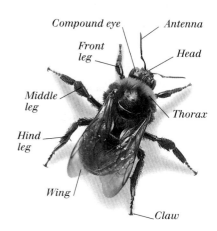

BUMBLEBEE

DAMSELFLY

EXTERNAL FEATURES OF A BEETLE

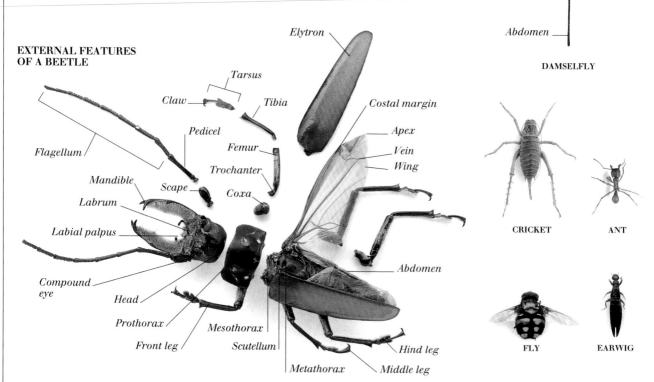

CRICKET

ANT

FLY

EARWIG

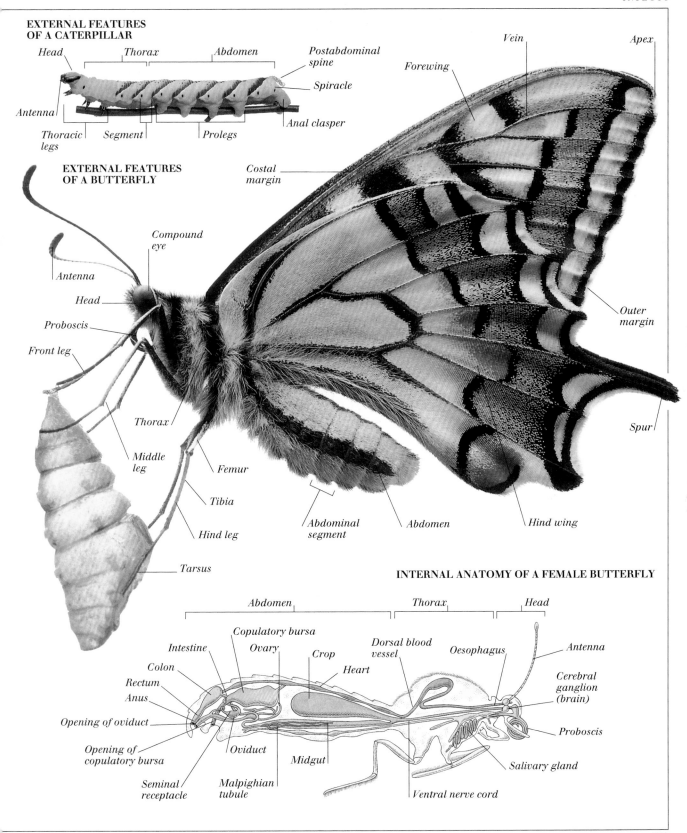

**EXTERNAL FEATURES
OF A CATERPILLAR**

Head

Thorax

Abdomen

Postabdominal
spine

Spiracle

Antenna

Anal clasper

Thoracic
legs

Segment

Prolegs

Vein

Apex

Forewing

**EXTERNAL FEATURES
OF A BUTTERFLY**

Costal
margin

Compound
eye

Antenna

Head

Proboscis

Front leg

Thorax

Middle
leg

Femur

Tibia

Hind leg

Tarsus

Outer
margin

Spur

Abdominal
segment

Abdomen

Hind wing

INTERNAL ANATOMY OF A FEMALE BUTTERFLY

Abdomen

Thorax

Head

Copulatory bursa

Intestine

Ovary

Crop

Dorsal blood
vessel

Oesophagus

Antenna

Colon

Heart

Cerebral
ganglion
(brain)

Rectum

Anus

Opening of oviduct

Proboscis

Opening of
copulatory bursa

Oviduct

Midgut

Salivary gland

Seminal
receptacle

Malpighian
tubule

Ventral nerve cord

169

Arachnids

THE CLASS ARACHNIDA INCLUDES SPIDERS (order Araneae) and scorpions (order Scorpiones). The class is part of the phylum Arthropoda, which also includes insects and crustaceans. Spiders and scorpions are characterized by having four pairs of walking legs; a pair of pincer-like mouthparts called chelicerae; another pair of frontal appendages called pedipalps, which are sensory in spiders but used for grasping in scorpions; and a body divided into two sections (a combined head and thorax called a cephalothorax, or prosoma, and an abdomen, or opisthosoma). Unlike other arthropods, spiders and scorpions lack antennae. Spiders and scorpions are carnivorous. Spiders poison prey by biting with the fanged chelicerae, scorpions by stinging with the end of the metasoma (tail).

MEXICAN TRUE RED-LEGGED TARANTULA
(Euathlus emilia)

INTERNAL ANATOMY OF A FEMALE SPIDER

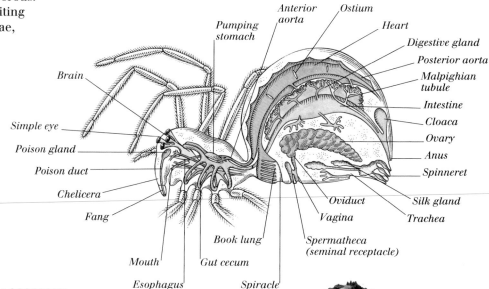

Pumping stomach
Anterior aorta
Ostium
Heart
Digestive gland
Posterior aorta
Malpighian tubule
Intestine
Cloaca
Ovary
Anus
Spinneret
Silk gland
Trachea
Spermatheca (seminal receptacle)
Oviduct
Vagina
Spiracle
Gut cecum
Book lung
Esophagus
Mouth
Fang
Chelicera
Poison duct
Poison gland
Simple eye
Brain

EXTERNAL FEATURES OF A SCORPION

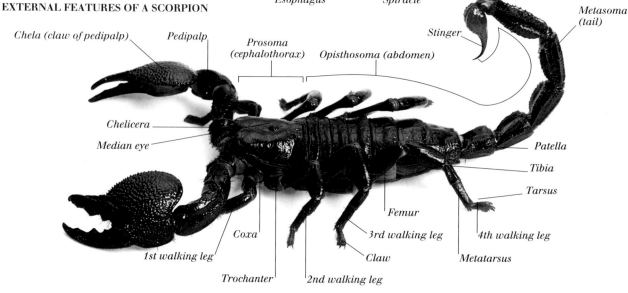

Chela (claw of pedipalp)
Pedipalp
Prosoma (cephalothorax)
Opisthosoma (abdomen)
Stinger
Metasoma (tail)
Chelicera
Median eye
Patella
Tibia
Tarsus
Femur
3rd walking leg
4th walking leg
Coxa
Claw
Metatarsus
1st walking leg
Trochanter
2nd walking leg

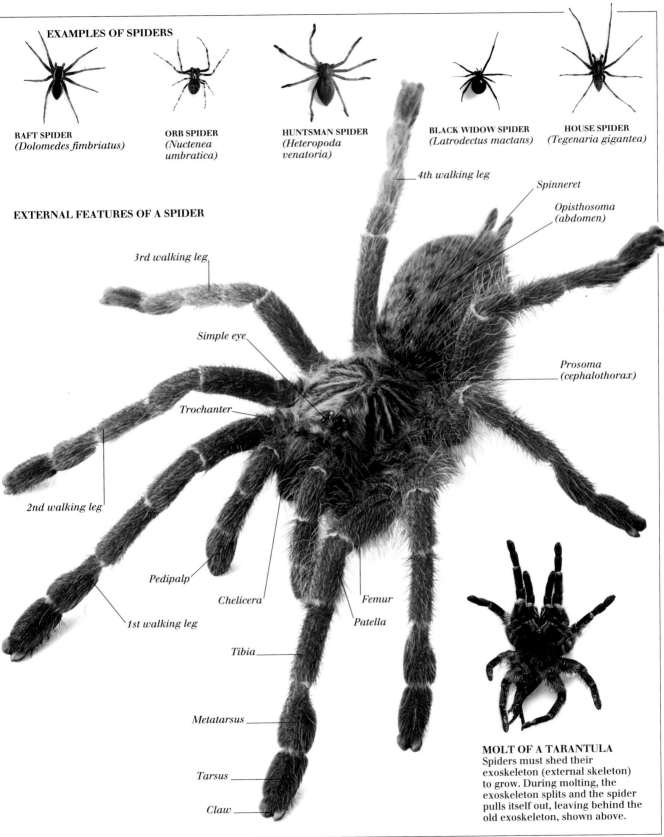

EXAMPLES OF SPIDERS

RAFT SPIDER
(*Dolomedes fimbriatus*)

ORB SPIDER
(*Nuctenea
umbratica*)

HUNTSMAN SPIDER
(*Heteropoda
venatoria*)

BLACK WIDOW SPIDER
(*Latrodectus mactans*)

HOUSE SPIDER
(*Tegenaria gigantea*)

EXTERNAL FEATURES OF A SPIDER

4th walking leg

Spinneret

*Opisthosoma
(abdomen)*

3rd walking leg

*Prosoma
(cephalothorax)*

Simple eye

Trochanter

2nd walking leg

Pedipalp

Chelicera

Femur

Patella

1st walking leg

Tibia

Metatarsus

Tarsus

Claw

MOLT OF A TARANTULA
Spiders must shed their
exoskeleton (external skeleton)
to grow. During molting, the
exoskeleton splits and the spider
pulls itself out, leaving behind the
old exoskeleton, shown above.

Crustaceans

THE SUBPHYLUM CRUSTACEA is one of the largest groups in the phylum Arthropoda. The subphylum is divided into several classes, the most important of which are Malacostraca and Cirripedia. The class Malacostraca includes crayfish, crabs, lobsters, and shrimps. Typical features of malacostracans include a body divided into two sections (a combined head and thorax called a cephalothorax, and an abdomen); an exoskeleton (external skeleton) with a large plate (carapace) covering the cephalothorax; stalked, compound eyes; and two pairs of antennae. The class Cirripedia includes barnacles, which, unlike other crustaceans, spend their adult lives attached to a surface, such as a rock. Other characteristics of cirripedes include an exoskeleton of overlapping calcareous plates; a body consisting almost entirely of thorax (the abdomen and head are minute); and six pairs of thoracic appendages (cirri) used for filter feeding.

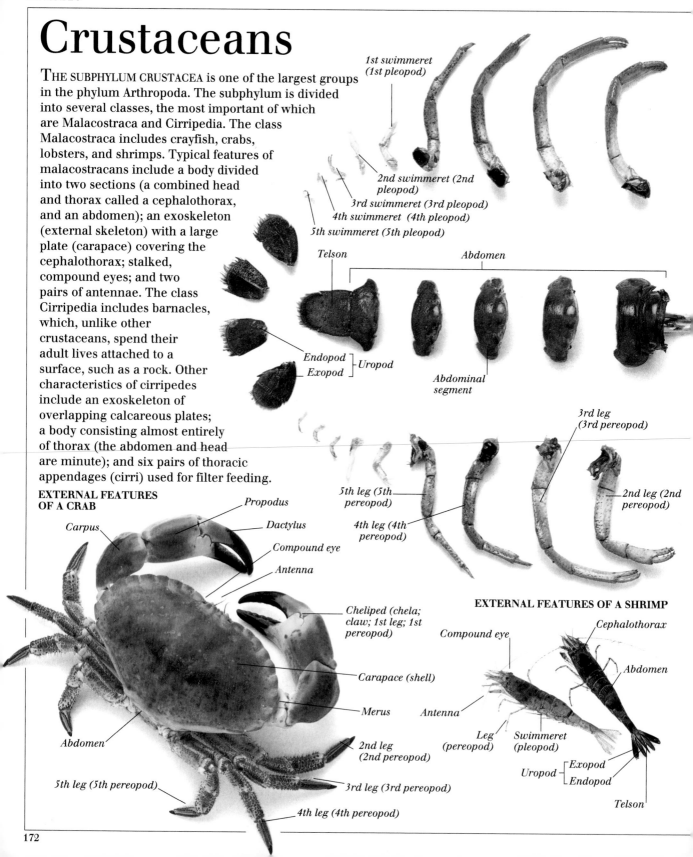

1st swimmeret (1st pleopod)

2nd swimmeret (2nd pleopod)

3rd swimmeret (3rd pleopod)

4th swimmeret (4th pleopod)

5th swimmeret (5th pleopod)

Telson

Abdomen

Endopod
Exopod
Uropod

Abdominal segment

3rd leg (3rd pereopod)

2nd leg (2nd pereopod)

5th leg (5th pereopod)

4th leg (4th pereopod)

EXTERNAL FEATURES OF A CRAB

Propodus

Dactylus

Compound eye

Antenna

Carpus

Cheliped (chela; claw; 1st leg; 1st pereopod)

Carapace (shell)

Merus

Abdomen

2nd leg (2nd pereopod)

5th leg (5th pereopod)

3rd leg (3rd pereopod)

4th leg (4th pereopod)

EXTERNAL FEATURES OF A SHRIMP

Compound eye

Cephalothorax

Abdomen

Antenna

Leg (pereopod)

Swimmeret (pleopod)

Uropod
Exopod
Endopod

Telson

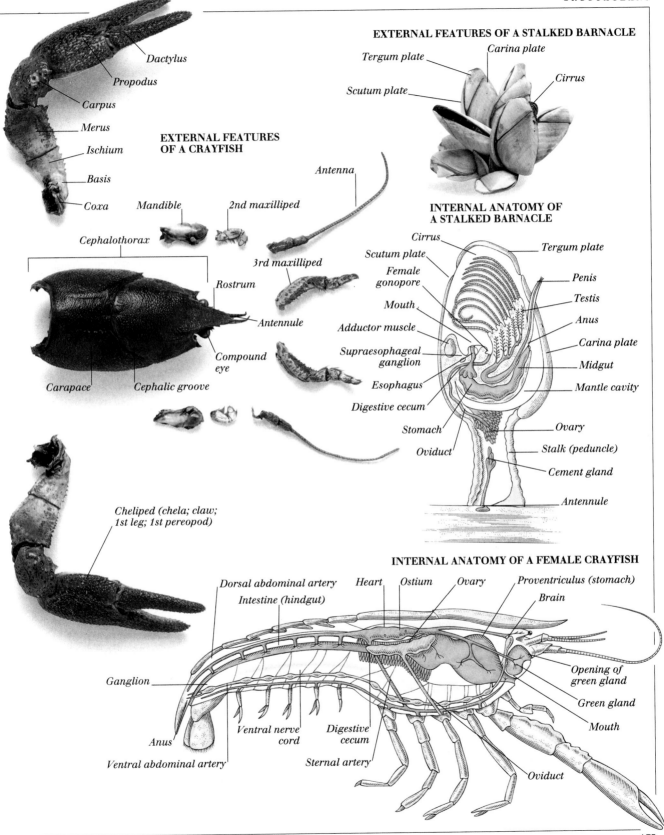

EXTERNAL FEATURES OF A CRAYFISH

Dactylus
Propodus
Carpus
Merus
Ischium
Basis
Coxa

Mandible
2nd maxilliped
Antenna
3rd maxilliped
Cephalothorax
Rostrum
Antennule
Compound eye
Carapace
Cephalic groove

Cheliped (chela; claw; 1st leg; 1st pereopod)

EXTERNAL FEATURES OF A STALKED BARNACLE

Carina plate
Tergum plate
Cirrus
Scutum plate

INTERNAL ANATOMY OF A STALKED BARNACLE

Cirrus
Scutum plate
Female gonopore
Mouth
Adductor muscle
Supraesophageal ganglion
Esophagus
Digestive cecum
Stomach
Oviduct
Tergum plate
Penis
Testis
Anus
Carina plate
Midgut
Mantle cavity
Ovary
Stalk (peduncle)
Cement gland
Antennule

INTERNAL ANATOMY OF A FEMALE CRAYFISH

Dorsal abdominal artery
Heart
Ostium
Ovary
Proventriculus (stomach)
Intestine (hindgut)
Brain
Ganglion
Opening of green gland
Green gland
Mouth
Anus
Ventral nerve cord
Digestive cecum
Sternal artery
Oviduct
Ventral abdominal artery

Starfish and sea urchins

STARFISH, SEA URCHINS, AND THEIR relatives (including feather stars, brittle stars, basket stars, sea daisies, sea lilies, and sea cucumbers) make up the phylum Echinodermata. A unique feature of echinoderms is the water vascular system, which consists of a series of water-filled canals from which protrude thousands of tiny tube feet. The tube feet may be used for movement, feeding, or respiration. Other features include pentaradiate symmetry (that is, the body can be divided into five parts radiating from the center); no head; a diffuse, decentralized nervous system that lacks a brain; and no excretory organs. Typically, echinoderms also have an endoskeleton (internal skeleton) consisting of hard calcite ossicles embedded in the body wall and often bearing protruding spines or tubercles. The ossicles may fit together to form a test (as in sea urchins) or remain separate (as in sea cucumbers).

EXTERNAL FEATURES OF A STARFISH (UPPER, OR ABORAL, SURFACE)

Disk

Madreporite

Spine

Arm

INTERNAL ANATOMY OF A STARFISH

Rectum

Pyloric stomach

Madreporite

Stone canal

Anus

Rectal cecum

Tube foot

Ring canal

Lateral canal

Radial canal

Ampulla

Cardiac stomach

Pyloric duct

Pyloric cecum

Mouth

Esophagus

Gonad

Gonopore

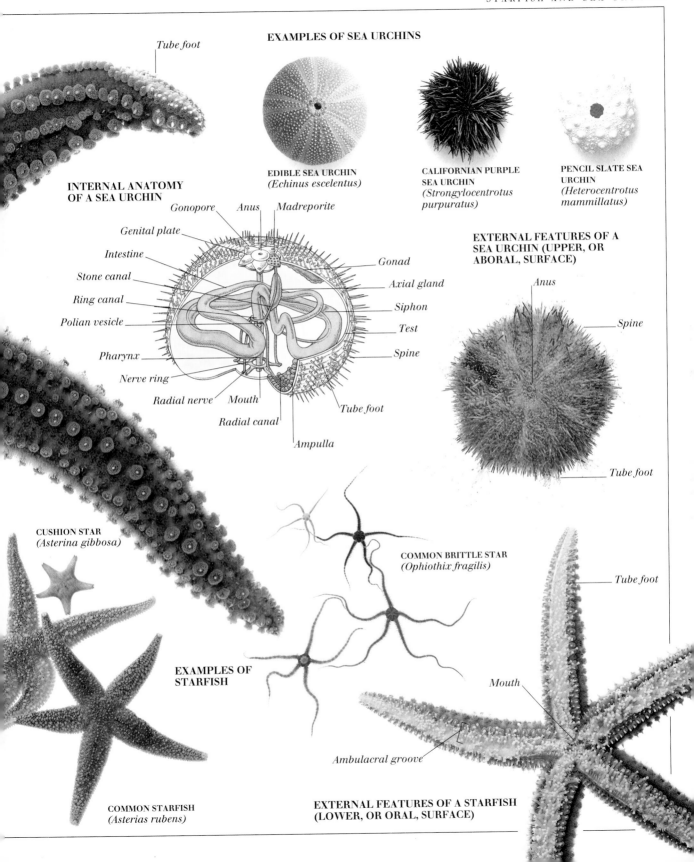

Tube foot

EXAMPLES OF SEA URCHINS

EDIBLE SEA URCHIN
(*Echinus escelentus*)

**CALIFORNIAN PURPLE
SEA URCHIN**
(*Strongylocentrotus
purpuratus*)

**PENCIL SLATE SEA
URCHIN**
(*Heterocentrotus
mammillatus*)

**INTERNAL ANATOMY
OF A SEA URCHIN**

Gonopore

Anus

Madreporite

Genital plate

Intestine

Gonad

Stone canal

Axial gland

Ring canal

Siphon

Polian vesicle

Test

Pharynx

Spine

Nerve ring

Radial nerve

Mouth

Radial canal

Ampulla

Tube foot

**EXTERNAL FEATURES OF A
SEA URCHIN (UPPER, OR
ABORAL, SURFACE)**

Anus

Spine

Tube foot

CUSHION STAR
(*Asterina gibbosa*)

COMMON BRITTLE STAR
(*Ophiothrix fragilis*)

Tube foot

**EXAMPLES OF
STARFISH**

Mouth

Ambulacral groove

COMMON STARFISH
(*Asterias rubens*)

**EXTERNAL FEATURES OF A STARFISH
(LOWER, OR ORAL, SURFACE)**

Mollusks

THE PHYLUM MOLLUSCA (MOLLUSKS) is a large group of animals that includes octopuses, snails, and scallops. Octopuses and their relatives —including squid and cuttlefish—form the class Cephalopoda. Cephalopods typically have a head with a radula (a file-like feeding organ) and beak; a well-developed nervous system; sucker-bearing tentacles; a muscular mantle (part of the body wall) that can expel water through the siphon, enabling movement by jet propulsion; and a small shell or no shell. Snails and their relatives—including slugs, limpets, and abalones—make up the class Gastropoda. Gastropods typically have a coiled external shell, although some, such as slugs, have a small internal shell or no shell; a flat foot; and a head with tentacles and a radula. Scallops and their relatives—including clams, mussels, and oysters—make up the class Bivalvia (also called Pelecypoda). Features of bivalves include a shell with two halves (valves); large gills that are used for breathing and filter feeding; and no radula.

EXTERNAL FEATURES OF A SCALLOP

Upper valve (shell)   Mantle   Ocellus (eye)

Lower valve (shell)   Shell rib   Sensory tentacle

Sensory tentacle   Ventral margin of shell   Shell rib

Anterior wing of shell

Umbo   Posterior wing of shell

Dorsal margin of shell

INTERNAL ANATOMY OF AN OCTOPUS

Cephalic vein
Skull
Brain
Siphon (funnel)
Buccal mass
Beak
Poison gland
Crop
Digestive cecum
Dorsal mantle cavity
Mantle muscles
Shell rudiment
Stomach
Cecum
Gonad
Systemic heart
Kidney
Branchial heart
Ctenidium
Ink sac
Anus
Muscular septum
Sucker

Tentacle

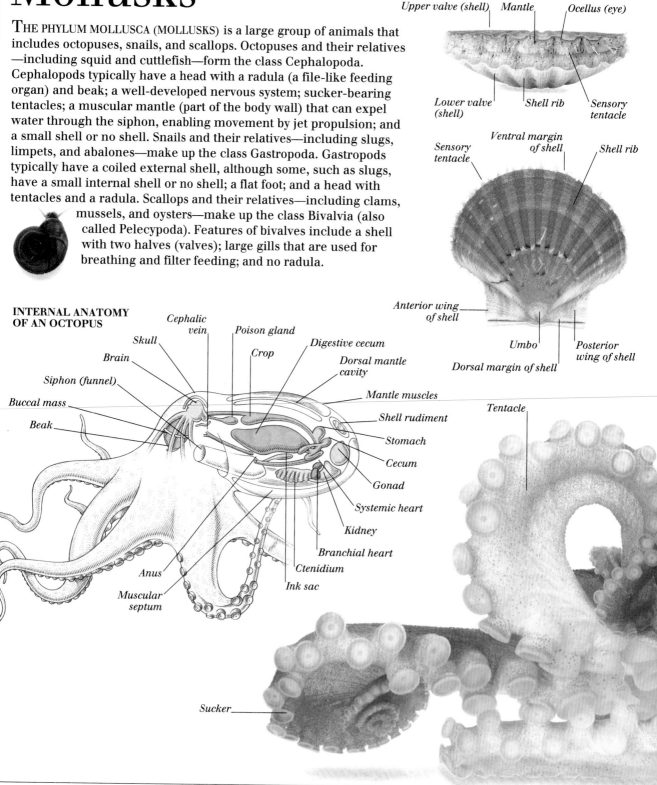

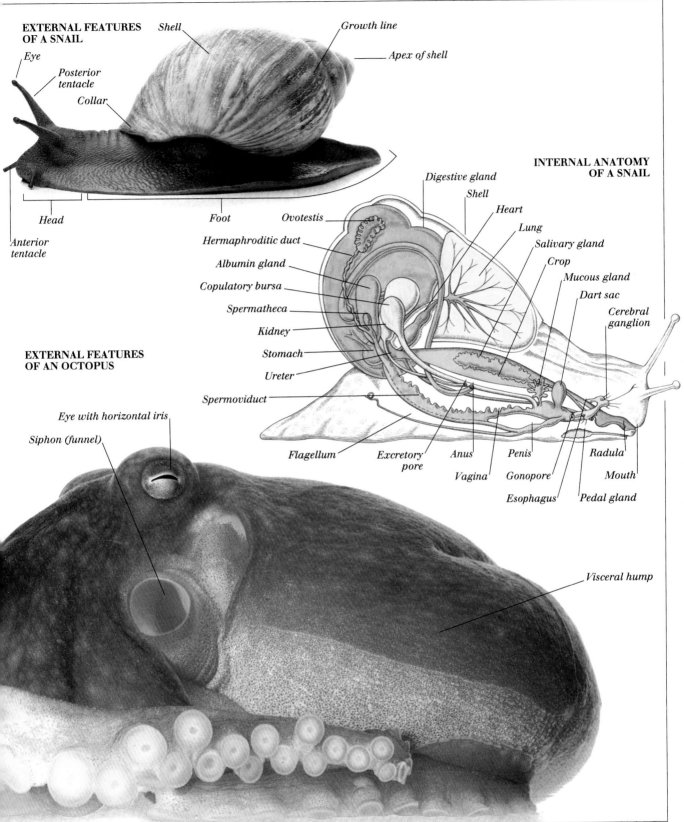

EXTERNAL FEATURES OF A SNAIL

Shell

Growth line

Eye

Apex of shell

Posterior tentacle

Collar

Head

Foot

Anterior tentacle

INTERNAL ANATOMY OF A SNAIL

Digestive gland

Shell

Heart

Lung

Salivary gland

Ovotestis

Crop

Hermaphroditic duct

Mucous gland

Albumin gland

Dart sac

Copulatory bursa

Cerebral ganglion

Spermatheca

Kidney

Stomach

Ureter

Spermoviduct

EXTERNAL FEATURES OF AN OCTOPUS

Flagellum

Excretory pore

Anus

Penis

Radula

Vagina

Gonopore

Mouth

Esophagus

Pedal gland

Eye with horizontal iris

Siphon (funnel)

Visceral hump

Sharks and jawless fish

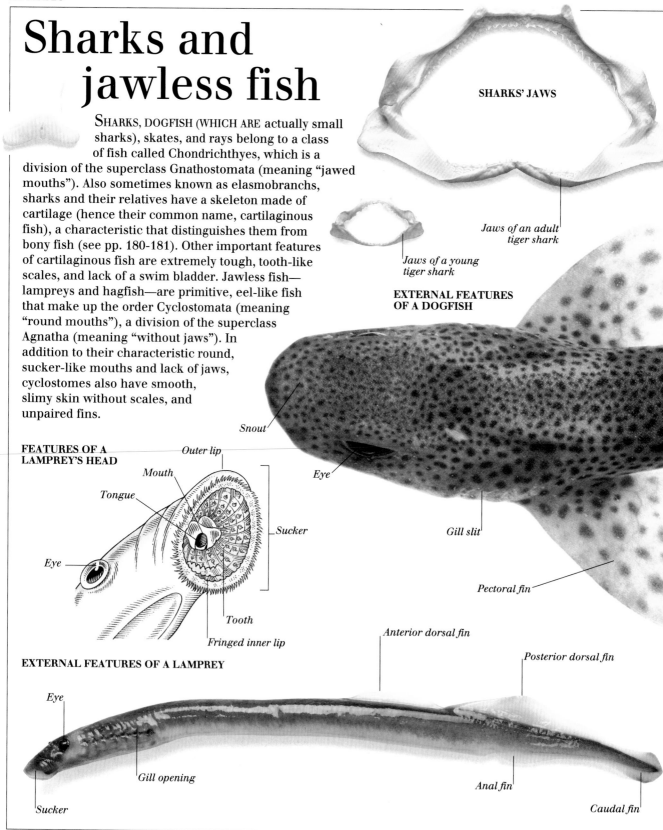

SHARKS, DOGFISH (WHICH ARE actually small sharks), skates, and rays belong to a class of fish called Chondrichthyes, which is a division of the superclass Gnathostomata (meaning "jawed mouths"). Also sometimes known as elasmobranchs, sharks and their relatives have a skeleton made of cartilage (hence their common name, cartilaginous fish), a characteristic that distinguishes them from bony fish (see pp. 180-181). Other important features of cartilaginous fish are extremely tough, tooth-like scales, and lack of a swim bladder. Jawless fish—lampreys and hagfish—are primitive, eel-like fish that make up the order Cyclostomata (meaning "round mouths"), a division of the superclass Agnatha (meaning "without jaws"). In addition to their characteristic round, sucker-like mouths and lack of jaws, cyclostomes also have smooth, slimy skin without scales, and unpaired fins.

SHARKS' JAWS

Jaws of an adult tiger shark

Jaws of a young tiger shark

EXTERNAL FEATURES OF A DOGFISH

Snout

Eye

Gill slit

Pectoral fin

FEATURES OF A LAMPREY'S HEAD

Outer lip

Mouth

Tongue

Eye

Sucker

Tooth

Fringed inner lip

EXTERNAL FEATURES OF A LAMPREY

Eye

Gill opening

Sucker

Anterior dorsal fin

Posterior dorsal fin

Anal fin

Caudal fin

EXAMPLES OF CARTILAGINOUS FISH

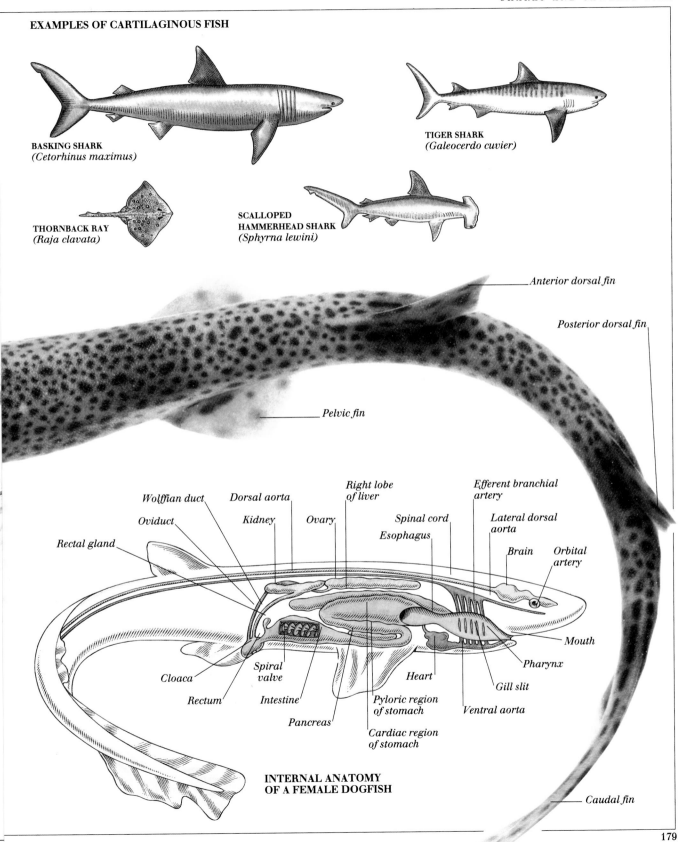

BASKING SHARK
(*Cetorhinus maximus*)

TIGER SHARK
(*Galeocerdo cuvier*)

THORNBACK RAY
(*Raja clavata*)

**SCALLOPED
HAMMERHEAD SHARK**
(*Sphyrna lewini*)

Anterior dorsal fin

Posterior dorsal fin

Pelvic fin

Wolffian duct

Oviduct

Rectal gland

Dorsal aorta

Kidney

Ovary

Right lobe
of liver

Spinal cord

Esophagus

Efferent branchial
artery

Lateral dorsal
aorta

Brain

Orbital
artery

Mouth

Pharynx

Gill slit

Ventral aorta

Heart

Cardiac region
of stomach

Pyloric region
of stomach

Pancreas

Intestine

Rectum

Spiral
valve

Cloaca

**INTERNAL ANATOMY
OF A FEMALE DOGFISH**

Caudal fin

Amphibians

THE CLASS AMPHIBIA INCLUDES FROGS and toads (which make up the order Anura) and newts and salamanders (which make up the order Urodela). Amphibians typically have moist, scaleless, hairless skin; lungs; and are cold-blooded. They also undergo complete metamorphosis, from eggs laid in water through various water-living larval stages (such as the tadpole stage) to land-living adults. Typical features of adult frogs and toads include a squat body with no tail; long, powerful hind legs; and large, often bulging, eyes. Adult newts and salamanders typically have a long body with a well-developed tail; and relatively short legs of equal size. However, newts and salamanders show considerable variation; for example, in some species the adults have minute legs, external gills rather than lungs, and spend their entire lives in water.

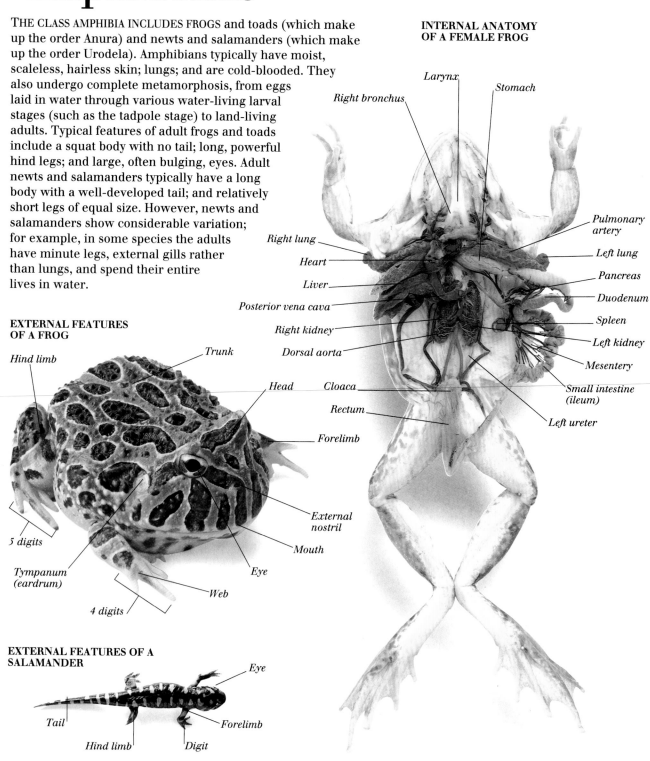

INTERNAL ANATOMY OF A FEMALE FROG

Larynx
Right bronchus
Stomach
Right lung
Pulmonary artery
Left lung
Heart
Pancreas
Liver
Duodenum
Posterior vena cava
Spleen
Right kidney
Left kidney
Dorsal aorta
Mesentery
Cloaca
Small intestine (ileum)
Rectum
Left ureter

EXTERNAL FEATURES OF A FROG

Hind limb
Trunk
Head
Forelimb
5 digits
External nostril
Tympanum (eardrum)
Mouth
Web
Eye
4 digits

EXTERNAL FEATURES OF A SALAMANDER

Eye
Tail
Forelimb
Hind limb
Digit

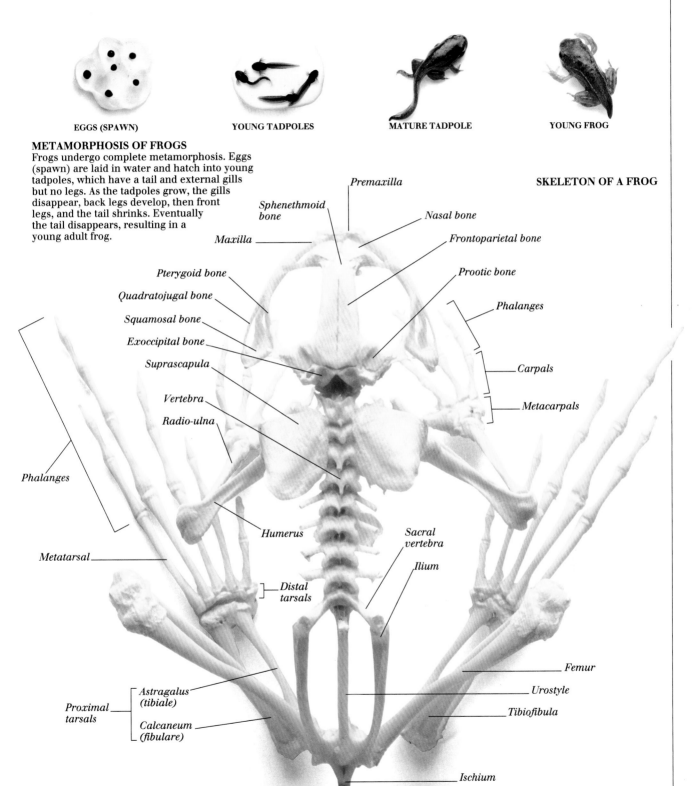

EGGS (SPAWN)

YOUNG TADPOLES

MATURE TADPOLE

YOUNG FROG

METAMORPHOSIS OF FROGS

Frogs undergo complete metamorphosis. Eggs (spawn) are laid in water and hatch into young tadpoles, which have a tail and external gills but no legs. As the tadpoles grow, the gills disappear, back legs develop, then front legs, and the tail shrinks. Eventually the tail disappears, resulting in a young adult frog.

SKELETON OF A FROG

Premaxilla

Sphenethmoid bone

Nasal bone

Maxilla

Frontoparietal bone

Pterygoid bone

Prootic bone

Quadratojugal bone

Phalanges

Squamosal bone

Exoccipital bone

Carpals

Suprascapula

Metacarpals

Vertebra

Radio-ulna

Phalanges

Humerus

Sacral vertebra

Ilium

Metatarsal

Distal tarsals

Femur

Astragalus (tibiale)

Urostyle

Proximal tarsals

Tibiofibula

Calcaneum (fibulare)

Ischium

Lizards and snakes

LIZARDS AND SNAKES BELONG to the order Squamata, a division of the class Reptilia. Characteristic reptilian features include scaly skin, lungs, and cold-bloodedness. Most reptiles lay leathery-shelled eggs, although some hatch the eggs inside their bodies and give birth to live young. Lizards belong to the suborder Lacertilia. Typically, they have long tails, and shed their skin in several pieces. Many lizards can regenerate a tail if it is lost; some can change color; and some are limbless. Snakes make up the suborder Ophidia (also called Serpentes). All snakes have long, limbless bodies; can dislocate their lower jaw to swallow large prey; and have eyelids that are joined together to form a single transparent covering over the front of the eye. Most snakes shed their skin in a single piece. Constrictor snakes kill their prey by squeezing; venomous snakes poison their prey.

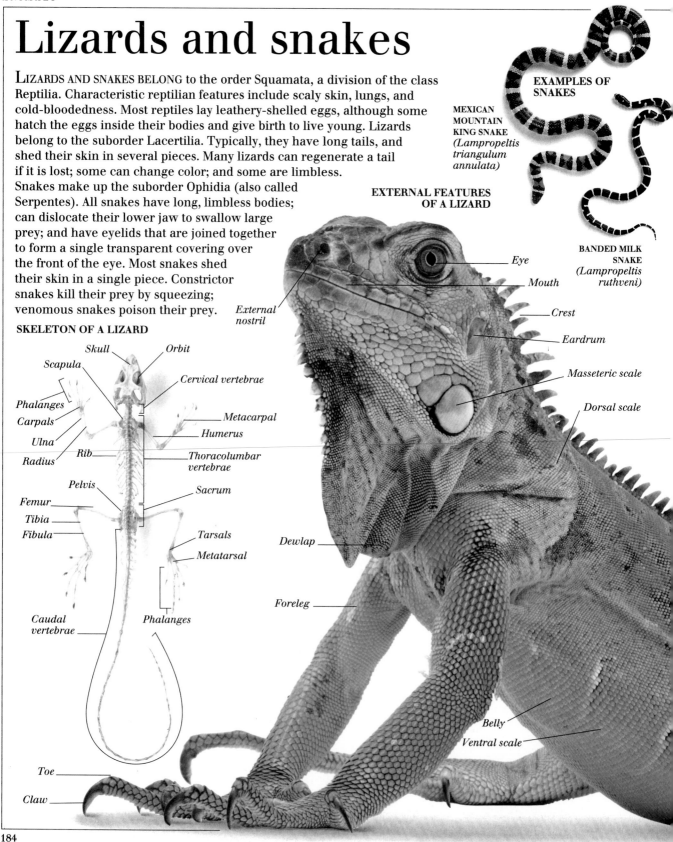

EXAMPLES OF SNAKES

MEXICAN MOUNTAIN KING SNAKE
(*Lampropeltis triangulum annulata*)

BANDED MILK SNAKE
(*Lampropeltis ruthveni*)

EXTERNAL FEATURES OF A LIZARD

Eye

Mouth

External nostril

Crest

Eardrum

Masseteric scale

Dorsal scale

Dewlap

Foreleg

Belly

Ventral scale

SKELETON OF A LIZARD

Skull

Orbit

Scapula

Cervical vertebrae

Phalanges

Carpals

Metacarpal

Humerus

Ulna

Rib

Radius

Thoracolumbar vertebrae

Pelvis

Femur

Sacrum

Tibia

Fibula

Tarsals

Metatarsal

Caudal vertebrae

Phalanges

Toe

Claw

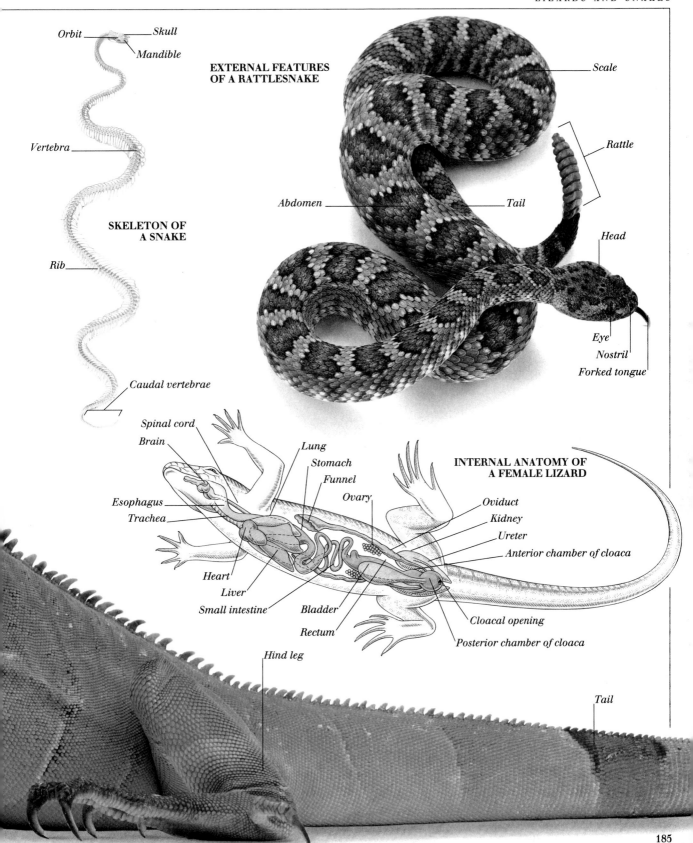

Orbit

Skull

Mandible

EXTERNAL FEATURES OF A RATTLESNAKE

Scale

Vertebra

Rattle

Abdomen

Tail

SKELETON OF A SNAKE

Head

Rib

Eye

Nostril

Forked tongue

Caudal vertebrae

Spinal cord

Brain

Lung

Stomach

Funnel

INTERNAL ANATOMY OF A FEMALE LIZARD

Ovary

Esophagus

Oviduct

Trachea

Kidney

Ureter

Anterior chamber of cloaca

Heart

Liver

Bladder

Small intestine

Rectum

Cloacal opening

Posterior chamber of cloaca

Hind leg

Tail

185

Crocodilians and turtles

CROCODILIANS AND TURTLES BELONG to different orders in the class Reptilia. The order Crocodilia includes crocodiles, alligators, caimans, and gharials. Typically, crocodilians are carnivores (flesh-eaters), and have a long snout, sharp teeth for gripping prey, and hard, square scales. All crocodilians are adapted to living on land and in water: they have four strong legs for moving on land; a powerful tail for swimming; and their eyes and nostrils are high on the head so that they stay above water while the rest of the body is submerged. The order Chelonia includes marine turtles, freshwater turtles (terrapins), and land turtles (tortoises). Characteristically, chelonians have a short, broad body encased in a bony shell with an outer horny covering, into which the head and limbs can be withdrawn; and a horny beak instead of teeth.

SKULLS OF CROCODILIANS

GHARIAL
(*Gavialis gangeticus*)

NILE CROCODILE
(*Crocodylus niloticus*)

MISSISSIPPI ALLIGATOR
(*Alligator mississippiensis*)

SKELETON OF A CROCODILE

Cervical vertebrae
Thoracic vertebrae
Lumbar vertebrae
Sacrum
Caudal vertebrae
Skull
Mandible
Scapula
Humerus
Radius
Ulna
Rib
Femur
Fibula
Phalanges
Metatarsals
Tarsals
Tibia

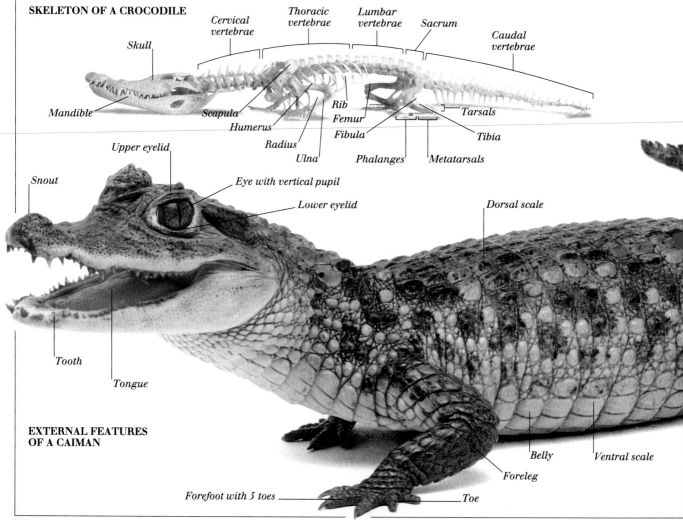

Upper eyelid
Snout
Eye with vertical pupil
Lower eyelid
Dorsal scale
Tooth
Tongue

EXTERNAL FEATURES OF A CAIMAN

Belly
Ventral scale
Foreleg
Forefoot with 5 toes
Toe

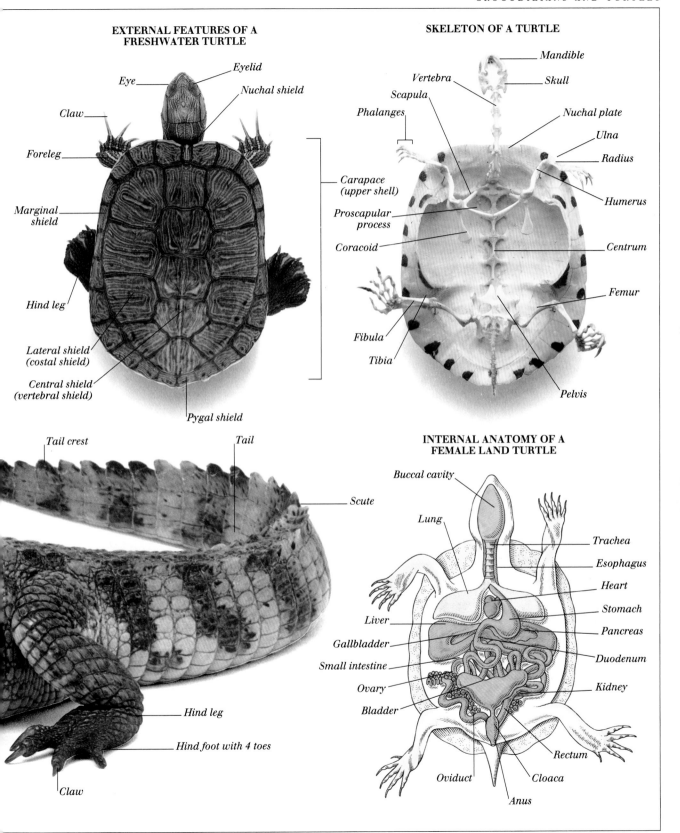

**EXTERNAL FEATURES OF A
FRESHWATER TURTLE**

Eyelid

Eye

Nuchal shield

Claw

Foreleg

Marginal
shield

Hind leg

Lateral shield
(costal shield)

Central shield
(vertebral shield)

Pygal shield

Carapace
(upper shell)

SKELETON OF A TURTLE

Mandible

Vertebra

Skull

Scapula

Phalanges

Nuchal plate

Ulna

Radius

Humerus

Proscapular
process

Coracoid

Centrum

Femur

Fibula

Tibia

Pelvis

Tail crest

Tail

Scute

Hind leg

Hind foot with 4 toes

Claw

**INTERNAL ANATOMY OF A
FEMALE LAND TURTLE**

Buccal cavity

Lung

Trachea

Esophagus

Heart

Stomach

Pancreas

Liver

Duodenum

Gallbladder

Small intestine

Kidney

Ovary

Bladder

Rectum

Oviduct

Cloaca

Anus

187

Birds 1

BIRDS MAKE UP THE CLASS AVES. There are more than 9,000 species, almost all of which can fly (the only flightless birds are penguins, ostriches, rheas, cassowaries, and kiwis). The ability to fly is reflected in the typical bird features: forelimbs modified as wings, a streamlined body, and hollow bones to reduce weight. All birds lay hard-shelled eggs, which the parents incubate. Birds' beaks and feet vary according to diet and way of life. Beaks range from general purpose types suitable for a mixed diet (those of thrushes, for example), to types specialized for particular foods (such as the large, curved, sieving beaks of flamingos). Feet range from the webbed "paddles" of ducks, to the talons of birds of prey. Plumage also varies widely, and in many species the male is brightly colored for courtship display whereas the female is drab.

EXTERNAL FEATURES OF A BIRD

Forehead

Eye

Crown

Nostril

Nape

Upper mandible

Beak

Lower mandible

Chin

Throat

Breast

Belly

Flank

Thigh

Claw

Toe

Tarsus

Under tail coverts

Tail feathers (retrices)

EXAMPLES OF BIRDS

MALE TUFTED DUCK
(Aythya fuligula)

Minor coverts

Lesser wing coverts

Median wing coverts

Greater wing coverts
(major coverts)

Secondary flight feathers
(secondary remiges)

Primary flight feathers
(primary remiges)

WHITE STORK
(Ciconia ciconia)

MALE OSTRICH
(Struthio camelus)

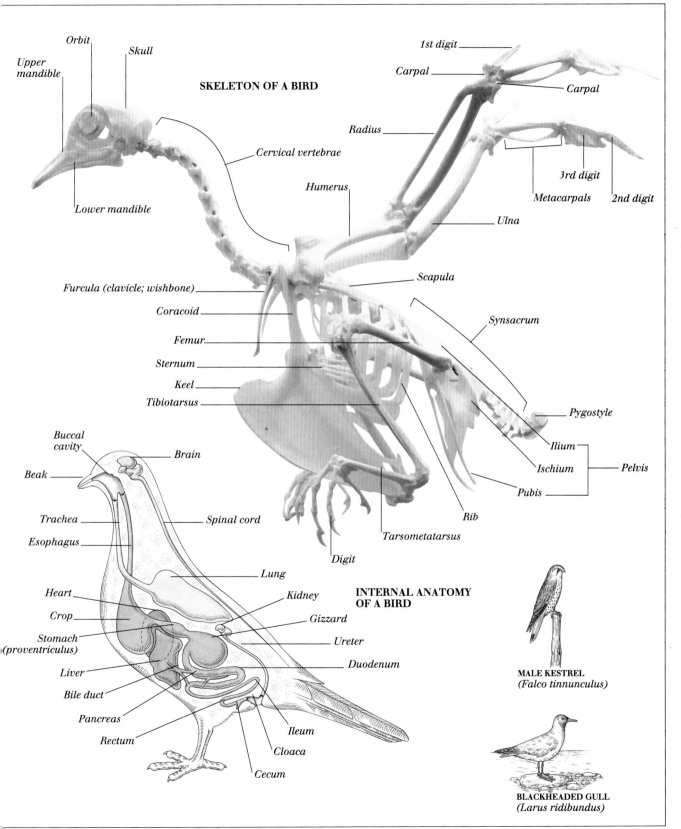

SKELETON OF A BIRD

Orbit

Skull

Upper mandible

Lower mandible

Cervical vertebrae

Humerus

1st digit

Carpal

Carpal

Radius

3rd digit

Metacarpals

2nd digit

Ulna

Scapula

Furcula (clavicle; wishbone)

Coracoid

Synsacrum

Femur

Sternum

Keel

Tibiotarsus

Pygostyle

Ilium

Ischium

Pelvis

Pubis

Rib

Tarsometatarsus

Digit

Buccal cavity

Brain

Beak

Spinal cord

Trachea

Esophagus

Lung

INTERNAL ANATOMY OF A BIRD

Heart

Kidney

Crop

Gizzard

Stomach (proventriculus)

Ureter

Liver

Duodenum

Bile duct

Pancreas

Ileum

Rectum

Cloaca

Cecum

MALE KESTREL
(Falco tinnunculus)

BLACKHEADED GULL
(Larus ridibundus)

Birds 2

EXAMPLES OF BIRDS' FEET

KITTIWAKE
(Rissa tridactyla)
The webbed feet are
adapted for paddling
through water.

LITTLE GREBE
(Tachybaptus ruficollis)
The lobed, flattened feet
are adapted for swimming
underwater.

TAWNY OWL
(Strix aluco)
The clawed feet are adapted
for gripping prey.

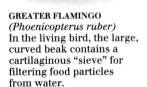

EXAMPLES OF BIRDS' BEAKS

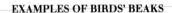

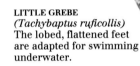

GREATER FLAMINGO
(Phoenicopterus ruber)
In the living bird, the large,
curved beak contains a
cartilaginous "sieve" for
filtering food particles
from water.

KING VULTURE
(Sarcorhamphus papa)
The hooked beak is adapted
for pulling apart flesh.

MAVIS, OR MISTLE THRUSH
(Turdus viscivorus)
The all-purpose beak is suitable
for gathering a wide range of
animal and plant foods.

BLUE-AND-YELLOW MACAW
(Ara ararauna)
The broad, powerful, hooked beak
is adapted for crushing seeds and
eating fruit.

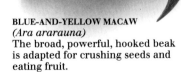

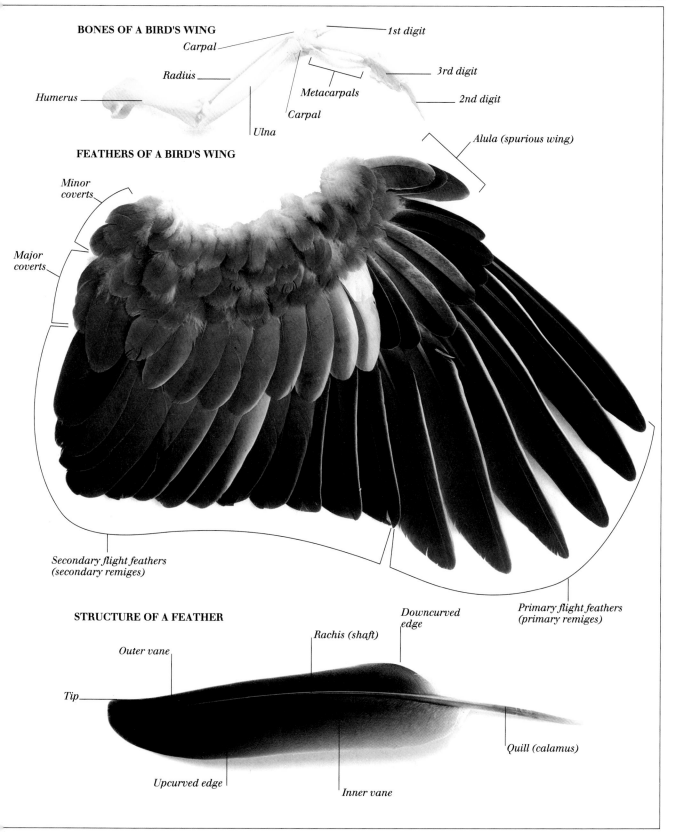

BONES OF A BIRD'S WING

1st digit

Carpal

Radius

3rd digit

Humerus

Metacarpals

2nd digit

Carpal

Ulna

Alula (spurious wing)

FEATHERS OF A BIRD'S WING

Minor coverts

Major coverts

Secondary flight feathers (secondary remiges)

Primary flight feathers (primary remiges)

STRUCTURE OF A FEATHER

Outer vane

Rachis (shaft)

Downcurved edge

Tip

Quill (calamus)

Upcurved edge

Inner vane

Eggs

AN EGG IS A SINGLE CELL, produced by the female, with the capacity to develop into a new individual. Development may take place inside the mother's body (as in most mammals) or outside, in which case the egg has a protective covering such as a shell. Egg yolk nourishes the growing young. Eggs developing inside the mother generally have little yolk, because the young are nourished from her body. Eggs developing outside may also have little yolk if they are produced by animals whose young go through a larval stage (such as a caterpillar) that feeds itself while developing into the adult form. The shelled eggs of birds and reptiles contain enough yolk to sustain the young until it hatches into a juvenile version of the adult.

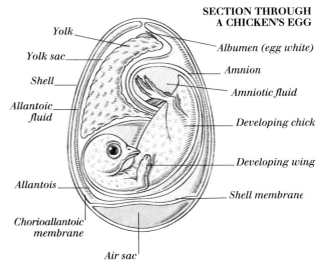

SECTION THROUGH A CHICKEN'S EGG

Yolk
Yolk sac
Shell
Allantoic fluid
Allantois
Chorioallantoic membrane
Air sac
Albumen (egg white)
Amnion
Amniotic fluid
Developing chick
Developing wing
Shell membrane

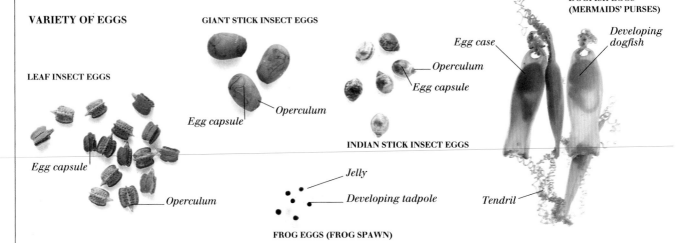

VARIETY OF EGGS

LEAF INSECT EGGS

Egg capsule
Operculum

GIANT STICK INSECT EGGS

Egg capsule
Operculum

INDIAN STICK INSECT EGGS

Operculum
Egg capsule

FROG EGGS (FROG SPAWN)

Jelly
Developing tadpole

DOGFISH EGGS (MERMAIDS' PURSES)

Egg case
Developing dogfish
Tendril

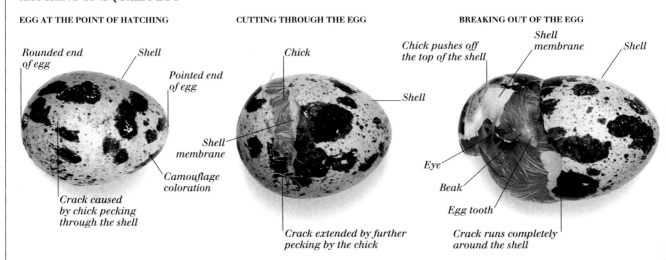

HATCHING OF A QUAIL'S EGG

EGG AT THE POINT OF HATCHING

Rounded end of egg
Shell
Pointed end of egg
Shell membrane
Camouflage coloration
Crack caused by chick pecking through the shell

CUTTING THROUGH THE EGG

Chick
Shell
Crack extended by further pecking by the chick

BREAKING OUT OF THE EGG

Chick pushes off the top of the shell
Shell membrane
Shell
Eye
Beak
Egg tooth
Crack runs completely around the shell

EXAMPLES OF BIRDS' EGGS

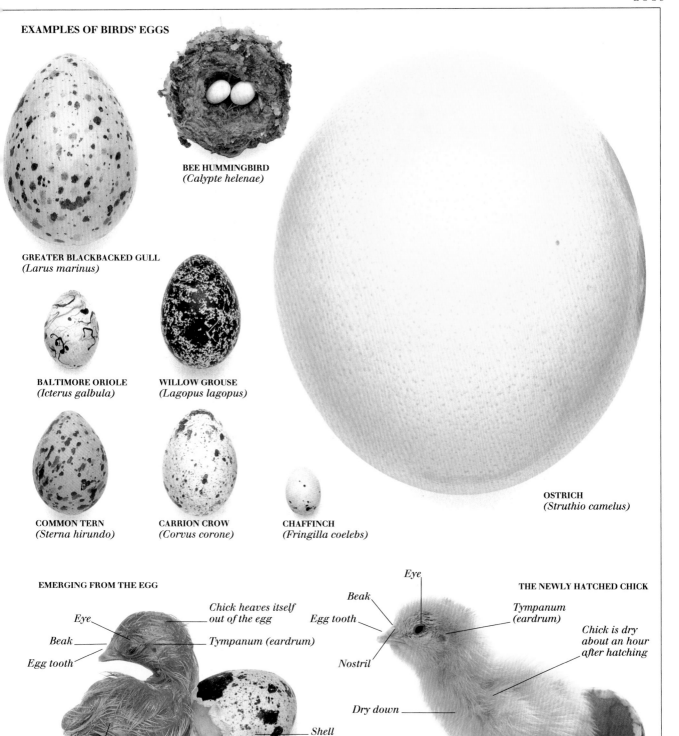

BEE HUMMINGBIRD
(Calypte helenae)

GREATER BLACKBACKED GULL
(Larus marinus)

BALTIMORE ORIOLE
(Icterus galbula)

WILLOW GROUSE
(Lagopus lagopus)

COMMON TERN
(Sterna hirundo)

CARRION CROW
(Corvus corone)

CHAFFINCH
(Fringilla coelebs)

OSTRICH
(Struthio camelus)

EMERGING FROM THE EGG

Eye

Beak

Egg tooth

Chick heaves itself out of the egg

Tympanum (eardrum)

Shell

Wet down

Remains of egg membranes (amnion and allantois)

THE NEWLY HATCHED CHICK

Eye

Beak

Egg tooth

Nostril

Tympanum (eardrum)

Chick is dry about an hour after hatching

Dry down

Toe

Claw

Leg

Eggshell

Carnivores

THE MAMMALIAN ORDER CARNIVORA includes cats, dogs, bears, raccoons, pandas, weasels, badgers, skunks, otters, civets, mongooses, and hyenas. The order's name is derived from the fact that most of its members are carnivores (flesh-eaters). Typical carnivore features therefore reflect a hunting lifestyle: speed and agility; sharp claws and well-developed canine teeth for holding and killing prey; carnassial teeth (cheek teeth) for cutting flesh; and forward-facing eyes for good distance judgment. However, some members of the order—bears, badgers, and foxes, for example—have a more mixed diet, and a few are entirely herbivorous (plant-eating), notably pandas. Such animals have no carnassial teeth and tend to be slower-moving than pure flesh-eaters.

EXTERNAL FEATURES OF A MALE LION

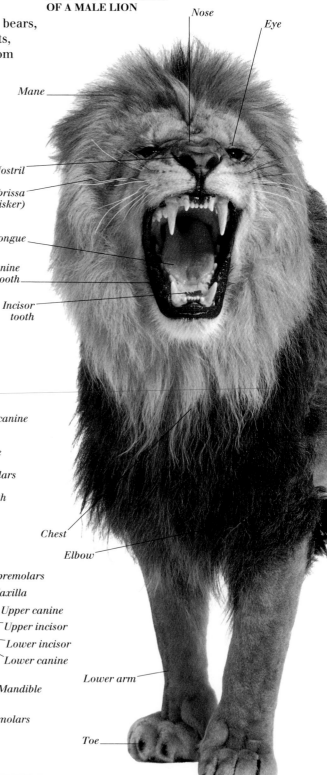

Nose
Eye
Mane
Nostril
Vibrissa (whisker)
Tongue
Canine tooth
Incisor tooth
Chest
Elbow
Lower arm
Toe

SKULL OF A LION

Zygomatic arch
Coronoid process
Sagittal crest
Nasal bone
Maxilla
Orbit
Upper premolars
Upper canine
Lower canine
Mandible
Lower premolars
Occipital condyle
Condyle
Tympanic bulla
Angular process
Upper carnassial tooth (4th upper premolar)

SKULL OF A BEAR

Sagittal crest
Occipital condyle
Zygomatic arch
Orbit
Upper molars
Nasal bone
Upper premolars
Maxilla
Upper canine
Upper incisor
Lower incisor
Lower canine
Mandible
Tympanic bulla
Angular process
Condyle
Lower molars
Lower premolars

EXAMPLES OF CARNIVORES

GERMAN SHEPHERD DOG
(Canis familiaris)

MANED WOLF
(Chrysocyon brachyurus)

RACCOON
(Procyon lotor)

AMERICAN BLACK BEAR
(Ursus americanus)

SKELETON OF A DOMESTIC CAT

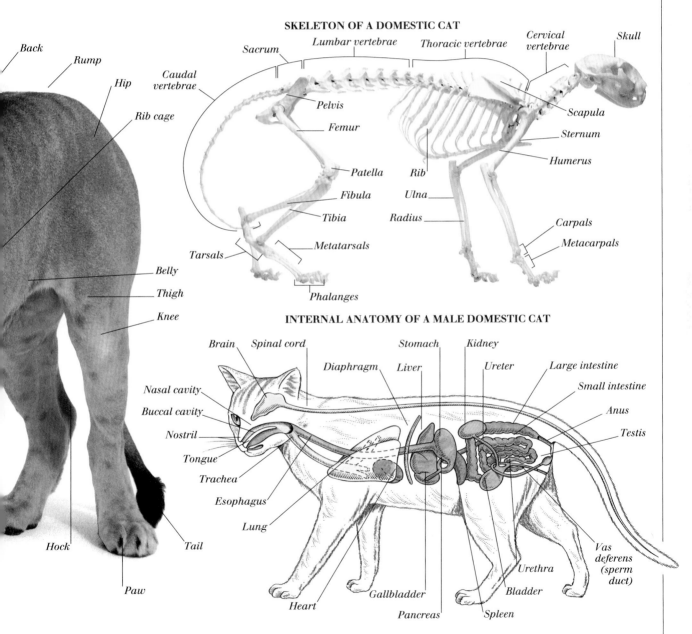

Back

Rump

Hip

Rib cage

Caudal vertebrae

Sacrum

Lumbar vertebrae

Thoracic vertebrae

Cervical vertebrae

Skull

Pelvis

Femur

Patella

Fibula

Tibia

Rib

Ulna

Radius

Scapula

Sternum

Humerus

Carpals

Metacarpals

Tarsals

Metatarsals

Phalanges

Belly

Thigh

Knee

Hock

Paw

Tail

INTERNAL ANATOMY OF A MALE DOMESTIC CAT

Brain

Spinal cord

Diaphragm

Stomach

Kidney

Liver

Ureter

Large intestine

Small intestine

Nasal cavity

Buccal cavity

Anus

Nostril

Testis

Tongue

Trachea

Esophagus

Lung

Heart

Gallbladder

Pancreas

Spleen

Bladder

Urethra

Vas deferens (sperm duct)

Rabbits and rodents

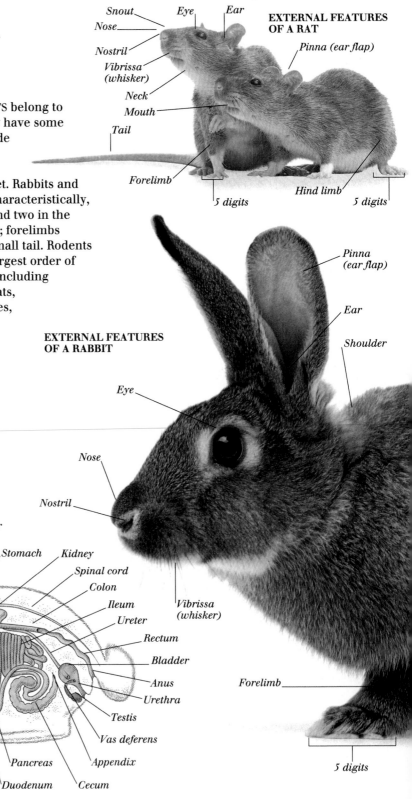

ALTHOUGH RABBITS AND RODENTS belong to different orders of mammals, they have some features in common. These features include chisel-shaped incisor teeth that grow continually, and eating their feces to extract more nutrients from their plant diet. Rabbits and hares belong to the order Lagomorpha. Characteristically, they have four incisors in the upper jaw and two in the lower jaw; powerful hind legs for jumping; forelimbs adapted for burrowing; long ears; and a small tail. Rodents make up the order Rodentia. This is the largest order of mammals, with more than 1,700 species, including squirrels, beavers, chipmunks, gophers, rats, mice, lemmings, gerbils, porcupines, cavies, and the capybara. Typical rodent features include two incisors in each jaw; short forelimbs for manipulating food; and cheek pouches for storing food.

EXTERNAL FEATURES OF A RAT

Snout
Nose
Nostril
Vibrissa (whisker)
Neck
Mouth
Tail
Eye
Ear
Pinna (ear flap)
Forelimb
5 digits
Hind limb
5 digits

EXTERNAL FEATURES OF A RABBIT

Pinna (ear flap)
Ear
Shoulder
Eye
Nose
Nostril
Vibrissa (whisker)
Forelimb
5 digits

INTERNAL ANATOMY OF A MALE RABBIT

Brain
Gallbladder
Liver
Stomach
Kidney
Spinal cord
Colon
Ileum
Ureter
Rectum
Bladder
Anus
Urethra
Testis
Vas deferens
Appendix
Nasal cavity
Mouth
Buccal cavity
Tongue
Esophagus
Lung
Trachea
Heart
Diaphragm
Pancreas
Duodenum
Cecum

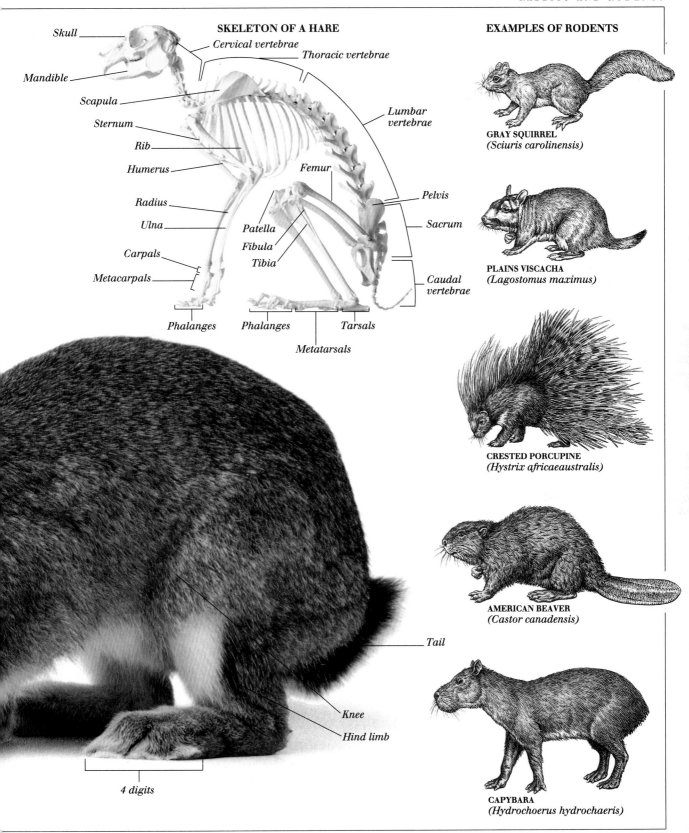

SKELETON OF A HARE

Skull
Cervical vertebrae
Thoracic vertebrae
Mandible
Scapula
Lumbar vertebrae
Sternum
Rib
Humerus
Femur
Radius
Pelvis
Ulna
Sacrum
Patella
Carpals
Fibula
Metacarpals
Tibia
Caudal vertebrae
Phalanges
Phalanges
Tarsals
Metatarsals

Tail

Knee

Hind limb

4 digits

EXAMPLES OF RODENTS

GRAY SQUIRREL
(Sciuris carolinensis)

PLAINS VISCACHA
(Lagostomus maximus)

CRESTED PORCUPINE
(Hystrix africaeaustralis)

AMERICAN BEAVER
(Castor canadensis)

CAPYBARA
(Hydrochoerus hydrochaeris)

197

Ungulates

UNGULATES IS A GENERAL TERM FOR a large, varied group of mammals that includes horses, cattle, and their relatives. The ungulates are divided into two orders on the basis of the number of toes. Members of the order Perissodactyla (odd-toed ungulates) have one or three toes. Perissodactyls include horses, asses, and zebras (all of which are one-toed), and rhinoceroses and tapirs (which are three-toed). Members of the order Artiodactyla (even-toed ungulates) have two or four toes. Most artiodactyls have two toes, which are typically encased in hooves to give the so-called cloven hoof. Two-toed, cloven-hoofed artiodactyls include cows and other cattle, sheep, goats, antelopes, deer, and giraffes. The other main two-toed artiodactyls are camels and llamas. Most two-toed artiodactyls are ruminants; that is, they have a four-chambered stomach and chew the cud. The principal four-toed artiodactyls are hogs and hippopotamuses.

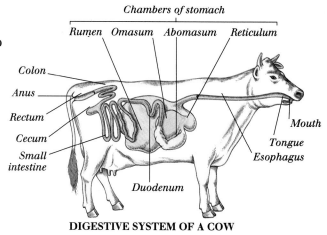

DIGESTIVE SYSTEM OF A COW

COMPARISON OF THE FRONT FEET OF A HORSE AND A COW

SKELETON OF THE LEFT FRONT FOOT OF A HORSE

SKELETON OF THE RIGHT FRONT FOOT OF A COW

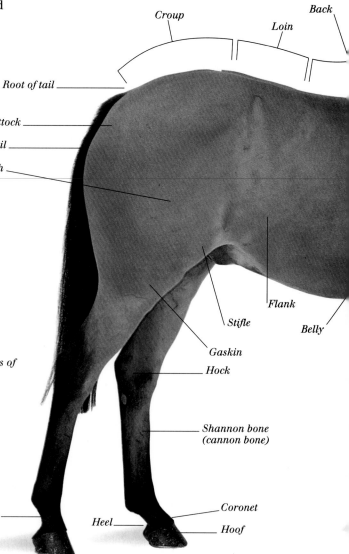

198

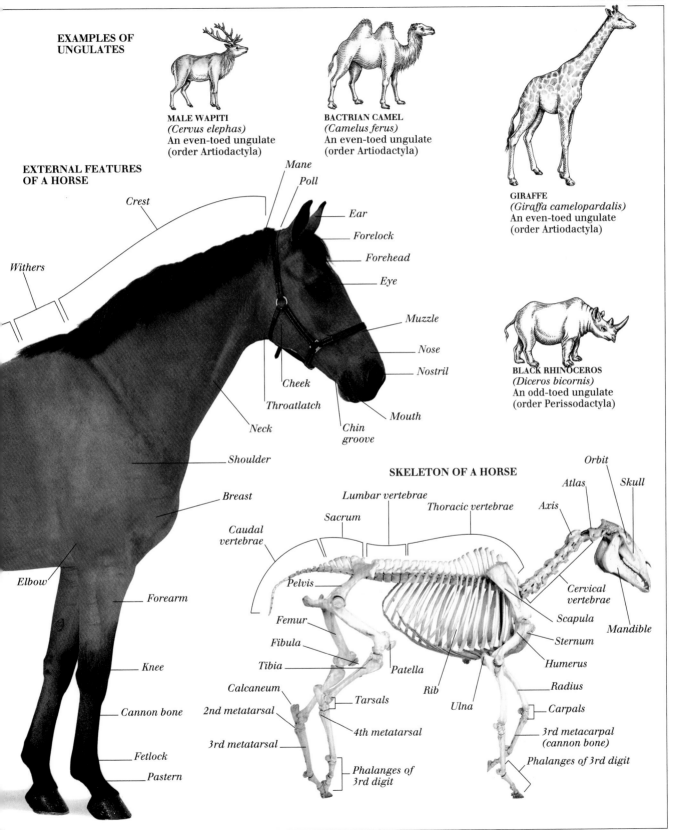

EXAMPLES OF UNGULATES

MALE WAPITI
(Cervus elephas)
An even-toed ungulate
(order Artiodactyla)

BACTRIAN CAMEL
(Camelus ferus)
An even-toed ungulate
(order Artiodactyla)

GIRAFFE
(Giraffa camelopardalis)
An even-toed ungulate
(order Artiodactyla)

BLACK RHINOCEROS
(Diceros bicornis)
An odd-toed ungulate
(order Perissodactyla)

EXTERNAL FEATURES OF A HORSE

Mane
Poll
Crest
Ear
Forelock
Forehead
Eye
Withers
Muzzle
Nose
Nostril
Cheek
Throatlatch
Mouth
Neck
Chin groove
Shoulder
Breast
Elbow
Forearm
Knee
Cannon bone
Fetlock
Pastern

SKELETON OF A HORSE

Orbit
Atlas
Skull
Axis
Lumbar vertebrae
Thoracic vertebrae
Sacrum
Caudal vertebrae
Cervical vertebrae
Pelvis
Scapula
Femur
Mandible
Fibula
Sternum
Tibia
Humerus
Patella
Calcaneum
Rib
Radius
Tarsals
2nd metatarsal
Ulna
Carpals
4th metatarsal
3rd metacarpal (cannon bone)
3rd metatarsal
Phalanges of 3rd digit
Phalanges of 3rd digit

Elephants

THE TWO SPECIES of elephants—African and Asian—are the only members of the mammalian order Proboscidea. The bigger African elephant is the largest land animal: a fully grown male may be up to 13 ft (4m) tall and weigh as much as 7.7 tons (7 tonnes). A fully grown male Asian elephant may be 11 ft (3.3 m) tall and weigh 6 tons (5.4 tonnes). The muscular trunk—an extension of the nose and upper lip—is the elephant's most obvious feature. It is used for manipulating and lifting, feeding, drinking and spraying water, smelling, touching, and producing trumpeting sounds. Other characteristic features of this mighty plant-eater include a pair of ivory tusks, used for defense and for crushing vegetation; thick, pillar-like legs and broad feet to support the massive body; and large ear flaps that act as radiators to keep the elephant cool.

DIFFERENCES BETWEEN AFRICAN AND ASIAN ELEPHANTS

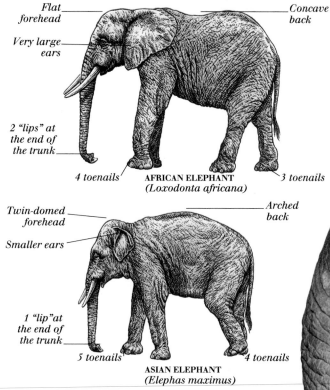

Flat forehead
Concave back
Very large ears
2 "lips" at the end of the trunk
4 toenails
AFRICAN ELEPHANT (*Loxodonta africana*)
3 toenails

Twin-domed forehead
Arched back
Smaller ears
1 "lip" at the end of the trunk
5 toenails
ASIAN ELEPHANT (*Elephas maximus*)
4 toenails

INTERNAL ANATOMY OF A FEMALE ELEPHANT

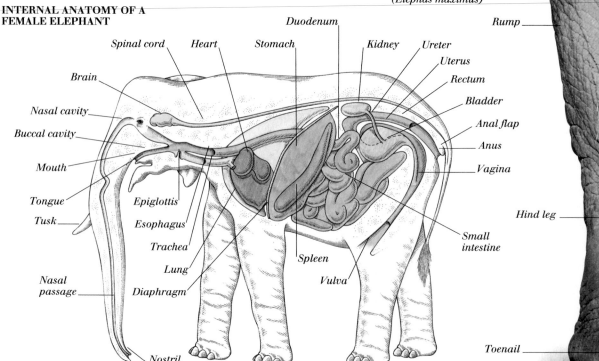

Spinal cord
Heart
Stomach
Duodenum
Kidney
Ureter
Rump
Brain
Uterus
Nasal cavity
Rectum
Buccal cavity
Bladder
Mouth
Anal flap
Tongue
Anus
Tusk
Vagina
Epiglottis
Esophagus
Trachea
Small intestine
Lung
Spleen
Hind leg
Diaphragm
Vulva
Nasal passage
Nostril
Toenail

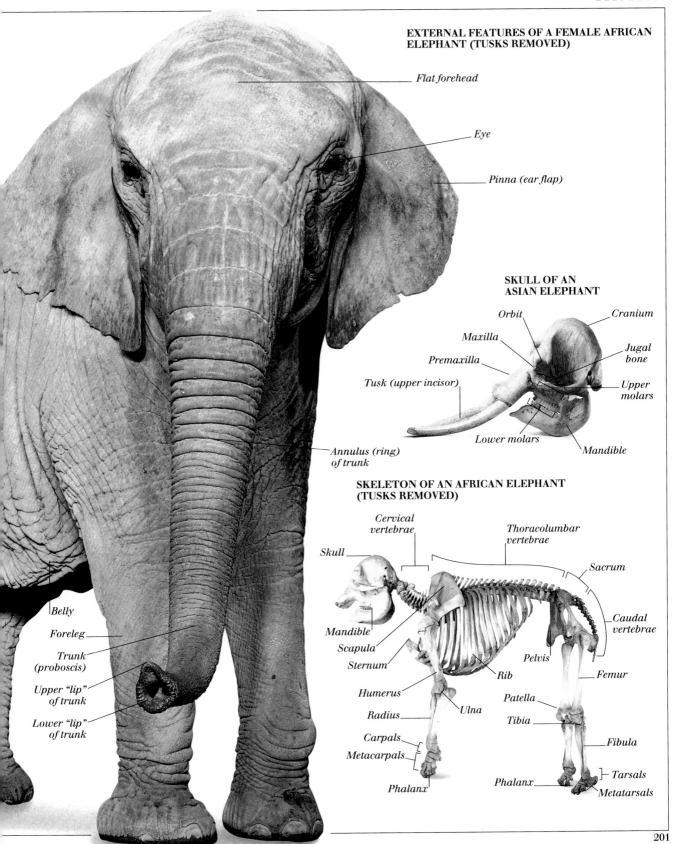

EXTERNAL FEATURES OF A FEMALE AFRICAN ELEPHANT (TUSKS REMOVED)

Flat forehead

Eye

Pinna (ear flap)

SKULL OF AN ASIAN ELEPHANT

Orbit

Cranium

Maxilla

Jugal bone

Premaxilla

Tusk (upper incisor)

Upper molars

Lower molars

Mandible

SKELETON OF AN AFRICAN ELEPHANT (TUSKS REMOVED)

Cervical vertebrae

Thoracolumbar vertebrae

Skull

Sacrum

Mandible

Scapula

Caudal vertebrae

Sternum

Rib

Pelvis

Humerus

Femur

Radius

Ulna

Patella

Carpals

Tibia

Metacarpals

Fibula

Phalanx

Tarsals

Phalanx

Metatarsals

Belly

Foreleg

Trunk (proboscis)

Upper "lip" of trunk

Lower "lip" of trunk

Annulus (ring) of trunk

Primates

THE MAMMALIAN ORDER PRIMATES consists of monkeys, apes, and their relatives (including humans). There are two suborders of primates: Prosimii, the primitive primates, which include lemurs, tarsiers, and lorises; and Anthropoidea, the advanced primates, which include monkeys, apes, and humans. The anthropoids are divided into New World monkeys, Old World monkeys, and hominids. New World monkeys typically have widespread nostrils that open to the side; and long tails, which are prehensile (grasping) in some species. This group of monkeys lives in South America, and includes marmosets, tamarins, and howler monkeys. Old World monkeys typically have close-set nostrils that open forward or downward and nonprehensile tails. This group of monkeys lives in Africa and Asia, and includes langurs, mandrills, macaques, and baboons. Hominids typically have large brains and no tail. This group includes the apes—chimpanzees, gibbons, gorillas, and orangutans—and humans.

INTERNAL ANATOMY OF A FEMALE CHIMPANZEE

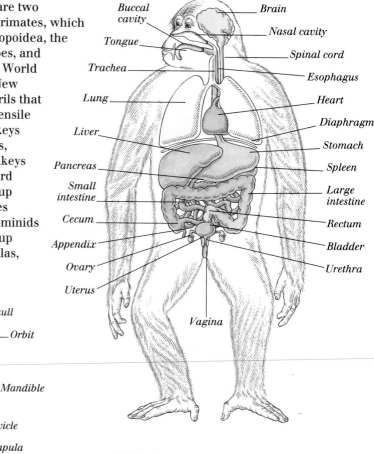

Buccal cavity
Tongue
Trachea
Lung
Liver
Pancreas
Small intestine
Cecum
Appendix
Ovary
Uterus
Vagina

Brain
Nasal cavity
Spinal cord
Esophagus
Heart
Diaphragm
Stomach
Spleen
Large intestine
Rectum
Bladder
Urethra

SKELETON OF A RHESUS MONKEY

Cervical vertebrae
Thoracic vertebrae
Lumbar vertebrae
Sacrum
Femur
Patella
Fibula
Pelvis
Caudal vertebrae
Tarsals
Metatarsals

Skull
Orbit
Mandible
Clavicle
Scapula
Rib
Humerus
Radius
Ulna
Carpals
Metacarpals
Phalanges
Phalanges

Tibia

SKULL OF A CHIMPANZEE

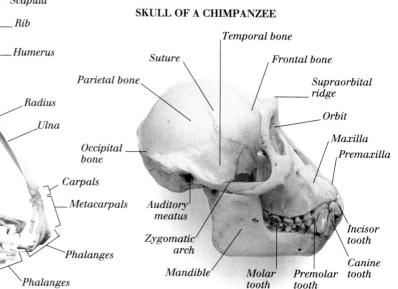

Suture
Parietal bone
Occipital bone
Auditory meatus
Zygomatic arch
Mandible
Molar tooth

Temporal bone
Frontal bone
Supraorbital ridge
Orbit
Maxilla
Premaxilla
Incisor tooth
Canine tooth
Premolar tooth

EXAMPLES OF PRIMATES

RING-TAILED LEMUR
(Lemur catta)
A prosimian

MALE RED HOWLER MONKEY
(Alouatta seniculus)
A New World monkey

MALE MANDRILL
(Mandrillus sphinx)
An Old World monkey

CHIMPANZEE
(Pan troglodytes)
An ape

**EXTERNAL FEATURES OF
A YOUNG GORILLA**

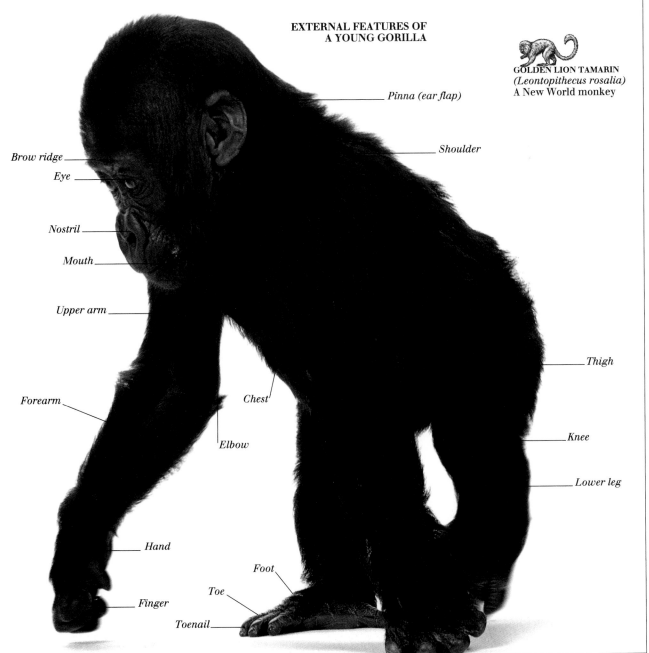

GOLDEN LION TAMARIN
(Leontopithecus rosalia)
A New World monkey

Pinna (ear flap)

Shoulder

Brow ridge

Eye

Nostril

Mouth

Upper arm

Thigh

Chest

Forearm

Elbow

Knee

Lower leg

Hand

Foot

Toe

Finger

Toenail

Dolphins, whales, and seals

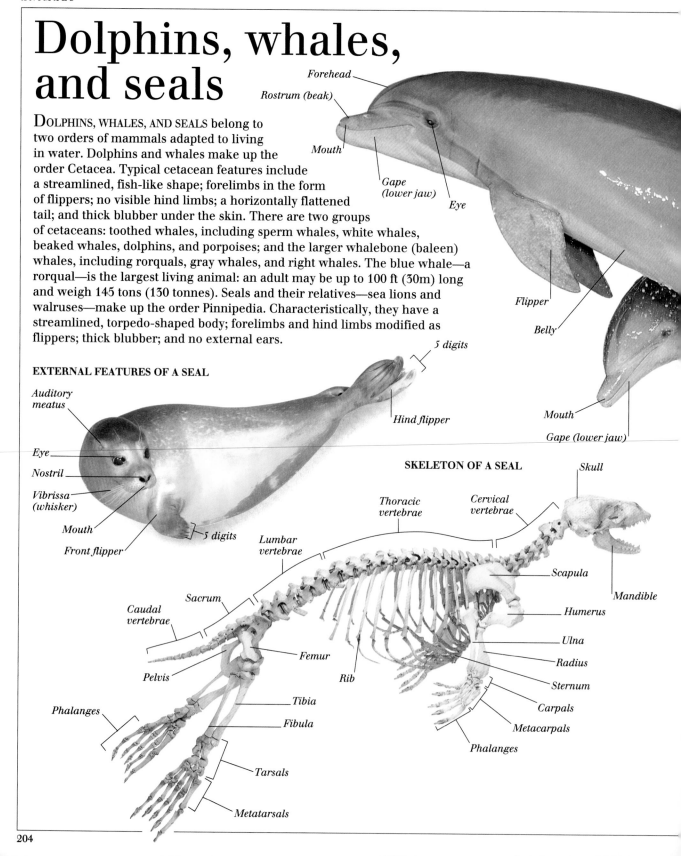

DOLPHINS, WHALES, AND SEALS belong to two orders of mammals adapted to living in water. Dolphins and whales make up the order Cetacea. Typical cetacean features include a streamlined, fish-like shape; forelimbs in the form of flippers; no visible hind limbs; a horizontally flattened tail; and thick blubber under the skin. There are two groups of cetaceans: toothed whales, including sperm whales, white whales, beaked whales, dolphins, and porpoises; and the larger whalebone (baleen) whales, including rorquals, gray whales, and right whales. The blue whale—a rorqual—is the largest living animal: an adult may be up to 100 ft (30m) long and weigh 145 tons (130 tonnes). Seals and their relatives—sea lions and walruses—make up the order Pinnipedia. Characteristically, they have a streamlined, torpedo-shaped body; forelimbs and hind limbs modified as flippers; thick blubber; and no external ears.

Forehead

Rostrum (beak)

Mouth

Gape (lower jaw)

Eye

Flipper

Belly

Mouth

Gape (lower jaw)

5 digits

Hind flipper

EXTERNAL FEATURES OF A SEAL

Auditory meatus

Eye

Nostril

Vibrissa (whisker)

Mouth

Front flipper

5 digits

SKELETON OF A SEAL

Skull

Thoracic vertebrae

Cervical vertebrae

Lumbar vertebrae

Scapula

Mandible

Sacrum

Humerus

Caudal vertebrae

Ulna

Radius

Femur

Sternum

Pelvis

Rib

Carpals

Phalanges

Tibia

Metacarpals

Fibula

Phalanges

Tarsals

Metatarsals

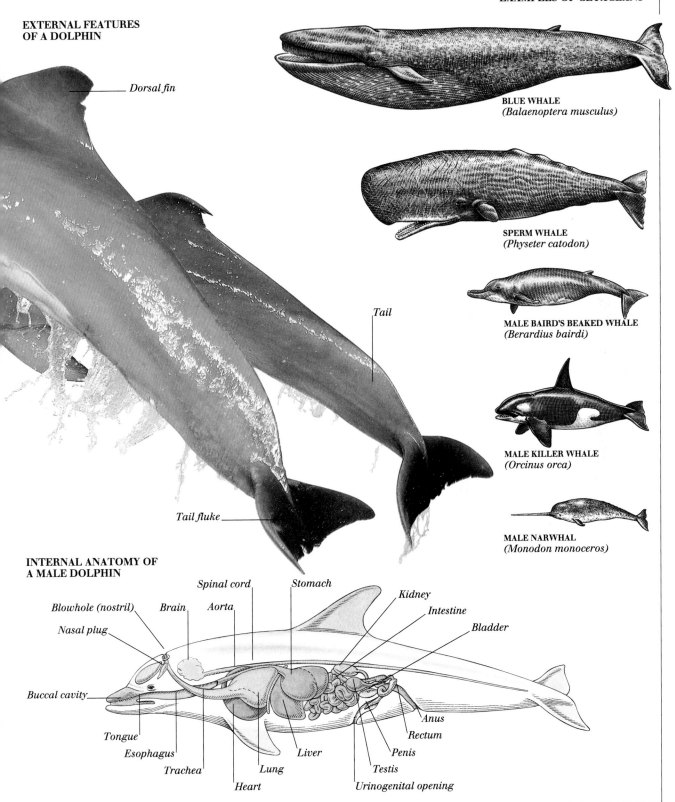

EXAMPLES OF CETACEANS

**EXTERNAL FEATURES
OF A DOLPHIN**

Dorsal fin

BLUE WHALE
(Balaenoptera musculus)

SPERM WHALE
(Physeter catodon)

MALE BAIRD'S BEAKED WHALE
(Berardius bairdi)

Tail

MALE KILLER WHALE
(Orcinus orca)

Tail fluke

MALE NARWHAL
(Monodon monoceros)

**INTERNAL ANATOMY OF
A MALE DOLPHIN**

Spinal cord

Stomach

Blowhole (nostril)

Brain

Aorta

Kidney

Intestine

Nasal plug

Bladder

Buccal cavity

Anus

Rectum

Tongue

Penis

Esophagus

Testis

Trachea

Liver

Urinogenital opening

Heart

Lung

205

Marsupials and Monotremes

MARSUPIALS AND MONOTREMES are two orders of mammals that differ from other mammalian groups in the ways that their young develop. The order Marsupalia, the pouched mammals, is made up of kangaroos and their relatives. Typically, marsupials give birth to their young at a very early stage of development. The young then crawls to the mother's pouch (which is on the outside of her abdomen), where it attaches itself to a nipple and remains until fully developed. Most marsupials live in Australia, although the opossums—which are classified as marsupials despite not having a pouch—live in the Americas. The order Monotremata is made up of the platypus and its relatives (the echidnas, or spiny anteaters). The monotremes are primitive mammals that lay eggs, which the mother incubates. The monotremes are found only in Australia and New Guinea.

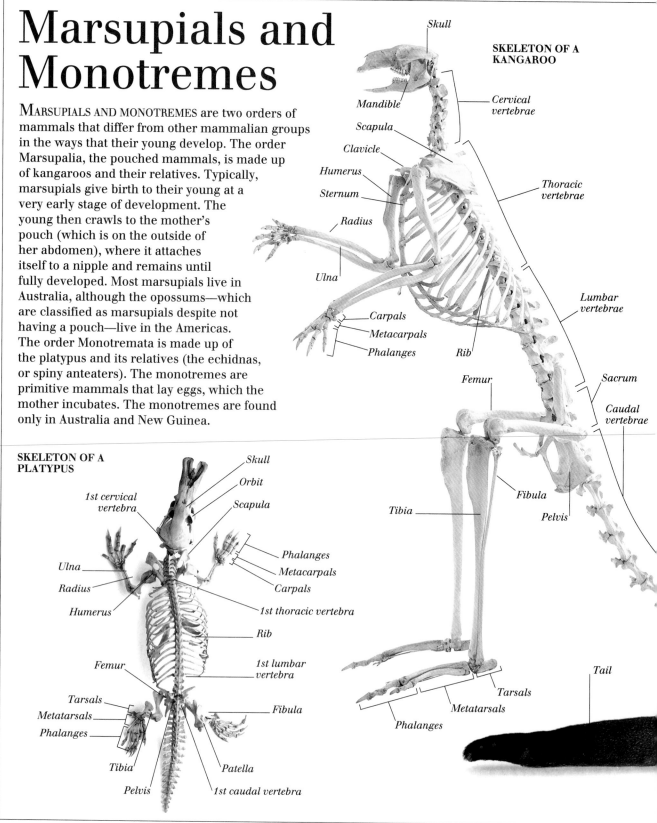

SKELETON OF A KANGAROO

Skull
Mandible
Cervical vertebrae
Scapula
Clavicle
Humerus
Sternum
Radius
Thoracic vertebrae
Ulna
Lumbar vertebrae
Carpals
Metacarpals
Phalanges
Rib
Femur
Sacrum
Caudal vertebrae
Fibula
Tibia
Pelvis
Tarsals
Metatarsals
Phalanges
Tail

SKELETON OF A PLATYPUS

Skull
Orbit
1st cervical vertebra
Scapula
Phalanges
Metacarpals
Carpals
Ulna
Radius
1st thoracic vertebra
Humerus
Rib
Femur
1st lumbar vertebra
Tarsals
Metatarsals
Phalanges
Fibula
Tibia
Patella
Pelvis
1st caudal vertebra

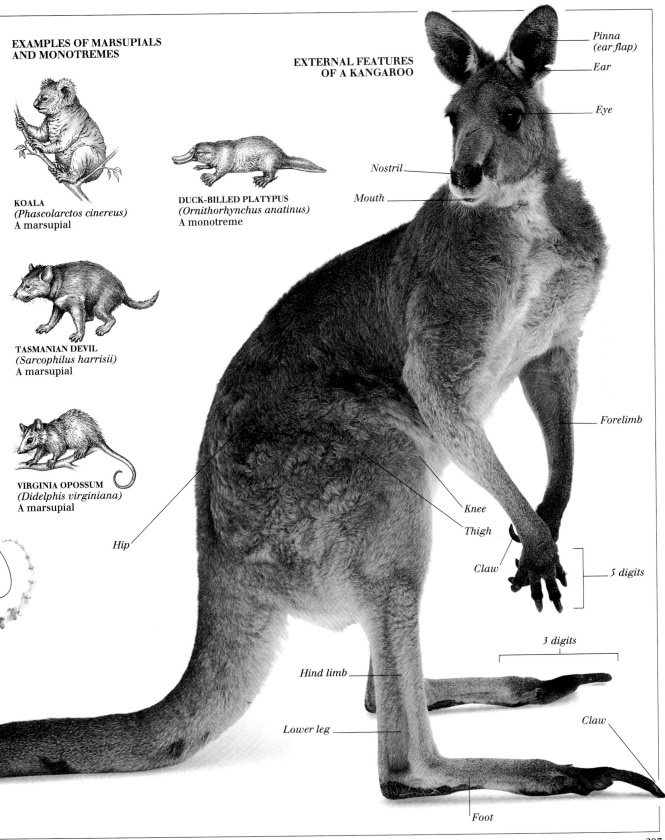

EXAMPLES OF MARSUPIALS AND MONOTREMES

EXTERNAL FEATURES OF A KANGAROO

KOALA
(Phascolarctos cinereus)
A marsupial

DUCK-BILLED PLATYPUS
(Ornithorhynchus anatinus)
A monotreme

TASMANIAN DEVIL
(Sarcophilus harrisii)
A marsupial

VIRGINIA OPOSSUM
(Didelphis virginiana)
A marsupial

Pinna (ear flap)

Ear

Eye

Nostril

Mouth

Forelimb

Knee

Thigh

Claw

5 digits

3 digits

Hip

Hind limb

Lower leg

Claw

Foot

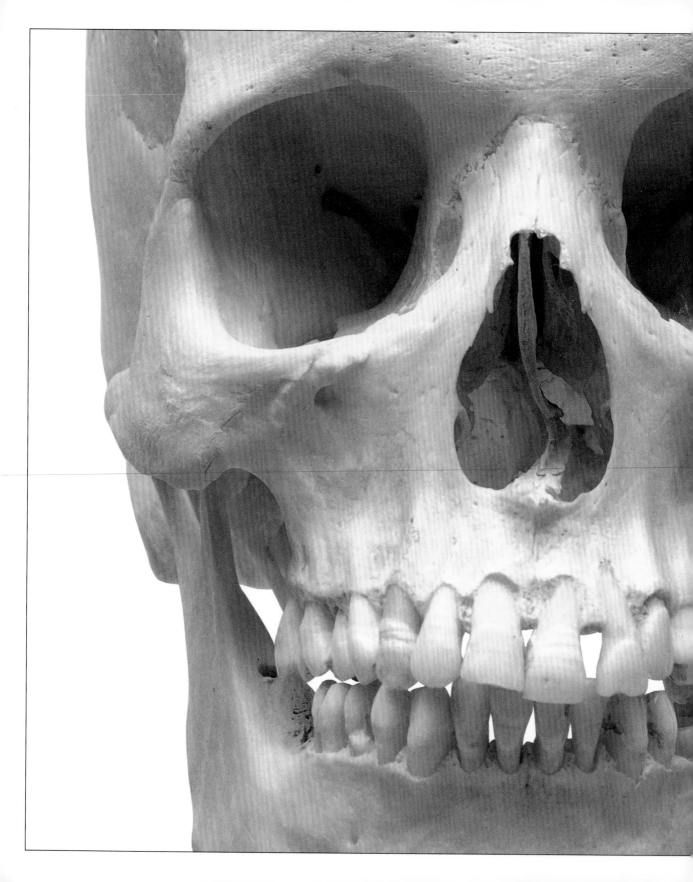

THE
HUMAN BODY

Body features

ALTHOUGH THERE IS enormous
variation between the external
appearances of humans, all bodies
contain the same basic features.
The outward form of the
human body depends on the
size of the skeleton, the shape
of the muscles, the thickness
of the fat layer beneath
the skin, the elasticity or
sagginess of the skin, and
the person's age and
gender. Males tend to be taller
than females, with broader
shoulders, more body hair,
and a different pattern of fat
deposits under the skin; the
female body tends to be
less muscular and has
a shallower and wider
pelvis to allow
for childbirth.

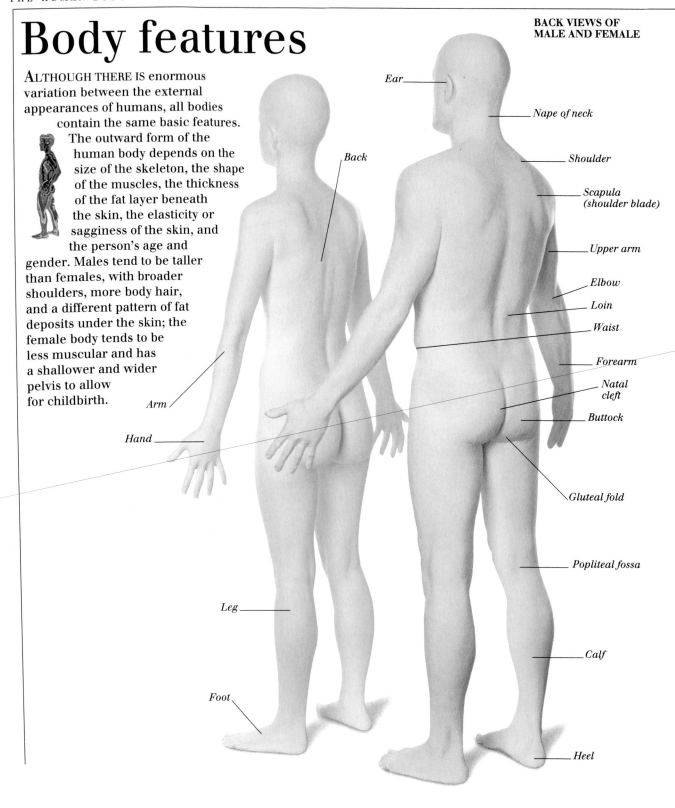

Ear

Nape of neck

Back

Shoulder

Scapula
(shoulder blade)

Upper arm

Elbow

Loin

Waist

Forearm

Natal
cleft

Arm

Buttock

Hand

Gluteal fold

Popliteal fossa

Leg

Calf

Foot

Heel

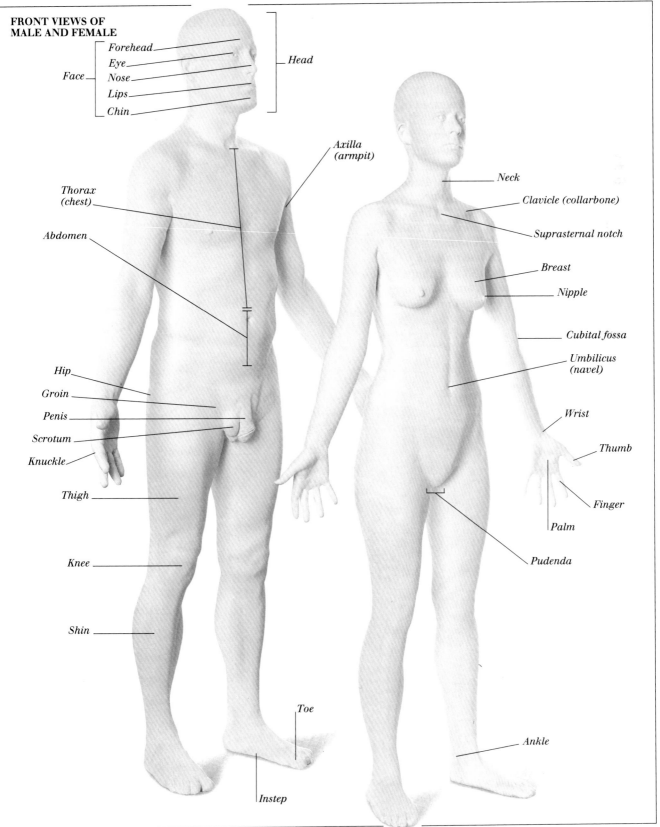

**FRONT VIEWS OF
MALE AND FEMALE**

Face

Forehead
Eye
Nose
Lips
Chin

Head

Axilla
(armpit)

Thorax
(chest)

Abdomen

Neck

Clavicle (collarbone)

Suprasternal notch

Breast

Nipple

Cubital fossa

Umbilicus
(navel)

Hip

Groin

Penis

Scrotum

Knuckle

Thigh

Knee

Shin

Wrist

Thumb

Finger

Palm

Pudenda

Toe

Ankle

Instep

Body organs

ALL THE VITAL BODY ORGANS except for the brain are enclosed within the trunk or torso (the body apart from the head and limbs). The trunk contains two large cavities separated by a muscular sheet called the diaphragm. The upper cavity, known as the thorax or chest cavity, contains the heart and lungs. The lower cavity, called the abdominal cavity, contains the stomach, intestines, liver, and pancreas, which all play a role in digesting food. Also within the trunk are the kidneys and bladder, which are part of the urinary system, and the reproductive organs, which hold the seeds of new human life. Modern imaging techniques, such as contrast X-rays and different types of scans, make it possible to see and study body organs without the need to cut through their protective coverings of skin, fat, muscle, and bone.

MAJOR INTERNAL STRUCTURES

Thyroid gland

Larynx

Heart

Right lung

Left lung

Diaphragm

Liver

Stomach

Large intestine

Small intestine

Greater omentum

IMAGING THE BODY

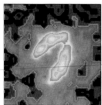

SCINTIGRAM OF HEART CHAMBERS

ANGIOGRAM OF RIGHT LUNG

CONTRAST X-RAY OF GALLBLADDER

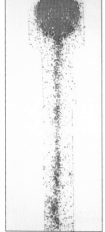

SCINTIGRAM OF NERVOUS SYSTEM

DOUBLE CONTRAST X-RAY OF COLON

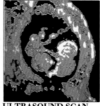

ULTRASOUND SCAN OF TWINS IN UTERUS

ANGIOGRAM OF KIDNEYS

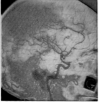

ANGIOGRAM OF ARTERIES OF HEAD

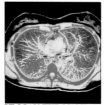

CT SCAN THROUGH FEMALE CHEST

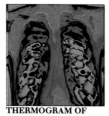

THERMOGRAM OF CHEST REGION

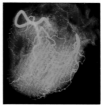

ANGIOGRAM OF ARTERIES OF HEART

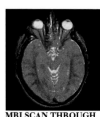

MRI SCAN THROUGH HEAD AT EYE LEVEL

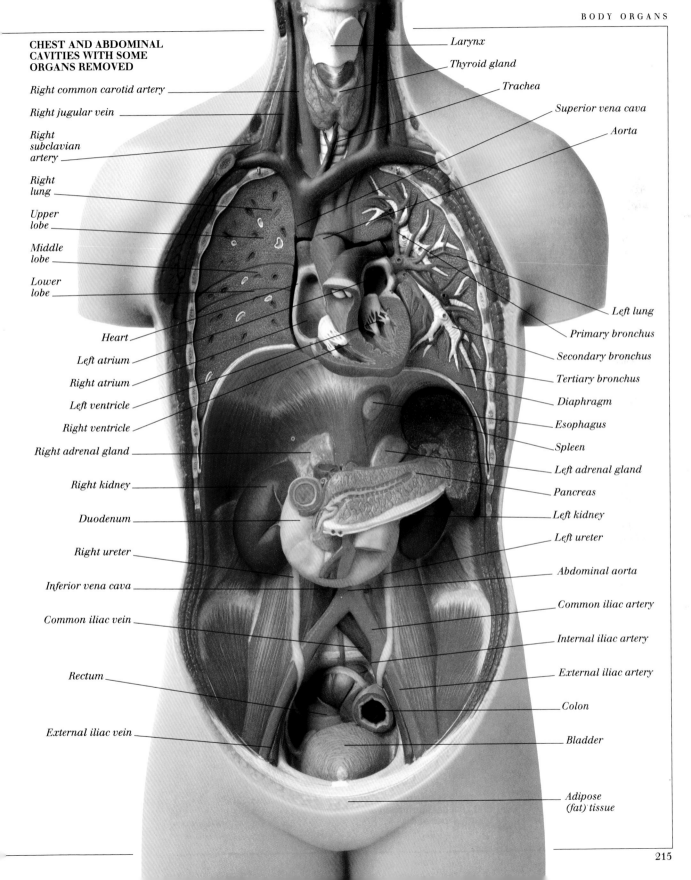

CHEST AND ABDOMINAL CAVITIES WITH SOME ORGANS REMOVED

Right common carotid artery

Right jugular vein

Right subclavian artery

Right lung

Upper lobe

Middle lobe

Lower lobe

Heart

Left atrium

Right atrium

Left ventricle

Right ventricle

Right adrenal gland

Right kidney

Duodenum

Right ureter

Inferior vena cava

Common iliac vein

Rectum

External iliac vein

Larynx

Thyroid gland

Trachea

Superior vena cava

Aorta

Left lung

Primary bronchus

Secondary bronchus

Tertiary bronchus

Diaphragm

Esophagus

Spleen

Left adrenal gland

Pancreas

Left kidney

Left ureter

Abdominal aorta

Common iliac artery

Internal iliac artery

External iliac artery

Colon

Bladder

Adipose (fat) tissue

Bones and joints

BONES FORM the body's hard, strong skeletal framework. Each bone has a hard, compact exterior surrounding a spongy, lighter interior. The long bones of the arms and legs, such as the femur (thigh bone), have a central cavity containing bone marrow. Bones are composed chiefly of calcium, phosphorus, and a fibrous substance known as collagen. Bones meet at joints, which are of several different types. For example, the hip is a ball-and-socket joint that allows the femur a wide range of movement, whereas finger joints are simple hinge joints that allow only bending and straightening. Joints are held in place by bands of tissue called ligaments. Movement of joints is facilitated by the smooth hyaline cartilage that covers the bone ends and by the synovial membrane that lines and lubricates the joint.

LIGAMENTS SURROUNDING HIP JOINT

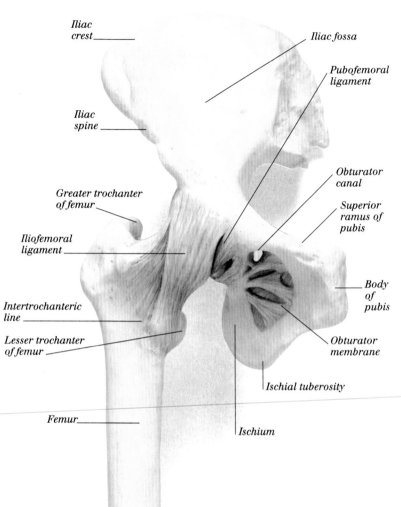

Iliac crest

Iliac fossa

Pubofemoral ligament

Iliac spine

Greater trochanter of femur

Obturator canal

Superior ramus of pubis

Iliofemoral ligament

Intertrochanteric line

Body of pubis

Lesser trochanter of femur

Obturator membrane

Ischial tuberosity

Femur

Ischium

SECTION THROUGH LEFT FEMUR

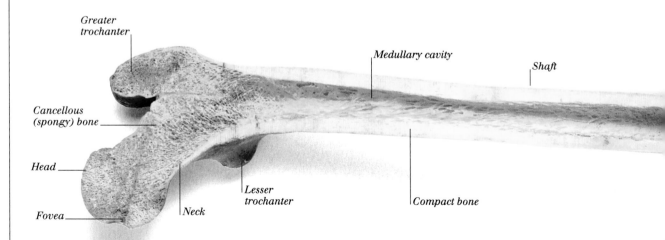

Greater trochanter

Medullary cavity

Shaft

Cancellous (spongy) bone

Head

Lesser trochanter

Compact bone

Fovea

Neck

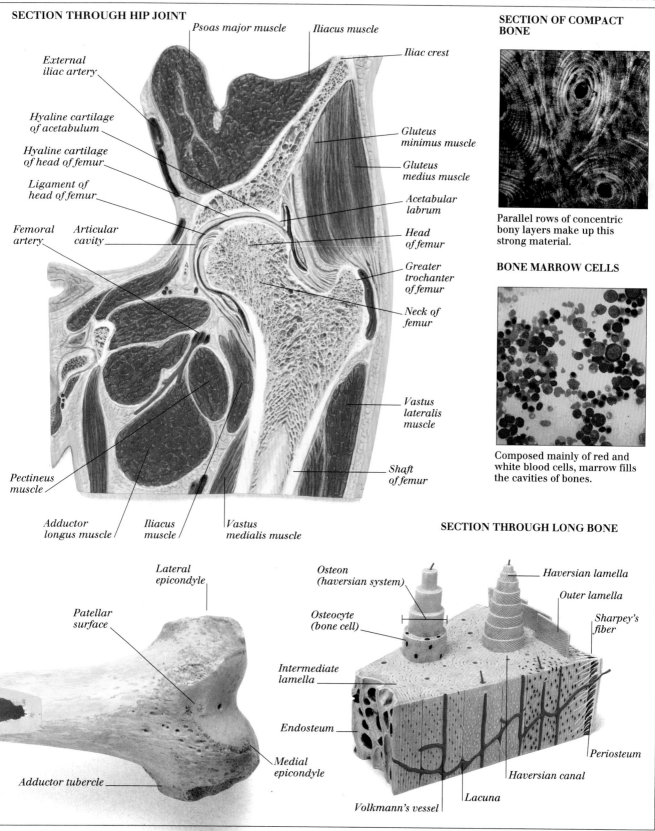

SECTION THROUGH HIP JOINT

Psoas major muscle

Iliacus muscle

External iliac artery

Iliac crest

Hyaline cartilage of acetabulum

Gluteus minimus muscle

Hyaline cartilage of head of femur

Gluteus medius muscle

Ligament of head of femur

Acetabular labrum

Femoral artery

Articular cavity

Head of femur

Greater trochanter of femur

Neck of femur

Vastus lateralis muscle

Pectineus muscle

Shaft of femur

Adductor longus muscle

Iliacus muscle

Vastus medialis muscle

SECTION OF COMPACT BONE

Parallel rows of concentric bony layers make up this strong material.

BONE MARROW CELLS

Composed mainly of red and white blood cells, marrow fills the cavities of bones.

SECTION THROUGH LONG BONE

Lateral epicondyle

Patellar surface

Osteon (haversian system)

Haversian lamella

Outer lamella

Osteocyte (bone cell)

Sharpey's fiber

Intermediate lamella

Endosteum

Medial epicondyle

Periosteum

Adductor tubercle

Haversian canal

Volkmann's vessel

Lacuna

Eye

THE EYE IS THE ORGAN OF SIGHT. The two eyeballs, protected within bony sockets called orbits and on the outside by the eyelids, eyebrows, and tear film, are directly connected to the brain by the optic nerves. Each eye is moved by six muscles, which are attached around the eyeball. Light rays entering the eye through the pupil are focused by the cornea and lens to form an image on the retina. The retina contains millions of light-sensitive cells, called rods and cones, which convert the image into a pattern of nerve impulses. These impulses are transmitted along the optic nerve to the brain. Information from the two optic nerves is processed in the brain to produce a single coordinated image.

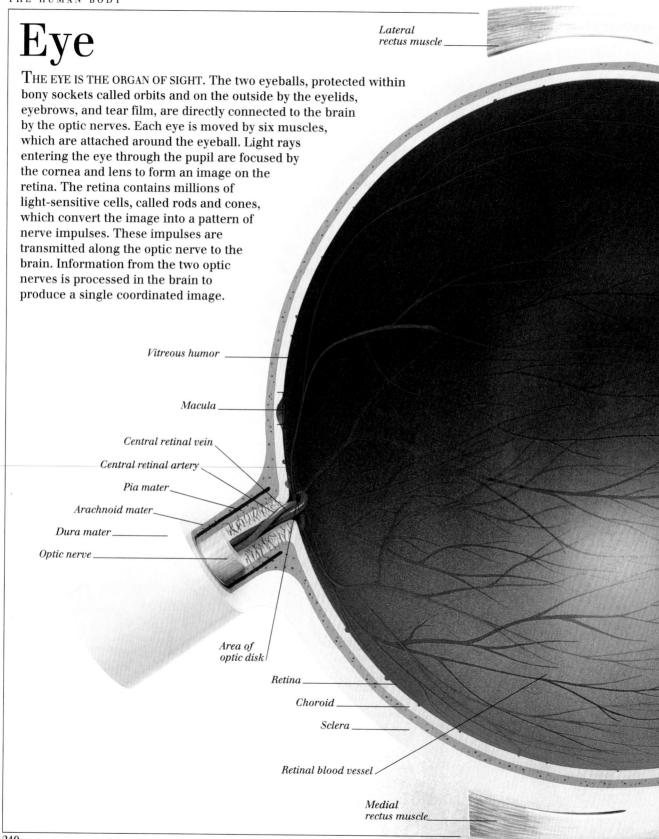

Lateral rectus muscle

Vitreous humor

Macula

Central retinal vein

Central retinal artery

Pia mater

Arachnoid mater

Dura mater

Optic nerve

Area of optic disk

Retina

Choroid

Sclera

Retinal blood vessel

Medial rectus muscle

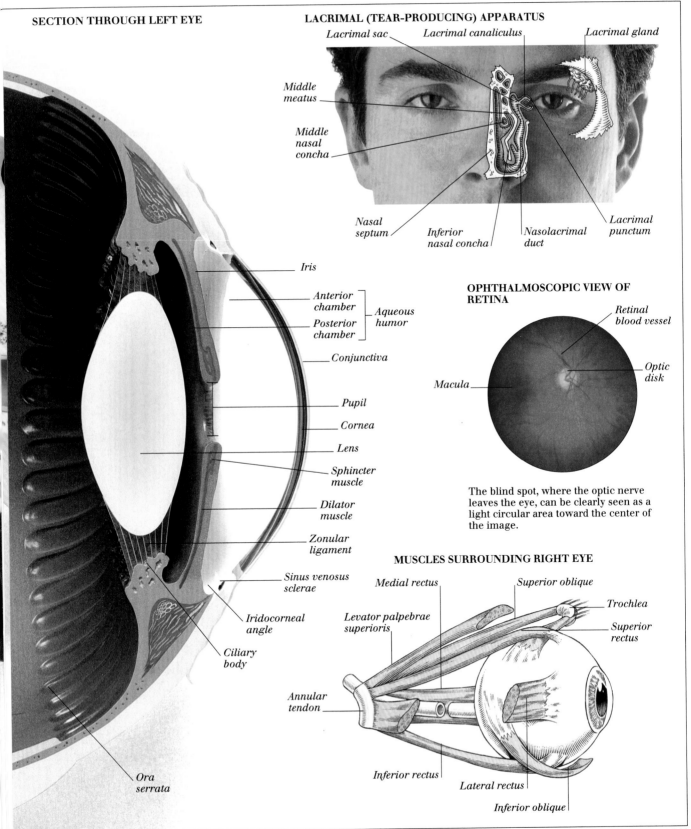

SECTION THROUGH LEFT EYE

LACRIMAL (TEAR-PRODUCING) APPARATUS

Lacrimal sac
Lacrimal canaliculus
Lacrimal gland
Middle meatus
Middle nasal concha
Nasal septum
Inferior nasal concha
Nasolacrimal duct
Lacrimal punctum

Iris

Anterior chamber
Posterior chamber
Aqueous humor

Conjunctiva

Pupil

Cornea

Lens

Sphincter muscle

Dilator muscle

Zonular ligament

Sinus venosus sclerae

Iridocorneal angle

Ciliary body

Ora serrata

OPHTHALMOSCOPIC VIEW OF RETINA

Retinal blood vessel
Optic disk
Macula

The blind spot, where the optic nerve leaves the eye, can be clearly seen as a light circular area toward the center of the image.

MUSCLES SURROUNDING RIGHT EYE

Medial rectus
Superior oblique
Trochlea
Levator palpebrae superioris
Superior rectus
Annular tendon
Inferior rectus
Lateral rectus
Inferior oblique

Urinary system

THE URINARY SYSTEM FILTERS WASTE PRODUCTS from the blood and removes them from the body via a system of tubes. Blood is filtered in the two kidneys, which are fist-sized, bean-shaped organs. The renal arteries carry blood to the kidneys; the renal veins remove blood after filtering. Each kidney contains about one million tiny units called nephrons. Each nephron is made up of a tubule and a filtering unit called a glomerulus, which consists of a collection of tiny blood vessels surrounded by the hollow Bowman's capsule. The filtering process produces a watery fluid that leaves the kidney as urine. The urine is carried via two tubes called ureters to the bladder, where it is stored until its release from the body through another tube called the urethra.

ARTERIAL SYSTEM OF KIDNEYS

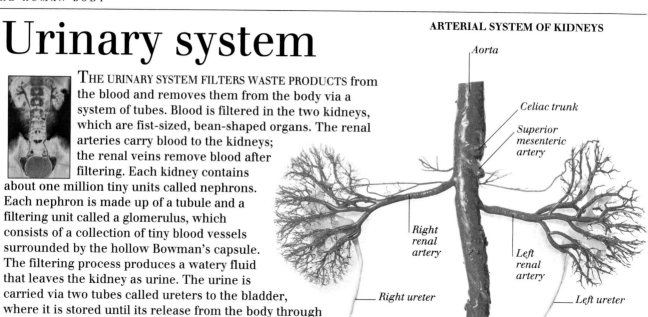

Aorta
Celiac trunk
Superior mesenteric artery
Right renal artery
Left renal artery
Right ureter
Left ureter

SECTION THROUGH LEFT KIDNEY

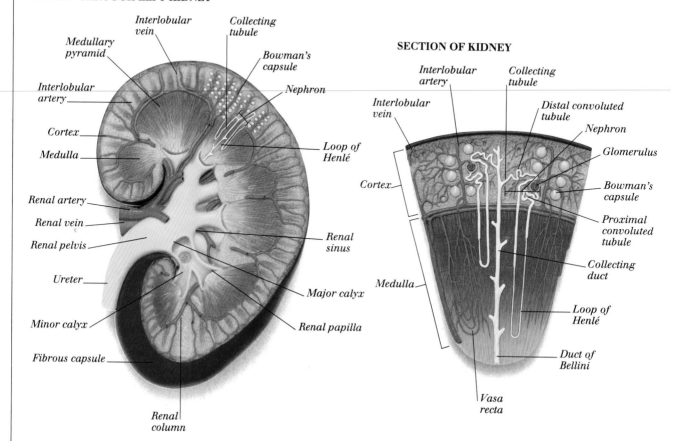

Interlobular vein
Medullary pyramid
Collecting tubule
Bowman's capsule
Interlobular artery
Nephron
Cortex
Medulla
Loop of Henlé
Renal artery
Renal vein
Renal pelvis
Renal sinus
Ureter
Minor calyx
Major calyx
Fibrous capsule
Renal papilla
Renal column

SECTION OF KIDNEY

Interlobular artery
Collecting tubule
Interlobular vein
Distal convoluted tubule
Nephron
Glomerulus
Cortex
Bowman's capsule
Proximal convoluted tubule
Medulla
Collecting duct
Loop of Henlé
Duct of Bellini
Vasa recta

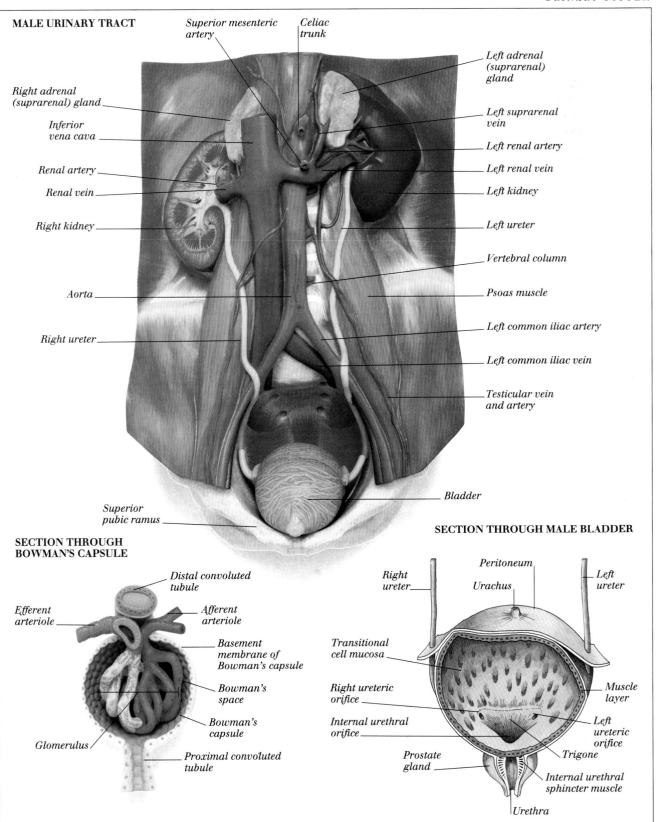

MALE URINARY TRACT

Superior mesenteric artery

Celiac trunk

Left adrenal (suprarenal) gland

Right adrenal (suprarenal) gland

Left suprarenal vein

Inferior vena cava

Left renal artery

Renal artery

Left renal vein

Renal vein

Left kidney

Right kidney

Left ureter

Vertebral column

Psoas muscle

Aorta

Left common iliac artery

Right ureter

Left common iliac vein

Testicular vein and artery

Bladder

Superior pubic ramus

SECTION THROUGH BOWMAN'S CAPSULE

Distal convoluted tubule

Efferent arteriole

Afferent arteriole

Basement membrane of Bowman's capsule

Bowman's space

Bowman's capsule

Glomerulus

Proximal convoluted tubule

SECTION THROUGH MALE BLADDER

Right ureter

Peritoneum

Urachus

Left ureter

Transitional cell mucosa

Right ureteric orifice

Muscle layer

Internal urethral orifice

Left ureteric orifice

Prostate gland

Trigone

Internal urethral sphincter muscle

Urethra

Development of a baby

A FERTILIZED EGG IS NOURISHED AND PROTECTED as it develops into an embryo and then a fetus during the 40 weeks of pregnancy. The placenta, a mass of blood vessels implanted in the uterus lining, delivers nourishment and oxygen, and removes waste through the umbilical cord. Meanwhile, the fetus lies snugly in its amniotic sac, a bag of fluid that protects it against any sudden jolts. In the last weeks of the pregnancy, the rapidly growing fetus turns head down: a baby ready to be born.

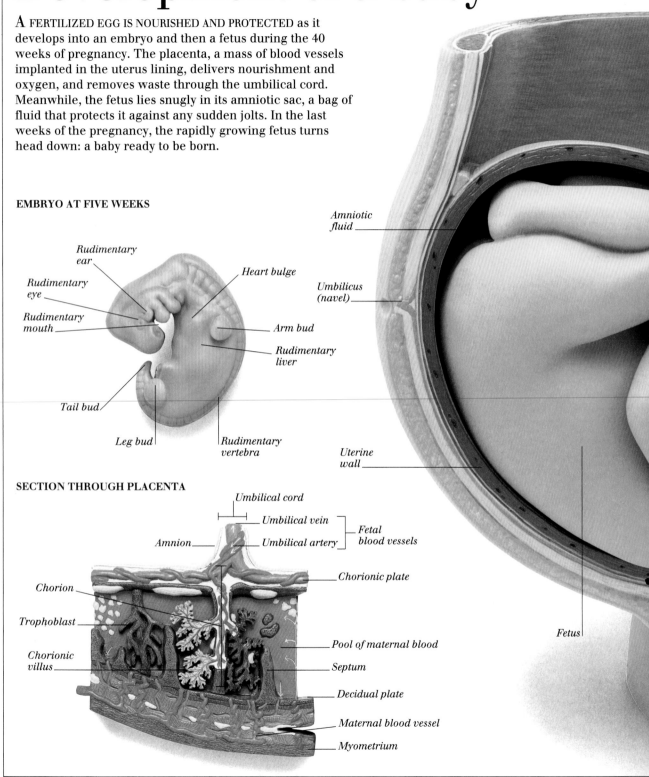

EMBRYO AT FIVE WEEKS

Rudimentary ear

Rudimentary eye

Rudimentary mouth

Heart bulge

Arm bud

Rudimentary liver

Tail bud

Leg bud

Rudimentary vertebra

Amniotic fluid

Umbilicus (navel)

Uterine wall

Fetus

SECTION THROUGH PLACENTA

Umbilical cord

Umbilical vein

Umbilical artery

Fetal blood vessels

Amnion

Chorionic plate

Chorion

Trophoblast

Chorionic villus

Pool of maternal blood

Septum

Decidual plate

Maternal blood vessel

Myometrium

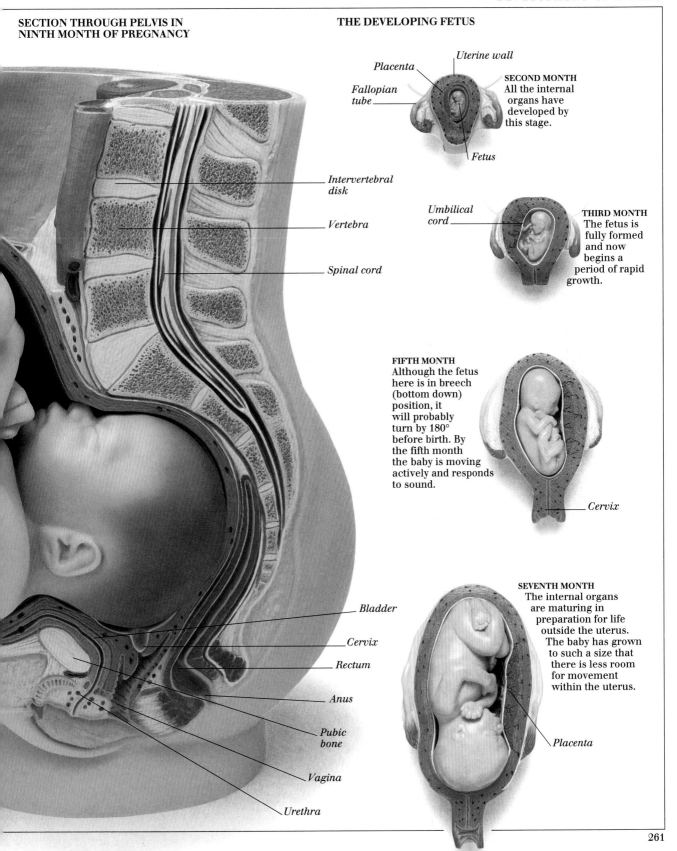

SECTION THROUGH PELVIS IN NINTH MONTH OF PREGNANCY

THE DEVELOPING FETUS

Uterine wall

Placenta

Fallopian tube

Fetus

SECOND MONTH
All the internal organs have developed by this stage.

Intervertebral disk

Vertebra

Spinal cord

Umbilical cord

THIRD MONTH
The fetus is fully formed and now begins a period of rapid growth.

FIFTH MONTH
Although the fetus here is in breech (bottom down) position, it will probably turn by 180° before birth. By the fifth month the baby is moving actively and responds to sound.

Cervix

SEVENTH MONTH
The internal organs are maturing in preparation for life outside the uterus. The baby has grown to such a size that there is less room for movement within the uterus.

Bladder

Cervix

Rectum

Anus

Pubic bone

Vagina

Placenta

Urethra

GEOLOGY, GEOGRAPHY, AND METEOROLGY

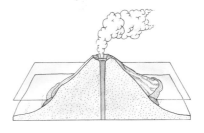

The rock cycle

HEXAGONAL BASALT COLUMNS, ICELAND

THE ROCK CYCLE IS A CONTINUOUS PROCESS through which old rocks are transformed into new ones. Rocks can be divided into three main groups: igneous, sedimentary, and metamorphic. Igneous rocks are formed when magma (molten rock) from the Earth's interior cools and solidifies (see pp. 274-275). Sedimentary rocks are formed when sediment (rock particles, for example) becomes compressed and cemented together in a process known as lithification (see pp. 276-277). Metamorphic rocks are formed when igneous, sedimentary, or other metamorphic rocks are changed by heat or pressure (see pp. 274-275). Rocks are added to the Earth's surface by crustal movements and volcanic activity. Once exposed on the surface, the rocks are broken down into rock particles by weathering (see pp. 282-283). The particles are then transported by glaciers, rivers, and wind and are deposited as sediment in lakes, deltas, deserts, and on the ocean floor. Some of this sediment undergoes lithification and forms sedimentary rock. This rock may be thrust back to the surface by crustal movements or forced deeper into the Earth's interior, where heat and pressure transform it into metamorphic rock. The metamorphic rock in turn may be pushed up to the surface or may be melted to form magma. Eventually, the magma cools and solidifies—below or on the surface—forming igneous rock. When the sedimentary, igneous, and metamorphic rocks are exposed once more on the Earth's surface, the cycle begins again.

THE ROCK CYCLE

Igneous rock

Cooling and solidification (crystallization)

Magma

Weathering, transport, and deposition

Sediment

Heat and pressure (metamorphism)

Weathering, transport, and deposition

Weathering, transport, and deposition

Compression and cementation (lithification)

Melting

Metamorphic rock

Heat and pressure (metamorphism)

Sedimentary rock

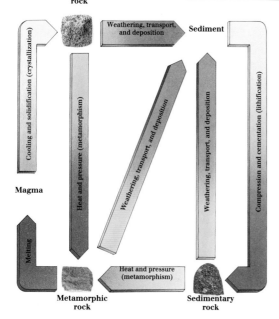

STAGES IN THE ROCK CYCLE

Magma extruded as lava, which solidifies to form igneous rock

Lava flow

Vent

Main conduit

Secondary conduit

Lava

Ash

Rock surrounding magma changed by heat to form metamorphic rock

Intense heat of rising magma melts some of the surrounding rock

Sedimentary rock crushed and folded to form metamorphic rock

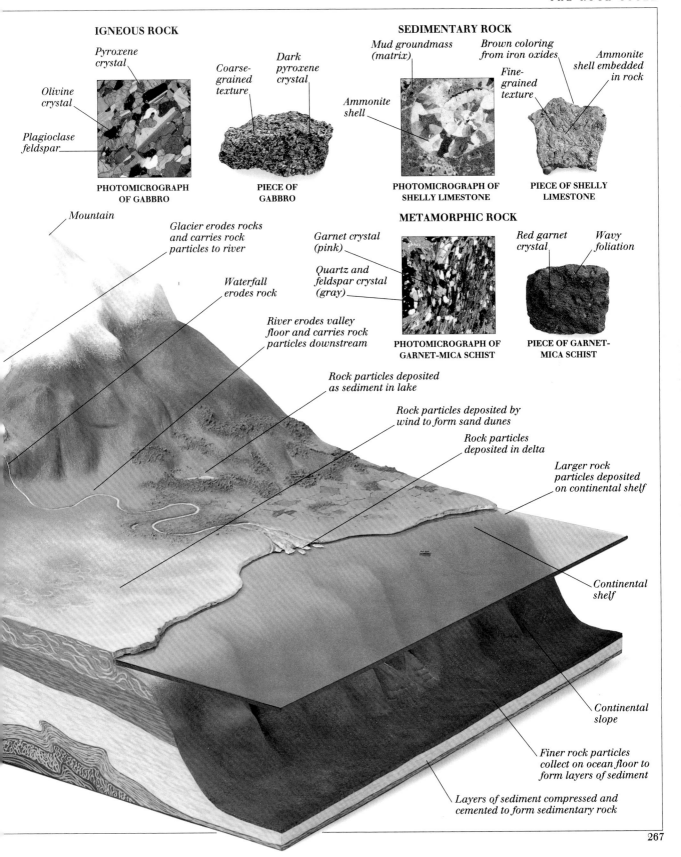

IGNEOUS ROCK

Pyroxene crystal

Olivine crystal

Plagioclase feldspar

PHOTOMICROGRAPH OF GABBRO

Coarse-grained texture

Dark pyroxene crystal

PIECE OF GABBRO

SEDIMENTARY ROCK

Mud groundmass (matrix)

Ammonite shell

PHOTOMICROGRAPH OF SHELLY LIMESTONE

Brown coloring from iron oxides

Fine-grained texture

Ammonite shell embedded in rock

PIECE OF SHELLY LIMESTONE

METAMORPHIC ROCK

Garnet crystal (pink)

Quartz and feldspar crystal (gray)

PHOTOMICROGRAPH OF GARNET-MICA SCHIST

Red garnet crystal

Wavy foliation

PIECE OF GARNET-MICA SCHIST

Mountain

Glacier erodes rocks and carries rock particles to river

Waterfall erodes rock

River erodes valley floor and carries rock particles downstream

Rock particles deposited as sediment in lake

Rock particles deposited by wind to form sand dunes

Rock particles deposited in delta

Larger rock particles deposited on continental shelf

Continental shelf

Continental slope

Finer rock particles collect on ocean floor to form layers of sediment

Layers of sediment compressed and cemented to form sedimentary rock

Minerals

A MINERAL IS A NATURALLY OCCURRING SUBSTANCE that has a characteristic chemical composition and specific physical properties, such as habit and streak (see pp. 270-271). A rock, by comparison, is an aggregate of minerals and need not have a specific chemical composition. Minerals are made up of elements (substances that cannot be broken down chemically into simpler substances), each of which can be represented by a chemical symbol. Minerals can be divided into two main groups: native elements and compounds. Native elements are made up of a pure element. Examples include gold (chemical symbol Au), silver (Ag), copper (Cu), and carbon (C); carbon occurs as a native element in two forms, diamond and graphite. Compounds are combinations of two or more elements. For example, sulfides are compounds of sulfur (S) and one or more other elements, such as lead (Pb) in the mineral galena, or antimony (Sb) in the mineral stibnite.

NATIVE ELEMENTS

Dendritic (branching) copper

Limonite groundmass (matrix)

COPPER
(Cu)

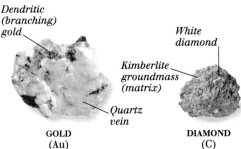

Dendritic (branching) gold

Quartz vein

GOLD
(Au)

White diamond

Kimberlite groundmass (matrix)

DIAMOND
(C)

Hexagonal graphite crystal

GRAPHITE
(C)

SULFIDES

Cubic galena crystal

GALENA
(PbS)

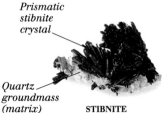

Prismatic stibnite crystal

Quartz groundmass (matrix)

STIBNITE
(Sb$_2$S$_5$)

Perfect octahedral pyrites crystal

Quartz crystal

PYRITES
(FeS$_2$)

OXIDES/HYDROXIDES

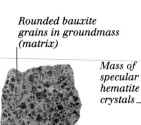

Milky quartz groundmass (matrix)

Smoky quartz crystal

SMOKY QUARTZ
(SiO$_2$)

Rounded bauxite grains in groundmass (matrix)

BAUXITE
(FeO(OH) and Al$_2$O$_5$.2H$_2$O)

Mass of specular hematite crystals

SPECULAR HEMATITE
(Fe$_2$O$_5$)

Parallel bands of onyx

ONYX
(SiO$_2$)

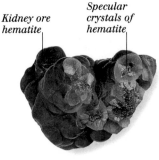

Kidney ore hematite

Specular crystals of hematite

KIDNEY ORE HEMATITE
(Fe$_2$O$_5$)

PHOSPHATES

Limonite groundmass (matrix)

Rock groundmass (matrix)

Radiating wavellite crystals

WAVELLITE
$(Al_3(PO_4)_2(OH,F)_3.5H_2O)$

Prismatic pyromorphite crystals

PYROMORPHITE
$(Pb_5(PO_4)_3Cl)$

CARBONATES

Striated cerussite crystal

Dog tooth calcite crystal

CERUSSITE
$(PbCO_3)$

CALCITE
$(CaCO_3)$

SULFATES

Rock groundmass (matrix)

Radiating crystal mass of daisy gypsum

Radiating cyanotrichite crystals

CYANOTRICHITE
$(Cu_4Al_2(SO_4)(OH)_{12}.2H_2O)$

DAISY GYPSUM
$(CaSO_4.2H_2O)$

MOLYBDATE

Tabular wulfenite crystal

Dark rock groundmass (matrix)

WULFENITE
$(PbMoO_4)$

SILICATES

Feldspar groundmass (matrix)

Transparent bicolored tourmaline crystal

Dodecahedral sodalite crystal

SODALITE
$(Na_8Al_6Si_6O_{24}Cl_2)$

Striated surface of olivine crystal

TOURMALINE
$(Na(Mg,Fe,Li,Mn,Al)_3Al_6(BO_3)_3Si_6.O_{18}(OH,F)_4)$

OLIVINE
$(Fe_2SiO_4 - Mg_2SiO_4)$

Striated prismatic epidote crystal

Tabular muscovite crystal

EPIDOTE
$(Ca_2(Al,Fe)_3(SiO_4)_3(OH))$

Orthoclase crystal

MUSCOVITE
$(KAl_2(Si_3Al)O_{10}(OH,F)_2)$

ORTHOCLASE
$(KAlSi_3O_8)$

HALIDES

Cubic rock salt crystal

Cubic fluorite crystal

GREEN FLUORITE
(CaF_2)

ORANGE HALITE (ROCK SALT)
$(NaCl)$

Mineral features

MINERALS CAN BE IDENTIFIED BY STUDYING features such as fracture, cleavage, crystal system, habit, hardness, color, and streak. Minerals can break in different ways. If a mineral breaks in an irregular way, leaving rough surfaces, it possesses fracture. If a mineral breaks along well-defined planes of weakness, it possesses cleavage. Specific minerals have distinctive patterns of cleavage. For example, mica cleaves along one plane. Most minerals form crystals that can be categorized into crystal systems according to their symmetry and number of faces. Within each system, several different but related forms of crystal are possible; for example, a cubic crystal can have six, eight, or twelve sides. A mineral's habit is the typical form taken by an aggregate of its crystals. Examples of habit include botryoidal (like a bunch of grapes) and massive (no definite form). The relative hardness of a mineral may be assessed by testing its resistance to scratching. This property is usually measured using Mohs' scale, which increases in hardness from 1 (talc) to 10 (diamond). The color of a mineral is not a dependable guide to its identity as some minerals have a range of colors. Streak (the color the powdered mineral makes when rubbed across an unglazed tile) is a more reliable indicator.

CLEAVAGE

Cleavage in one direction

CLEAVAGE ALONG ONE PLANE

Cleavage in three directions, forming a block cube

CLEAVAGE ALONG THREE PLANES

Horizontal cleavage

Vertical cleavage

CLEAVAGE ALONG TWO PLANES

Cleavage in four directions, forming a double-pyramid crystal

CLEAVAGE ALONG FOUR PLANES

CRYSTAL SYSTEMS

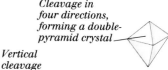

Cubic iron pyrites crystal

Tetragonal idocrase crystal

Representation of tetragonal system

TETRAGONAL SYSTEM

CUBIC SYSTEM

Representation of cubic system

FRACTURE

Fire opal with conchoidal (shell-like) fracture

CONCHOIDAL FRACTURE

Nickel-iron with hackly (jagged) fracture

HACKLY FRACTURE

Orpiment with uneven fracture

UNEVEN FRACTURE

Garnierite with splintery fracture

SPLINTERY FRACTURE

Hexagonal beryl crystal

Representation of hexagonal/trigonal system

HEXAGONAL/TRIGONAL SYSTEM

Monoclinic selenite crystal

Representation of monoclinic system

MONOCLINIC SYSTEM

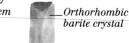

Orthorhombic barite crystal

Representation of orthorhombic system

ORTHORHOMBIC SYSTEM

Representation of triclinic system

Triclinic axinite crystal

TRICLINIC SYSTEM

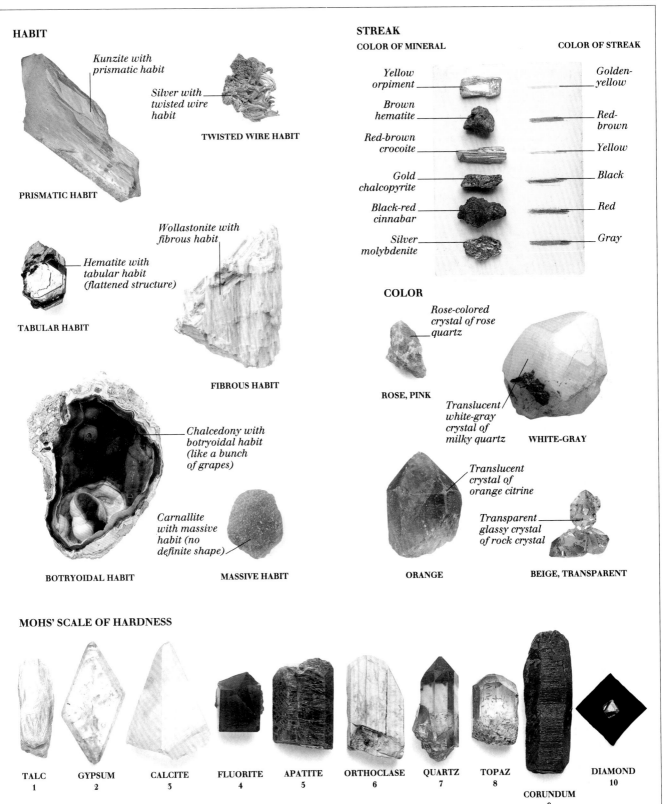

HABIT

Kunzite with prismatic habit

Silver with twisted wire habit

TWISTED WIRE HABIT

PRISMATIC HABIT

Wollastonite with fibrous habit

Hematite with tabular habit (flattened structure)

TABULAR HABIT

FIBROUS HABIT

Chalcedony with botryoidal habit (like a bunch of grapes)

Carnallite with massive habit (no definite shape)

BOTRYOIDAL HABIT

MASSIVE HABIT

STREAK

COLOR OF MINERAL

COLOR OF STREAK

Yellow orpiment — *Golden-yellow*

Brown hematite — *Red-brown*

Red-brown crocoite — *Yellow*

Gold chalcopyrite — *Black*

Black-red cinnabar — *Red*

Silver molybdenite — *Gray*

COLOR

Rose-colored crystal of rose quartz

ROSE, PINK

Translucent white-gray crystal of milky quartz

WHITE-GRAY

Translucent crystal of orange citrine

Transparent glassy crystal of rock crystal

ORANGE

BEIGE, TRANSPARENT

MOHS' SCALE OF HARDNESS

TALC
1

GYPSUM
2

CALCITE
3

FLUORITE
4

APATITE
5

ORTHOCLASE
6

QUARTZ
7

TOPAZ
8

CORUNDUM
9

DIAMOND
10

Volcanoes

VOLCANOES ARE VENTS OR FISSURES IN THE EARTH'S crust through which magma (molten rock that originates from deep beneath the crust) is forced onto the surface as lava. They occur most commonly along the boundaries of crustal plates; most volcanoes lie in a belt called the "Ring of Fire," which runs along the edge of the Pacific Ocean. Volcanoes can be classified according to the violence and frequency of their eruptions.

Nonexplosive volcanic eruptions generally occur where crustal plates pull apart. These eruptions produce runny basaltic lava that spreads quickly over a wide area to form relatively flat cones. The most violent eruptions take place where plates collide. Such eruptions produce thick rhyolitic lava and may also blast out clouds of dust and pyroclasts (lava fragments). The lava does not flow far before cooling and therefore builds up steep-sided, conical volcanoes. Some volcanoes produce lava and ash eruptions, which build up composite volcanic cones. Volcanoes that erupt frequently are described as active, those that erupt rarely are termed dormant, and those that have stopped erupting altogether are termed extinct. Besides the volcanoes themselves, other features associated with volcanic regions include geysers, hot mineral springs, solfataras, fumaroles, and bubbling mud pools.

Folded, rope-like surface

PAHOEHOE (ROPY LAVA)

HORU GEYSER, NEW ZEALAND

VOLCANO TYPES

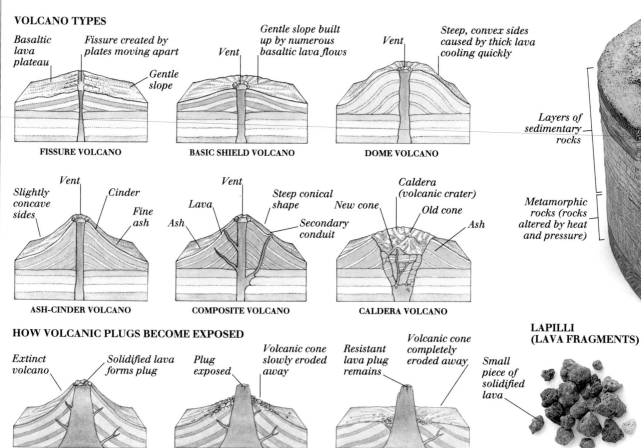

FISSURE VOLCANO
Basaltic lava plateau
Fissure created by plates moving apart
Gentle slope

BASIC SHIELD VOLCANO
Gentle slope built up by numerous basaltic lava flows
Vent

DOME VOLCANO
Vent
Steep, convex sides caused by thick lava cooling quickly

ASH-CINDER VOLCANO
Slightly concave sides
Vent
Cinder
Fine ash

COMPOSITE VOLCANO
Vent
Lava
Ash
Steep conical shape
Secondary conduit

CALDERA VOLCANO
Caldera (volcanic crater)
New cone
Old cone
Ash

Layers of sedimentary rocks

Metamorphic rocks (rocks altered by heat and pressure)

HOW VOLCANIC PLUGS BECOME EXPOSED

PLUG FORMATION
Extinct volcano
Solidified lava forms plug

INITIAL EROSION AROUND PLUG
Plug exposed
Volcanic cone slowly eroded away

COMPLETE DENUDATION OF PLUG
Resistant lava plug remains
Volcanic cone completely eroded away

LAPILLI (LAVA FRAGMENTS)
Small piece of solidified lava

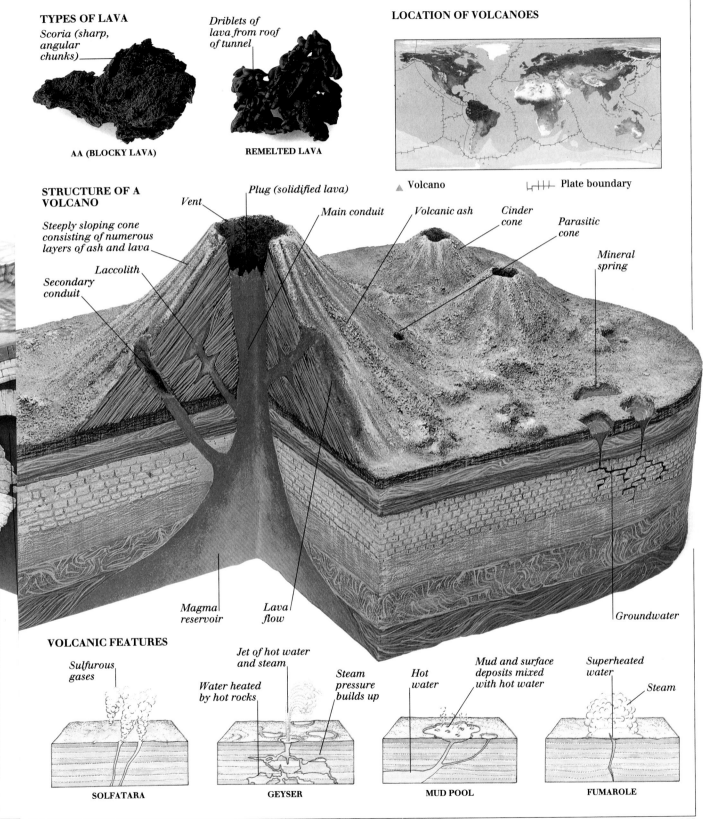

TYPES OF LAVA

Scoria (sharp, angular chunks)

Driblets of lava from roof of tunnel

AA (BLOCKY LAVA)

REMELTED LAVA

LOCATION OF VOLCANOES

▲ Volcano   Plate boundary

STRUCTURE OF A VOLCANO

Steeply sloping cone consisting of numerous layers of ash and lava

Laccolith

Secondary conduit

Vent

Plug (solidified lava)

Main conduit

Volcanic ash

Cinder cone

Parasitic cone

Mineral spring

Magma reservoir

Lava flow

Groundwater

VOLCANIC FEATURES

Sulfurous gases

SOLFATARA

Jet of hot water and steam

Water heated by hot rocks

Steam pressure builds up

GEYSER

Hot water

Mud and surface deposits mixed with hot water

MUD POOL

Superheated water

Steam

FUMAROLE

Rivers

RIVERS FORM PART of the water cycle—the continuous circulation of water between the land, sea, and atmosphere. The source of a river may be a mountain spring, or lake, or a melting glacier. The course that the river subsequently takes depends on the slope of the terrain and on the rock types and formations over which it flows. In its early, upland stages, a river tumbles steeply over rocks and boulders and cuts a steep-sided V-shaped valley. Farther downstream, it flows smoothly over sediments and forms winding meanders, eroding sideways to create broad valleys and plains. On reaching the coast, the river may deposit sediment, forming an estuary or delta (see pp. 290-291).

RIVER CAPTURE

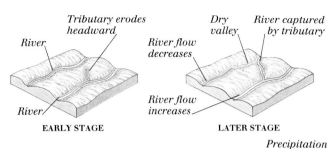

Tributary erodes headward
River
River
EARLY STAGE

Dry valley *River captured by tributary*
River flow decreases
River flow increases
LATER STAGE

SATELLITE IMAGE OF GANGES RIVER DELTA, BANGLADESH

River Ganges
Ganges delta
Infertile swampland *Distributary* *Large volume of sediment*

THE WATER CYCLE

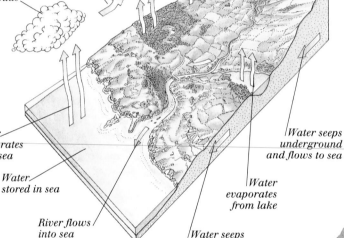

Precipitation falls on high ground
Wind
Water carried downstream by river
Water vapor released into atmosphere by trees and other plants
Wind
Water vapor forms clouds
Water seeps underground and flows to sea
Water evaporates from sea
Water stored in sea
Water evaporates from lake
River flows into sea
Water seeps underground and flows to sea

RIVER DRAINAGE PATTERNS

RADIAL

CENTRIPETAL

PARALLEL

DENDRITIC

DERANGED

TRELLISED

ANNULAR

RECTANGULAR

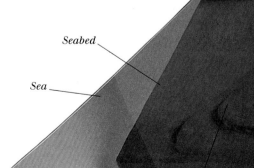

Seabed
Sea
Sediment layers

STAGES IN A RIVER'S DEVELOPMENT

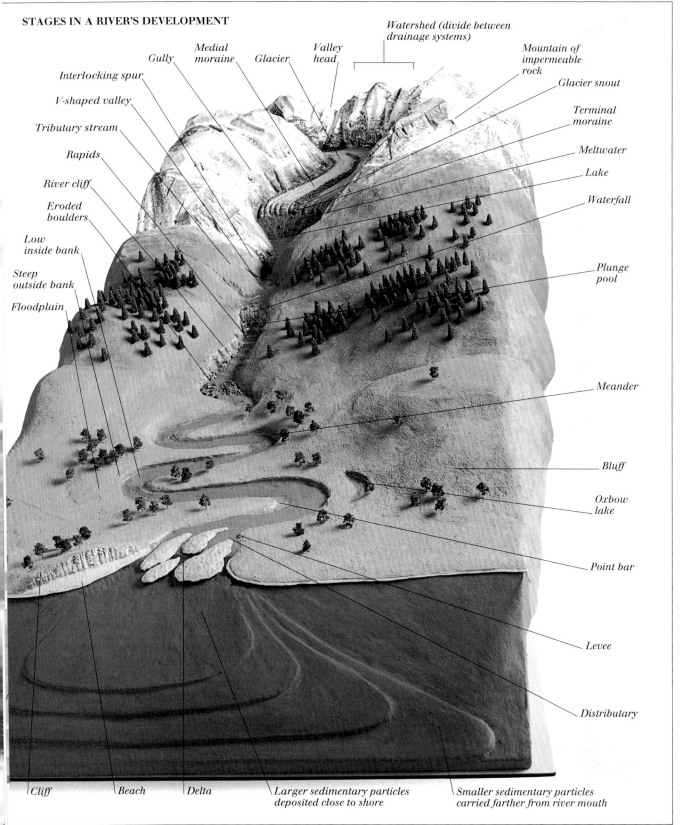

Watershed (divide between drainage systems)

Medial moraine

Gully

Glacier

Valley head

Interlocking spur

Mountain of impermeable rock

Glacier snout

V-shaped valley

Terminal moraine

Tributary stream

Meltwater

Rapids

Lake

River cliff

Waterfall

Eroded boulders

Low inside bank

Plunge pool

Steep outside bank

Floodplain

Meander

Bluff

Oxbow lake

Point bar

Levee

Distributary

Cliff   Beach   Delta   Larger sedimentary particles deposited close to shore   Smaller sedimentary particles carried farther from river mouth

Weather

WEATHER IS DEFINED AS THE ATMOSPHERIC CONDITIONS at a particular
time and place; climate is the average weather conditions for a given
region over time. Weather conditions include temperature, wind,
cloud cover, and precipitation, such as rain or snow. Good weather
is associated with high-pressure areas, where air is sinking. Cloudy,
wet, changeable weather is common in low-pressure zones with
rising, unstable air. Such conditions occur at temperate latitudes,
where warm air meets cool air along the polar fronts. Here, spiraling
low-pressure cells known as depressions (mid-latitude cyclones) often
form. A depression usually contains a sector of warmer air, beginning
at a warm front and ending at a cold front. If the two fronts merge,
forming an occluded front, the warm air is pushed upward. An
extreme form of low-pressure cell is a hurricane (also called a
typhoon or tropical cyclone), which brings torrential rain,
and exceptionally strong winds.

TYPES OF OCCLUDED FRONT

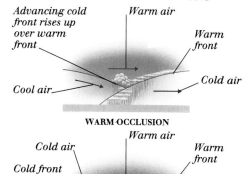

WARM OCCLUSION

COLD OCCLUSION

FORMS OF PRECIPITATION

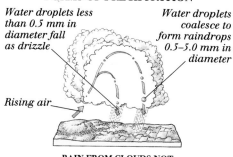

**RAIN FROM CLOUDS NOT
REACHING FREEZING LEVEL**

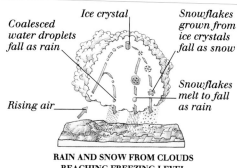

**RAIN AND SNOW FROM CLOUDS
REACHING FREEZING LEVEL**

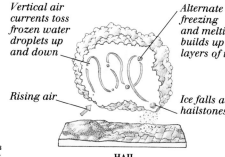

HAIL

TYPES OF CLOUD

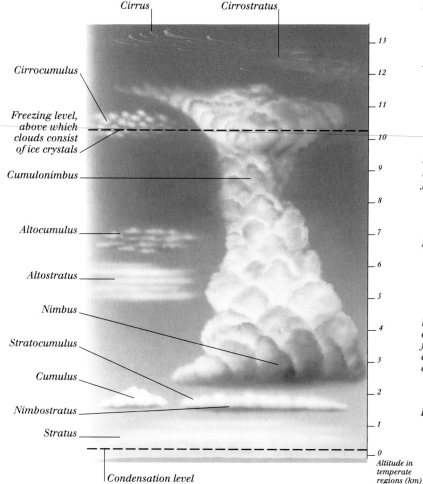

STRUCTURE OF A HURRICANE

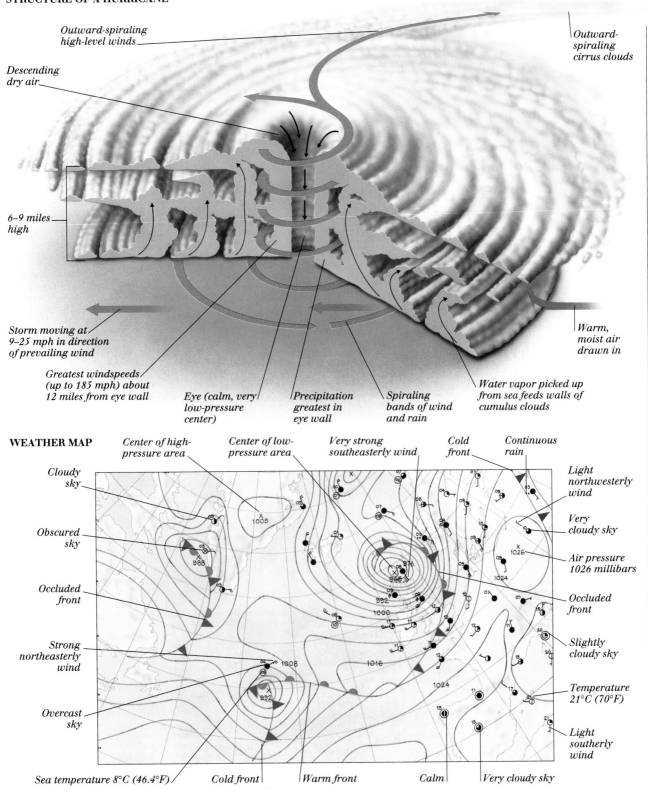

Outward-spiraling
high-level winds

Outward-
spiraling
cirrus clouds

Descending
dry air

6–9 miles
high

Storm moving at
9–25 mph in direction
of prevailing wind

Warm,
moist air
drawn in

Greatest windspeeds
(up to 185 mph) about
12 miles from eye wall

Eye (calm, very
low-pressure
center)

Precipitation
greatest in
eye wall

Spiraling
bands of wind
and rain

Water vapor picked up
from sea feeds walls of
cumulus clouds

WEATHER MAP

Center of high-
pressure area

Center of low-
pressure area

Very strong
southeasterly wind

Cold
front

Continuous
rain

Cloudy
sky

Light
northwesterly
wind

Obscured
sky

Very
cloudy sky

Air pressure
1026 millibars

Occluded
front

Occluded
front

Strong
northeasterly
wind

Slightly
cloudy sky

Overcast
sky

Temperature
21°C (70°F)

Light
southerly
wind

Sea temperature 8°C (46.4°F)   Cold front   Warm front   Calm   Very cloudy sky

Physics and Chemistry

The variety of matter

**PLANT AND INSECT
(LIVING MATTER)**

MATTER IS ANYTHING THAT OCCUPIES SPACE. It includes everything from natural substances, such as minerals or living organisms, to synthetic materials. Matter can exist in three distinct states—solid, liquid, and gas. A solid is rigid and retains its shape. A liquid is fluid, has a definite volume, and will take the shape of its container. A gas (also fluid) fills a space, so its volume will be the same as the volume of its container. Most substances can exist as a solid, a liquid, or a gas: the state is determined by temperature. At very high temperatures, matter becomes plasma, often considered to be a fourth state of matter. All matter is composed of microscopic particles, such as atoms and molecules (see pp. 308-309). The arrangement and interactions of these particles give a substance its physical and chemical properties, by which matter can be identified. There is a huge variety of matter because particles can arrange themselves in countless ways, in one substance or by mixing with others. Natural glass, for example, seems to be a solid but is, in fact, a supercool liquid: the atoms are not locked into a pattern and can flow. Pure substances known as elements (see p. 310) combine to form compounds or mixtures. Mixtures called colloids are made up of larger particles of matter suspended in a solid, liquid, or gas, while a solution is one substance dissolved in another.

TYPES OF COLLOID

HAIR GEL (SOLID IN LIQUID)

**SHAVING CREAM
(AIR IN LIQUID)**

**MIST
(LIQUID IN GAS)**

EXAMPLES OF MATTER

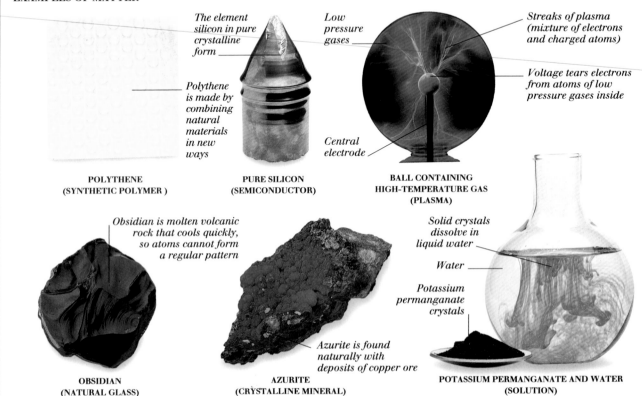

The element silicon in pure crystalline form

Low pressure gases

Streaks of plasma (mixture of electrons and charged atoms)

Polythene is made by combining natural materials in new ways

Voltage tears electrons from atoms of low pressure gases inside

Central electrode

**POLYTHENE
(SYNTHETIC POLYMER)**

**PURE SILICON
(SEMICONDUCTOR)**

**BALL CONTAINING
HIGH-TEMPERATURE GAS
(PLASMA)**

Obsidian is molten volcanic rock that cools quickly, so atoms cannot form a regular pattern

Solid crystals dissolve in liquid water

Water

Potassium permanganate crystals

Azurite is found naturally with deposits of copper ore

**OBSIDIAN
(NATURAL GLASS)**

**AZURITE
(CRYSTALLINE MINERAL)**

**POTASSIUM PERMANGANATE AND WATER
(SOLUTION)**

STATES OF MATTER

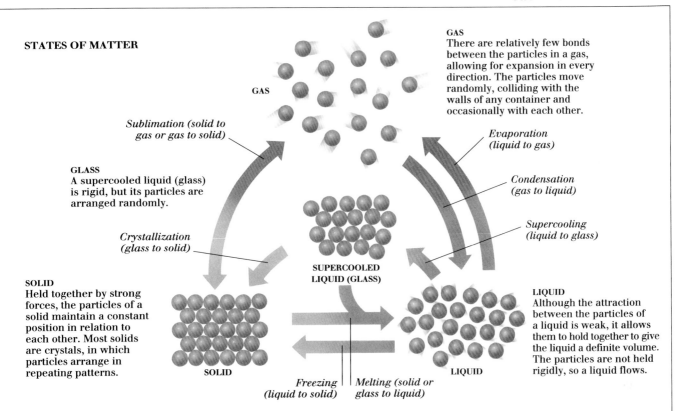

GAS

GAS
There are relatively few bonds between the particles in a gas, allowing for expansion in every direction. The particles move randomly, colliding with the walls of any container and occasionally with each other.

Sublimation (solid to gas or gas to solid)

Evaporation (liquid to gas)

GLASS
A supercooled liquid (glass) is rigid, but its particles are arranged randomly.

Condensation (gas to liquid)

Crystallization (glass to solid)

Supercooling (liquid to glass)

SUPERCOOLED LIQUID (GLASS)

SOLID
Held together by strong forces, the particles of a solid maintain a constant position in relation to each other. Most solids are crystals, in which particles arrange in repeating patterns.

LIQUID
Although the attraction between the particles of a liquid is weak, it allows them to hold together to give the liquid a definite volume. The particles are not held rigidly, so a liquid flows.

SOLID

LIQUID

Freezing (liquid to solid)

Melting (solid or glass to liquid)

CHANGING STATES OF WATER

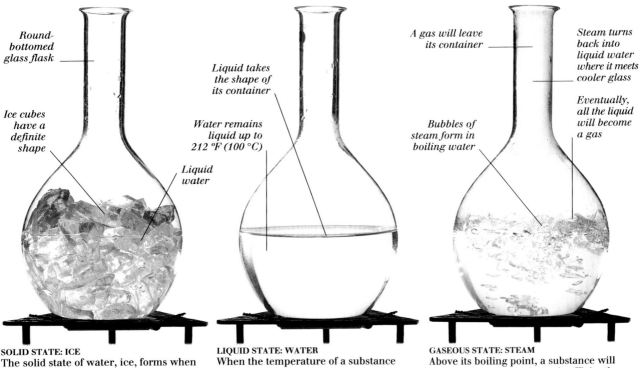

Round-bottomed glass flask

Ice cubes have a definite shape

Liquid water

Liquid takes the shape of its container

Water remains liquid up to 212 °F (100 °C)

A gas will leave its container

Bubbles of steam form in boiling water

Steam turns back into liquid water where it meets cooler glass

Eventually, all the liquid will become a gas

SOLID STATE: ICE
The solid state of water, ice, forms when liquid water is cooled sufficiently. Ice cubes are rigid, with a definite shape and volume.

LIQUID STATE: WATER
When the temperature of a substance rises above its freezing point, it melts to become a liquid. Ice changes to water.

GASEOUS STATE: STEAM
Above its boiling point, a substance will become a gas. When heated sufficiently, liquid water turns to steam, a colorless gas.

Force and motion

FORCES ARE PUSHES OR PULLS that change the motion of objects. To make a stationary object move, or a moving object stop, a force is needed. A force is also required to change the speed or direction of an object. This change in speed or direction is known as acceleration. Acceleration depends on the size (magnitude) of the force, and on the mass of the object. The effects of forces were first summarized by Isaac Newton in his three laws of motion. The international unit of force, named after him, is the newton (N), which is approximately equal to the weight of one apple. Gravity—the force of attraction between any two masses—can be measured using a newton meter (spring balance). Forces are put to useful effect in machines. A simple machine, such as a wheel and axle, is a device that changes the size or direction of an applied force. It allows an applied force (the effort) to produce another force (the load). A lever uses a bar that turns on a fulcrum to exert force. In all simple machines, there is a relationship between force and distance. A small force (in a compound pulley, for instance) moves through a large distance to lift a heavy object a small distance. This is called the Law of Simple Machines.

SIMPLE MACHINES

Single-pulley system (simple pulley)

Two-pulley system (simple pulley)

Four-pulley system (compound pulley)

Pulley wheel

Pulley wheel

Two pulley wheels

Simple pulley only changes direction of a force

Effort is the same size as the load (10 N) and is pulled the same distance

Effort is half the load (5 N), but the rope must be pulled twice the distance

Effort is one quarter of the load (2.5 N), but the rope must be pulled four times the distance

One rope attached to load

Two ropes share the force and distance

Four ropes share the force and distance

Load of 10 N

Pulley wheel

Load of 10 N

SIMPLE AND COMPOUND PULLEYS

Two pulley wheels

Load of 10 N

NEWTON METERS (SPRING BALANCES)

Weight is measured using a spring

When weight pulls downward, pointer moves along scale and measures force

Weight is 10 N

Weight is 20 N

Mass of 1 kg

Mass of 2 kg

WEIGHT AND MASS
The mass of an object is a measure of the quantity of matter that it possesses. Mass is usually measured in grams (g) or kilograms (kg). The weight of an object is the force exerted on the object's mass by gravity. Since weight is a force, its unit is the newton (N).

Wheel and axle multiplies the effort

Force is transmitted to the wheels by the chain

Pedal

Crank

Effort, provided by cyclist's muscles, is smaller than the load, but moves through a greater distance

A larger force, the load, is produced at the axle

WHEEL AND AXLE

A screw, acting like a wedge wrapped around a shaft, multiplies the effort

Effort, a turning force supplied through a screwdriver

Pitch (the angle of the screw thread)

The smaller the angle of pitch, the less force is required, but more turns are needed to move it through a greater distance

A larger force, the load, pulls the screw into wood

SCREW

Effort pushes axe into wood

A larger force, the load, moves through a smaller distance to push wood apart

Axe blade has wedge shape

Wedge multiplies effort

WEDGE

NEWTON'S THREE LAWS OF MOTION

NEWTON'S FIRST LAW
When no force acts on a body, it will continue in a state of rest or uniform motion.

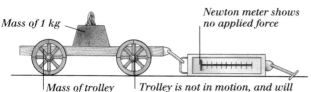

Mass of 1 kg

Newton meter shows no applied force

Mass of trolley is negligible

Trolley is not in motion, and will remain at rest until a force acts

NO FORCE, NO ACCELERATION: STATE OF REST

Constant speed

Mass of 1 kg

Newton meter shows no applied force

Trolley is in motion, and will continue at a constant speed in a straight line until a force acts

NO FORCE, NO ACCELERATION: UNIFORM MOTION

NEWTON'S SECOND LAW
When a force acts on a body, the motion of the body will change. The size of the change will depend upon the mass of the object and the magnitude of the applied force.

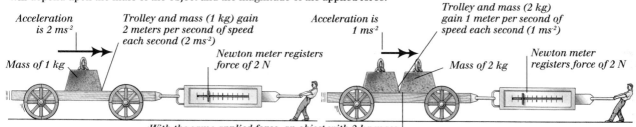

Acceleration is 2 ms^{-2}

Trolley and mass (1 kg) gain 2 meters per second of speed each second (2 ms^{-2})

Newton meter registers force of 2 N

Mass of 1 kg

Acceleration is 1 ms^{-2}

Trolley and mass (2 kg) gain 1 meter per second of speed each second (1 ms^{-2})

Newton meter registers force of 2 N

Mass of 2 kg

With the same applied force, an object with 2 kg mass accelerates at half the rate of object with 1 kg mass

FORCE AND ACCELERATION: SMALL MASS, LARGE ACCELERATION   **FORCE AND ACCELERATION: LARGE MASS, SMALL ACCELERATION**

NEWTON'S THIRD LAW
If one object exerts a force on another, an equal and opposite force, called the reaction force, is applied by the second object on the first.

Acceleration: the trolley and mass accelerate at 2 ms^{-2}

Newton meter registers force of 2 N to the left

Newton meters pull on each other with equal and opposite forces

Newton meter registers force of 2 N to the right

Mass of 1 kg

Person experiences a reaction force

ACTION AND REACTION

THREE CLASSES OF LEVER

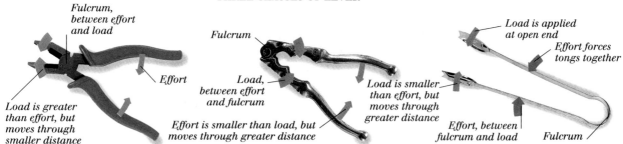

Fulcrum, between effort and load

Effort

Load is greater than effort, but moves through smaller distance

CLASS 1 LEVER
Pliers consist of two class 1 levers.

Fulcrum

Load, between effort and fulcrum

Effort is smaller than load, but moves through greater distance

CLASS 2 LEVER
Nutcrackers consist of two class 2 levers.

Load is applied at open end

Effort forces tongs together

Load is smaller than effort, but moves through greater distance

Effort, between fulcrum and load

Fulcrum

CLASS 3 LEVER
Tongs consist of two class 3 levers.

RAIL AND ROAD

Steam locomotives

WAGONS THAT ARE PULLED along tracks have been used to transport material since the 16th century, but these trains were drawn by men or horses until the invention of the steam locomotive. Steam locomotives enabled the basic railroad system to realize its true potential. In 1804, Richard Trevithick built the world's first working steam locomotive in South Wales. It was not entirely successful, but it encouraged others to develop new designs. By 1829, the British engineer Robert Stephenson had built the Rocket, considered to be the forerunner of the modern locomotive. The Rocket was a self-sufficient unit, carrying coal to heat the boiler and a water supply for generating steam. Steam passed from the boiler to force the pistons back and forth, and this movement turned the driving wheels, propelling the train forward. Used steam was then expelled in characteristic puffs. Later steam locomotives, like Ellerman Lines and the Mallard, worked in a similar way, but on a much larger scale. The simple design and reliability of steam locomotives ensured that they changed very little in 120 years of use, before being replaced in the 1950s by more efficient diesel and electric power (see pp. 326–329).

ROCKET STEAM LOCOMOTIVE, 1829

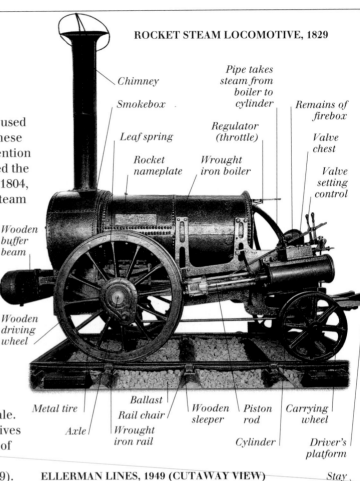

Chimney

Smokebox

Pipe takes steam from boiler to cylinder

Remains of firebox

Leaf spring

Regulator (throttle)

Valve chest

Rocket nameplate

Wrought iron boiler

Valve setting control

Wooden buffer beam

Wooden driving wheel

Metal tire

Axle

Ballast

Rail chair

Wrought iron rail

Wooden sleeper

Piston rod

Cylinder

Carrying wheel

Driver's platform

ELLERMAN LINES, 1949 (CUTAWAY VIEW)

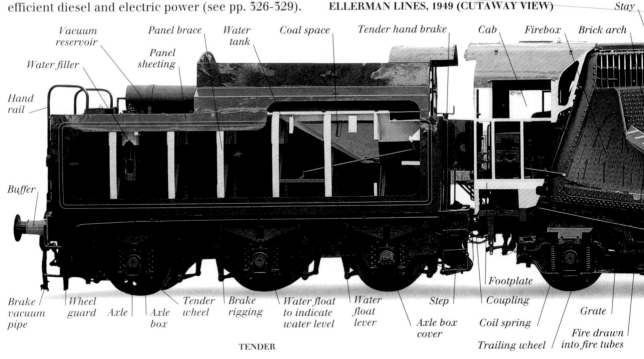

Vacuum reservoir

Panel brace

Water tank

Coal space

Tender hand brake

Cab

Firebox

Brick arch

Stay

Water filler

Panel sheeting

Hand rail

Buffer

Brake vacuum pipe

Wheel guard

Axle

Axle box

Tender wheel

Brake rigging

Water float to indicate water level

Water float lever

Axle box cover

Step

Coil spring

Trailing wheel

Footplate

Coupling

Grate

Fire drawn into fire tubes

TENDER

CAB INTERIOR OF MALLARD EXPRESS STEAM LOCOMOTIVE, 1938

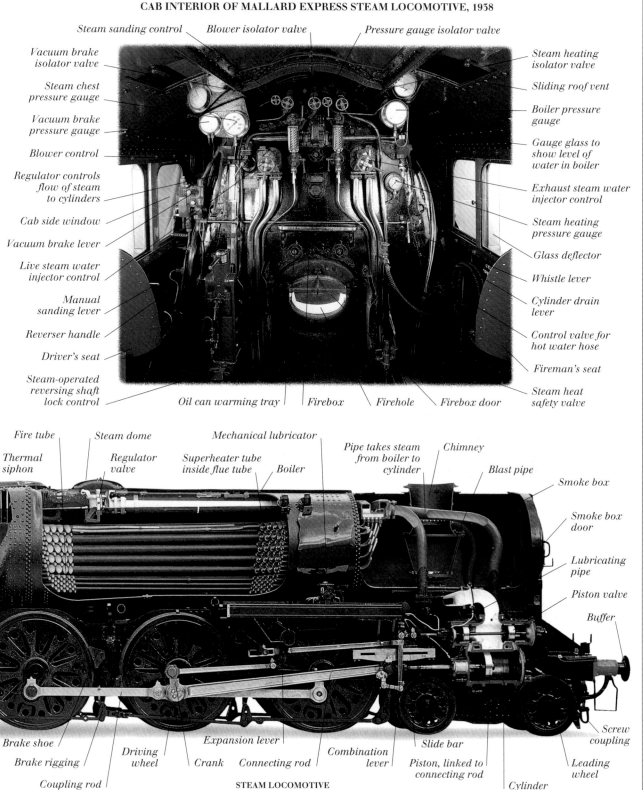

Steam sanding control

Blower isolator valve

Pressure gauge isolator valve

Vacuum brake isolator valve

Steam chest pressure gauge

Vacuum brake pressure gauge

Blower control

Regulator controls flow of steam to cylinders

Cab side window

Vacuum brake lever

Live steam water injector control

Manual sanding lever

Reverser handle

Driver's seat

Steam-operated reversing shaft lock control

Steam heating isolator valve

Sliding roof vent

Boiler pressure gauge

Gauge glass to show level of water in boiler

Exhaust steam water injector control

Steam heating pressure gauge

Glass deflector

Whistle lever

Cylinder drain lever

Control valve for hot water hose

Fireman's seat

Oil can warming tray

Firebox

Firehole

Firebox door

Steam heat safety valve

Fire tube

Thermal siphon

Steam dome

Regulator valve

Mechanical lubricator

Superheater tube inside flue tube

Boiler

Pipe takes steam from boiler to cylinder

Chimney

Blast pipe

Smoke box

Smoke box door

Lubricating pipe

Piston valve

Buffer

Brake shoe

Brake rigging

Coupling rod

Driving wheel

Crank

Expansion lever

Connecting rod

Combination lever

Slide bar

Piston, linked to connecting rod

Screw coupling

Leading wheel

Cylinder

STEAM LOCOMOTIVE

Diesel trains

RUDOLF DIESEL FIRST DEMONSTRATED the diesel engine in
Germany in 1898, but it was not until the 1940s that diesel
locomotives were successfully established on both passenger
and freight services in the U.S. Early diesel locomotives like
the Union Pacific were more expensive to build than steam
locomotives, but were more efficient and cheaper to operate,
especially where oil was plentiful. One feature of diesel engines
is that the power output cannot be coupled directly to the wheels.
To convert the mechanical energy produced by diesel engines,
a transmission system is needed. Almost all diesel locomotives
have electric transmissions, and are known as diesel-electric
locomotives. The diesel engine works by drawing air into the
cylinders and compressing it to increase its temperature; a small
quantity of diesel fuel is then injected into it. The resulting
combustion drives the generator (more recently an alternator)
to produce electricity, which is fed to electric motors connected
to the wheels. Diesel-electric locomotives are essentially
electric locomotives that carry their own power plants, and
are used worldwide today. The Deltic diesel-electric
locomotive, similar to the one shown here, replaced
classic express steam locomotives, and ran
at speeds up to 100 mph.

**FRONT VIEW OF UNION PACIFIC
DIESEL-ELECTRIC LOCOMOTIVE, 1950s**

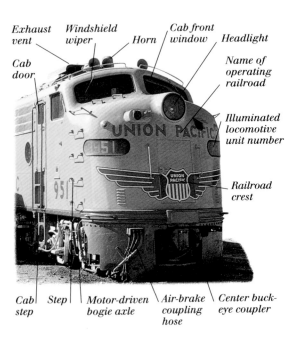

Exhaust vent · Windshield wiper · Horn · Cab front window · Headlight · Cab door · Name of operating railroad · Illuminated locomotive unit number · Railroad crest · Cab step · Step · Motor-driven bogie axle · Air-brake coupling hose · Center buck-eye coupler

PROTOTYPE DELTIC DIESEL-ELECTRIC LOCOMOTIVE, 1956

Engine room vent · Inspection hatch · Engine exhaust port · Radiator fan · Engine room window · Engine room vent · Fuel tank · Water for heating boiler · Inspection socket · Folding step · Drain for radiator coolant · Radiator coolant · Sand box · Telescopic damper · Drain for control reservoir

DELTIC

DIESEL ENGINE OF BRITISH RAIL CLASS 20 DIESEL-ELECTRIC LOCOMOTIVE

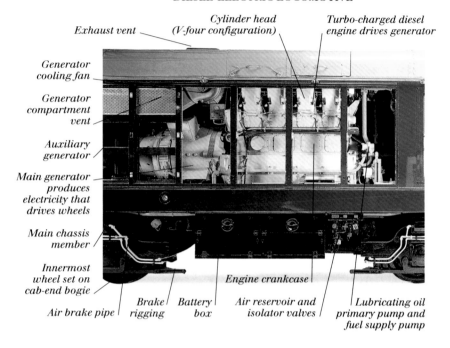

Exhaust vent

Cylinder head (V-four configuration)

Turbo-charged diesel engine drives generator

Generator cooling fan

Generator compartment vent

Auxiliary generator

Main generator produces electricity that drives wheels

Main chassis member

Innermost wheel set on cab-end bogie

Air brake pipe

Brake rigging

Battery box

Engine crankcase

Air reservoir and isolator valves

Lubricating oil primary pump and fuel supply pump

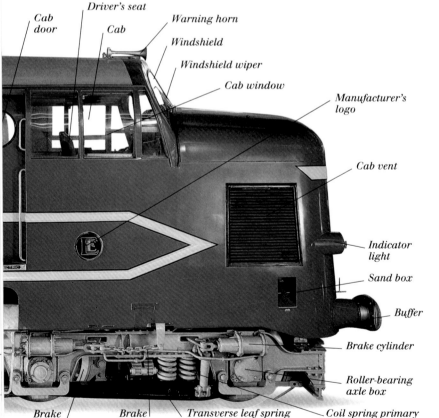

Cab door

Driver's seat

Cab

Warning horn

Windshield

Windshield wiper

Cab window

Manufacturer's logo

Cab vent

Indicator light

Sand box

Buffer

Brake cylinder

Roller-bearing axle box

Brake shoe

Brake actuating chain

Transverse leaf spring secondary suspension

Coil spring primary suspension

EXAMPLES OF FREIGHT CARS

BOX CAR

HOPPER CAR

REFRIGERATOR CAR

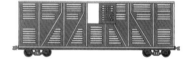

LIVESTOCK CAR

FLAT CAR WITH BULKHEADS

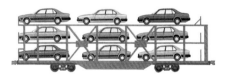

AUTOMOBILE CAR

Elegance and utility

DURING THE FIRST DECADE OF THIS CENTURY, the motorist who could afford it had a choice of some of the finest cars ever made. These handbuilt cars were powerful and luxurious, using the finest wood, leather, and cloth, and bodywork made to the customer's individual requirements. Some had six-cylinder engines as big as 15 liters. The price of such cars was several times that of an average house, and their yearly running costs were also very high. As a result, basic, utilitarian cars became popular. Costing perhaps one-tenth of the price of a luxury car, these cars had very little trim and often had only single-cylinder engines.

1904 OLDSMOBILE SINGLE-CYLINDER ENGINE

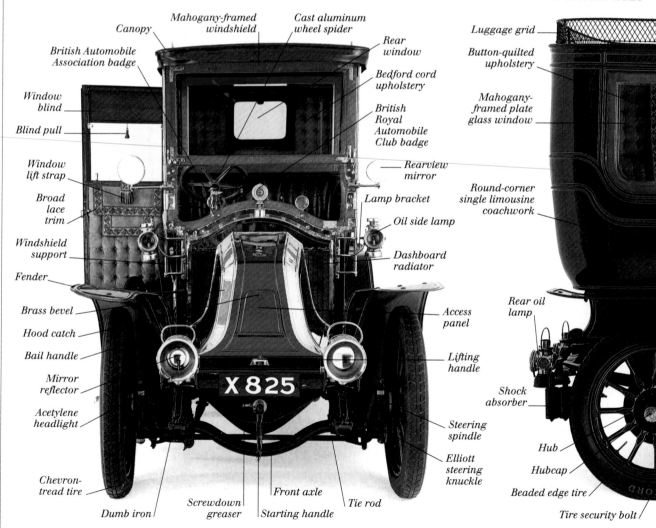

FRONT VIEW OF 1906 RENAULT

SIDE VIEW OF 1906 RENAULT

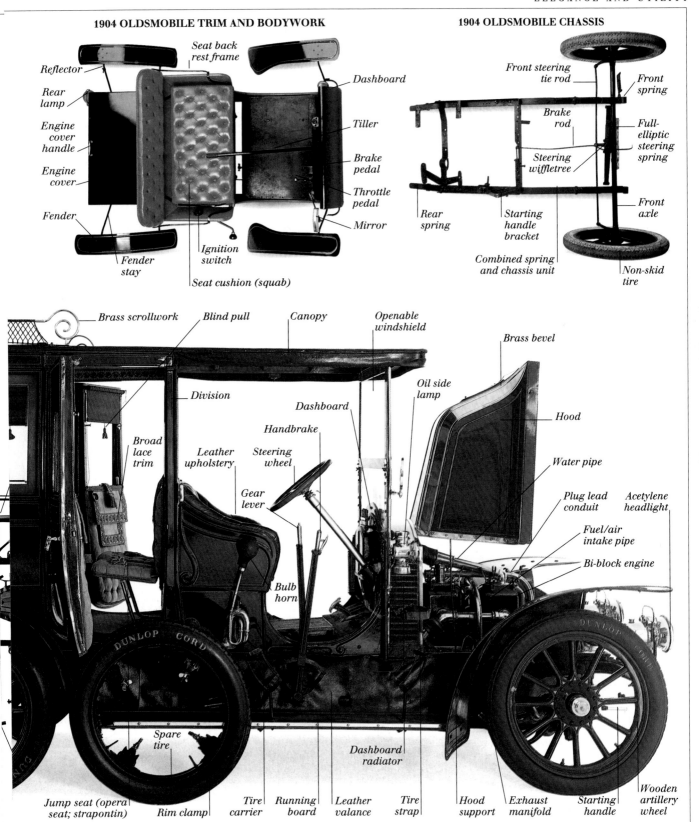

1904 OLDSMOBILE TRIM AND BODYWORK

Seat back rest frame

Reflector

Rear lamp

Engine cover handle

Engine cover

Fender

Fender stay

Ignition switch

Seat cushion (squab)

Dashboard

Tiller

Brake pedal

Throttle pedal

Mirror

1904 OLDSMOBILE CHASSIS

Front steering tie rod

Brake rod

Steering wiffletree

Rear spring

Starting handle bracket

Combined spring and chassis unit

Front spring

Full-elliptic steering spring

Front axle

Non-skid tire

Brass scrollwork

Blind pull

Canopy

Openable windshield

Brass bevel

Division

Dashboard

Oil side lamp

Hood

Broad lace trim

Leather upholstery

Steering wheel

Handbrake

Water pipe

Gear lever

Plug lead conduit

Acetylene headlight

Fuel/air intake pipe

Bi-block engine

Bulb horn

Jump seat (opera seat; strapontin)

Spare tire

Rim clamp

Tire carrier

Running board

Leather valance

Dashboard radiator

Tire strap

Hood support

Exhaust manifold

Starting handle

Wooden artillery wheel

337

Modern trim

A MODERN CAR HAS TWO TYPES OF TRIM, according to the materials used: hard (chrome and plastics) and soft (upholstered materials). Safety and comfort are priorities in the trim's design: seats help the occupants maintain a comfortable posture, rubber seals keep out dirt and moisture, and headlights light the way. Older cars had interior or leather paneling cut and fitted by craftsmen; modern cars use precisely molded plastics and seat fabrics cut by robot-controlled lasers to reduce costs and production time. Doors are now assembled off the production line so that complex wiring can be built in.

TRIM OF A RENAULT CLIO, 1991

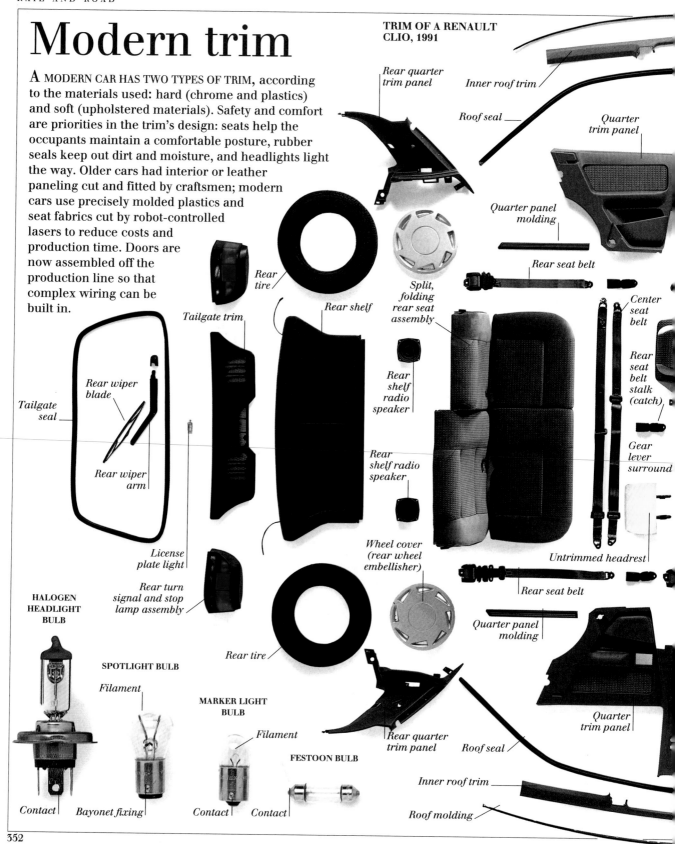

Rear quarter trim panel

Inner roof trim

Roof seal

Quarter trim panel

Quarter panel molding

Rear seat belt

Center seat belt

Rear seat belt stalk (catch)

Gear lever surround

Rear tire

Rear shelf

Split, folding rear seat assembly

Rear shelf radio speaker

Rear shelf radio speaker

Tailgate trim

Rear wiper blade

Tailgate seal

Rear wiper arm

License plate light

Wheel cover (rear wheel embellisher)

Untrimmed headrest

Rear seat belt

Quarter panel molding

HALOGEN HEADLIGHT BULB

Rear turn signal and stop lamp assembly

Rear tire

Quarter trim panel

SPOTLIGHT BULB

Filament

MARKER LIGHT BULB

Filament

FESTOON BULB

Rear quarter trim panel

Roof seal

Inner roof trim

Roof molding

Contact

Bayonet fixing

Contact

Contact

Contact

Contact

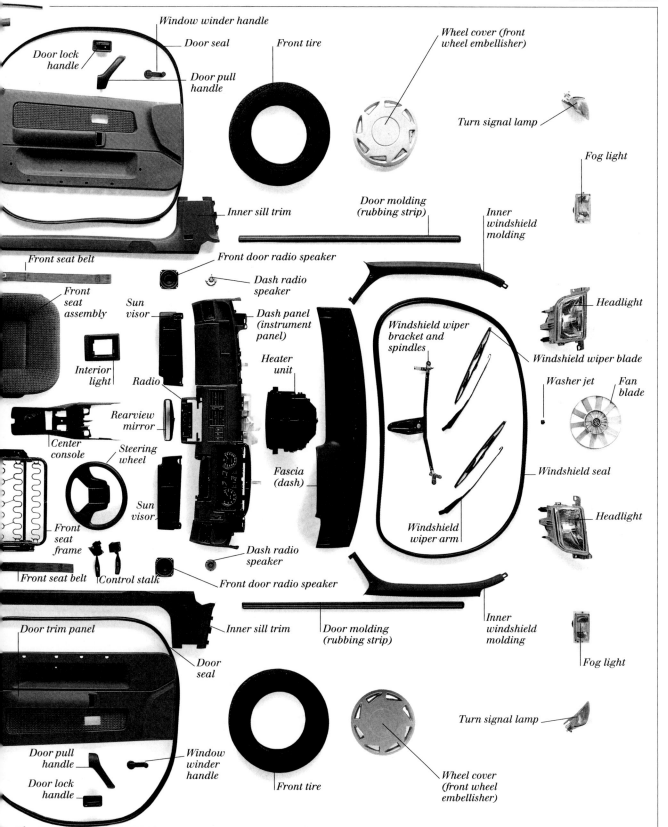

Window winder handle

Door seal

Front tire

Wheel cover (front wheel embellisher)

Door lock handle

Door pull handle

Turn signal lamp

Fog light

Inner sill trim

Door molding (rubbing strip)

Inner windshield molding

Front seat belt

Front door radio speaker

Dash radio speaker

Headlight

Front seat assembly

Sun visor

Dash panel (instrument panel)

Windshield wiper bracket and spindles

Windshield wiper blade

Heater unit

Washer jet

Fan blade

Interior light

Radio

Rearview mirror

Center console

Steering wheel

Fascia (dash)

Windshield seal

Sun visor

Windshield wiper arm

Headlight

Front seat frame

Dash radio speaker

Front seat belt

Control stalk

Front door radio speaker

Inner windshield molding

Door trim panel

Inner sill trim

Door molding (rubbing strip)

Door seal

Door pull handle

Window winder handle

Front tire

Turn signal lamp

Door lock handle

Wheel cover (front wheel embellisher)

All-terrain vehicles

THE MODERN ALL-TERRAIN VEHICLE has its origins in the American military Jeep of the 1940s and the British Land Rover. Such vehicles have been used for a wide range of purposes, from safari travel to fire fighting. The principal special features of such cars—including four- or six-wheel drive, high ground clearance, and toughened braking, suspension, and transmission systems—are designed to enable driving under the most difficult off-road conditions. The vehicle shown here is equipped for safari travel and carries a comprehensive range of survival gear.

COOKING EQUIPMENT

TWO–BURNER ALCOHOL STOVE

Handle for all pans

Zipper

Flame regulator

Wick

Cooking pot

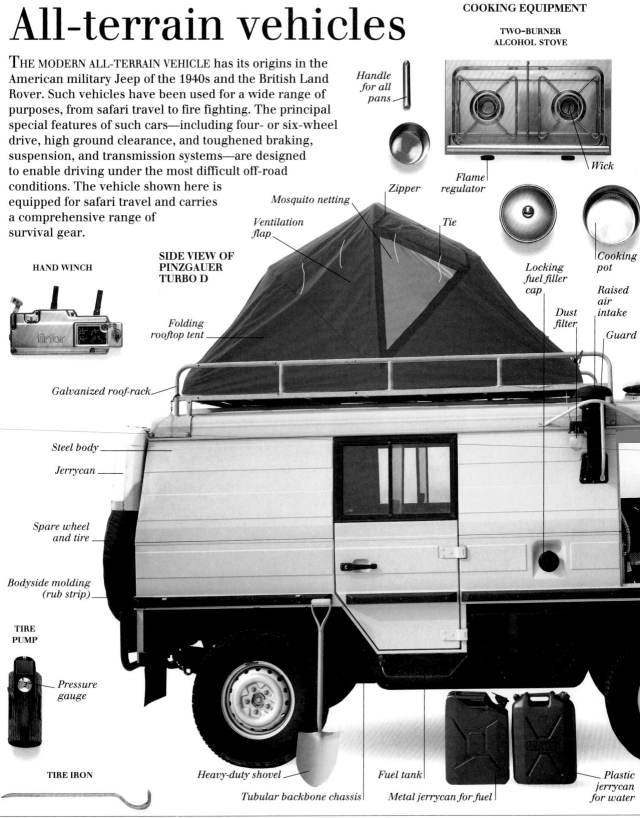

Mosquito netting

Ventilation flap

Tie

Locking fuel filler cap

Dust filter

Raised air intake

Guard

HAND WINCH

SIDE VIEW OF PINZGAUER TURBO D

Folding rooftop tent

Galvanized roof-rack

Steel body

Jerrycan

Spare wheel and tire

Bodyside molding (rub strip)

TIRE PUMP

Pressure gauge

TIRE IRON

Heavy-duty shovel

Tubular backbone chassis

Fuel tank

Metal jerrycan for fuel

Plastic jerrycan for water

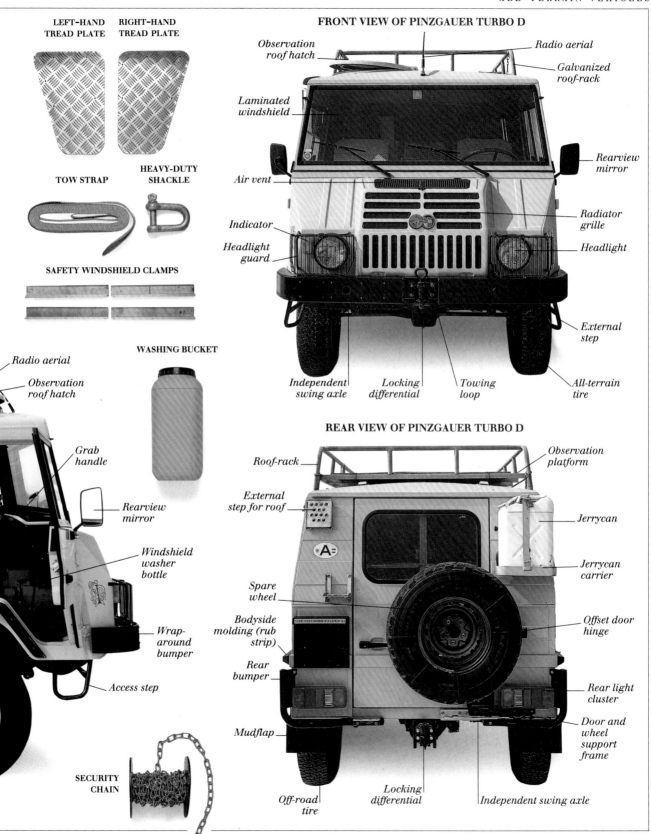

LEFT-HAND
TREAD PLATE

RIGHT-HAND
TREAD PLATE

TOW STRAP

HEAVY-DUTY
SHACKLE

SAFETY WINDSHIELD CLAMPS

WASHING BUCKET

Radio aerial

Observation
roof hatch

Grab
handle

Rearview
mirror

Windshield
washer
bottle

Wrap-
around
bumper

Access step

SECURITY
CHAIN

FRONT VIEW OF PINZGAUER TURBO D

Observation
roof hatch

Radio aerial

Galvanized
roof-rack

Laminated
windshield

Rearview
mirror

Air vent

Indicator

Radiator
grille

Headlight
guard

Headlight

External
step

Independent
swing axle

Locking
differential

Towing
loop

All-terrain
tire

REAR VIEW OF PINZGAUER TURBO D

Roof-rack

Observation
platform

External
step for roof

Jerrycan

Jerrycan
carrier

Spare
wheel

Offset door
hinge

Bodyside
molding (rub
strip)

Rear
bumper

Rear light
cluster

Door and
wheel
support
frame

Mudflap

Off-road
tire

Locking
differential

Independent swing axle

Racing cars

SINCE MOTORING BEGAN, racing cars have been a major focus of innovation in car design. Features that are now commonplace, such as disc brakes, turbochargers, and even safety belts, were used first on competition cars. Research into racing cars has contributed to a new understanding of engine performance, aerodynamics, and tire adhesion, and has led to the development of ultra-light materials such as carbon-fiber for car bodies. Like the 1937 Bugatti Type 57S below, a modern Williams Formula One car has a low, streamlined body and an open cockpit. Unlike its forerunner, it also has a front wing that pushes the front wheels firmly onto the track, huge slick tires for extra grip, and electrical sensors that continually relay information to the pits about the car's performance.

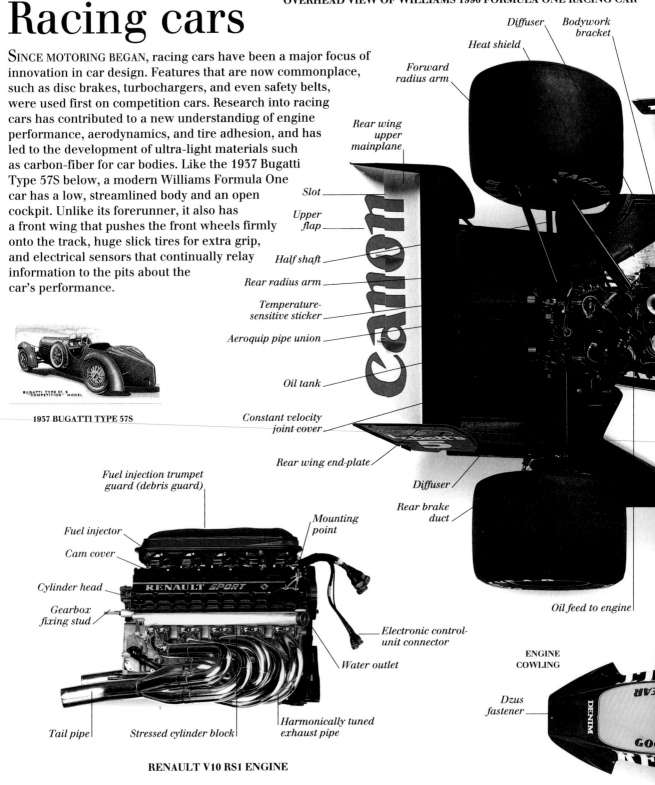

1937 BUGATTI TYPE 57S

Diffuser

Bodywork bracket

Heat shield

Forward radius arm

Rear wing upper mainplane

Slot

Upper flap

Half shaft

Rear radius arm

Temperature-sensitive sticker

Aeroquip pipe union

Oil tank

Constant velocity joint cover

Rear wing end-plate

Diffuser

Rear brake duct

Oil feed to engine

Fuel injection trumpet guard (debris guard)

Mounting point

Fuel injector

Cam cover

Cylinder head

Gearbox fixing stud

Electronic control-unit connector

Water outlet

Tail pipe

Stressed cylinder block

Harmonically tuned exhaust pipe

RENAULT V10 RS1 ENGINE

ENGINE COWLING

Dzus fastener

SIDE FAIRING

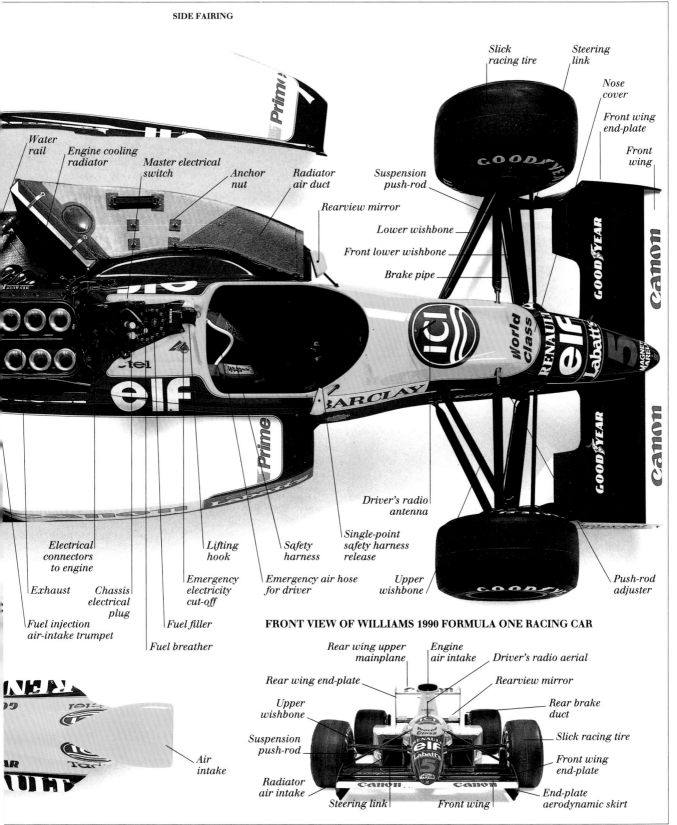

Slick racing tire

Steering link

Nose cover

Front wing end-plate

Front wing

Water rail

Engine cooling radiator

Master electrical switch

Anchor nut

Radiator air duct

Suspension push-rod

Rearview mirror

Lower wishbone

Front lower wishbone

Brake pipe

Driver's radio antenna

Single-point safety harness release

Electrical connectors to engine

Lifting hook

Safety harness

Exhaust

Chassis electrical plug

Emergency electricity cut-off

Emergency air hose for driver

Upper wishbone

Push-rod adjuster

Fuel injection air-intake trumpet

Fuel filler

Fuel breather

Air intake

FRONT VIEW OF WILLIAMS 1990 FORMULA ONE RACING CAR

Rear wing upper mainplane

Engine air intake

Driver's radio aerial

Rear wing end-plate

Rearview mirror

Upper wishbone

Rear brake duct

Suspension push-rod

Slick racing tire

Radiator air intake

Front wing end-plate

Steering link

Front wing

End-plate aerodynamic skirt

The motorcycle

THE MOTORCYCLE HAS EVOLVED from a motorized cycle—a basic bicycle with an engine—into a sophisticated, high-performance machine. In 1901, the Werner brothers established the most viable location for the engine, positioning it low in the center of the chassis (see pp. 364-365): the new Werner became the basis for the modern motorcycle. Motorcycles are used for many purposes —for commuting, delivering messages, touring, and racing—and different machines have been developed to suit the demands of different types of riders. The Vespa scooter, for instance, which is small-wheeled, economical, and easy-to-ride, was designed to meet the needs of the commuter. Sidecars provided transportation for the family until the arrival of cheap cars caused their popularity to decline. Serious riders generally favor larger capacity machines that are capable of greater performance and offer more comfort. Four-cylinder machines have been common since the Honda CB750 appeared in 1969. Despite advances in motorcycle technology, many riders are attracted to the traditional look of motorcycles like the twin-cylinder Harley-Davidson. Harley-Davidson Glides exploit the style of the classic American V-twin engine, where the cylinders are placed in a V-formation.

1901 WERNER MOTORCYCLE

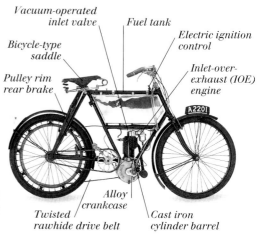

Vacuum-operated inlet valve
Fuel tank
Bicycle-type saddle
Electric ignition control
Pulley rim rear brake
Inlet-over-exhaust (IOE) engine
A 2201
Alloy crankcase
Twisted rawhide drive belt
Cast iron cylinder barrel

1988 HARLEY-DAVIDSON FLHS ELECTRA GLIDE

1965 BMW R/60 WITH 1952 STEIB CHAIR

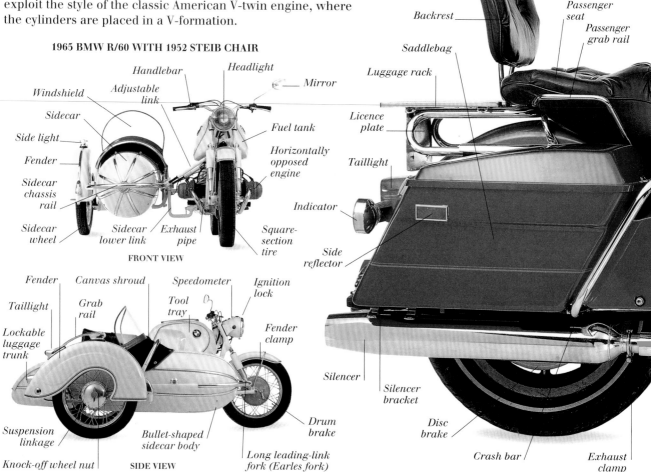

Backrest
Passenger seat
Passenger grab rail
Saddlebag
Luggage rack

Handlebar
Headlight
Windshield
Adjustable link
Mirror
Sidecar
Side light
Fender
Fuel tank
Licence plate
Horizontally opposed engine
Sidecar chassis rail
Taillight
Sidecar wheel
Sidecar lower link
Exhaust pipe
Square-section tire
Indicator
Side reflector

FRONT VIEW

Fender
Canvas shroud
Speedometer
Ignition lock
Taillight
Grab rail
Tool tray
Fender clamp
Lockable luggage trunk
Silencer
Silencer bracket
Disc brake
Suspension linkage
Bullet-shaped sidecar body
Drum brake
Crash bar
Exhaust clamp
Knock-off wheel nut
SIDE VIEW
Long leading-link fork (Earles fork)

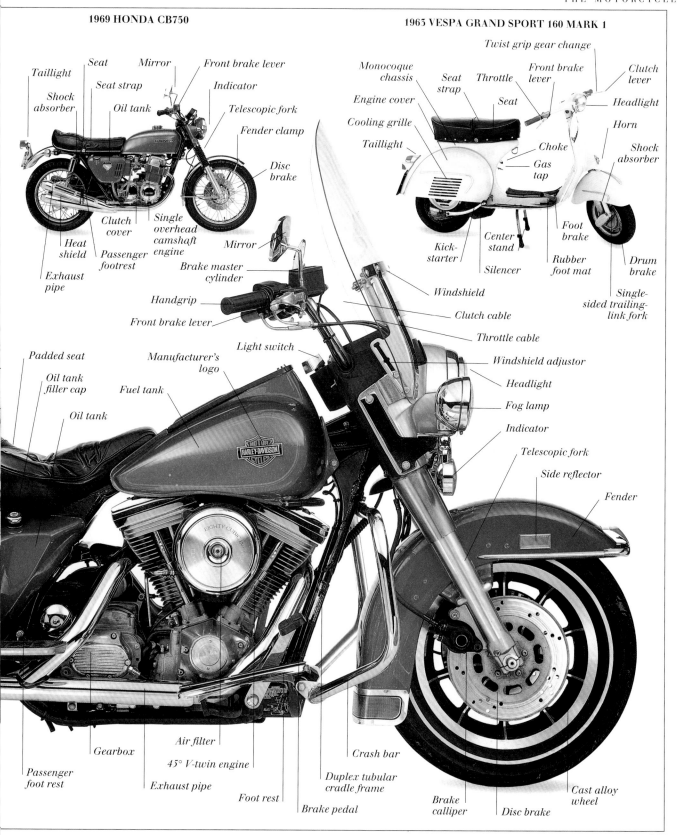

1969 HONDA CB750

Taillight
Seat
Mirror
Front brake lever
Seat strap
Indicator
Shock absorber
Oil tank
Telescopic fork
Fender clamp
Disc brake
Clutch cover
Single overhead camshaft engine
Mirror
Heat shield
Passenger footrest
Exhaust pipe
Brake master cylinder
Handgrip
Front brake lever
Light switch
Manufacturer's logo
Padded seat
Oil tank filler cap
Fuel tank
Oil tank
Passenger foot rest
Gearbox
Air filter
45° V-twin engine
Exhaust pipe
Foot rest
Crash bar
Duplex tubular cradle frame
Brake pedal
Brake calliper

1963 VESPA GRAND SPORT 160 MARK 1

Twist grip gear change
Monocoque chassis
Seat strap
Throttle
Front brake lever
Clutch lever
Engine cover
Seat
Headlight
Cooling grille
Horn
Taillight
Choke
Shock absorber
Gas tap
Kick-starter
Center stand
Foot brake
Drum brake
Silencer
Rubber foot mat
Single-sided trailing-link fork
Windshield
Clutch cable
Throttle cable
Windshield adjustor
Headlight
Fog lamp
Indicator
Telescopic fork
Side reflector
Fender
Disc brake
Cast alloy wheel

Competition motorcycles

THERE ARE MANY TYPES of motorcycle sports and in each, a special machine has evolved to perform to specific requirements. Races take place on roads or tracks or "off-road," in fields, dirt tracks, and even the desert. "Grand Prix" world championships in roadracing exist for 125cc, 250cc, and 500cc classes, as well as for sidecars. The latest racing sidecars have more in common with racing cars than motorcycles. The rider and passenger operate within an all-enclosing, aerodynamic fairing. The Suzuki RGV500 shown here, like other Grand Prix machines, carries advertising, which promotes the manufacturer and helps to cover the cost of developing motorcycle technology. In Speedway, which originated in the U.S. in 1902, motorcycles operate without brakes or a gearbox. Off-road competition motorcycles have less emphasis on high power output. In Motocross, for example, which is held on rough terrain, they must have high ground clearance, flexible long-travel suspension, and tires with a chunky tread pattern, to allow them to grip in sand or mud.

1992 HUSQVARNA MOTOCROSS TC610

Throttle cable
Handlebar brace
Long seat
Racing number
Hand protector
Radiator air vent
Flexible plastic fender
Lightweight exhaust system
Telescopic fork
Plastic guard
Axle
Overhead camshaft engine
Gear lever
Shock absorber
Disc brake
Knobby tire
Disc brake
Brake calliper
Alloy swing arm
Shock absorber linkage

1992 SUZUKI RGV500
SIDE VIEW

Exhaust pipe
Racing number
Air vent
One-piece seat and tail unit
Shock absorber
Minimal seat padding
Arched alloy swing arm

Exhaust pipe
Vent
Handlebar
Silencer
Exhaust pipe
Foot rest
Shock absorber mounting
Rear brake pedal
Three-spoke alloy wheel
Drive chain
Exhaust pipe
Wide, slick tire
Axle adjustor
Disc brake
Rear brake calliper
Slick racing tire
Foot rest
Drive chain
Brake pedal
Disc brake master cylinder
Lightweight alloy frame

REAR VIEW

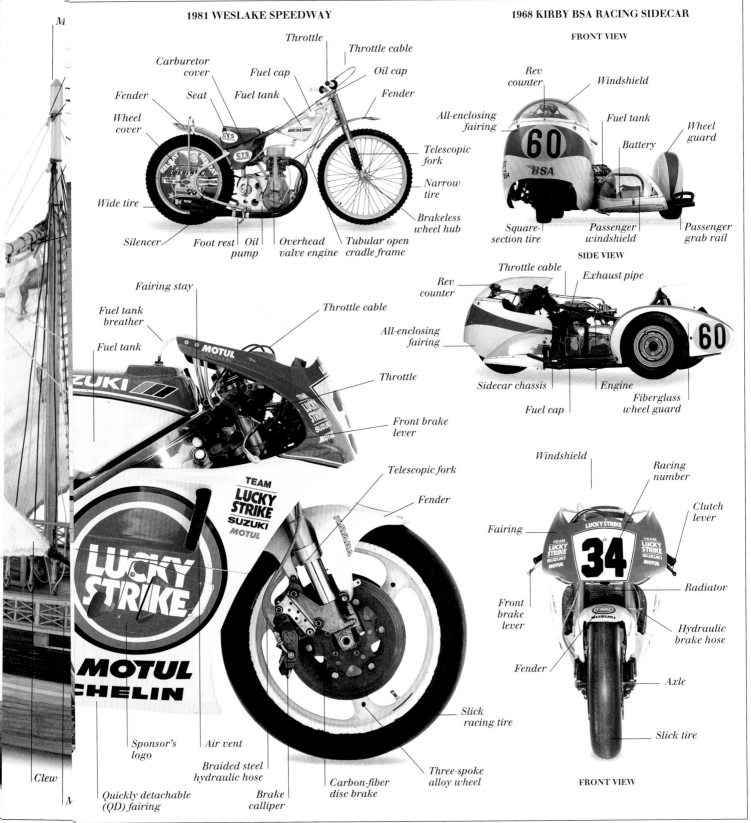

1981 WESLAKE SPEEDWAY

Throttle
Throttle cable
Carburetor cover
Fuel cap
Oil cap
Fender
Seat
Fuel tank
Fender
Wheel cover
Telescopic fork
Narrow tire
Wide tire
Brakeless wheel hub
Silencer
Foot rest
Oil pump
Overhead valve engine
Tubular open cradle frame

Fairing stay
Fuel tank breather
Throttle cable
Fuel tank
Throttle
Front brake lever
MOTUL
SUZUKI
TEAM LUCKY STRIKE SUZUKI MOTUL
Telescopic fork
Fender
LUCKY STRIKE
MOTUL
CHELIN
Sponsor's logo
Air vent
Braided steel hydraulic hose
Brake calliper
Carbon-fiber disc brake
Three-spoke alloy wheel
Slick racing tire
Quickly detachable (QD) fairing

1968 KIRBY BSA RACING SIDECAR

FRONT VIEW

Rev counter
Windshield
All-enclosing fairing
Fuel tank
Wheel guard
Battery
60
BSA
Square-section tire
Passenger windshield
Passenger grab rail

SIDE VIEW

Throttle cable
Exhaust pipe
Rev counter
All-enclosing fairing
60
Sidecar chassis
Engine
Fuel cap
Fiberglass wheel guard

Windshield
Racing number
Clutch lever
Fairing
TEAM LUCKY STRIKE SUZUKI MOTUL
34
Front brake lever
Radiator
Hydraulic brake hose
Fender
Axle
Slick tire

FRONT VIEW

M

Clew

M

369

A ship of the line

THE 74-GUN THIRD-RATER WAS A MAINSTAY of British and French battlefleets in the late 18th and early 19th centuries. (The biggest ships in the fledgling American navy of the time were 44-gun frigates.) The length of such a man-of-war was determined by the number of guns needed for each deck, allowing room for crews to man them. The gun deck of this vessel was about 170 ft (52 m) long. Her decks had to be strong to carry the weight of the guns. The deck planks have been removed in the model below to illustrate the number of beams needed to make the hull strong enough. Only timber with perfect grain was used. The upper deck was open at the waist, but forward and aft were officers' cabins. The forecastle (foc's'l) and quarterdeck carried light guns and provided platforms for handling the rigging and for reconnaissance. The ship's longboats, or launches, were carried on skids between the gangways.

LONGBOAT

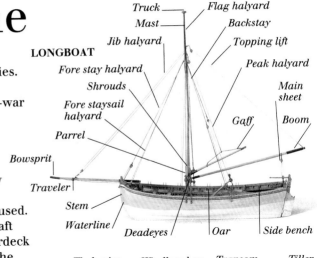

Truck · Flag halyard · Mast · Backstay · Jib halyard · Topping lift · Fore stay halyard · Peak halyard · Shrouds · Main sheet · Fore staysail halyard · Gaff · Boom · Parrel · Bowsprit · Traveler · Stem · Waterline · Deadeyes · Oar · Side bench

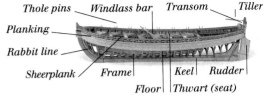

Thole pins · Windlass bar · Transom · Tiller · Planking · Rabbit line · Sheerplank · Frame · Keel · Rudder · Floor · Thwart (seat)

UPPER DECK OF A 74-GUN SHIP

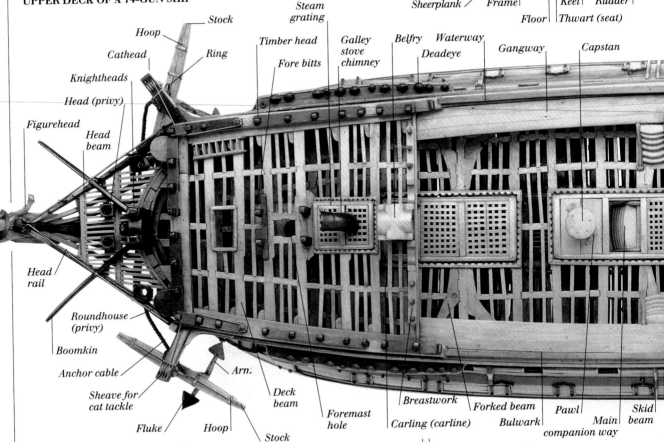

Stock · Hoop · Ring · Steam grating · Cathead · Timber head · Galley stove chimney · Belfry · Waterway · Gangway · Capstan · Knightheads · Fore bits · Deadeye · Head (privy) · Figurehead · Head beam · Head rail · Roundhouse (privy) · Boomkin · Anchor cable · Arm · Deck beam · Breastwork · Forked beam · Pawl · Skid beam · Sheave for cat tackle · Foremast hole · Carling (carline) · Bulwark · Main companion way · Fluke · Hoop · Stock · Head · Forecastle (foc's'l) · Waist

SEA A
RO
Sha
spic
thes
plan
Som
voya
To n
corb
"arte
lean
fore
carri
of th
ATTI
A GRI
Kalo
(bra
rope
Mo
Emb
(ram
beak
Op
(ey

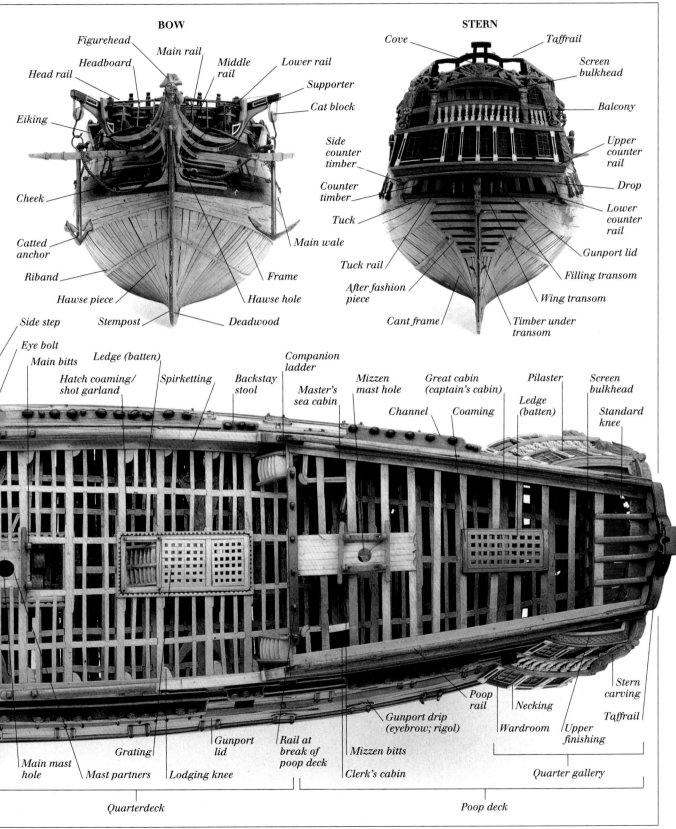

BOW

Figurehead
Main rail
Middle rail
Lower rail
Headboard
Head rail
Supporter
Eiking
Cat block
Cheek
Catted anchor
Riband
Main wale
Frame
Hawse piece
Hawse hole
Side step
Stempost
Deadwood

STERN

Cove
Taffrail
Screen bulkhead
Balcony
Side counter timber
Upper counter rail
Counter timber
Drop
Tuck
Lower counter rail
Tuck rail
Gunport lid
After fashion piece
Filling transom
Cant frame
Wing transom
Timber under transom

Side step
Eye bolt
Main bitts
Ledge (batten)
Companion ladder
Mizzen mast hole
Great cabin (captain's cabin)
Pilaster
Screen bulkhead
Hatch coaming/shot garland
Spirketting
Backstay stool
Master's sea cabin
Channel
Coaming
Ledge (batten)
Standard knee

Poop rail
Necking
Stern carving
Gunport drip (eyebrow; rigol)
Taffrail
Wardroom
Upper finishing
Grating
Gunport lid
Rail at break of poop deck
Mizzen bitts
Quarter gallery
Main mast hole
Mast partners
Lodging knee
Clerk's cabin

Quarterdeck
Poop deck

Rigging

MOST SAILING SHIPS HAVE TWO TYPES OF RIGGING. Standing rigging—kept taut by turnbuckles or old-fashioned lanyards and deadeyes—refers to the ropes, wires, and chains that support the masts and yards (horizontal spars). Running rigging, which includes types of block and tackle, halyards, and sheets, is used to hoist, lower, or trim sails.

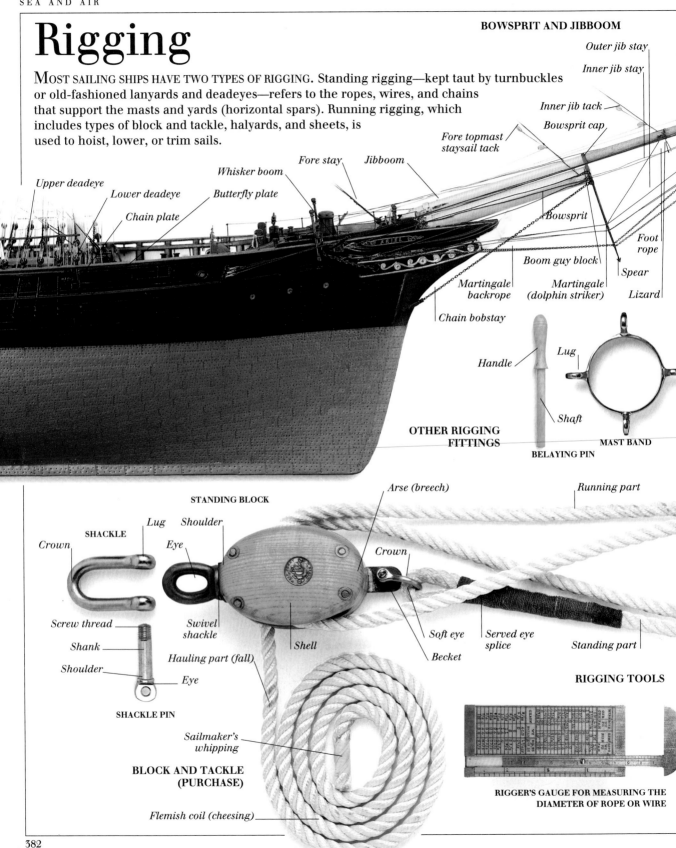

BOWSPRIT AND JIBBOOM

Outer jib stay

Inner jib stay

Inner jib tack

Bowsprit cap

Fore topmast staysail tack

Fore stay

Jibboom

Whisker boom

Butterfly plate

Upper deadeye

Lower deadeye

Chain plate

Bowsprit

Boom guy block

Martingale backrope

Martingale (dolphin striker)

Foot rope

Spear

Lizard

Chain bobstay

OTHER RIGGING FITTINGS

Handle

Lug

Shaft

Shell

BELAYING PIN

MAST BAND

STANDING BLOCK

Arse (breech)

Running part

SHACKLE

Crown

Lug

Shoulder

Eye

Shoulder

Crown

Screw thread

Shank

Shoulder

Eye

SHACKLE PIN

Swivel shackle

Shell

Soft eye

Becket

Served eye splice

Standing part

RIGGING TOOLS

Hauling part (fall)

Sailmaker's whipping

BLOCK AND TACKLE (PURCHASE)

Flemish coil (cheesing)

RIGGER'S GAUGE FOR MEASURING THE DIAMETER OF ROPE OR WIRE

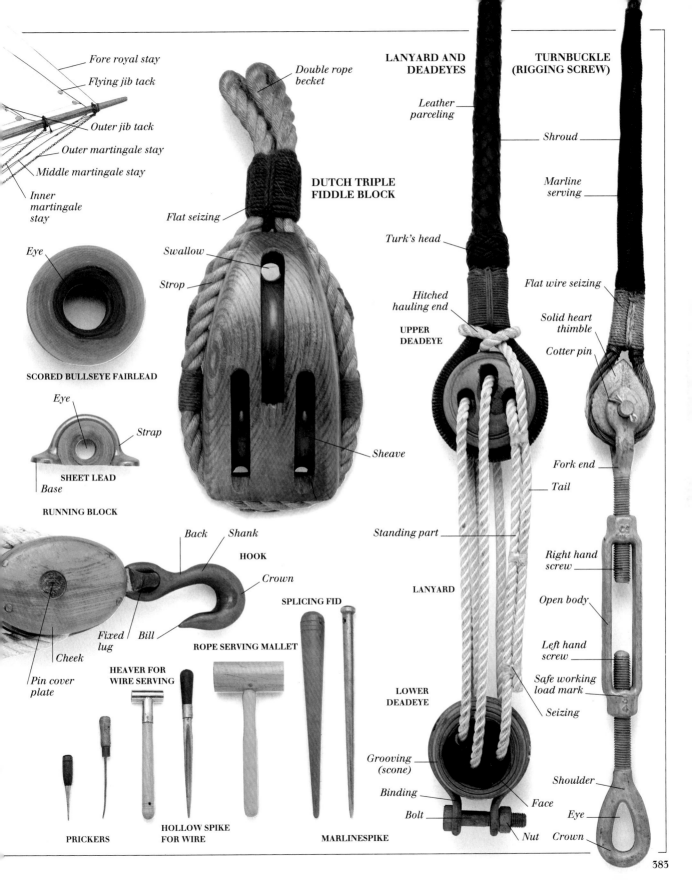

Fore royal stay

Flying jib tack

Outer jib tack

Outer martingale stay

Middle martingale stay

Inner martingale stay

Eye

SCORED BULLSEYE FAIRLEAD

Eye

Strap

SHEET LEAD

Base

RUNNING BLOCK

Double rope becket

DUTCH TRIPLE FIDDLE BLOCK

Flat seizing

Swallow

Strop

Sheave

Back

Shank

HOOK

Crown

SPLICING FID

Fixed lug

Bill

ROPE SERVING MALLET

Cheek

HEAVER FOR WIRE SERVING

Pin cover plate

PRICKERS

HOLLOW SPIKE FOR WIRE

MARLINESPIKE

LANYARD AND DEADEYES

Leather parceling

Shroud

Turk's head

Marline serving

Hitched hauling end

UPPER DEADEYE

Standing part

LANYARD

LOWER DEADEYE

Grooving (scone)

Binding

Bolt

Face

Nut

TURNBUCKLE (RIGGING SCREW)

Flat wire seizing

Solid heart thimble

Cotter pin

Fork end

Tail

Right hand screw

Open body

Left hand screw

Safe working load mark

Seizing

Shoulder

Eye

Crown

383

Sails

THERE ARE TWO MAIN TYPES OF SAILS: Old-fashioned square sails hang from yards at right angles to the mast, and are powerful drivers with following winds; fore-and-aft sails are set parallel to the length of the boat, with the luff (leading edge) of the sail attached to a mast or a stay. They are more efficient for all-round sailing, and almost all modern sailboats are rigged this way. Some fore-and-aft sails have a gaff at the head; Marconi-rig sails are pointed at the top (below). The bottom (foot) of the sail is on a boom. Sails are made of strips of cloth sewn together. Cotton and flax are traditional sail materials but synthetic fabrics are now more often used.

TOP OF A MARCONI SAIL

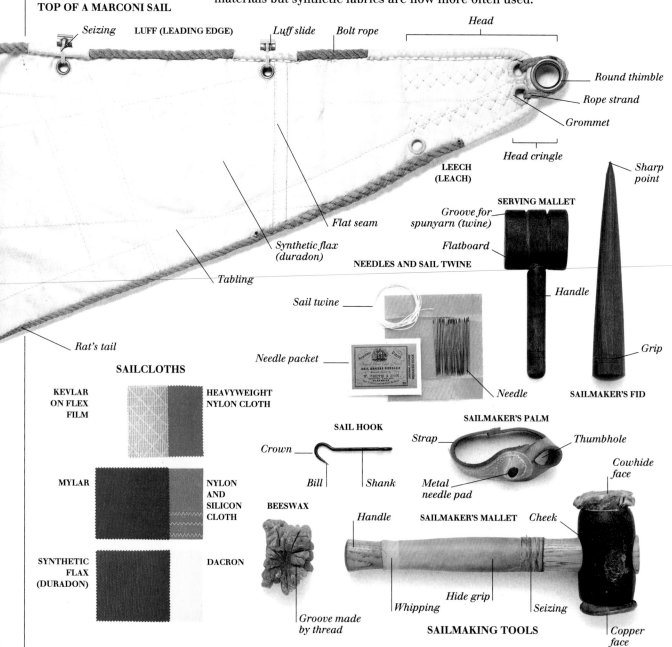

Seizing **LUFF (LEADING EDGE)** Luff slide Bolt rope Head

Round thimble

Rope strand

Grommet

Head cringle

LEECH (LEACH)

Flat seam

Synthetic flax (duradon)

NEEDLES AND SAIL TWINE

Tabling

Rat's tail

Sail twine

Needle packet

Needle

Sharp point

SERVING MALLET

Groove for spunyarn (twine)

Flatboard

Handle

Grip

SAILMAKER'S FID

SAILCLOTHS

KEVLAR ON FLEX FILM

HEAVYWEIGHT NYLON CLOTH

MYLAR

NYLON AND SILICON CLOTH

SYNTHETIC FLAX (DURADON)

DACRON

SAIL HOOK

Crown

Bill Shank

BEESWAX

Groove made by thread

SAILMAKER'S PALM

Strap

Thumbhole

Metal needle pad

Cowhide face

Handle

SAILMAKER'S MALLET Cheek

Whipping Hide grip Seizing

Copper face

SAILMAKING TOOLS

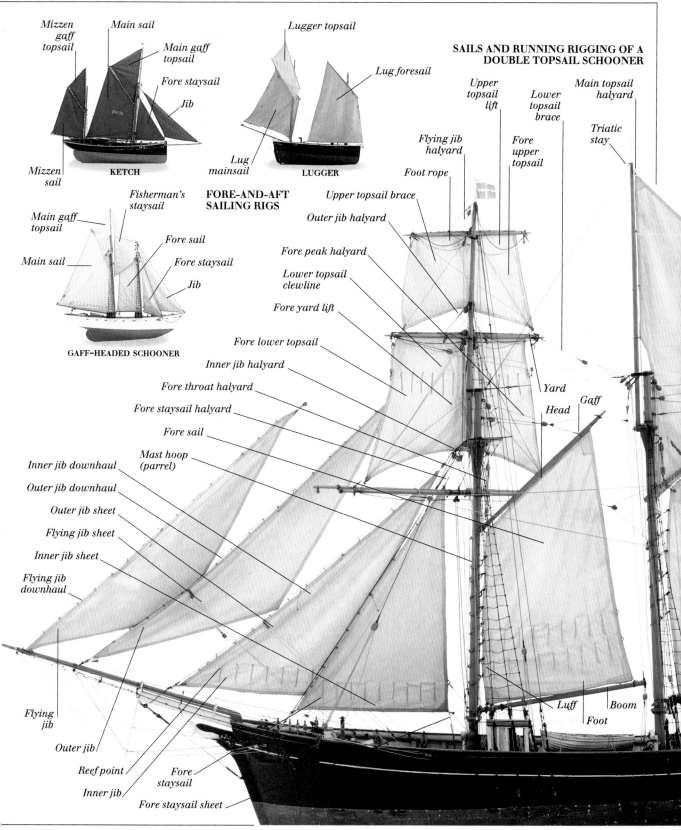

Mizzen gaff topsail

Main sail

Main gaff topsail

Fore staysail

Jib

Mizzen sail

KETCH

Lugger topsail

Lug foresail

Lug mainsail

LUGGER

SAILS AND RUNNING RIGGING OF A DOUBLE TOPSAIL SCHOONER

Upper topsail lift

Lower topsail brace

Main topsail halyard

Flying jib halyard

Fore upper topsail

Triatic stay

Foot rope

Upper topsail brace

Outer jib halyard

Main gaff topsail

Fisherman's staysail

Fore sail

Fore staysail

Jib

Main sail

FORE-AND-AFT SAILING RIGS

GAFF-HEADED SCHOONER

Fore peak halyard

Lower topsail clewline

Fore yard lift

Fore lower topsail

Inner jib halyard

Fore throat halyard

Fore staysail halyard

Fore sail

Mast hoop (parrel)

Inner jib downhaul

Outer jib downhaul

Outer jib sheet

Flying jib sheet

Inner jib sheet

Flying jib downhaul

Flying jib

Outer jib

Reef point

Fore staysail

Inner jib

Fore staysail sheet

Yard

Head

Gaff

Luff

Boom

Foot

385

Mooring and anchoring

IN MOST HARBORS AND PORTS, a ship can moor (tie up or "make fast") directly to a pier, wharf, or quay (pronounced "key"), using heavy hawsers and docking lines attached to bitts or bollards. Hawsers are tied to each other with knots called bends. In open water, however, ships that are not under way must drop an anchor, which attaches the ship securely to the seabed. The earliest anchors were simply heavy stones. Later, various anchor designs were developed for different uses. Most small vessels today use Danforth or plow anchors, which dig deeply into the sea bottom. A permanent mooring is an anchor set in the bottom to which a ship can tie up without using its own anchor. On old sailing ships, anchors were pulled up, or "weighed," by sailors pushing against bars that turned a capstan, which wound up the anchor cable. Now, most capstans are powered by electricity.

STONE ANCHOR (KILLICK)

Rope hole

TYPES OF ANCHOR

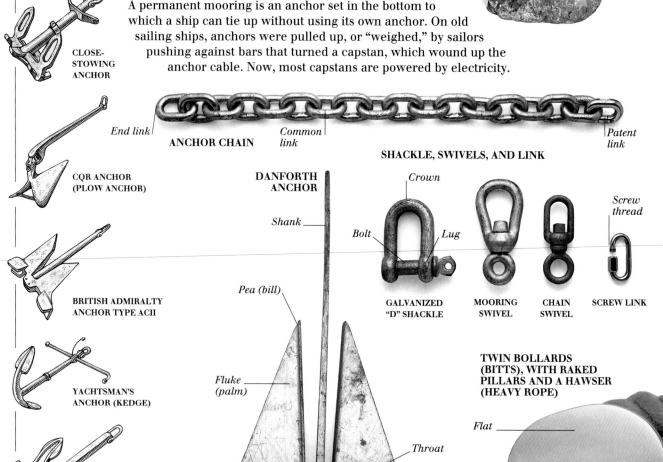

CLOSE-STOWING ANCHOR

CQR ANCHOR (PLOW ANCHOR)

BRITISH ADMIRALTY ANCHOR TYPE ACII

YACHTSMAN'S ANCHOR (KEDGE)

STOCKLESS ANCHOR

End link | ANCHOR CHAIN | Common link | Patent link

SHACKLE, SWIVELS, AND LINK

DANFORTH ANCHOR

Shank

Crown

Bolt

Lug

Screw thread

GALVANIZED "D" SHACKLE

MOORING SWIVEL

CHAIN SWIVEL

SCREW LINK

Pea (bill)

Fluke (palm)

Throat

TWIN BOLLARDS (BITTS), WITH RAKED PILLARS AND A HAWSER (HEAVY ROPE)

Flat

Rim

Stock

Base

Tripping palm

Crown

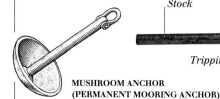

MUSHROOM ANCHOR (PERMANENT MOORING ANCHOR)

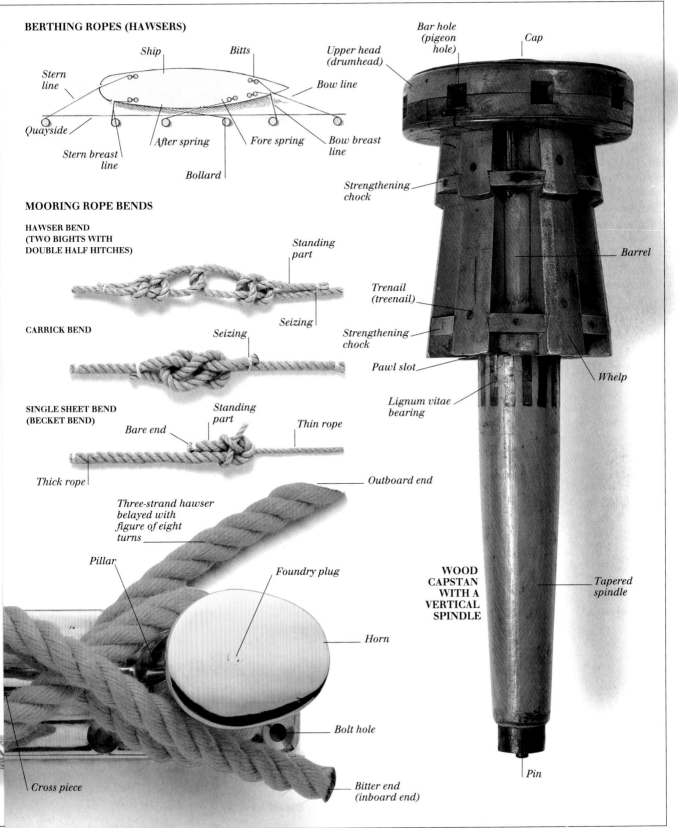

BERTHING ROPES (HAWSERS)

Ship

Bitts

Stern line

Upper head (drumhead)

Bow line

Stern breast line

Quayside

After spring

Fore spring

Bow breast line

Stern breast line

Bollard

MOORING ROPE BENDS

HAWSER BEND (TWO BIGHTS WITH DOUBLE HALF HITCHES)

Standing part

Seizing

CARRICK BEND

Seizing

SINGLE SHEET BEND (BECKET BEND)

Bare end

Standing part

Thin rope

Thick rope

Three-strand hawser belayed with figure of eight turns

Outboard end

Pillar

Foundry plug

Horn

Bolt hole

Cross piece

Bitter end (inboard end)

Bar hole (pigeon hole)

Cap

Strengthening chock

Barrel

Trenail (treenail)

Strengthening chock

Whelp

Pawl slot

Lignum vitae bearing

WOOD CAPSTAN WITH A VERTICAL SPINDLE

Tapered spindle

Pin

Paddle wheels and propellers

THE INVENTION OF THE STEAM ENGINE IN THE 18TH CENTURY made mechanically driven ships fitted with paddle wheels or propellers a viable alternative to sails. Paddle wheels have fixed or feathered floats, and the model shown below features both types. Feathered floats give more propulsive power than fixed floats because they are almost upright at all times in the water. Paddle wheels were superseded by the propeller on oceangoing vessels in the mid-19th century. Propellers are more efficient, work better in rough water, and are less vulnerable in collisions. The first propellers were two-bladed, but later three- and four-bladed versions are more powerful; the shape and pitch of the blades have also been refined over the years. At the beginning of the 18th century, tillers were replaced on many larger ships by the ship's wheel as a means of steering.

SHIP'S WHEEL

King spoke handle

Handle

Spoke

Rim plate

Felloe (rim section)

Maker's name

Nave plate

Nave

PADDLE WHEEL WITH FIXED FLOATS

Wrist pin

Limb

Fixed float

Hub

Deck beam

OSCILLATING STEAM ENGINE

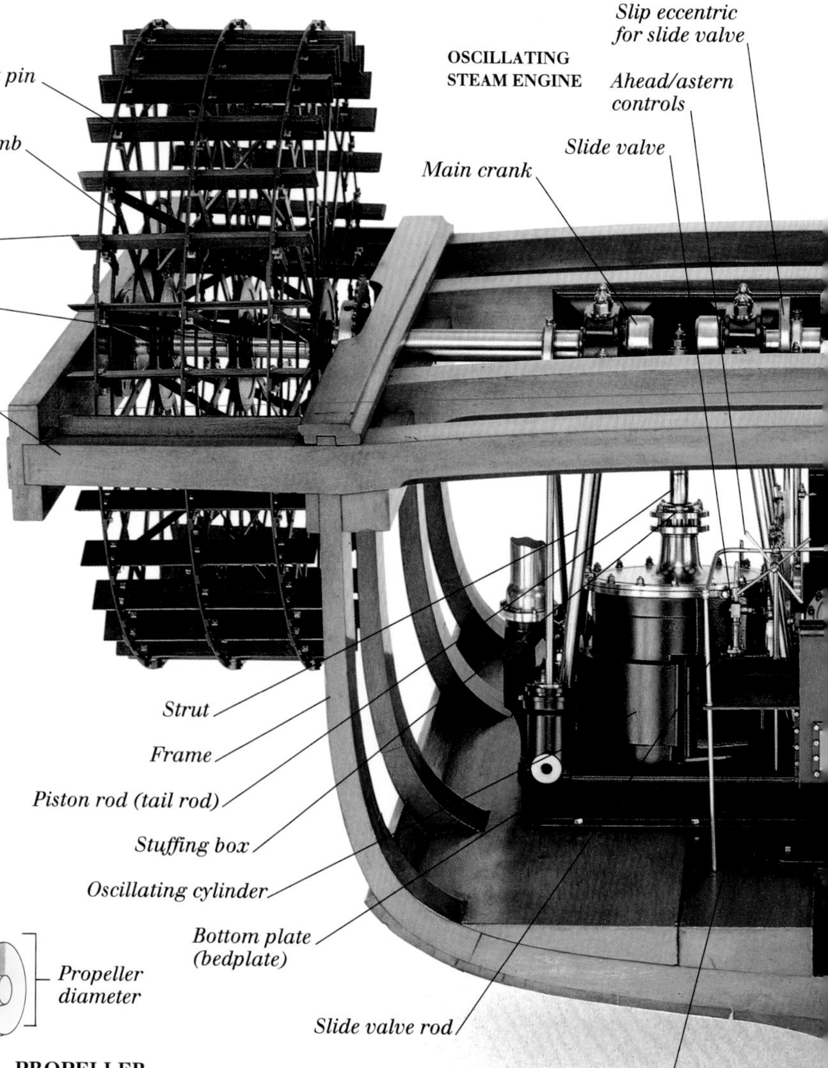

Slip eccentric for slide valve

Ahead/astern controls

Slide valve

Main crank

THREE-BLADED PROPELLER

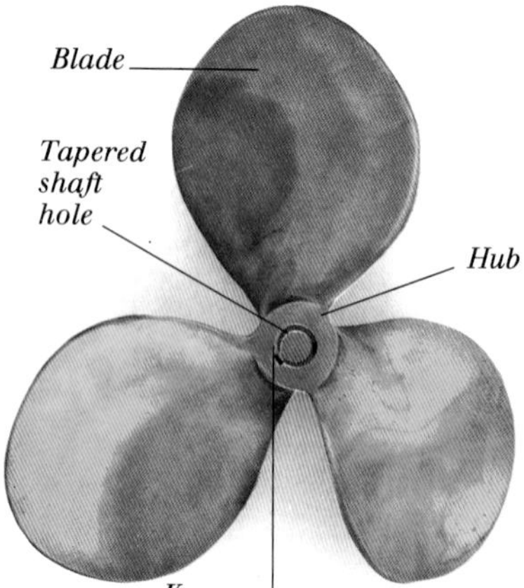

Blade

Tapered shaft hole

Hub

Keyway

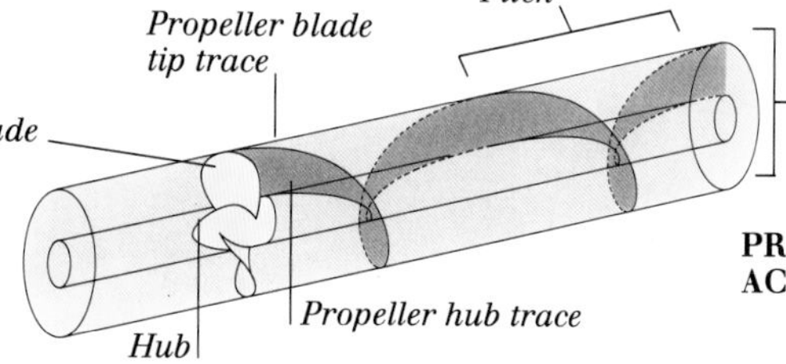

Strut

Frame

Piston rod (tail rod)

Stuffing box

Oscillating cylinder

Bottom plate (bedplate)

Slide valve rod

Control platform

Pitch

Propeller blade tip trace

Blade

Propeller diameter

Hub

Propeller hub trace

PROPELLER ACTION

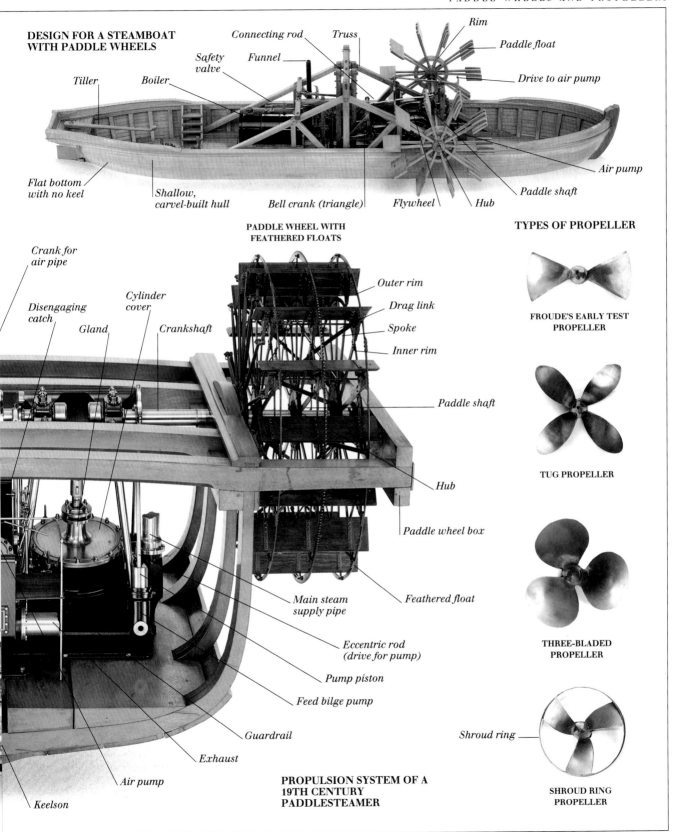

DESIGN FOR A STEAMBOAT WITH PADDLE WHEELS

Connecting rod

Truss

Rim

Paddle float

Safety valve

Funnel

Drive to air pump

Tiller

Boiler

Air pump

Flat bottom with no keel

Shallow, carvel-built hull

Bell crank (triangle)

Flywheel

Hub

Paddle shaft

PADDLE WHEEL WITH FEATHERED FLOATS

TYPES OF PROPELLER

Crank for air pipe

Outer rim

Drag link

Disengaging catch

Spoke

Cylinder cover

Gland

Inner rim

Crankshaft

Paddle shaft

Hub

Paddle wheel box

Main steam supply pipe

Eccentric rod (drive for pump)

Feathered float

Pump piston

Feed bilge pump

Guardrail

Exhaust

Air pump

Keelson

PROPULSION SYSTEM OF A 19TH CENTURY PADDLESTEAMER

FROUDE'S EARLY TEST PROPELLER

TUG PROPELLER

THREE-BLADED PROPELLER

Shroud ring

SHROUD RING PROPELLER

The battleship

IN THE EARLY YEARS OF THE 20TH CENTURY, sea warfare—
attacking enemy vessels or defending a ship—was
revolutionized by the introduction of Dreadnought-type
battleships like the Brazilian vessel below. These new
ships combined the latest advances in steam
propulsion, gunnery, and armor plating. Their gun
turrets, protected by armor up to 12 in (30 cm) thick,
were designed to fire shells over great distances.
The ship shown here, the Minas Geraes, was 500 ft
(152 m) long. It was built at Elswick, England, and
launched in 1908. Its chief armament was of 12 in (30 cm)
guns (firing shells with a 12 in diameter). Other naval
weapons developed in the 20th century include the torpedo—
as portrayed on the upper cigarette card (right). This was
a self-propelled underwater missile, often steered by
gyro-control. Depth charges were designed in the
First World War for use against submerged U-boats.
They are canisters filled with explosives that are
detonated by depth-sensitive pistols. The lower
cigarette card shows depth charges being
fired by a "thrower," fired from a
torpedo tube, and rolled from the
stern. Ship's shields were fitted to
warships from the late 19th century
onwards. The shield shown
opposite depicts a traditional
ship's cannon.

20TH CENTURY WEAPONRY

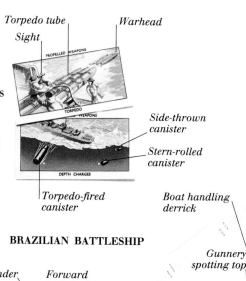

Torpedo tube
Sight
Warhead

TORPEDOES

DEPTH
CHARGES

Side-thrown
canister

Stern-rolled
canister

Torpedo-fired
canister

BRAZILIAN BATTLESHIP

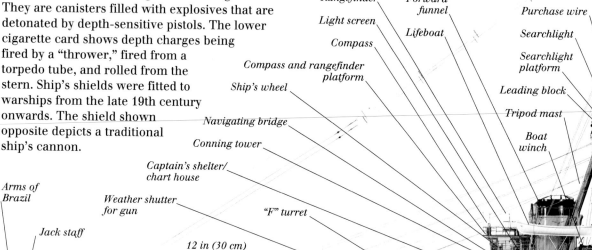

Rangefinder
Light screen
Compass
Compass and rangefinder platform
Ship's wheel
Navigating bridge
Conning tower
Captain's shelter/ chart house
Weather shutter for gun
Arms of Brazil
Jack staff
12 in (30 cm) gun
Skylight
"F" turret

Forward funnel
Lifeboat
Boat handling derrick
Gunnery spotting top
Purchase wire
Searchlight
Searchlight platform
Leading block
Tripod mast
Boat winch

Stem (false ram bow)
Porthole
Belt armor
Forward accommodation ladder
Sighting hood
"A" turret
Turret barbette
Open gun mounting
4.7 in (12 cm) gun
Steam launch
Guest boat boom

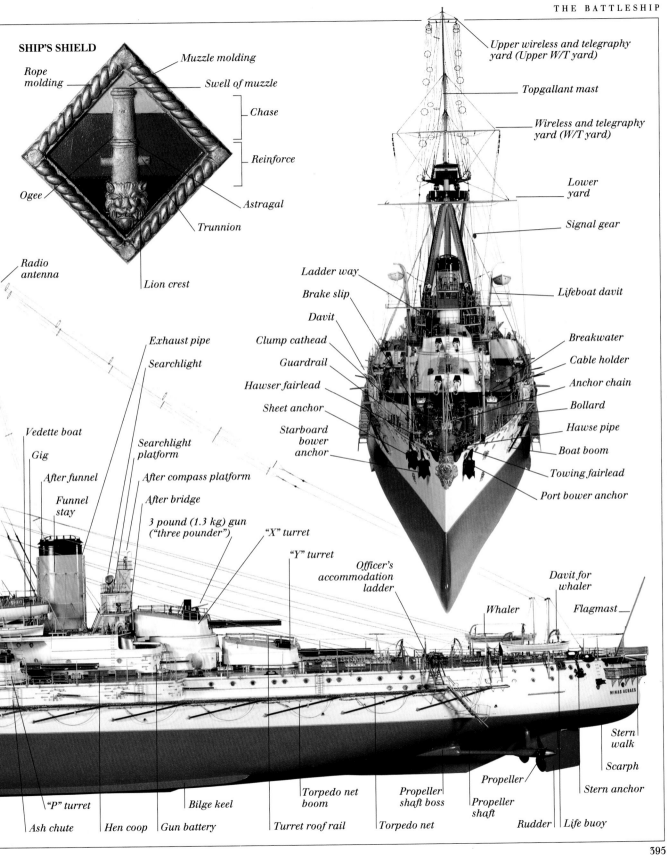

SHIP'S SHIELD

Rope molding
Muzzle molding
Swell of muzzle
Chase
Reinforce
Astragal
Trunnion
Ogee
Lion crest
Radio antenna

Upper wireless and telegraphy yard (Upper W/T yard)
Topgallant mast
Wireless and telegraphy yard (W/T yard)
Lower yard
Signal gear

Ladder way
Brake slip
Davit
Clump cathead
Guardrail
Hawser fairlead
Sheet anchor
Starboard bower anchor

Lifeboat davit
Breakwater
Cable holder
Anchor chain
Bollard
Hawse pipe
Boat boom
Towing fairlead
Port bower anchor

Exhaust pipe
Searchlight
Searchlight platform
After compass platform
After bridge
3 pound (1.3 kg) gun ("three pounder")
"X" turret
"Y" turret
Officer's accommodation ladder

Vedette boat
Gig
After funnel
Funnel stay

Davit for whaler
Whaler
Flagmast

Stern walk
Scarph
Stern anchor

"P" turret
Ash chute
Hen coop
Gun battery
Bilge keel
Torpedo net boom
Turret roof rail
Propeller shaft boss
Torpedo net
Propeller shaft
Propeller
Rudder
Life buoy
Stern anchor

Frigates and submarines

Fʀᴏᴍ ᴛʜᴇ ᴍɪᴅ-19ᴛʜ ᴄᴇɴᴛᴜʀʏ, ᴀʀᴍᴏʀᴇᴅ ꜱʜɪᴘꜱ provided a new challenge to enemy craft. In response, huge revolving gun turrets were developed. These could shoot in any direction, were loaded quickly from the breech, and fired exploding shells. Today's fighting ships, like the Royal Navy frigate opposite, also carry missile launchers and helicopters. Submarines operate underwater, have great speed, and some can fire missiles while submerged. A nuclear sub can operate for several years without refueling.

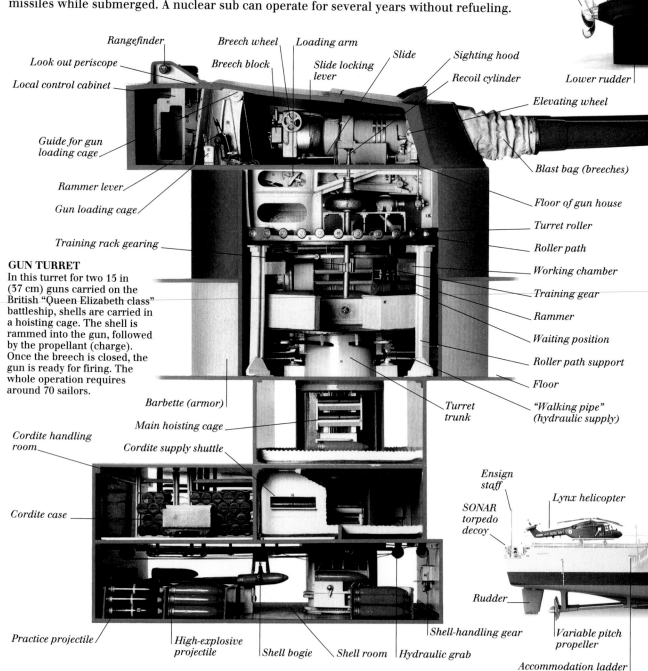

Stabilizer fin

Aft hydroplane

Propeller

Lower rudder

Rangefinder

Look out periscope

Local control cabinet

Breech wheel

Breech block

Loading arm

Slide locking lever

Slide

Sighting hood

Recoil cylinder

Elevating wheel

Guide for gun loading cage

Blast bag (breeches)

Floor of gun house

Rammer lever

Gun loading cage

Turret roller

Roller path

Training rack gearing

Working chamber

GUN TURRET
In this turret for two 15 in (37 cm) guns carried on the British "Queen Elizabeth class" battleship, shells are carried in a hoisting cage. The shell is rammed into the gun, followed by the propellant (charge). Once the breech is closed, the gun is ready for firing. The whole operation requires around 70 sailors.

Training gear

Rammer

Waiting position

Roller path support

Floor

"Walking pipe" (hydraulic supply)

Barbette (armor)

Main hoisting cage

Turret trunk

Cordite handling room

Cordite supply shuttle

Ensign staff

Lynx helicopter

SONAR torpedo decoy

Cordite case

Rudder

Practice projectile

High-explosive projectile

Shell bogie

Shell room

Hydraulic grab

Shell-handling gear

Variable pitch propeller

Accommodation ladder

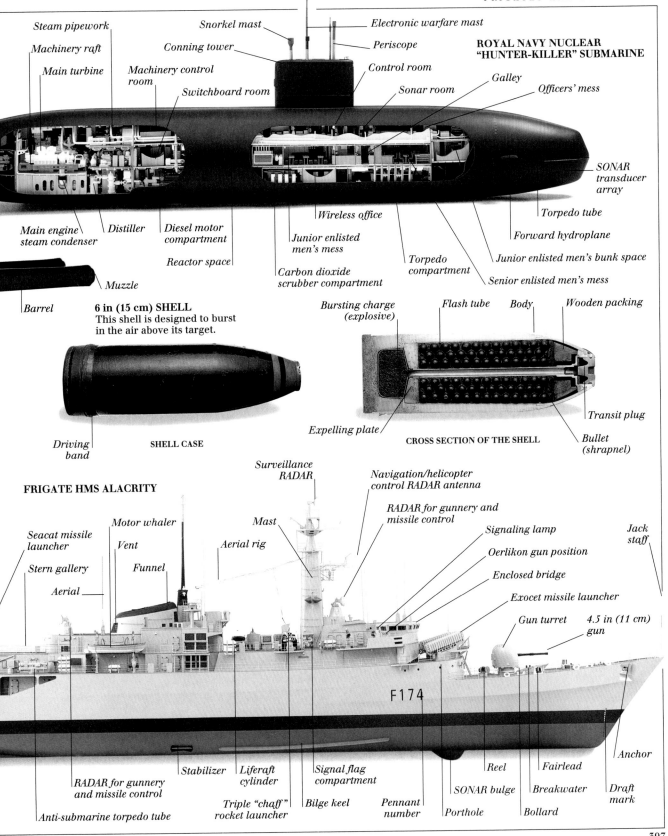

Steam pipework

Machinery raft

Main turbine

Snorkel mast

Conning tower

Machinery control room

Switchboard room

Electronic warfare mast

Periscope

Control room

Sonar room

Galley

ROYAL NAVY NUCLEAR "HUNTER-KILLER" SUBMARINE

Officers' mess

SONAR transducer array

Main engine steam condenser

Distiller

Diesel motor compartment

Reactor space

Wireless office

Junior enlisted men's mess

Carbon dioxide scrubber compartment

Torpedo compartment

Torpedo tube

Forward hydroplane

Junior enlisted men's bunk space

Senior enlisted men's mess

Muzzle

Barrel

6 in (15 cm) SHELL
This shell is designed to burst in the air above its target.

Driving band

SHELL CASE

Bursting charge (explosive)

Flash tube

Body

Wooden packing

Expelling plate

CROSS SECTION OF THE SHELL

Transit plug

Bullet (shrapnel)

FRIGATE HMS ALACRITY

Surveillance RADAR

Navigation/helicopter control RADAR antenna

RADAR for gunnery and missile control

Mast

Aerial rig

Signaling lamp

Oerlikon gun position

Enclosed bridge

Exocet missile launcher

Jack staff

Seacat missile launcher

Stern gallery

Aerial

Motor whaler

Vent

Funnel

Gun turret

4.5 in (11 cm) gun

F174

RADAR for gunnery and missile control

Anti-submarine torpedo tube

Stabilizer

Liferaft cylinder

Triple "chaff" rocket launcher

Signal flag compartment

Bilge keel

Pennant number

Porthole

Reel

SONAR bulge

Bollard

Fairlead

Breakwater

Anchor

Draft mark

Pioneers of flight

FLIGHT HAS FASCINATED MANKIND for centuries, and countless unsuccessful flying machines have been designed. The first successful flight was made by the French Montgolfier brothers in 1783, when they flew a balloon over Paris. The next major advance was the development of gliders, notably by the Englishman Sir George Cayley, who in 1845 designed the first glider to make a sustained flight, and by the German Otto Lilienthal, who became known as the world's first pilot because he managed to achieve controlled flights. However, powered flight did not become a practical possibility until the invention of lightweight, gas-driven internal-combustion engines at the end of the 19th century. Then, in 1903, the American brothers Orville and Wilbur Wright made the first powered flight in their Wright Flyer biplane, which used a four-cylinder, gas-driven engine. Aircraft design advanced rapidly, and in 1909 the Frenchman Louis Blériot made his pioneering flight across the English Channel (see pp. 400-401). The American Glenn Curtiss also achieved several "firsts" in his Model-D Pusher and its variants, most notably winning the world's first competition for airspeed at Reims in 1909.

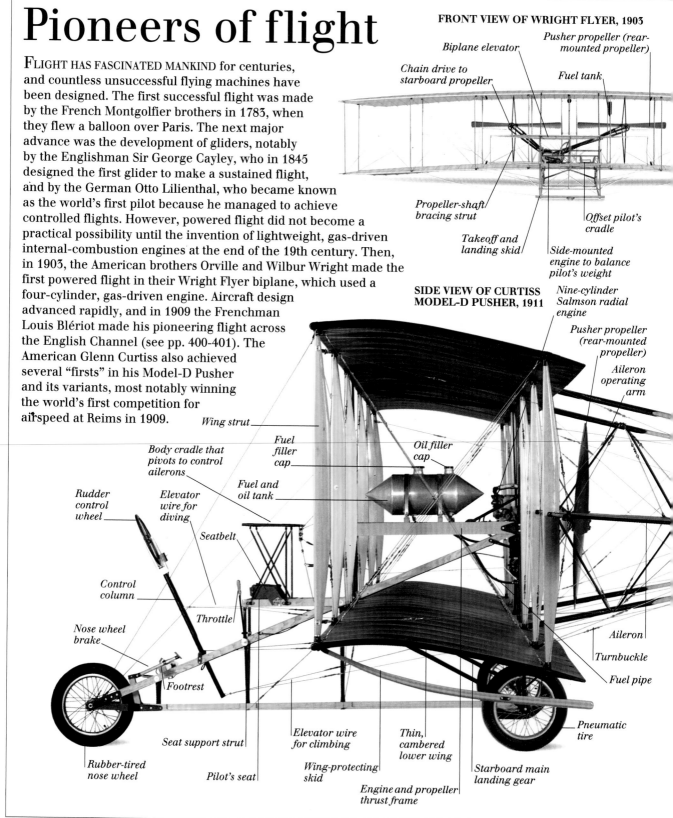

FRONT VIEW OF WRIGHT FLYER, 1903

Biplane elevator

Pusher propeller (rear-mounted propeller)

Chain drive to starboard propeller

Fuel tank

Propeller-shaft bracing strut

Offset pilot's cradle

Takeoff and landing skid

Side-mounted engine to balance pilot's weight

SIDE VIEW OF CURTISS MODEL-D PUSHER, 1911

Nine-cylinder Salmson radial engine

Pusher propeller (rear-mounted propeller)

Aileron operating arm

Wing strut

Fuel filler cap

Oil filler cap

Body cradle that pivots to control ailerons

Fuel and oil tank

Rudder control wheel

Elevator wire for diving

Seatbelt

Control column

Throttle

Nose wheel brake

Footrest

Aileron

Turnbuckle

Fuel pipe

Pneumatic tire

Seat support strut

Elevator wire for climbing

Thin, cambered lower wing

Rubber-tired nose wheel

Pilot's seat

Wing-protecting skid

Starboard main landing gear

Engine and propeller thrust frame

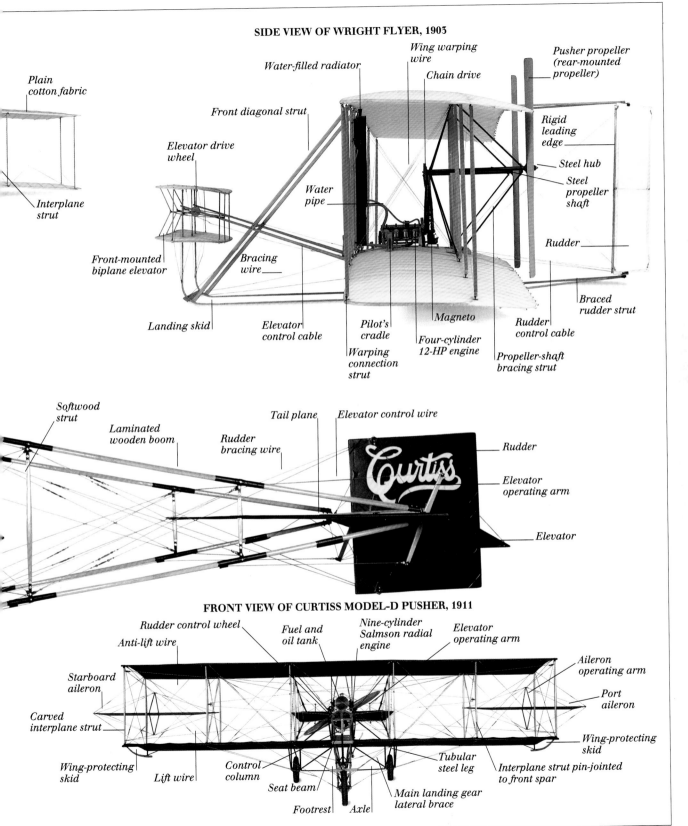

SIDE VIEW OF WRIGHT FLYER, 1903

Plain cotton fabric

Interplane strut

Water-filled radiator

Wing warping wire

Chain drive

Pusher propeller (rear-mounted propeller)

Front diagonal strut

Elevator drive wheel

Rigid leading edge

Steel hub

Steel propeller shaft

Water pipe

Rudder

Front-mounted biplane elevator

Bracing wire

Landing skid

Elevator control cable

Pilot's cradle

Magneto

Rudder control cable

Braced rudder strut

Warping connection strut

Four-cylinder 12-HP engine

Propeller-shaft bracing strut

Softwood strut

Laminated wooden boom

Tail plane

Elevator control wire

Rudder bracing wire

Rudder

Elevator operating arm

Elevator

Curtiss

FRONT VIEW OF CURTISS MODEL-D PUSHER, 1911

Rudder control wheel

Anti-lift wire

Fuel and oil tank

Nine-cylinder Salmson radial engine

Elevator operating arm

Aileron operating arm

Starboard aileron

Port aileron

Carved interplane strut

Wing-protecting skid

Wing-protecting skid

Lift wire

Control column

Seat beam

Footrest

Axle

Tubular steel leg

Main landing gear lateral brace

Interplane strut pin-jointed to front spar

Early monoplanes

RUMPLER MONOPLANE, 1908

MONOPLANES HAVE ONE WING on each side of the fuselage. The principal disadvantage of this arrangement in early wooden-framed aircraft was that single wings were weak. They required strong wires to brace them to king posts above and below the fuselage. However, single wings also had advantages: they experienced less drag than multiple wings, allowing greater speed; they also made aircraft more maneuverable because single wings were easier to warp (twist) than double wings, and warping the wings was how pilots controlled the roll of early aircraft. By 1912, the French pilot Louis Blériot had used a monoplane to make the first flight across the English Channel, and the Briton Robert Blackburn and the Frenchman Armand Deperdussin had proved the greater speed of monoplanes. However, a spate of crashes caused by broken wings discouraged monoplane production, except in Germany, where all-metal monoplanes were developed in 1917. The wings of all-metal monoplanes did not need strengthening by struts or bracing wires, but despite this, such planes were not widely adopted until the 1930s.

FRONT VIEW OF BLACKBURN MONOPLANE, 1912

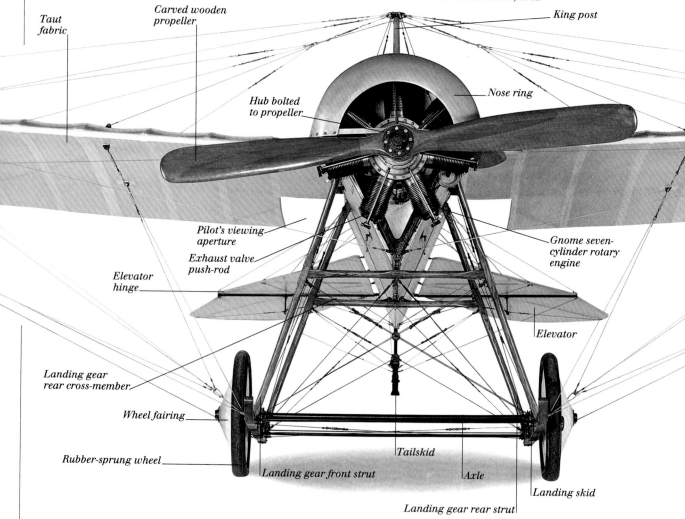

Taut fabric

Carved wooden propeller

King post

Nose ring

Hub bolted to propeller

Pilot's viewing aperture

Exhaust valve push-rod

Gnome seven-cylinder rotary engine

Elevator hinge

Elevator

Landing gear rear cross-member

Wheel fairing

Rubber-sprung wheel

Landing gear front strut

Tailskid

Axle

Landing skid

Landing gear rear strut

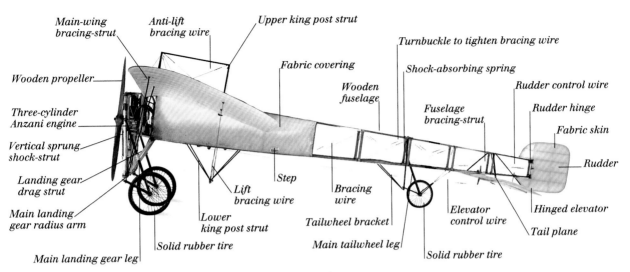

Main-wing bracing-strut
Anti-lift bracing wire
Upper king post strut
Fabric covering
Turnbuckle to tighten bracing wire
Shock-absorbing spring
Wooden propeller
Wooden fuselage
Rudder control wire
Rudder hinge
Three-cylinder Anzani engine
Fuselage bracing-strut
Fabric skin
Vertical sprung shock-strut
Rudder
Landing gear drag strut
Step
Lift bracing wire
Bracing wire
Main landing gear radius arm
Elevator control wire
Hinged elevator
Lower king post strut
Tailwheel bracket
Tail plane
Main landing gear leg
Solid rubber tire
Main tailwheel leg
Solid rubber tire

SIDE VIEW OF BLÉRIOT XI, 1909

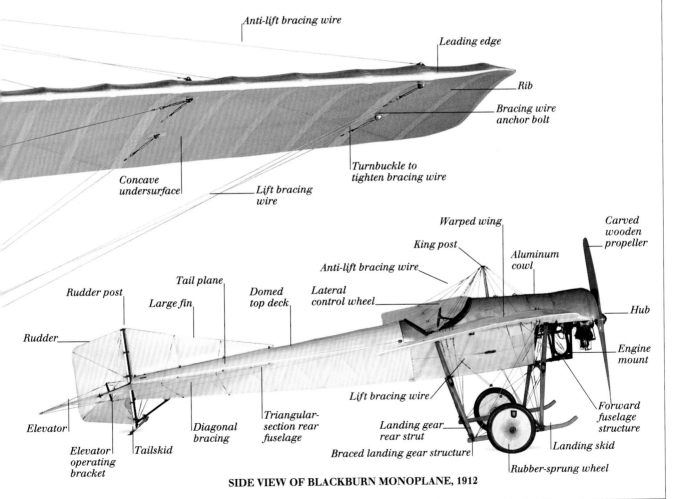

Anti-lift bracing wire
Leading edge
Rib
Bracing wire anchor bolt
Concave undersurface
Turnbuckle to tighten bracing wire
Lift bracing wire

Warped wing
Carved wooden propeller
King post
Aluminum cowl
Anti-lift bracing wire
Rudder post
Tail plane
Domed top deck
Lateral control wheel
Large fin
Hub
Rudder
Engine mount
Lift bracing wire
Forward fuselage structure
Elevator
Diagonal bracing
Triangular-section rear fuselage
Landing gear rear strut
Landing skid
Elevator operating bracket
Tailskid
Braced landing gear structure
Rubber-sprung wheel

SIDE VIEW OF BLACKBURN MONOPLANE, 1912

Biplanes and triplanes

BIPLANES DOMINATED AIRCRAFT DESIGN until the 1930s, largely because some early monoplanes (see pp. 400-401) were too fragile to withstand the stresses of flight. The struts between biplanes' wings made the wings strong compared with those of early monoplanes, although the greater surface area of biplanes' wings increased drag and reduced speed. Many aircraft designers also developed triplanes, which had a particular advantage over biplanes: more wings meant a shorter wingspan to achieve the same lifting power, and a shorter wingspan gave greater maneuverability. Triplanes were most successful as fighters during World War I, the German Fokker triplane being a notable example. However, the greater maneuverability of triplanes was no advantage for normal flying, so most manufacturers continued to make biplanes. Many other aircraft designs were attempted. Some were quadruplanes, with four pairs of wings. Some had tandem wings (two pairs of monoplane wings, one behind the other). One of the most bizarre designs was by the Englishman Horatio Phillips; it had 20 sets of narrow wings and looked rather like a Venetian blind.

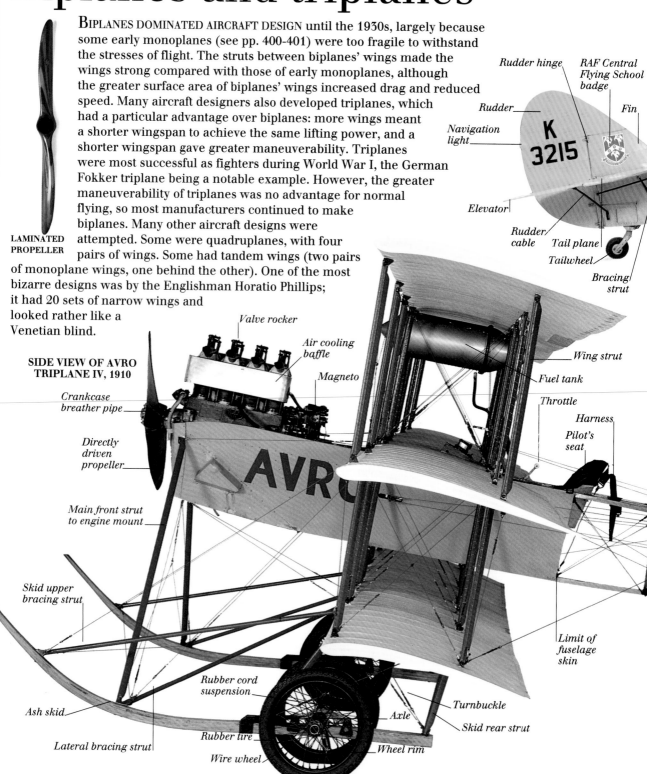

LAMINATED
PROPELLER

Rudder hinge

RAF Central
Flying School
badge

Rudder

Fin

Navigation
light

K
3215

Elevator

Rudder
cable

Tail plane

Tailwheel

Bracing
strut

**SIDE VIEW OF AVRO
TRIPLANE IV, 1910**

Valve rocker

Air cooling
baffle

Magneto

Wing strut

Fuel tank

Throttle

Harness

Pilot's
seat

Crankcase
breather pipe

Directly
driven
propeller

AVRO

Main front strut
to engine mount

Skid upper
bracing strut

Limit of
fuselage
skin

Rubber cord
suspension

Turnbuckle

Ash skid

Axle

Skid rear strut

Lateral bracing strut

Rubber tire

Wheel rim

Wire wheel

AVRO TUTOR BIPLANE, 1931

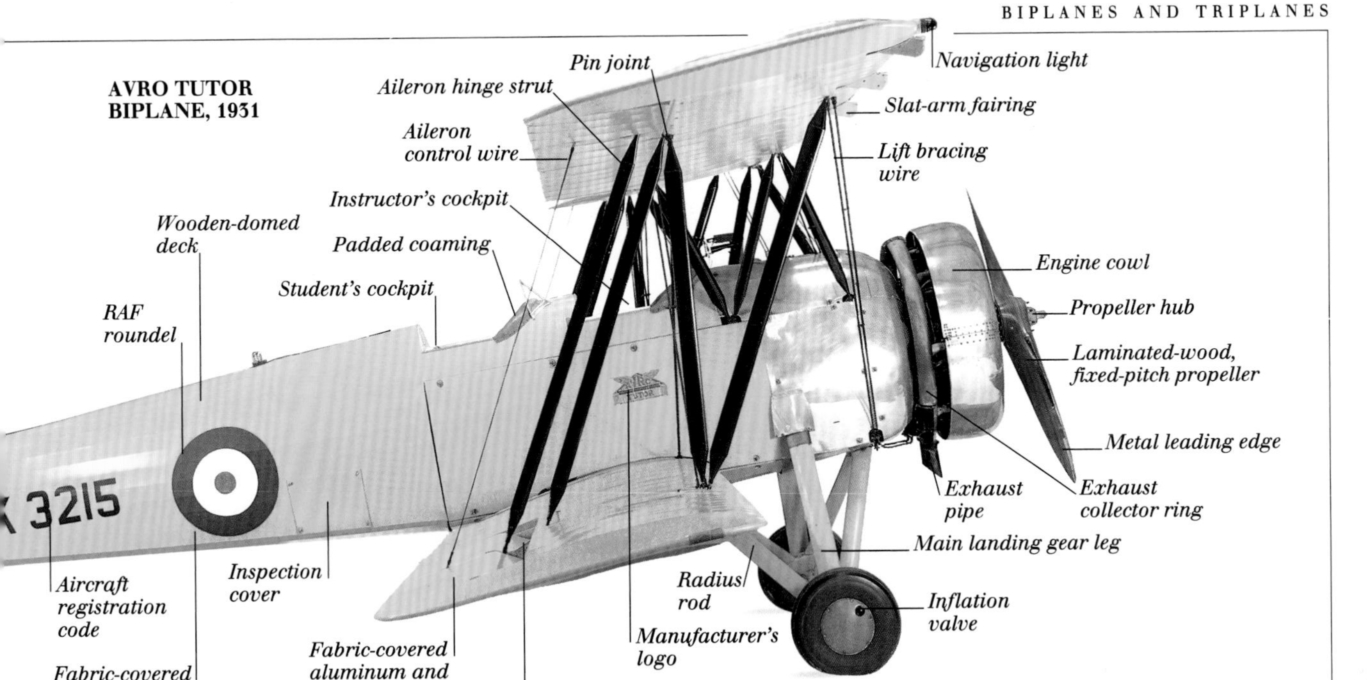

Pin joint

Aileron hinge strut

Aileron control wire

Instructor's cockpit

Padded coaming

Navigation light

Slat-arm fairing

Lift bracing wire

Wooden-domed deck

Student's cockpit

Engine cowl

Propeller hub

Laminated-wood, fixed-pitch propeller

RAF roundel

Metal leading edge

X 3215

Exhaust pipe

Exhaust collector ring

Main landing gear leg

Aircraft registration code

Inspection cover

Radius rod

Manufacturer's logo

Inflation valve

Fabric-covered steel-tube fuselage

Fabric-covered aluminum and steel wing

Recessed nose of aileron

FRONT VIEW OF AVRO TRIPLANE IV, 1910

Unpainted, varnished fabric

Top wing

Wing strut

Middle wing

Rib

Bottom wing

Leading edge

Fuel filler and vent

Fixed-pitch wooden propeller

Anti-lift bracing wire

Landing skid

Axle

Elevator

Tail plane

Lift bracing wire

Triangular-section fuselage

Triangular-section fuselage

Fuselage bracing wire

Rudder control cable

Lateral bracing strut

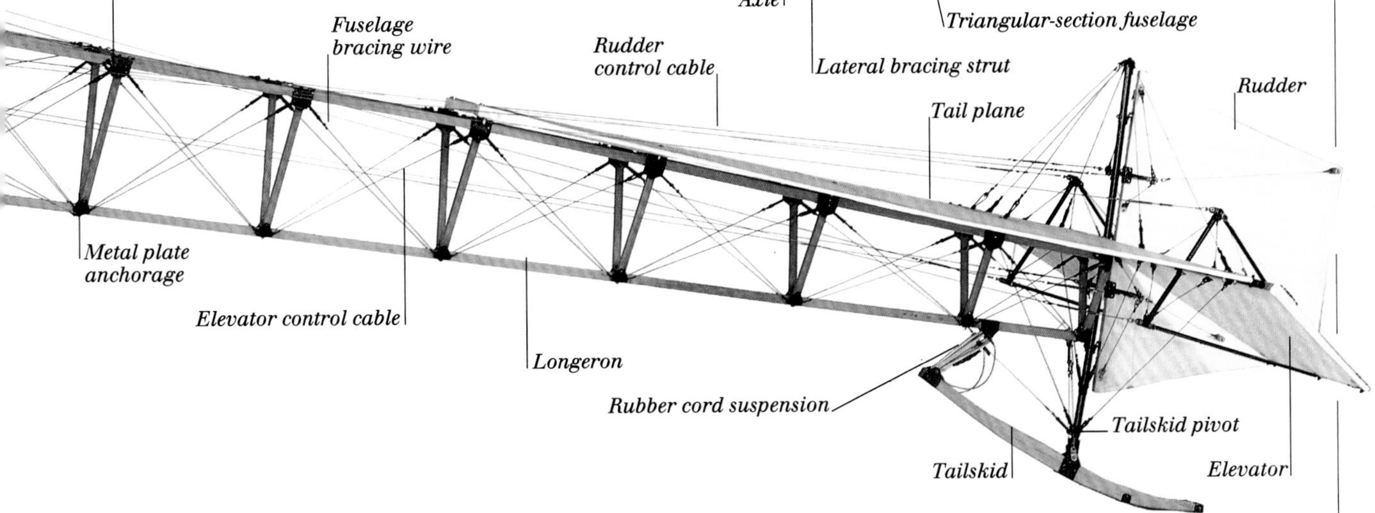

Tail plane

Rudder

Metal plate anchorage

Elevator control cable

Longeron

Rubber cord suspension

Tailskid pivot

Tailskid

Elevator

403

World War I aircraft

WHEN WORLD WAR I STARTED in 1914, the main purpose of military aircraft was reconnaissance. The British-built BE 2, of which the BE 2B was a variant, was well suited to this duty; it was very stable in flight, allowing the occupants to study the terrain, take photographs, and make notes. The BE 2 was also one of the first aircraft to drop bombs. One of the biggest problems for aircraft designers during the war was mounting machine guns. On aircraft that had front-mounted propellers, the field of fire was restricted by the propeller and other parts of the aircraft. The problem was solved in 1915 by the Dutchman Anthony Fokker, who designed an interrupter gear that prevented a machine gun from firing when a propeller blade passed in front of the barrel. The German LVG CVI had a forward-firing gun to the right of the engine, as well as a rear-cockpit gun, and bombing capability. It was one of the most versatile aircraft of the war.

FLYING HELMET

PORT WINGS FROM A BE 2B

Interplane-strut attachment
Intermediate leading-edge rib
Airspeed-indicator tube
Leading edge
Wingtip
Airspeed-indicator tube
Main rib
Root
Interplane strut
Trailing edge
Airspeed pitot tube
Interplane-strut attachment
Upper side of lower wing
Attachment lug

BE 2B, 1914

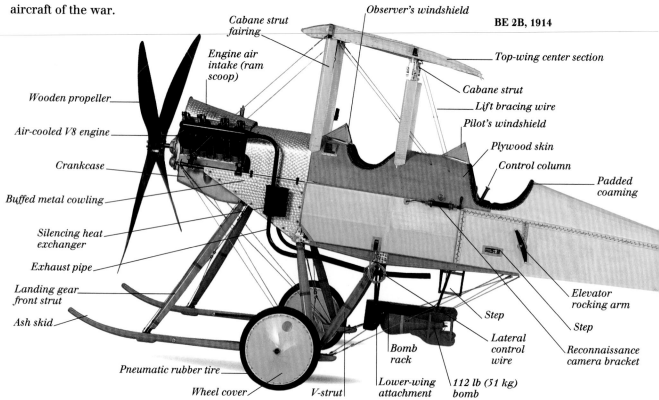

Cabane strut fairing
Observer's windshield
Engine air intake (ram scoop)
Top-wing center section
Wooden propeller
Cabane strut
Lift bracing wire
Air-cooled V8 engine
Pilot's windshield
Crankcase
Plywood skin
Control column
Buffed metal cowling
Padded coaming
Silencing heat exchanger
Exhaust pipe
Landing gear front strut
Elevator rocking arm
Ash skid
Step
Step
Lateral control wire
Reconnaissance camera bracket
Pneumatic rubber tire
Bomb rack
Wheel cover
V-strut
Lower-wing attachment
112 lb (51 kg) bomb

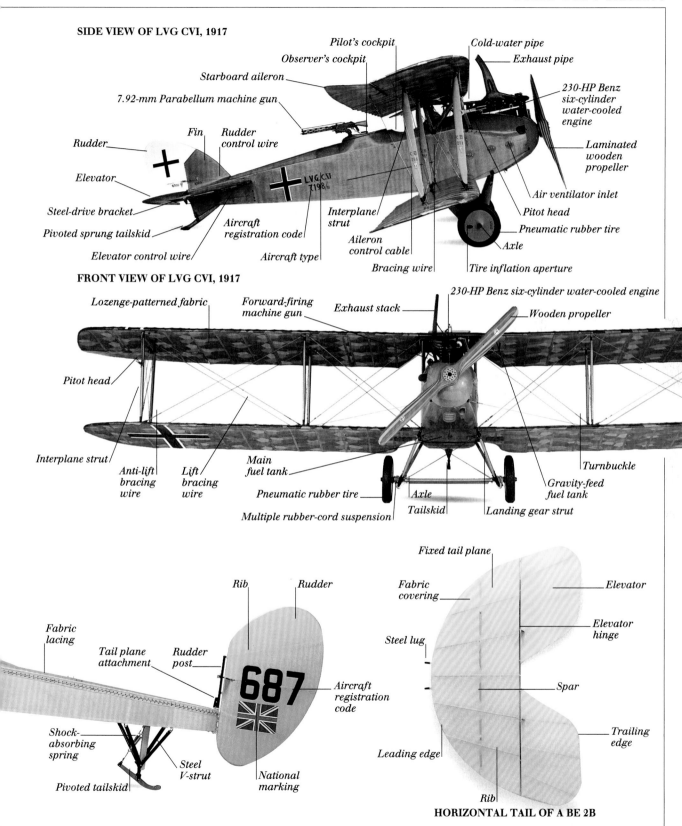

SIDE VIEW OF LVG CVI, 1917

Pilot's cockpit

Observer's cockpit

Starboard aileron

7.92-mm Parabellum machine gun

Cold-water pipe

Exhaust pipe

230-HP Benz six-cylinder water-cooled engine

Rudder

Fin

Rudder control wire

Elevator

Steel-drive bracket

Pivoted sprung tailskid

Elevator control wire

Aircraft registration code

Aircraft type

Interplane strut

Aileron control cable

Bracing wire

Laminated wooden propeller

Air ventilator inlet

Pitot head

Pneumatic rubber tire

Axle

Tire inflation aperture

FRONT VIEW OF LVG CVI, 1917

Lozenge-patterned fabric

Forward-firing machine gun

Exhaust stack

230-HP Benz six-cylinder water-cooled engine

Wooden propeller

Pitot head

Interplane strut

Anti-lift bracing wire

Lift bracing wire

Main fuel tank

Pneumatic rubber tire

Multiple rubber-cord suspension

Axle

Tailskid

Landing gear strut

Turnbuckle

Gravity-feed fuel tank

Fabric lacing

Tail plane attachment

Rudder post

Rib

Rudder

Shock-absorbing spring

Pivoted tailskid

Steel V-strut

National marking

687

Aircraft registration code

Fixed tail plane

Fabric covering

Steel lug

Leading edge

Rib

Elevator

Elevator hinge

Spar

Trailing edge

HORIZONTAL TAIL OF A BE 2B

Early passenger aircraft

FRONT VIEW OF LOCKHEED ELECTRA, 1934

UNTIL THE 1930s, most passenger aircraft were biplanes, with two pairs of wings and a wooden or metal framework covered with fabric or, sometimes, plywood. Such aircraft were restricted to low speeds and low altitudes because of the drag on their wings. Many had an open cockpit, situated behind or in front of an enclosed—but unpressurized—cabin that carried a maximum of 10 people. The passengers usually sat in wicker chairs that were not bolted to the floor, and the journey could be bumpy when flying through turbulence. Warm clothing, and earplugs to reduce the effects of prolonged noise, were often required. During the 1930s, powerful, streamlined, all-metal monoplanes, such as the Lockheed Electra shown here, became widespread. By 1939, the advent of pressurized cabins allowed fast flights at high altitudes, where there is less turbulence. Flying boats were still necessary on many routes until 1945 because of inadequate runways and the frequency of emergency sea landings. World War II, however, resulted in enough good runways being built for land planes to become standard on all major airline routes.

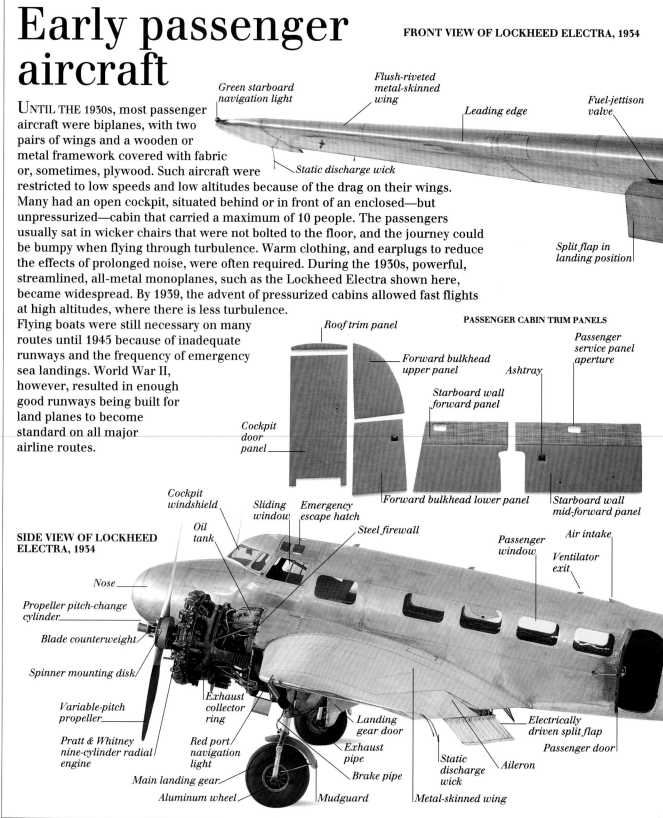

Green starboard navigation light

Flush-riveted metal-skinned wing

Leading edge

Fuel-jettison valve

Static discharge wick

Split flap in landing position

PASSENGER CABIN TRIM PANELS

Roof trim panel

Forward bulkhead upper panel

Passenger service panel aperture

Ashtray

Starboard wall forward panel

Cockpit door panel

Forward bulkhead lower panel

Starboard wall mid-forward panel

SIDE VIEW OF LOCKHEED ELECTRA, 1934

Cockpit windshield

Oil tank

Sliding window

Emergency escape hatch

Steel firewall

Passenger window

Air intake

Ventilator exit

Nose

Propeller pitch-change cylinder

Blade counterweight

Spinner mounting disk

Variable-pitch propeller

Pratt & Whitney nine-cylinder radial engine

Exhaust collector ring

Red port navigation light

Landing gear door

Exhaust pipe

Electrically driven split flap

Passenger door

Static discharge wick

Aileron

Main landing gear

Brake pipe

Aluminum wheel

Mudguard

Metal-skinned wing

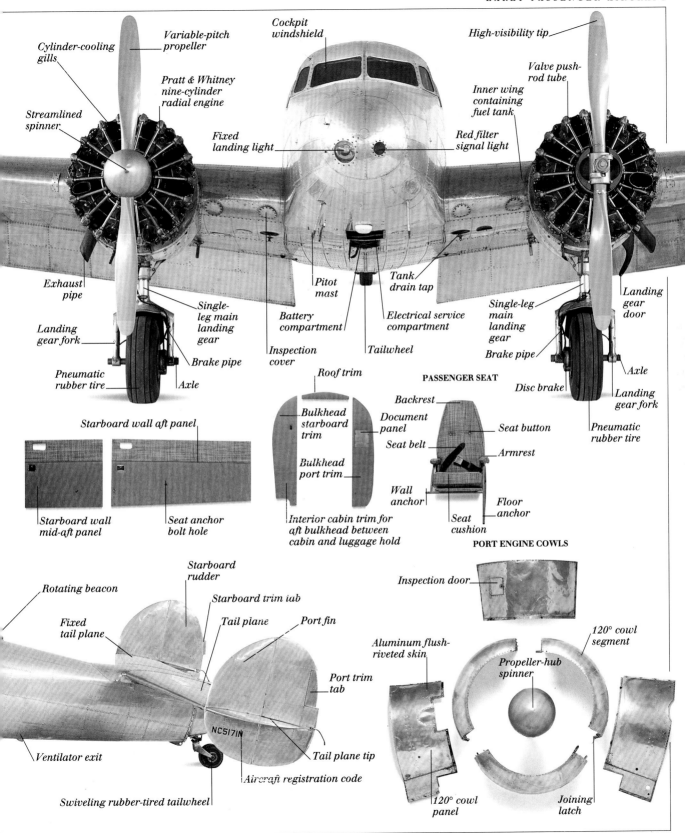

Variable-pitch propeller

Cylinder-cooling gills

Cockpit windshield

High-visibility tip

Pratt & Whitney nine-cylinder radial engine

Valve push-rod tube

Inner wing containing fuel tank

Streamlined spinner

Fixed landing light

Red filter signal light

Exhaust pipe

Single-leg main landing gear

Pitot mast

Tank drain tap

Single-leg main landing gear

Landing gear door

Landing gear fork

Battery compartment

Electrical service compartment

Brake pipe

Axle

Pneumatic rubber tire

Axle

Inspection cover

Tailwheel

Disc brake

Landing gear fork

Brake pipe

Pneumatic rubber tire

Roof trim

PASSENGER SEAT

Starboard wall aft panel

Bulkhead starboard trim

Backrest

Document panel

Seat button

Bulkhead port trim

Seat belt

Armrest

Starboard wall mid-aft panel

Seat anchor bolt hole

Wall anchor

Floor anchor

Interior cabin trim for aft bulkhead between cabin and luggage hold

Seat cushion

PORT ENGINE COWLS

Inspection door

Starboard rudder

Rotating beacon

Starboard trim tab

Tail plane

120° cowl segment

Fixed tail plane

Port fin

Aluminum flush-riveted skin

Propeller-hub spinner

Port trim tab

Ventilator exit

Tail plane tip

Swiveling rubber-tired tailwheel

Aircraft registration code

120° cowl panel

Joining latch

NC5171N

World War II aircraft

WHEN WORLD WAR II began in 1939, air forces had already replaced most of their fabric-skinned biplanes with all-metal stressed-skin monoplanes. Aircraft played a far greater role in military operations during World War II than ever before. The wide range of aircraft duties and the introduction of radar tracking and guidance systems put pressure on designers to improve aircraft performance. The main areas of improvement were speed, range, and engine power. Bombers became larger and more powerful—converting from two to four engines—in order to carry a heavier bomb load; the U.S. B-17 Flying Fortress could carry up to 6 tons of bombs over a distance of about 2,000 miles (3,200 km). Some aircraft increased their range by using drop tanks (fuel tanks that were jettisoned when empty to reduce drag). Fighters needed speed and maneuverability: the Hawker Tempest shown here had a maximum speed of 435 mph (700 kph) and was one of the few Allied aircraft capable of catching the German jet-powered V1 "flying bomb." By 1944, Britain had introduced its first turbojet-powered aircraft, the Gloster Meteor fighter, and Germany had introduced the fastest fighter in the world, the turbojet-powered Me 262, which had a maximum speed of 540 mph (868 kph).

PROPELLER

High-visibility yellow tip

Light-alloy propeller spinner

Variable-pitch aluminum-alloy blade

COMPONENTS OF A HAWKER TEMPEST MARK V, c.1943

STARBOARD ENGINE COWLINGS

Radiator-access cowling

Lower side cowling

Upper side cowling

Cowling fastener

Propeller governor

Radiator header tank

Propeller drive shaft

Distributor

Ejector exhaust

Magneto

Starter motor

2,400-HP Napier Sabre 24-cylinder engine

Cartridge starter

Engine top cowling

Upper side cowling

Lower side cowling

Radiator-access cowling

Cowling fastener

PORT ENGINE COWLINGS

SECTIONED B-17G FLYING FORTRESS BOMBER, c.1943

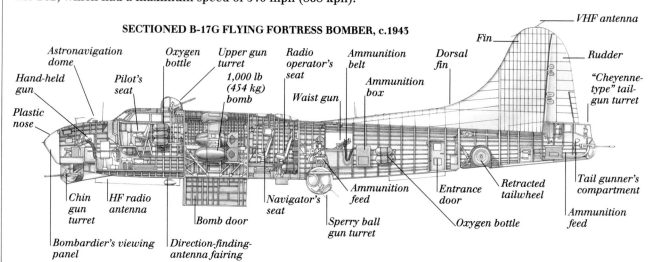

VHF antenna

Fin

Rudder

Dorsal fin

"Cheyenne-type" tail-gun turret

Astronavigation dome

Oxygen bottle

Upper gun turret

Radio operator's seat

Ammunition belt

Hand-held gun

Pilot's seat

1,000 lb (454 kg) bomb

Waist gun

Ammunition box

Plastic nose

Tail gunner's compartment

Chin gun turret

HF radio antenna

Navigator's seat

Ammunition feed

Entrance door

Retracted tailwheel

Ammunition feed

Bombardier's viewing panel

Bomb door

Direction-finding-antenna fairing

Sperry ball gun turret

Oxygen bottle

408

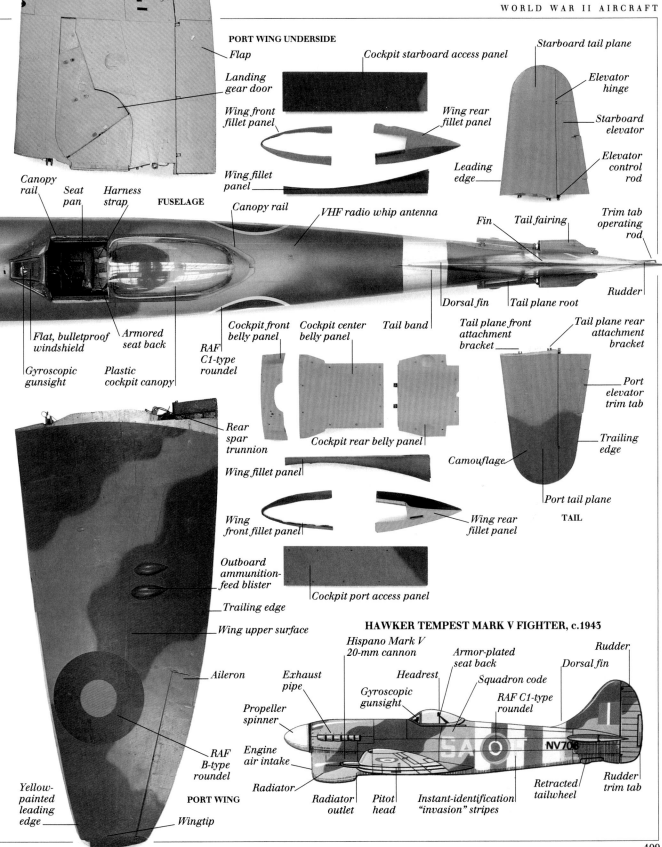

PORT WING UNDERSIDE

Flap

Landing gear door

Wing front fillet panel

Wing fillet panel

Cockpit starboard access panel

Wing rear fillet panel

Starboard tail plane

Elevator hinge

Starboard elevator

Elevator control rod

Leading edge

Canopy rail

Seat pan

Harness strap

FUSELAGE

Canopy rail

VHF radio whip antenna

Fin

Tail fairing

Trim tab operating rod

Rudder

Flat, bulletproof windshield

Armored seat back

Dorsal fin

Tail plane root

Tail band

Gyroscopic gunsight

Plastic cockpit canopy

Cockpit front belly panel

Cockpit center belly panel

RAF C1-type roundel

Cockpit rear belly panel

Tail plane front attachment bracket

Tail plane rear attachment bracket

Port elevator trim tab

Trailing edge

Rear spar trunnion

Wing fillet panel

Camouflage

Port tail plane

TAIL

Wing front fillet panel

Wing rear fillet panel

Outboard ammunition-feed blister

Trailing edge

Wing upper surface

Cockpit port access panel

HAWKER TEMPEST MARK V FIGHTER, c.1943

Aileron

RAF B-type roundel

Yellow-painted leading edge

PORT WING

Wingtip

Hispano Mark V 20-mm cannon

Exhaust pipe

Propeller spinner

Engine air intake

Radiator

Headrest

Gyroscopic gunsight

Armor-plated seat back

Squadron code

RAF C1-type roundel

Rudder

Dorsal fin

Radiator outlet

Pitot head

Instant-identification "invasion" stripes

Retracted tailwheel

Rudder trim tab

SA T

NV70

Modern piston aircraft engines

PISTON ENGINES today are used mainly to power the vast numbers of light aircraft and ultralights, as well as crop sprayers and crop dusters, small helicopters, and fire-bombers (which dump water on large fires). Virtually all heavier aircraft are now powered by jet engines. Modern piston aircraft engines work on the same basic principles as the engine used by the Wright brothers in the first powered flight in 1903. However, today's engines are more sophisticated than earlier engines. For example, modern aircraft engines may use a two-stroke or a four-stroke combustion cycle; they may have from one to nine air- or liquid-cooled cylinders, which may be arranged horizontally, in-line, in V formation, or radially; and they may drive the aircraft's propeller either directly or through a reduction gearbox. One of the more unconventional types of modern aircraft engine is the rotary engine shown here, which has a trilobate (three-sided) rotor spinning in a chamber shaped like a fat figure-eight.

MID WEST TWO-STROKE, THREE-CYLINDER ENGINE

MID WEST 75-HP TWO-STROKE, THREE-CYLINDER ENGINE

Spark plug

Coolant outlet

Cylinder head

Piston

Cylinder barrel

Exhaust manifold

Exhaust port

Cylinder liner

Upper crankcase

Reduction gearbox

Driven gear

Gearbox drive splines

Connecting rod (con-rod)

Pump drive belt

Coolant pump

Propeller drive flange

Small end

Generator rotor

Torsional vibration damper

Sprag clutch

Big end

Counterweight

Crankshaft

Ignition trigger housing

Stator

Gearbox mounting plate

Lower crankcase

Engine mounting plate

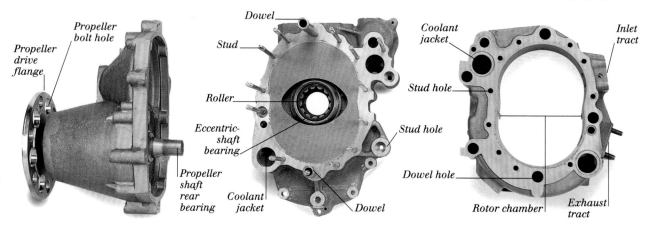

ROTOR AND HOUSINGS OF A MID WEST SINGLE-ROTOR ENGINE

Propeller bolt hole

Propeller drive flange

Dowel

Stud

Coolant jacket

Inlet tract

Roller

Stud hole

Eccentric-shaft bearing

Stud hole

Propeller shaft rear bearing

Coolant jacket

Dowel

Dowel hole

Rotor chamber

Exhaust tract

GEARBOX CASE

FRONT HOUSING (FRONT END PLATE)

TROCHOID HOUSING

MID WEST 90-HP TWIN-ROTOR ENGINE

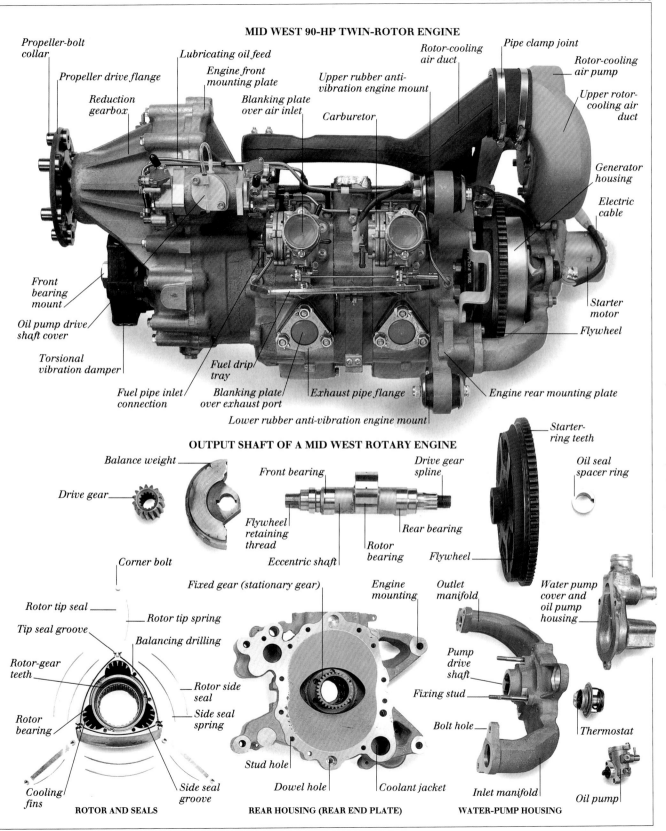

Propeller-bolt collar
Propeller drive flange
Reduction gearbox
Lubricating oil feed
Engine front mounting plate
Blanking plate over air inlet
Carburetor
Upper rubber anti-vibration engine mount
Rotor-cooling air duct
Pipe clamp joint
Rotor-cooling air pump
Upper rotor-cooling air duct
Generator housing
Electric cable
Starter motor
Flywheel
Front bearing mount
Oil pump drive shaft cover
Torsional vibration damper
Fuel pipe inlet connection
Fuel drip tray
Blanking plate over exhaust port
Exhaust pipe flange
Engine rear mounting plate
Lower rubber anti-vibration engine mount

OUTPUT SHAFT OF A MID WEST ROTARY ENGINE

Balance weight
Drive gear
Front bearing
Drive gear spline
Starter-ring teeth
Oil seal spacer ring
Flywheel retaining thread
Rear bearing
Corner bolt
Eccentric shaft
Rotor bearing
Flywheel

Fixed gear (stationary gear)
Engine mounting
Outlet manifold
Water pump cover and oil pump housing

Rotor tip seal
Rotor tip spring
Tip seal groove
Balancing drilling
Rotor-gear teeth
Rotor side seal
Side seal spring
Pump drive shaft
Fixing stud
Bolt hole
Thermostat
Rotor bearing
Stud hole
Dowel hole
Coolant jacket
Inlet manifold
Oil pump
Cooling fins
Side seal groove

ROTOR AND SEALS   **REAR HOUSING (REAR END PLATE)**   **WATER-PUMP HOUSING**

Modern jetliners 1

BAE 146 JETLINER

MODERN JETLINERS HAVE ENABLED ordinary people to travel to places where once only the wealthy could afford to go. Compared with the first jetliners (which were introduced in the 1940s), modern jetliners are much quieter, burn fuel more efficiently, and produce less air pollution. These advances are largely due to the replacement of turbojet engines with turbofan engines (see pp. 418-419). The greater power of turbofan engines at low speeds enables modern jetliners to carry more fuel and passengers than turbojet aircraft; a modern Boeing 747-400 (popularly known as a "jumbo jet") can fly 400 people for 8,500 miles (13,700 km) without needing to refuel. Jetliners fly at high altitudes, typically cruising at 26,000-36,000 ft (8,000-11,000 m), where they can use fuel efficiently and usually avoid bad weather. The pilot always controls the aircraft during takeoff and landing, but at other times the aircraft is usually controlled by an autopilot. Autopilots are complex onboard mechanisms that detect deviations from an aircraft's route and make appropriate adjustments to the flight controls. Flight decks are also equipped with radar that warns pilots of approaching hazards, such as mountain ranges, bad weather, and other aircraft.

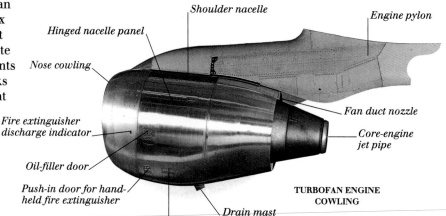

Shoulder nacelle

Engine pylon

Hinged nacelle panel

Nose cowling

Fan duct nozzle

Fire extinguisher discharge indicator

Core-engine jet pipe

Oil-filler door

Push-in door for hand-held fire extinguisher

TURBOFAN ENGINE COWLING

Drain mast

STRUCTURAL COMPONENTS OF A BAE 146 JETLINER

Oil-filler door for integrated-drive generator

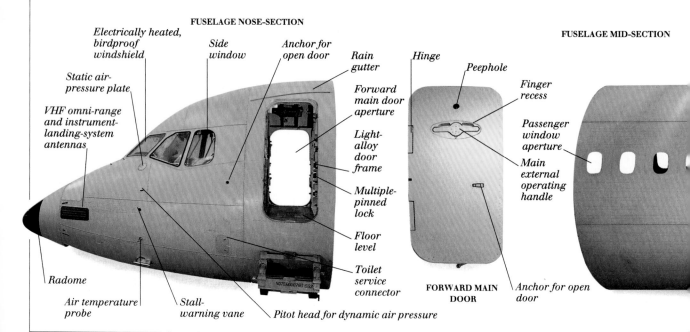

FUSELAGE NOSE-SECTION

FUSELAGE MID-SECTION

Electrically heated, birdproof windshield

Side window

Anchor for open door

Rain gutter

Hinge

Peephole

Finger recess

Static air-pressure plate

Forward main door aperture

VHF omni-range and instrument-landing-system antennas

Light-alloy door frame

Passenger window aperture

Main external operating handle

Multiple-pinned lock

Floor level

Radome

Toilet service connector

FORWARD MAIN DOOR

Anchor for open door

Air temperature probe

Stall-warning vane

Pitot head for dynamic air pressure

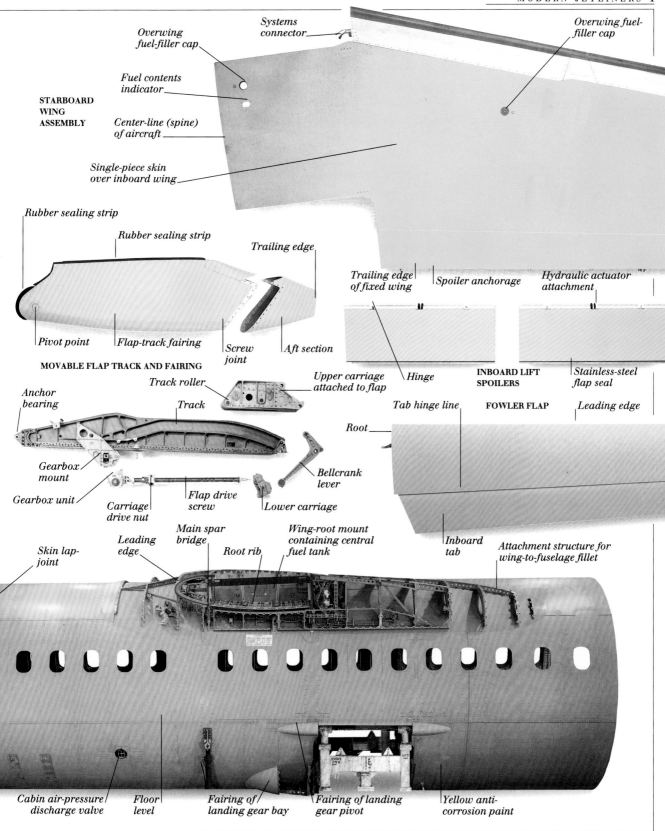

STARBOARD WING ASSEMBLY

Overwing fuel-filler cap

Systems connector

Overwing fuel-filler cap

Fuel contents indicator

Center-line (spine) of aircraft

Single-piece skin over inboard wing

Rubber sealing strip

Rubber sealing strip

Trailing edge

Trailing edge of fixed wing

Spoiler anchorage

Hydraulic actuator attachment

Pivot point

Flap-track fairing

Screw joint

Aft section

Hinge

INBOARD LIFT SPOILERS

Stainless-steel flap seal

MOVABLE FLAP TRACK AND FAIRING

Track roller

Upper carriage attached to flap

FOWLER FLAP

Leading edge

Tab hinge line

Anchor bearing

Track

Root

Gearbox mount

Bellcrank lever

Gearbox unit

Carriage drive nut

Flap drive screw

Lower carriage

Skin lap-joint

Leading edge

Main spar bridge

Root rib

Wing-root mount containing central fuel tank

Inboard tab

Attachment structure for wing-to-fuselage fillet

Cabin air-pressure discharge valve

Floor level

Fairing of landing gear bay

Fairing of landing gear pivot

Yellow anti-corrosion paint

413

Modern jetliners 2

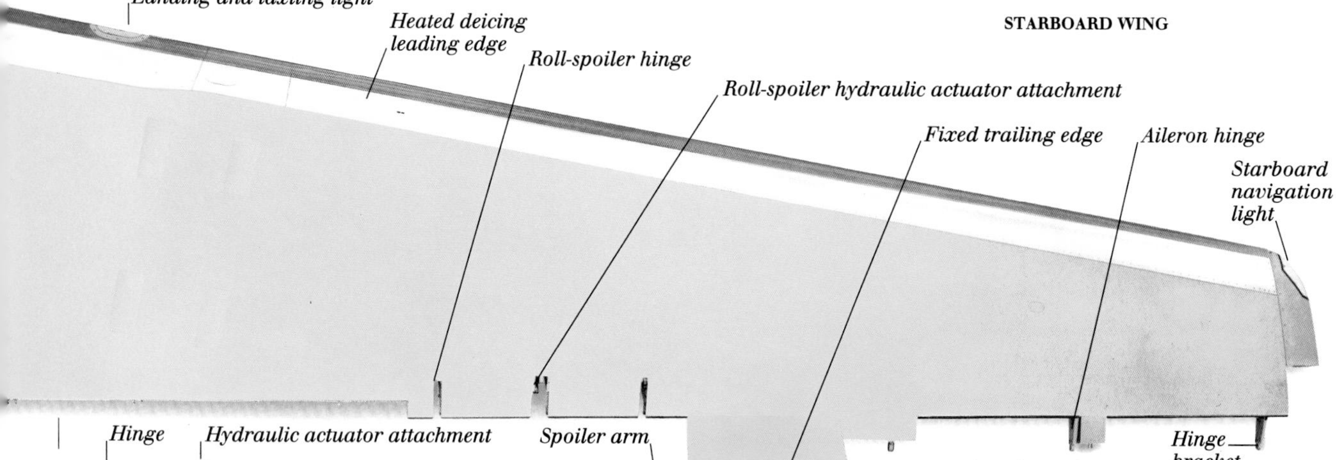

Landing and taxiing light

STARBOARD WING

Heated deicing
leading edge

Roll-spoiler hinge

Roll-spoiler hydraulic actuator attachment

Fixed trailing edge

Aileron hinge

Starboard
navigation
light

Hinge   Hydraulic actuator attachment

Spoiler arm

Hinge
bracket

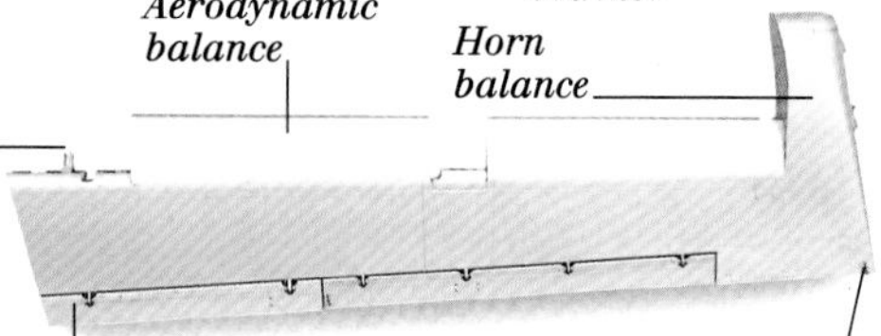

Aerodynamic
balance

Horn
balance

Recessed hinge

**INTERMEDIATE
LIFT SPOILER**

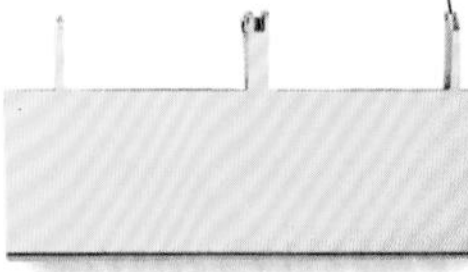

Flap
seal

OUTBOARD ROLL SPOILER

AILERON

Trim tab

MAIN FOWLER FLAP

Leading edge

Static discharge wick attachment

Flap tip

Outboard tab

Tab-hinge line

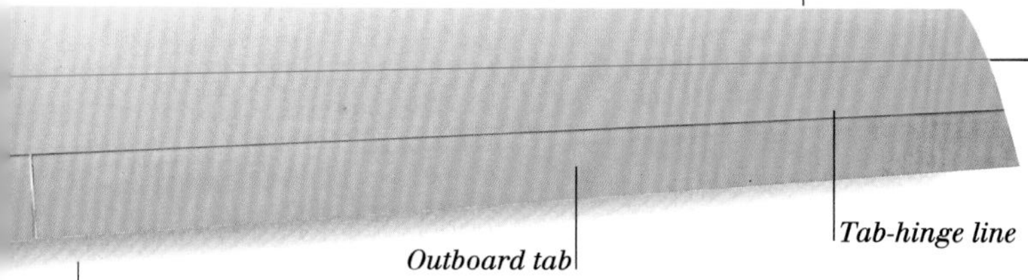

FUSELAGE SPINE FAIRING

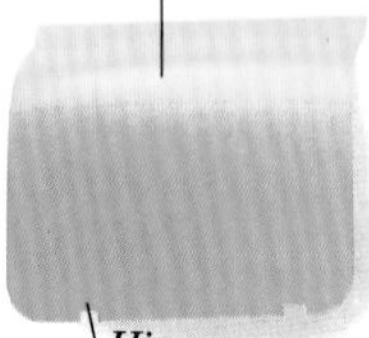

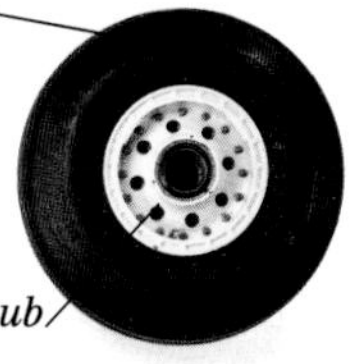

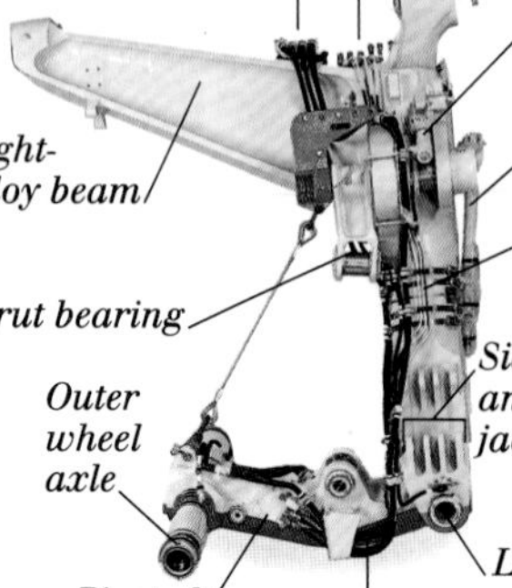

Landing gear
door

Hydraulic brake line

Main pivot

Finger
recess

Peephole

Hot-air deicing duct

Electrical harness

Oleo
lock-jack

Skin lap joint

Passenger
window
aperture

Light-
alloy beam

Direction
bar

Main
external
operating
handle

Shock-strut bearing

Brake
line

Hinge

Pneumatic
tire

Side brace
and retraction
jack trunnions

Outer
wheel
axle

Lower pivot

Wheel hub

Pivoted
trailing-
link arm

Hydraulic
brake line

Anchor for open door

Cabin air-
discharge aperture

Hinge

STARBOARD TWIN-WHEEL MAIN LANDING GEAR

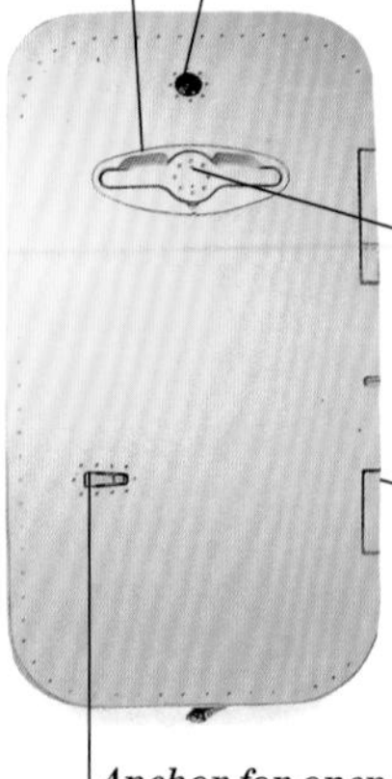

AFT MAIN DOOR

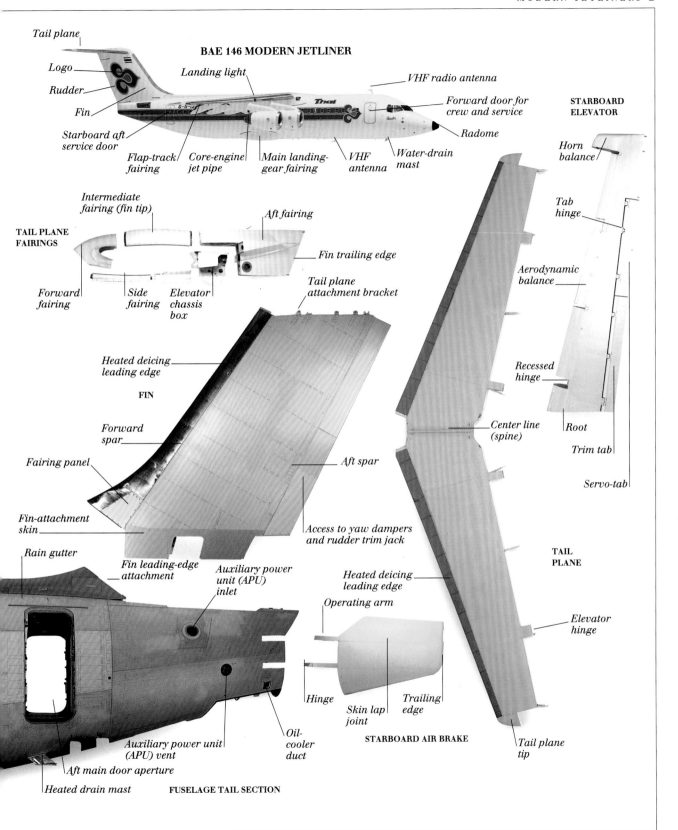

BAE 146 MODERN JETLINER

Tail plane

Logo

Rudder

Fin

Starboard aft
service door

Flap-track
fairing

Core-engine
jet pipe

Main landing-
gear fairing

VHF
antenna

Water-drain
mast

Landing light

VHF radio antenna

Forward door for
crew and service

Radome

**STARBOARD
ELEVATOR**

Horn
balance

Tab
hinge

Aerodynamic
balance

Recessed
hinge

Center line
(spine)

Root

Trim tab

Servo-tab

**TAIL PLANE
FAIRINGS**

Intermediate
fairing (fin tip)

Aft fairing

Fin trailing edge

Forward
fairing

Side
fairing

Elevator
chassis
box

Tail plane
attachment bracket

Heated deicing
leading edge

FIN

Forward
spar

Fairing panel

Aft spar

Fin-attachment
skin

Access to yaw dampers
and rudder trim jack

Rain gutter

Fin leading-edge
attachment

Auxiliary power
unit (APU)
inlet

Heated deicing
leading edge

Operating arm

**TAIL
PLANE**

Elevator
hinge

Auxiliary power unit
(APU) vent

Oil-
cooler
duct

Hinge

Skin lap
joint

Trailing
edge

Tail plane
tip

Aft main door aperture

STARBOARD AIR BRAKE

Heated drain mast

FUSELAGE TAIL SECTION

Supersonic jetliners

COMPUTER-DESIGNED SST

SUPERSONIC AIRCRAFT FLY FASTER than the speed of sound (Mach 1). There are many supersonic military aircraft, but only two supersonic passenger-carrying aircraft (also called SSTs, or supersonic transports) have been produced: the Russian Tu-144, and the Concorde, produced jointly by Britain and France. The Tu-144 had a greater maximum speed than the Concorde but was withdrawn in 1978, after only seven months in service. The Concorde has remained in service since 1976. It features many innovations, including a droop nose, which is lowered during takeoff and landing to aid visibility from the cockpit, and the pumping of fuel between forward and aft trim tanks to help stabilize the aircraft. The Concorde has a narrow fuselage and short-span wings to reduce drag during supersonic flight. Its noisy turbojet engines with afterburners enable it to carry 100 passengers at a cruising speed of Mach 2 at 50,000-60,000 ft (15,000-18,000 m). Once an aircraft is flying faster than Mach 1, it produces a continuous air-pressure wave, which is heard as a "sonic boom."

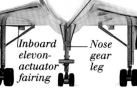

FRONT VIEW OF CONCORDE

Strake
Fin
Standby pitot head
Starboard outboard engine air intake
Inboard elevon-actuator fairing
Nose gear leg

OVERHEAD VIEW OF CONCORDE

Variable nozzle
Leading edge

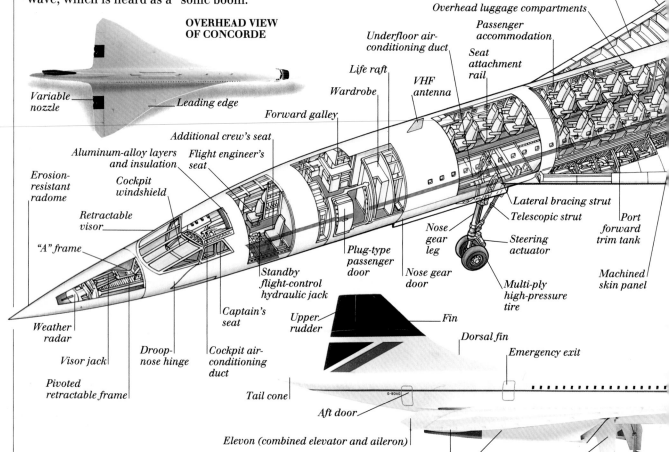

Toilets
Electrothermal deicing panel
Starboard forward trim tank
Overhead luggage compartments
Passenger accommodation
Seat attachment rail
Underfloor air-conditioning duct
Life raft
VHF antenna
Wardrobe
Forward galley
Additional crew's seat
Flight engineer's seat
Aluminum-alloy layers and insulation
Cockpit windshield
Erosion-resistant radome
Retractable visor
"A" frame
Weather radar
Visor jack
Pivoted retractable frame
Droop-nose hinge
Captain's seat
Cockpit air-conditioning duct
Standby flight-control hydraulic jack
Plug-type passenger door
Upper rudder
Nose gear leg
Nose gear door
Lateral bracing strut
Telescopic strut
Steering actuator
Multi-ply high-pressure tire
Port forward trim tank
Machined skin panel
Fin
Dorsal fin
Emergency exit
Tail cone
Aft door
Elevon (combined elevator and aileron)
Hot-section steel and titanium skin
Engine cowling
Landing gear door
Bogie main landing gear

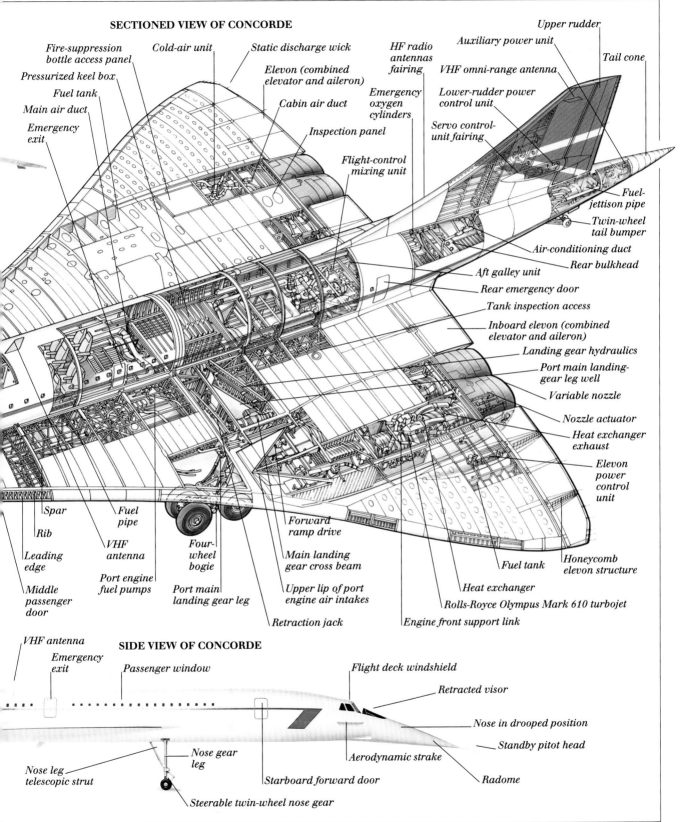

SECTIONED VIEW OF CONCORDE

Fire-suppression bottle access panel
Pressurized keel box
Fuel tank
Main air duct
Emergency exit
Cold-air unit
Static discharge wick
Elevon (combined elevator and aileron)
Cabin air duct
Inspection panel
Flight-control mixing unit
HF radio antennas fairing
Emergency oxygen cylinders
Auxiliary power unit
VHF omni-range antenna
Upper rudder
Tail cone
Lower-rudder power control unit
Servo control-unit fairing
Fuel-jettison pipe
Twin-wheel tail bumper
Air-conditioning duct
Rear bulkhead
Aft galley unit
Rear emergency door
Tank inspection access
Inboard elevon (combined elevator and aileron)
Landing gear hydraulics
Port main landing-gear leg well
Variable nozzle
Nozzle actuator
Heat exchanger exhaust
Elevon power control unit
Honeycomb elevon structure
Fuel tank
Heat exchanger
Rolls-Royce Olympus Mark 610 turbojet
Engine front support link
Upper lip of port engine air intakes
Main landing gear cross beam
Retraction jack
Forward ramp drive
Four-wheel bogie
Port main landing gear leg
Port engine fuel pumps
VHF antenna
Fuel pipe
Spar
Rib
Leading edge
Middle passenger door

SIDE VIEW OF CONCORDE

VHF antenna
Emergency exit
Passenger window
Flight deck windshield
Retracted visor
Nose in drooped position
Standby pitot head
Aerodynamic strake
Radome
Starboard forward door
Steerable twin-wheel nose gear
Nose leg telescopic strut
Nose gear leg

417

Jet engines

JET ENGINES ARE USED BY MOST MILITARY and heavy aircraft and by many helicopters. The simplest type of jet engine, or gas turbine, is the turbojet. It works by continuously burning a mixture of fuel and air in a combustion chamber to produce a jet of hot exhaust gas that is expelled through a nozzle to produce thrust. The hot gas also spins turbine blades which, in turn, spin the blades of an air compressor; the compressor forces air into the combustion chamber. Many of the fastest aircraft use turbojets, with additional booster units called afterburners, but their use is restricted by their high noise emission. Most jetliners use quieter turbofan jet engines. An enormous fan, driven by a low-pressure turbine, feeds some air into the compressor but feeds most of it through bypass ducts to join the exhaust jetstream in the tail cone. The bypass stream produces most of the thrust. Many smaller, propeller-driven aircraft use turboprop jet engines, in which the engine powers a propeller.

NPT 301 MODERN TURBOJET

Fuel sprayer
Turbine rotor
Reverse-flow combustion chamber
Radial diffuser
Centrifugal compressor
Exhaust diffuser
Inducer
Air intake
Tail cone
Jet pipe
Exhaust nozzle
Nose cone
Igniter
Alternator
Air impingement starter
Nozzle guide vane
Combustion chamber casing

Temperature and pressure sensor
Low-pressure fan
Inlet cone (rotating spinner)
Pressure line
Fan case with special structure to contain broken fan
Electronic engine control and airframe interface connector
Electronic engine control (EEC) unit
Compressor front bearing
Engine front mount
Electrical wiring harness
Fuel and oil heat exchanger
Oil filter
Compressor air-bleed connection

Plenum ring for hot anti-icing air
Flow splitter
Transmission bevel drive
Integral oil tank
High-pressure compressor
Combustion chamber
Centrifugal compressor
Fuel manifold
Fuel nozzle
High-pressure turbine
Fan duct

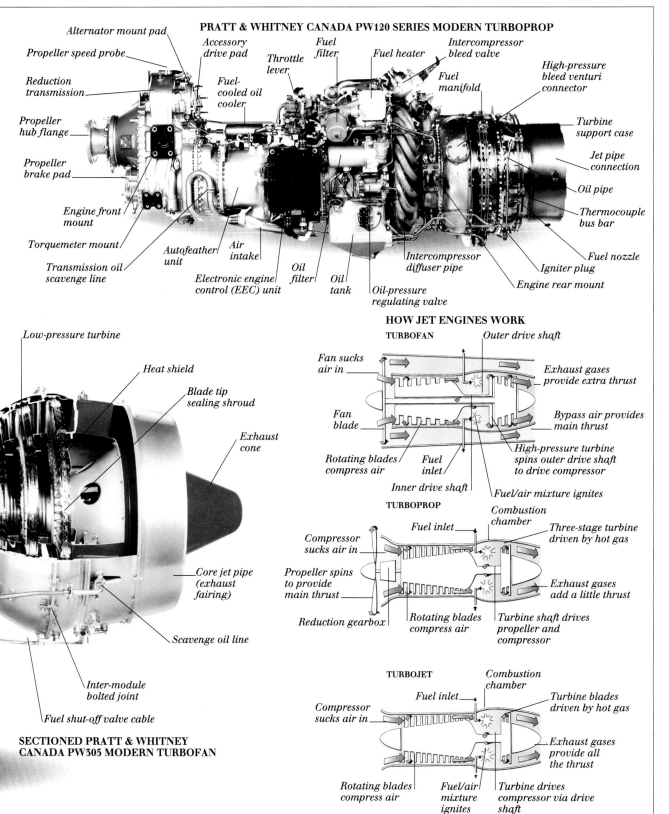

PRATT & WHITNEY CANADA PW120 SERIES MODERN TURBOPROP

Alternator mount pad
Propeller speed probe
Reduction transmission
Propeller hub flange
Propeller brake pad
Engine front mount
Torquemeter mount
Transmission oil scavenge line
Accessory drive pad
Throttle lever
Fuel-cooled oil cooler
Autofeather unit
Air intake
Electronic engine control (EEC) unit
Oil filter
Oil tank
Fuel filter
Fuel heater
Fuel manifold
Intercompressor bleed valve
Oil-pressure regulating valve
Intercompressor diffuser pipe
High-pressure bleed venturi connector
Turbine support case
Jet pipe connection
Oil pipe
Thermocouple bus bar
Fuel nozzle
Igniter plug
Engine rear mount

HOW JET ENGINES WORK

TURBOFAN

Fan sucks air in
Fan blade
Rotating blades compress air
Inner drive shaft
Fuel inlet
Outer drive shaft
Exhaust gases provide extra thrust
Bypass air provides main thrust
High-pressure turbine spins outer drive shaft to drive compressor
Fuel/air mixture ignites

TURBOPROP

Compressor sucks air in
Propeller spins to provide main thrust
Reduction gearbox
Rotating blades compress air
Fuel inlet
Combustion chamber
Three-stage turbine driven by hot gas
Exhaust gases add a little thrust
Turbine shaft drives propeller and compressor

TURBOJET

Compressor sucks air in
Rotating blades compress air
Fuel inlet
Fuel/air mixture ignites
Combustion chamber
Turbine blades driven by hot gas
Exhaust gases provide all the thrust
Turbine drives compressor via drive shaft

Low-pressure turbine
Heat shield
Blade tip sealing shroud
Exhaust cone
Core jet pipe (exhaust fairing)
Scavenge oil line
Inter-module bolted joint
Fuel shut-off valve cable

SECTIONED PRATT & WHITNEY CANADA PW305 MODERN TURBOFAN

419

Modern military aircraft

MODERN MILITARY AIRCRAFT ARE AMONG THE MOST SOPHISTICATED and expensive products of the 20th century. Fighters need computer-operated controls for maneuverability, powerful engines, and effective air-to-air weapons. Most modern fighters also have guided missiles, radar, and passive, infrared sensors. These developments enable today's fighters to engage in combat with adversaries who are outside visual range. Bombers carry a large weapon load and enough fuel for long-range flights. A few military aircraft, such as the Tornado and the F-14 Tomcat, have variable-sweep ("swing") wings. During takeoff and landing their wings are fully extended, but for high-speed flight and low-level attacks the wings are pivoted fully back. A recent development is the "stealth" bomber, which is designed to absorb or deflect enemy radar in order to remain undetected. Earlier bombers, such as the Tornado, use terrain-following radars to fly so close to the ground that they avoid enemy radar detection.

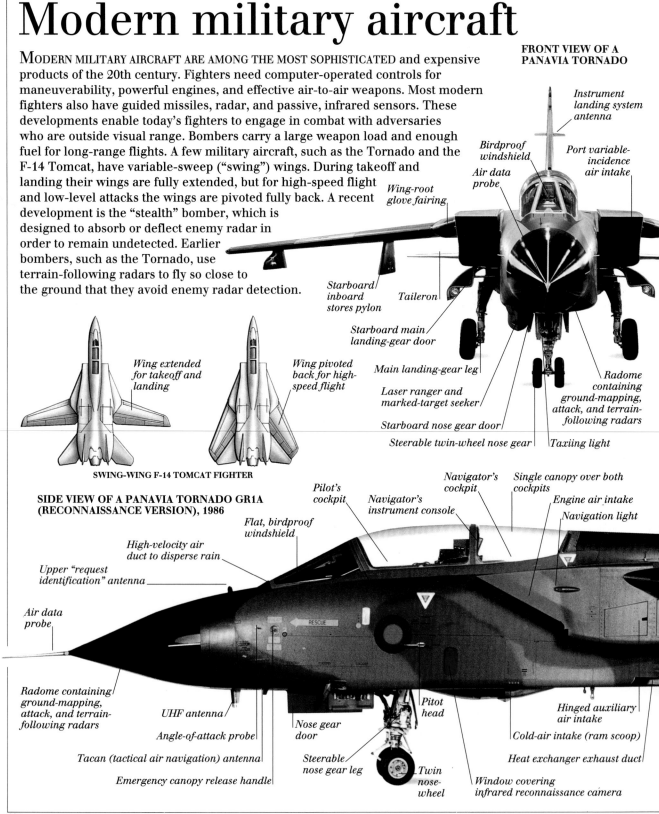

FRONT VIEW OF A PANAVIA TORNADO

Instrument landing system antenna

Birdproof windshield

Air data probe

Wing-root glove fairing

Port variable-incidence air intake

Starboard inboard stores pylon

Taileron

Starboard main landing-gear door

Main landing-gear leg

Laser ranger and marked-target seeker

Starboard nose gear door

Steerable twin-wheel nose gear

Radome containing ground-mapping, attack, and terrain-following radars

Taxiing light

Wing extended for takeoff and landing

Wing pivoted back for high-speed flight

SWING-WING F-14 TOMCAT FIGHTER

SIDE VIEW OF A PANAVIA TORNADO GR1A (RECONNAISSANCE VERSION), 1986

Pilot's cockpit

Navigator's instrument console

Navigator's cockpit

Single canopy over both cockpits

Engine air intake

Navigation light

Flat, birdproof windshield

High-velocity air duct to disperse rain

Upper "request identification" antenna

Air data probe

Radome containing ground-mapping, attack, and terrain-following radars

UHF antenna

Angle-of-attack probe

Tacan (tactical air navigation) antenna

Emergency canopy release handle

Nose gear door

Steerable nose gear leg

Twin nose-wheel

Pitot head

Window covering infrared reconnaissance camera

Hinged auxiliary air intake

Cold-air intake (ram scoop)

Heat exchanger exhaust duct

NORTHROP B-2 ("STEALTH" BOMBER), 1989

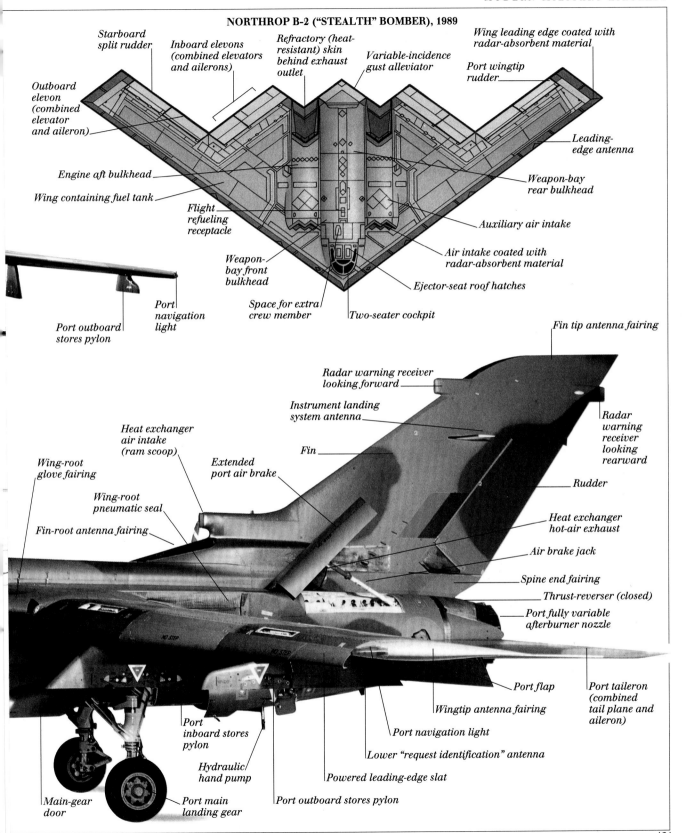

Starboard split rudder

Inboard elevons (combined elevators and ailerons)

Refractory (heat-resistant) skin behind exhaust outlet

Variable-incidence gust alleviator

Wing leading edge coated with radar-absorbent material

Port wingtip rudder

Outboard elevon (combined elevator and aileron)

Leading-edge antenna

Engine aft bulkhead

Wing containing fuel tank

Flight refueling receptacle

Weapon-bay rear bulkhead

Weapon-bay front bulkhead

Auxiliary air intake

Air intake coated with radar-absorbent material

Ejector-seat roof hatches

Space for extra crew member

Two-seater cockpit

Port navigation light

Port outboard stores pylon

Fin tip antenna fairing

Radar warning receiver looking forward

Instrument landing system antenna

Fin

Heat exchanger air intake (ram scoop)

Extended port air brake

Radar warning receiver looking rearward

Rudder

Wing-root glove fairing

Wing-root pneumatic seal

Fin-root antenna fairing

Heat exchanger hot-air exhaust

Air brake jack

Spine end fairing

Thrust-reverser (closed)

Port fully variable afterburner nozzle

Port flap

Port taileron (combined tail plane and aileron)

Wingtip antenna fairing

Port navigation light

Lower "request identification" antenna

Powered leading-edge slat

Port outboard stores pylon

Port inboard stores pylon

Hydraulic hand pump

Main-gear door

Port main landing gear

Gliders, hang gliders, and ultralights

NOSE SHELL

Grommet for front pylon strut

Instrument panel

HANG GLIDER

MODERN GLIDERS ARE AMONG the most graceful and aerodynamically efficient of all aircraft. Unpowered but with a large wingspan (up to about 82 ft, or 25 m), gliders use currents of hot, rising air (thermals) to stay aloft, and a rudder, elevators, and ailerons for control. Modern gliders have achieved flights of more than 900 miles (1,450 km) and altitudes above 49,000 ft (15,000 m). Hang gliders consist of a simple frame across which rigid or flexible material is stretched to form the wings. The pilot is suspended below the wings in a harness or body bag and, gripping a triangular A-frame, steers by shifting weight from side to side. Like gliders, hang gliders rely on thermals for lift. Ultralights are basically powered hang gliders. A small engine and an open fiberglass car (trike), which can hold a crew of two, are suspended beneath a stronger version of a hang glider frame; the frame may have rigid or flexible wings. Ultralight pilots, like hang glider pilots, steer by shifting their weight against an A-frame. Ultralights can reach speeds of up to 100 mph (160 kph).

King post

Apex

PEGASUS XL SE ULTRALIGHT

Stiffening rib

Center-line beam

Apex wire

Main suspension

Nose shell

Rear-mounted propeller (pusher propeller)

Nose gear mount

Fuel tank

Main wheel

Wheel part

Trike nacelle

Fixed nose wheel

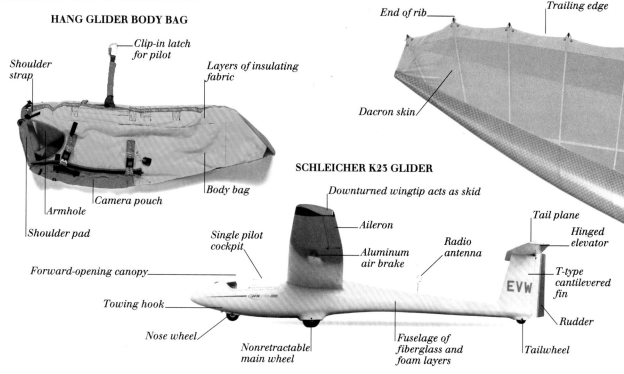

HANG GLIDER BODY BAG

End of rib

Trailing edge

Clip-in latch for pilot

Shoulder strap

Layers of insulating fabric

Dacron skin

Camera pouch

Body bag

Armhole

Shoulder pad

SCHLEICHER K23 GLIDER

Downturned wingtip acts as skid

Single pilot cockpit

Aileron

Radio antenna

Tail plane

Hinged elevator

Aluminum air brake

T-type cantilevered fin

Forward-opening canopy

EVW

Towing hook

Rudder

Nose wheel

Nonretractable main wheel

Fuselage of fiberglass and foam layers

Tailwheel

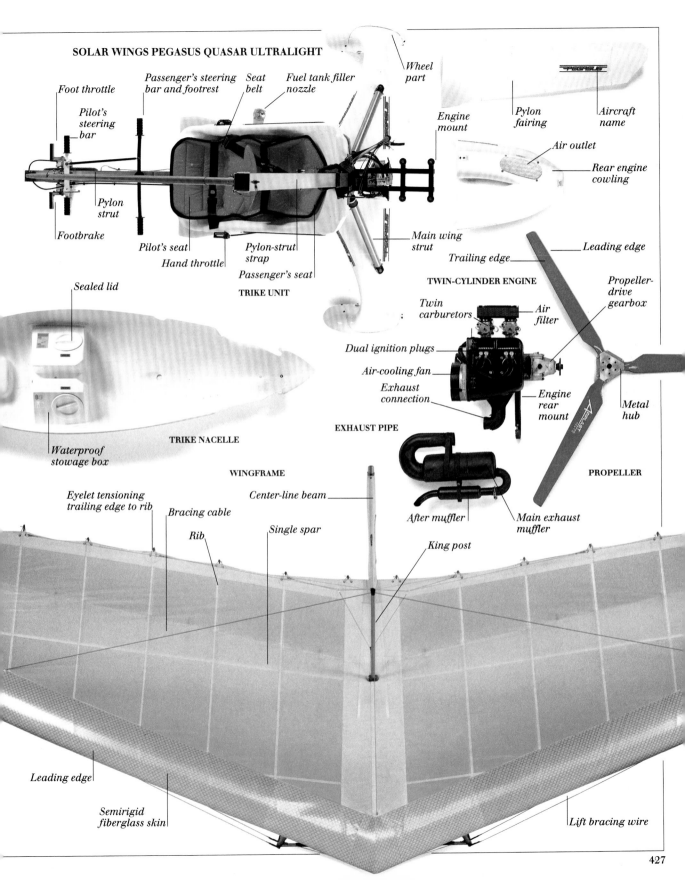

SOLAR WINGS PEGASUS QUASAR ULTRALIGHT

Foot throttle

Passenger's steering
bar and footrest

Seat
belt

Fuel tank filler
nozzle

Wheel
part

Pilot's
steering
bar

Engine
mount

Pylon
fairing

Aircraft
name

Air outlet

Rear engine
cowling

Pylon
strut

Footbrake

Pilot's seat

Hand throttle

Pylon-strut
strap

Passenger's seat

Main wing
strut

Trailing edge

Leading edge

Propeller-
drive
gearbox

TRIKE UNIT

TWIN-CYLINDER ENGINE

Sealed lid

Twin
carburetors

Air
filter

Dual ignition plugs

Air-cooling fan

Exhaust
connection

Engine
rear
mount

Metal
hub

Waterproof
stowage box

TRIKE NACELLE

EXHAUST PIPE

PROPELLER

WINGFRAME

Eyelet tensioning
trailing edge to rib

Bracing cable

Rib

Center-line beam

Single spar

King post

After muffler

Main exhaust
muffler

Leading edge

Semirigid
fiberglass skin

Lift bracing wire

427

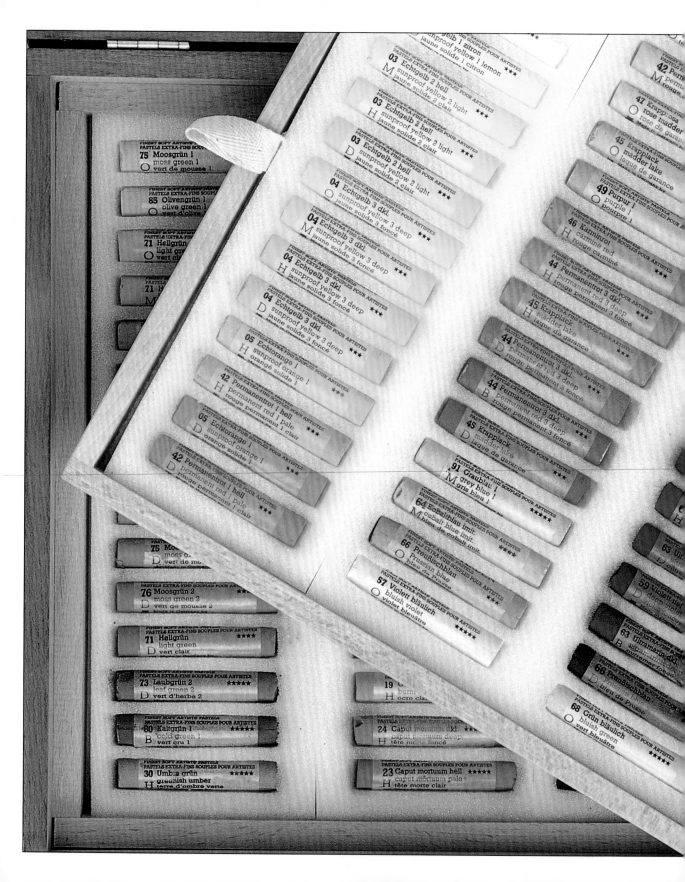

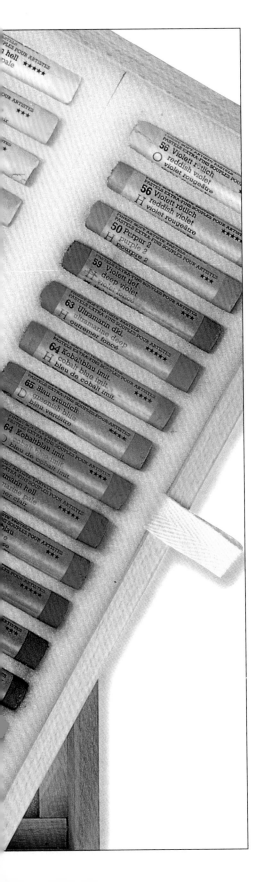

THE
VISUAL ARTS

Drawing

DRAWINGS CAN BE FINISHED WORKS OF ART, or preparatory studies for paintings and other visual arts. They can be made using a wide variety of drawing instruments such as pencils, graphite sticks, chalks, charcoal, pens and inks, and silver wires. The most common drawing instrument is the graphite pencil. A graphite pencil consists of a thin rod of graphite mixed with clay, encased in wood. Charcoal is one of the oldest drawing instruments. It is produced by firing twigs of willow, vine, or other woods at high temperatures in airtight containers. Erasers can be used to rub out marks made by drawing materials such as graphite pencils or charcoal, or to achieve a particular effect—such as smudging. Fixative is often applied—using a mouth diffuser or aerosol spray fixative—to prevent smudging once a drawing is finished. Silver lines can be produced by drawing silver wire across specially prepared paper— a technique known as silverpoint. The lines are permanent and cannot be erased. In time the silver lines oxidize and turn brown.

FIXATIVE AND MOUTH DIFFUSER

Hinge

Liquid fixative consisting of dissolved resin

Fixative is sucked into tube and sprayed onto drawing

DRAWING INSTRUMENTS

2B GRAPHITE PENCIL

8B GRAPHITE PENCIL

SILVER WIRE IN A METAL HOLDER

DRAWING BOARD

Medium-soft, light line

Very soft, dark line

ERASERS

Hard texture

PLASTIC ERASER

Soft texture

KNEADED ERASER

CHALK, CRAYON, AND CHARCOAL

Calcite (calcium carbonate) mixed with pigment

BLUE CHALK

Iron oxide mixed with chalk

SANGUINE CRAYON

Carbonized wood

WILLOW CHARCOAL

DRAWING MATERIALS

Drawing board

Paper

Drawing clip

Colored pencil

Graphite stick

Binder clip

Dip pen

Pencil sharpener

Sketch book

Ink bottle

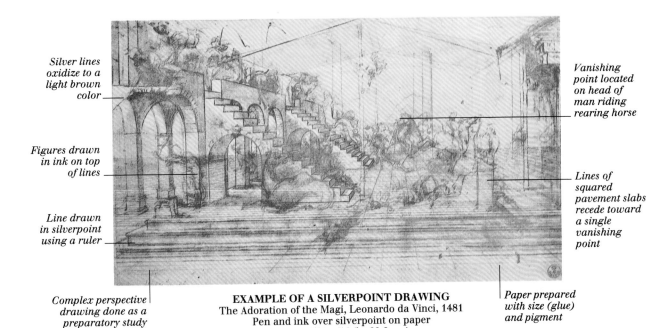

Silver lines
oxidize to a
light brown
color

Figures drawn
in ink on top
of lines

Line drawn
in silverpoint
using a ruler

Complex perspective
drawing done as a
preparatory study
for a painting

Vanishing
point located
on head of
man riding
rearing horse

Lines of
squared
pavement slabs
recede toward
a single
vanishing
point

Paper prepared
with size (glue)
and pigment

EXAMPLE OF A SILVERPOINT DRAWING
The Adoration of the Magi, Leonardo da Vinci, 1481
Pen and ink over silverpoint on paper
6½ x 11½ in (16.5 x 29.2 cm)

One of a series
of drawings
recording
London during
1944–1945

Charcoal lines
softened by
rubbing and
smudging

Charcoal
gives strong,
expressive lines

Handmade, tinted
paper

Broad charcoal
mark

Lines rapidly
drawn on site

EXAMPLE OF A CHARCOAL DRAWING
St. Paul's and the River, David Bomberg, 1945
Charcoal on paper
20 x 25⅛ in (50.8 x 65.8 cm)

Tempera

ILLUMINATED MANUSCRIPT

THE TERM TEMPERA is applied to any paint in which pigment is tempered (mixed) with a water-based binding medium—usually egg yolk. Egg tempera is applied to a smooth surface such as vellum (for illuminated manuscripts) or more commonly to hardwood panels prepared with gesso—a mixture of chalk and size (glue). Bristle brushes are used to apply the gesso. A layer of gesso grosso (coarse gesso) is followed by successive layers of gesso sotile (fine gesso) that are sanded between coats to provide a smooth, yet absorbent ground. The paint is applied with fine sable brushes in thin layers, using light brushstrokes. Tempera dries quickly to form a tough skin with a satin sheen. The luminous white surface of the gesso combined with the overlaid paint produces the brilliant crispness and rich colors particular to this medium. Egg tempera paintings are frequently gilded with gold. Leaves of finely beaten gold are applied to a bole (reddish-brown clay) base and polished by burnishing.

MATERIALS FOR GILDING

Parchment for protecting gold leaf from drafts

Brush

Bowl containing diluted bole

Gold leaf

Gilder's knife

Gilder's tip for picking up gold leaf

Gilder's cushion

Surface prepared with gesso

Gold leaf smoothed and polished with a burnisher

Gold leaf applied in overlapping layers

Bole brushed onto gesso

Burnisher

Agate tip

MATERIALS FOR TEMPERA PANEL PAINTING

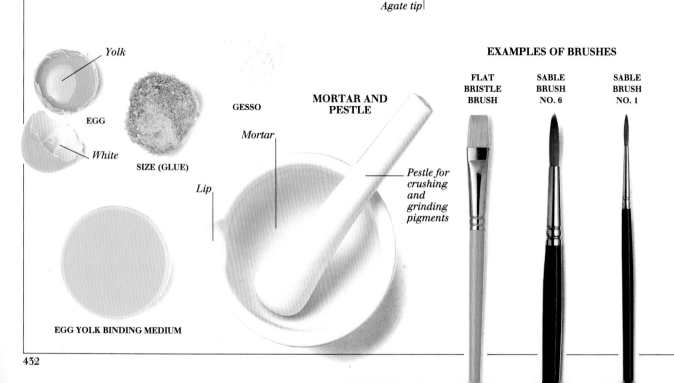

Yolk

EGG

White

SIZE (GLUE)

GESSO

MORTAR AND PESTLE

Mortar

Lip

Pestle for crushing and grinding pigments

EXAMPLES OF BRUSHES

FLAT BRISTLE BRUSH

SABLE BRUSH NO. 6

SABLE BRUSH NO. 1

EGG YOLK BINDING MEDIUM

EXAMPLE OF A TEMPERA PAINTING
Presentation in the Temple, Ambrogio Lorenzetti, 1342
Tempera on wood, 8 ft 5⅛ in x 5 ft 6⅛ in (257 x 168 cm)

PIGMENTS FOR FLESH-COLOR PAINTING

Altarpiece commissioned for Siena Cathedral, Italy

Textured gold ornament made by punching motifs into the gilded surface

The red tinge of the bole is just visible beneath the gold

Edge of a sheet of gold leaf

Crisp edge characteristic of tempera painting

Vine black used to create the dim cathedral interior

Highlights on the beard made by applying thin layers of white over dried paint

Red drapery painted in vermilion

Raised right hand and pointing finger is the gesture of prophecy

Receding floor tiles create the impression of depth

Patch of discolored varnish, left from last cleaning

VERDACCIO

VERMILION AND LEAD WHITE

VERMILION

RED EARTH (IRON OXIDE)

EXAMPLES OF PIGMENTS

MALACHITE

ULTRAMARINE LAPIS LAZULI

Warm flesh tones achieved by layering vermilion and white over an undercoat of verdaccio

Patterned gold halo glitters in candlelight

Ultramarine lapis lazuli, as costly as gold, was reserved for significant figures such as the Virgin Mary

Craquelure (pattern of cracks in the paint)

DETAIL FROM "PRESENTATION IN THE TEMPLE"

VINE BLACK

LEAD TIN YELLOW

433

Fresco

FRESCO IS A METHOD OF WALL PAINTING. In buon fresco (true fresco), pigments are mixed with water and applied to an intonaco (layer of fresh, damp lime-plaster). The intonaco absorbs and binds the pigments as it dries making the picture a permanent part of the wall surface. The intonaco is applied in sections called giornate (daily sections). The size of each giornata depends on the artist's estimate of how much can be painted before the plaster sets. The junctions between giornate are sometimes visible on a finished fresco. The range of colors used in buon fresco are limited to lime-resistant pigments such as earth colors (below). Slaked lime (burnt lime mixed with water), bianco di San Giovanni (slaked lime that has been partly exposed to air), and chalk can be used to produce fresco whites. In fresco secco (dry fresco), pigments are mixed with a binding medium and applied to dry plaster. The pigments are not completely absorbed into the plaster and may flake off over time.

CROSS-SECTION SHOWING FRESCO LAYERS

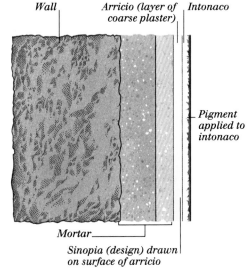

Wall

Arricio (layer of coarse plaster)

Intonaco

Pigment applied to intonaco

Mortar

Sinopia (design) drawn on surface of arricio

EXAMPLES OF EARTH COLOR PIGMENTS

RAW UMBER

RED EARTH (IRON OXIDE)

GREEN EARTH

RAW SIENNA

INGREDIENTS FOR FRESCO WHITES

Marble slab for mixing ingredients

Bianco di San Giovanni

Slaked lime

Chalk

EXAMPLES OF FRESCO BRUSHES

Round bristle brush

Rust-resistant twine binding

Dome-shaped bristle brush

Pointed bristle brush

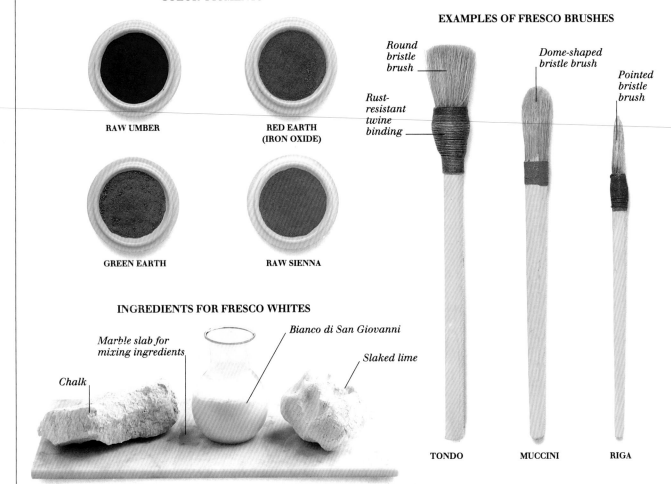

TONDO

MUCCINI

RIGA

EXAMPLE OF A FRESCO
The Expulsion of the Merchants from the Temple, Giotto, c.1306
Fresco, 78 x 72 in (200 x 185 cm)

Temple acts as a backdrop for the action

Bianco di San Giovanni often used for fresco whites

Gold leaf applied to apostle's halo

Green earth pigment applied to robe

Child painted on top of apostle's robe

One of a series of frescoes in the Arena Chapel, Padua, Italy

Patches of azurite blue have turned green due to reaction with carbon dioxide

Hairline junction between giornate is visible

Red earth pigment applied in buon fresco has retained rich hue

Azurite blue applied in fresco secco has flaked off to reveal the plaster beneath

Dry, matt surface characteristic of buon fresco

Paint applied in buon fresco to child's face

White dove represents the Holy Ghost

Paint applied in fresco secco to child's body has flaked off

DETAIL FROM "THE EXPULSION"

Artist has to finish giornata before plaster dries

Junction between giornate

A fresco was generally worked in zones from the top down

Area with little detail can be painted quickly, allowing a larger giornata to be completed

Highly detailed area takes a longer time to paint, restricting the size of the giornata

Sinopia (design) sketched in red earth

GIORNATE (DAILY SECTIONS) IN "THE EXPULSION"

Oils

KIDNEY-SHAPED PALETTE

OIL PAINTS ARE MADE BY MIXING and grinding pigment with a drying vegetable oil such as linseed oil. The paint can be applied to many different surfaces and textures—the most common being canvas. Before painting, the canvas is stretched on a wooden frame and its surface is prepared with layers of size (glue) and primer. The two main types of brushes used in oil painting are stiff hog hair bristle brushes—generally used for covering large areas; and soft hair brushes made from sable or synthetic material—generally used for fine detail. Other tools, including painting knives, can also be used to achieve different effects. Oil paint can be applied thickly (a technique known as impasto), or can be thinned down using a solvent such as turpentine. Varnishes are sometimes applied to finished paintings to protect their surface and to give them a matt or gloss finish.

DAMMAR RESIN VARNISH

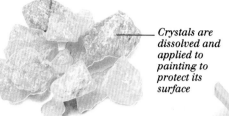

Crystals are dissolved and applied to painting to protect its surface

COMMERCIAL OIL PAINTS

CADMIUM RED

ULTRAMARINE

Lightfast opaque color

Transparent color

LINSEED OIL

EXAMPLES OF PIGMENTS

CADMIUM RED

Oil derived from seeds of flax plant

CERULEAN BLUE

DOUBLE DIPPER (PALETTE ATTACHMENT)

Screw-top lid

Container for storing solvent or drying oil

EXAMPLES OF BRUSHES

SYNTHETIC BRUSH

BRISTLE BRUSHES

Flat bristle brush

Filbert bristle brush

Flat bristle brush

Filbert bristle brush

Round bristle brush

EQUIPMENT FOR MAKING OIL PAINT

Airtight jar for storing paint

Palette knife for mixing drying oil and pigment

PAINTING KNIVES

TROWEL-SHAPED PAINTING KNIFE

DIAMOND-SHAPED PAINTING KNIFE

SABLE BRUSH

Blade

Blade

Glass muller for grinding drying oil and pigment

Glass slab with abrasive surface

Cranked, steel shank

Cranked, steel shank

Long, wooden handle

Protective, plastic case

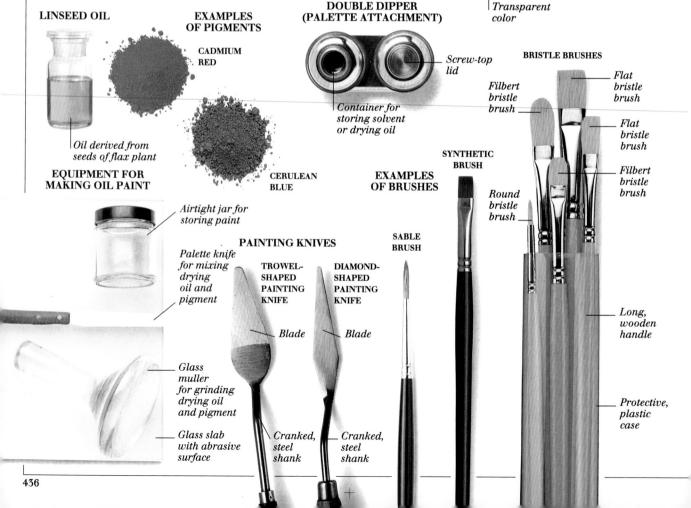

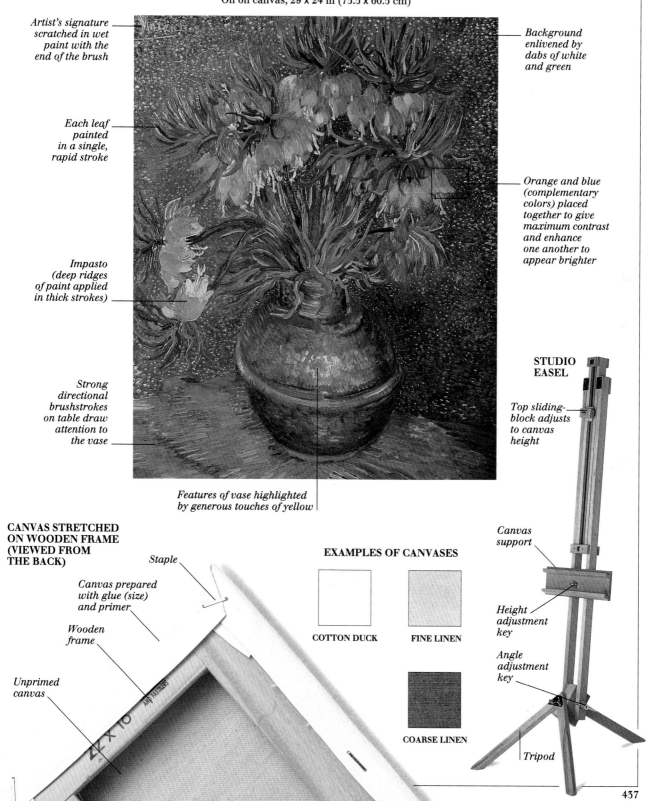

EXAMPLE OF AN OIL PAINTING
Fritillarias, Vincent van Gogh, 1886
Oil on canvas, 29 x 24 in (73.5 x 60.5 cm)

Artist's signature scratched in wet paint with the end of the brush

Background enlivened by dabs of white and green

Each leaf painted in a single, rapid stroke

Orange and blue (complementary colors) placed together to give maximum contrast and enhance one another to appear brighter

Impasto (deep ridges of paint applied in thick strokes)

Strong directional brushstrokes on table draw attention to the vase

Features of vase highlighted by generous touches of yellow

STUDIO EASEL

Top sliding-block adjusts to canvas height

Canvas support

Height adjustment key

Angle adjustment key

Tripod

CANVAS STRETCHED ON WOODEN FRAME (VIEWED FROM THE BACK)

Staple

Canvas prepared with glue (size) and primer

Wooden frame

Unprimed canvas

EXAMPLES OF CANVASES

COTTON DUCK

FINE LINEN

COARSE LINEN

437

Watercolor

WATERCOLOR PAINT IS MADE OF GROUND PIGMENT mixed with a water-soluble binding medium, usually gum arabic. It is usually applied to paper using soft hair brushes such as sable, goat hair, squirrel, and synthetic brushes. Watercolors are often diluted and applied as overlaying washes (thin, transparent layers) to build up depth of color. Washes can be laid in a variety of ways to create a range of different effects. For example, a wet-in-wet wash can be achieved by laying a wash on top of another wet wash. The two washes blend together to give a fused effect. Sponges are used to modify washes by soaking up paint so that areas of pigment are lightened or removed from the paper. Watercolors can also be applied undiluted—a technique known as dry brush—to create a broken-color effect. Watercolors are generally transparent and allow light to reflect from the surface of the paper through the layers of paint to give a luminous effect. They can be thickened and made opaque by adding body color (Chinese white).

GUM ARABIC

*Natural sap
from acacia tree*

NATURAL SPONGE

ANATOMY OF A SABLE BRUSH

*Soft red
sable hair*

Toe (tip)

Wooden handle

SOFT HAIR BRUSHES

*Hair trimmed
and cemented
into ferrule*

ROUND SABLE BRUSH (NO. 6)

*Round
ferrule*

*Hair tied with
clove hitch knot*

ROUND SABLE BRUSH (NO. 1)

**TUBES OF
WATERCOLOR PAINT**

WINSOR GREEN

SYNTHETIC WASH BRUSH

Winsor Green
Vert Winsor
Winsorgrün
Verde Winsor
Verde Winsor
0102 720 SL Series 1 A

Cadmium Yellow
Jaune de Cadmium
Kadmiumgelb
Amarillo de Cadmio
Giallo di cadmio
0102 108 SL Series 4 A

SQUIRREL MOP
WASH BRUSH

**PORTABLE BOX OF
WATERCOLOR PAINTS**

CADMIUM YELLOW

Painted color swatch

Chinese white

*Pan of
watercolor paint*

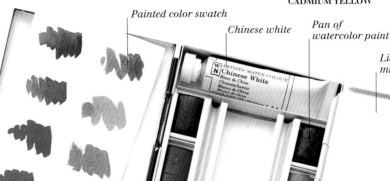

ARTISTS' WATER COLOUR
Chinese White
Blanc de Chine
Chinesischweiss
Blanco de China

*Lid can be used for
mixing colors*

LARGE GOAT HAKE
WASH BRUSH

EXAMPLE OF A WATERCOLOR
Burning of the Houses of Parliament, Turner, 1834
Watercolor on paper, 11½ x 17½ in (29.2 x 44.5 cm)

Transparent washes laid on top of each other to create tonal depth

Transparent washes allow light to reflect off the surface of the paper to give a luminous effect

Highlight scratched out with a scalpel

Paper shows through thin wash to give flames added highlight

Crowd painted with thin strokes laid over a pale wash

Undiluted paint applied, then partly washed out, to create the impression of water

EXAMPLES OF WATERCOLOR PAPERS

SMOOTH-TEXTURED PAPER

MEDIUM-TEXTURED PAPER

ROUGH-TEXTURED PAPER

EXAMPLES OF WASHES

WASH OVER DRY BRUSH
Wash laid over paint applied with dry brush gives two-tone effect

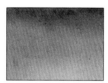

GRADED WASH
Strong wash applied to tilted paper gives graded effect

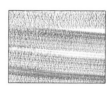

DRY BRUSH
Undiluted paint dragged across surface of paper gives broken effect

WET-IN-WET
Two diluted washes left to run together to give fused effect

COLOR WHEEL OF WATERCOLOR PAINTS

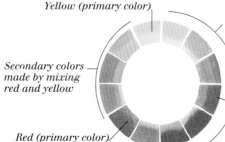

Yellow (primary color)

Secondary colors made by mixing yellow and blue

Secondary colors made by mixing red and yellow

Blue (primary color)

Red (primary color)

Secondary colors made by mixing blue and red

Acrylics

ACRYLIC PAINT IS MADE BY MIXING PIGMENT with a synthetic resin. It can be thinned with water but dries to become water insoluble. Acrylics are applied to many surfaces, such as paper and acrylic-primed board and canvas. A variety of brushes, painting knives, rollers, air-brushes, plastic scrapers, and other tools are used in acrylic painting. The versatility of acrylics makes them suitable for a wide range of techniques. They can be used opaquely or—by adding water—in a transparent, watercolor style. Acrylic mediums can be added to the paint to adjust its consistency for special effects such as glazing and impasto (ridges of paint applied in thick strokes) or to make it more matt or glossy. Acrylics are quick-drying, which allows layers of paint to be applied on top of each other almost immediately.

EXAMPLES OF BRUSHES

Sable brush

Bristle sash brush

Synthetic bristle brush

Synthetic sable brush

Bristle brush

Goat hair brush

Synthetic wash brush

Ox hair brush

EXAMPLES OF PAINTS USED IN ACRYLICS

Azo yellow

Phthalo green

Cerulean blue

Phthalo blue

Quinacridone red

Titanium white

Yellow ochre

Burnt umber

Burnt sienna

Pad of disposable paper palettes

PAINTING TOOLS

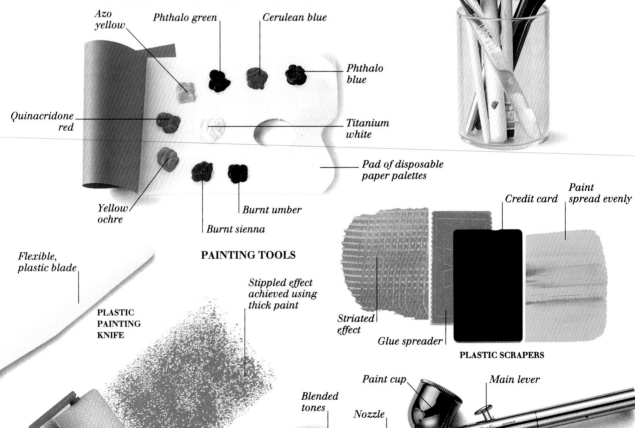

Flexible, plastic blade

PLASTIC PAINTING KNIFE

Stippled effect achieved using thick paint

Credit card

Paint spread evenly

Striated effect

Glue spreader

PLASTIC SCRAPERS

Blended tones

Paint cup

Main lever

Nozzle

AIR-BRUSH

Plastic handle

SPONGE ROLLER

Uniform tone

Air hose

EXAMPLE OF AN ACRYLIC PAINTING
A Bigger Splash, David Hockney, 1967
Acrylic on canvas, 95½ x 96 in (242.5 x 243.8 cm)

Paint applied evenly using a roller

Cotton duck canvas support (surface)

Flatness of rollered areas enhanced by adding gel medium to the paint

Masking tape stuck onto canvas to define main shapes, and paint applied within these areas using a roller

Thin strip of pool edge left unpainted

Splash painted using thicker paint and small brush

Imprecise edge on end of spring board where paint has seeped under masking tape

EXAMPLES OF ACRYLIC PAINTS AND TECHNIQUES

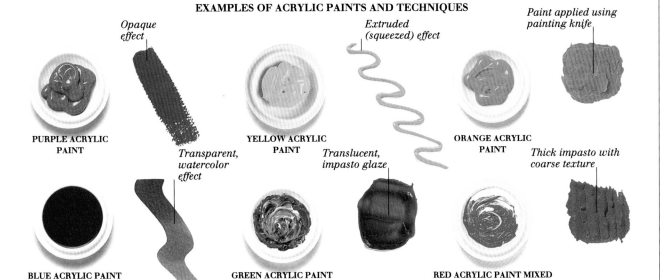

Opaque effect

Extruded (squeezed) effect

Paint applied using painting knife

PURPLE ACRYLIC PAINT

YELLOW ACRYLIC PAINT

ORANGE ACRYLIC PAINT

Transparent, watercolor effect

Translucent, impasto glaze

Thick impasto with coarse texture

BLUE ACRYLIC PAINT DILUTED WITH WATER

GREEN ACRYLIC PAINT MIXED WITH GEL MEDIUM

RED ACRYLIC PAINT MIXED WITH TEXTURE PASTE

Printmaking 1

PRINTS ARE MADE BY FOUR BASIC printing processes – intaglio, lithographic, relief, and screen. In intaglio printing, lines are engraved or etched onto the surface of a metal plate. Lines are engraved using sharp metal tools. They are etched by corroding the metal plate with acid, using acid-resistant ground to protect the areas not to be etched. The plate is then inked and wiped, leaving the grooves filled with ink and the surface clean. Dampened paper is laid over the plate, and both paper and plate are passed through the rollers of an etching press. The pressure of the rollers forces the paper into the grooves, so that it takes up the ink, leaving an impression on the paper. Lithographic printing is based on the antipathy between grease and water. An image is drawn on a surface—usually a stone or metal plate—with a greasy medium, such as tusche (lihographic ink). The greasy drawing is fixed onto the plate by applying an acidic solution, such as gum arabic. The surface is then dampened and rolled with ink. The ink adheres only to the greasy areas and is repelled by the water. Paper is laid on the plate and pressure is applied by means of a press. In relief printing, the non-printing areas of a wood or linoleum block are cut away using gouges, knives, and other tools. The printing areas are left raised in relief and are rolled with ink. Paper is laid on the inked block and pressure is applied by means of a press or by burnishing (rubbing) the back of the paper. The most common forms of relief printing are woodcut, wood engraving, and linocut. In screen printing, the printing surface is a mesh stretched across a wooden frame. A stencil is applied to the mesh to seal the non-printing areas and ink is scraped through the mesh to produce an image.

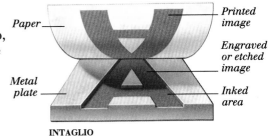

INTAGLIO

Paper · Printed image · Engraved or etched image · Metal plate · Inked area

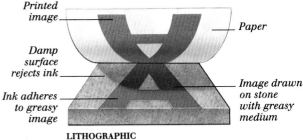

LITHOGRAPHIC

Printed image · Damp surface rejects ink · Ink adheres to greasy image · Paper · Image drawn on stone with greasy medium

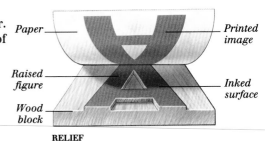

RELIEF

Paper · Printed image · Raised figure · Inked surface · Wood block

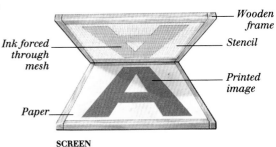

SCREEN

Ink forced through mesh · Paper · Wooden frame · Stencil · Printed image

LEATHER INK DABBER

EQUIPMENT USED IN INTAGLIO PRINTING

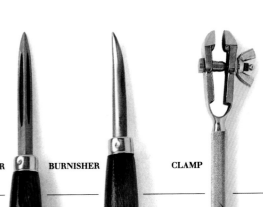

ROCKER   **SCRIBER**   **ROULETTE**   **SCRAPER**   **BURNISHER**   **CLAMP**

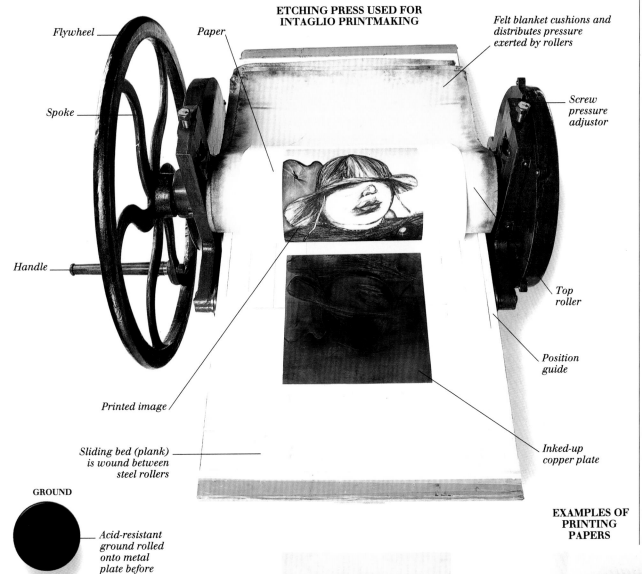

ETCHING PRESS USED FOR INTAGLIO PRINTMAKING

Flywheel

Paper

Felt blanket cushions and distributes pressure exerted by rollers

Spoke

Screw pressure adjustor

Handle

Top roller

Position guide

Printed image

Sliding bed (plank) is wound between steel rollers

Inked-up copper plate

GROUND

Acid-resistant ground rolled onto metal plate before etching

EXAMPLES OF PRINTING PAPERS

GROUND ROLLER

Gelatine roller

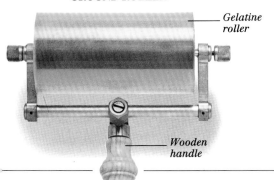

Wooden handle

EXAMPLE OF AN INTAGLIO PRINT
Annie with a Sun Hat, Jock McFadyen, 1993
Etched copper plate, 16 x 15¾ in (41 x 40 cm)

Printmaking 2

EXAMPLE OF A LITHOGRAPHIC STONE AND PRINT
Crown Gateway 2, Mandy Bonnell, 1987
Lithograph, 19½ x 15¾ in (50 x 40 cm)

IMAGE DRAWN ON STONE

LITHOGRAPIC PRINT

EXAMPLE OF A SCREEN PRINT
Sea Change, Patrick Hughes, 1992
Screen print, 30 x 37 in (77 x 94.5 cm)

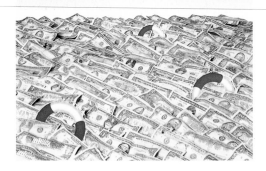

SCREEN AND SQUEEGEE

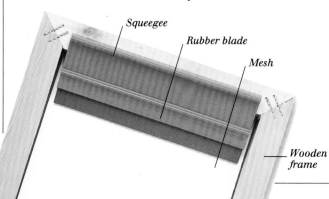

Squeegee

Rubber blade

Mesh

Wooden frame

EQUIPMENT USED IN LITHOGRAPHIC PRINTING

CRAYON AND HOLDER

LITHOGRAPHIC PENCIL

TUSCHE (LITHOGRAPHIC INK) PEN

ERASING STICK

EXPANDABLE SPONGE

TUSCHE (LITHOGRAPHIC INK) STICK

RUBBING INK

INK ROLLER

MILD ACIDIC SOLUTION

GUM ARABIC SOLUTION

WATER-BASED SCREEN PRINTING INKS

BLUE ACRYLIC INK

RED ACRYLIC INK

BROWN TEXTILE INK

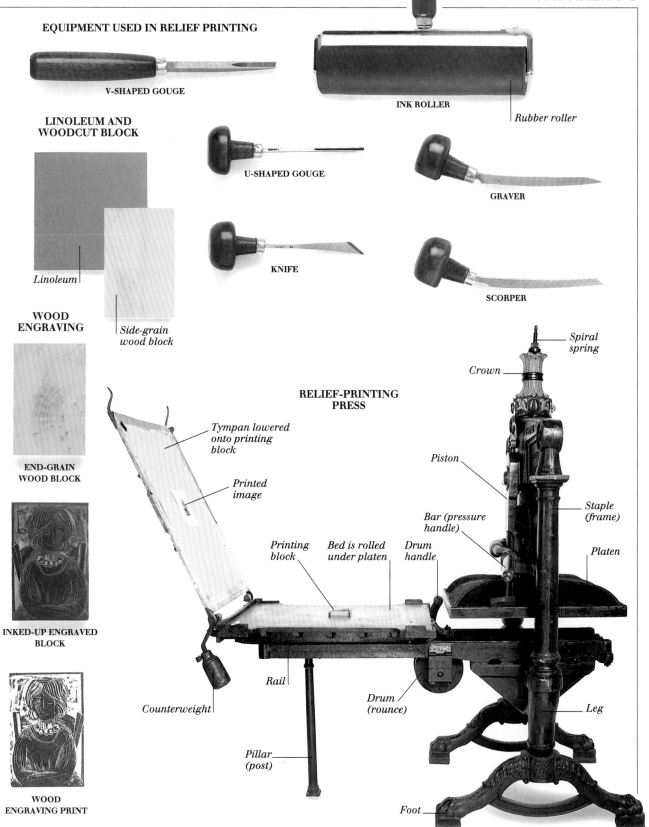

EQUIPMENT USED IN RELIEF PRINTING

V-SHAPED GOUGE

INK ROLLER

Rubber roller

LINOLEUM AND WOODCUT BLOCK

U-SHAPED GOUGE

GRAVER

Linoleum

KNIFE

SCORPER

Side-grain wood block

WOOD ENGRAVING

END-GRAIN WOOD BLOCK

INKED-UP ENGRAVED BLOCK

WOOD ENGRAVING PRINT

RELIEF-PRINTING PRESS

Spiral spring

Crown

Piston

Staple (frame)

Tympan lowered onto printing block

Bar (pressure handle)

Platen

Printed image

Printing block

Bed is rolled under platen

Drum handle

Rail

Counterweight

Drum (rounce)

Leg

Pillar (post)

Foot

Mosaic

MOSAIC IS THE ART OF MAKING patterns and pictures from tesserae (small, colored pieces of glass, marble, and other materials). Different materials are cut into tesserae using different tools. Smalti (glass enamel) and marble are cut into pieces using a hammer and a hardy (a pointed blade) embedded in a log. Vitreous glass is cut into pieces using a pair of pliers. Mosaics can be made using a direct or indirect method. In the direct method, the tesserae are laid directly into a bed of cement–based adhesive. In the indirect method, the design is drawn in reverse on paper or cloth. The tesserae are then stuck face down on the paper or cloth using water-soluble glue. Adhesive is spread with a trowel onto a solid surface—such as a wall—and the back of the mosaic is laid into the adhesive. Finally, the paper or cloth is soaked off to reveal the mosaic. Gaps between tesserae can be filled with grout. Grout is forced into gaps by dragging a grouting squeegee across the face of the mosaic. Mosaics are usually used to decorate walls and floors, but they can also be applied to smaller objects.

EQUIPMENT FOR BREAKING MARBLE

Strip of marble, ready for breaking into cubes

Mosaic hammer

Alicante (red marble) pieces

Hardy (pointed blade) embedded in a log

PLIERS

Hardwearing, tungsten carbide tip

Handle with rubber grip

SMALTI (GLASS ENAMEL)

RED SMALTI

EXAMPLE OF A MOSAIC (DIRECT METHOD)
Seascape, Tessa Hunkin, 1993
Smalti mosaic on board
31½ in (80 cm) diameter

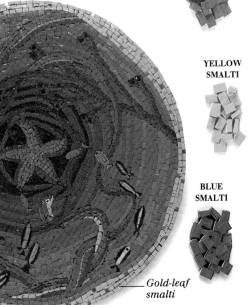

Gold-leaf smalti

YELLOW SMALTI

BLUE SMALTI

MOSAIC TOOLS

CEMENT-BASED ADHESIVE

GROUT

TROWEL

Notch

Steel blade

Wooden handle

GROUTING SQUEEGEE

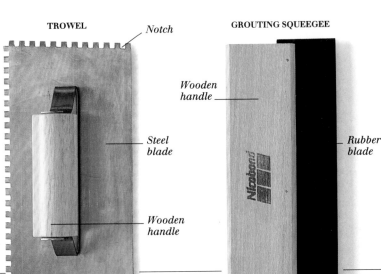

Wooden handle

Rubber blade

Nicobond

STAGES IN THE CREATION OF A MOSAIC (INDIRECT METHOD)

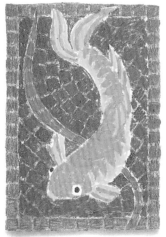

COLOR SKETCH
A color sketch is drawn
in oil pastel to give a clear
impression of how the finished
mosaic will look.

REVERSE IMAGE
Tesserae are glued face down
on reverse image on paper.
Mosaic is then attached to solid
surface and paper is removed.

MOSAIC POT

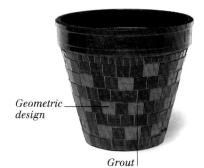

Geometric
design

Grout

MOSAIC MOSQUE DESIGN

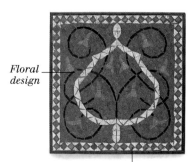

Floral
design

Geometric border

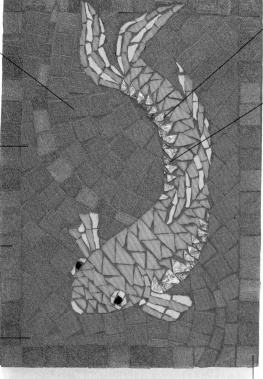

Andamenti
(line along
which tesserae
are laid)

Grout fills
the gaps
between the
tesserae

Mosaic
mounted
on board

Vitreous
glass cut into
triangular
shape with
pliers

Gold tessera
with ripple
finish

Gold tessera
placed upside-
down

FINISHED MOSAIC
Goldfish, Tessa Hunkin, 1993
Vitreous glass mosaic on board
14 x 10 in (35.5 x 25.5 cm)

Border of square
vitreous glass

VITREOUS GLASS

**GREEN VITREOUS
GLASS WITH GOLD LEAF**

Plain
finish

Ripple
finish

**RED VITREOUS
GLASS**

SHEETS OF VITREOUS GLASS

**BLUE VITREOUS
GLASS**

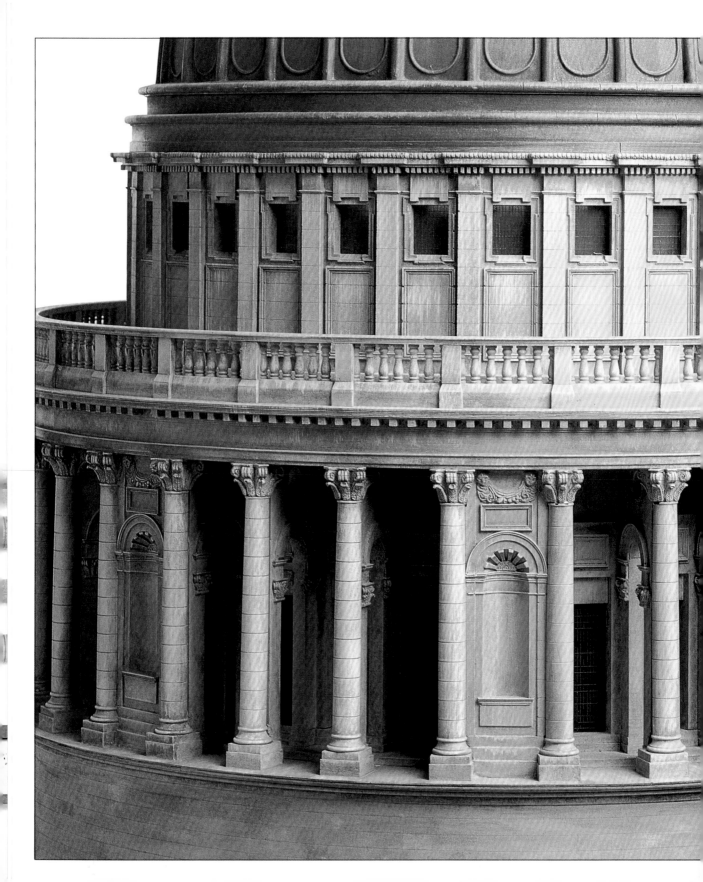

ARCHITECTURE

Ancient Egypt

THE CIVILIZATION OF THE ANCIENT EGYPTIANS (which lasted from about 3100 BC until it was finally absorbed into the Roman empire in 30 BC) is famous for its temples and tombs. Egyptian temples were often huge and geometric, like the Temple of Amon-Re (below and right). They were usually decorated with hieroglyphs (sacred characters used for picture writing) and painted reliefs depicting gods, Pharaohs (kings), and queens. Tombs were particularly important to the Egyptians, who believed that the dead were resurrected in the afterlife. The tombs were often decorated—for example, the surround of the false door opposite— in order to give comfort to the dead. The best-known ancient Egyptian tombs are the pyramids, which were designed to symbolize the rays of the sun. Many of the architectural forms used by the ancient Egyptians were later adopted by other civilizations. For example, columns and capitals were later used by the ancient Greeks (see pp. 460-461) and ancient Romans (see pp. 462-465).

SIDE VIEW OF HYPOSTYLE HALL, TEMPLE OF AMON-RE, KARNAK, EGYPT, c.1290 BC

FRONT VIEW OF HYPOSTYLE HALL, TEMPLE OF AMON-RE

Cornice decorated with cavetto molding

Campaniform (open papyrus) capital

Architrave

Papyrus-bud capital

Socle

Side aisle | Central nave | Side aisle

Horus, the sun-god

Architrave

Stone slab forming flat roof of side aisle

Kepresh crown with disc

Chons, the moon-god | Amon-Re, king of the gods | Hathor, the sky-goddess | Papyrus motif | Cartouche (oval border) containing the titles of the Pharaoh (king) | Socle | Aisle running north–south

LIMESTONE FALSE DOOR WITH HIEROGLYPHS, TOMB OF KING TJETJI, GIZA, EGYPT, c.2400 BC

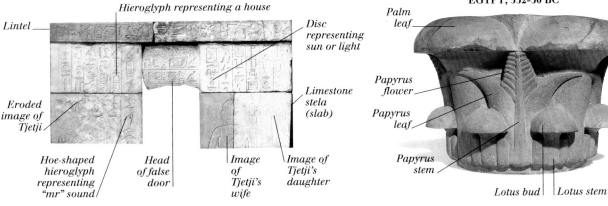

Hieroglyph representing a house

Lintel

Disc representing sun or light

Eroded image of Tjetji

Limestone stela (slab)

Hoe-shaped hieroglyph representing "mr" sound

Head of false door

Image of Tjetji's wife

Image of Tjetji

Image of Tjetji's daughter

PLANT CAPITAL OF THE PTOLEMAIC-ROMAN PERIOD, EGYPT, 332-30 BC

Palm leaf

Papyrus flower

Papyrus leaf

Papyrus stem

Lotus bud | *Lotus stem*

Cornice decorated with cavetto molding

Bead molding

Trellis window

Rectangular pier decorated with hieroglyphs

Elevated roof of central nave

Clerestory

Disc representing sun or light

Architrave

Square abacus

Papyrus-bud capital

Papyriform column

Shaft

Scene depicting a Pharaoh (king) paying homage to the god Amon-Re

Central nave

ANCIENT EGYPTIAN BUILDING DECORATION

DECORATED WINDOW, MEDINET HABU, EGYPT, C.1198 BC

ROPE AND PATERAE DECORATION

CAPITAL WITH THE HEAD OF THE SKY-GODDESS HATHOR, TEMPLE OF ISIS, PHILAE, EGYPT, 283-47 BC

LOTUS AND PAPYRUS FRIEZE DECORATION

Ancient Rome 2

SIDE VIEW OF A ROMAN MILL

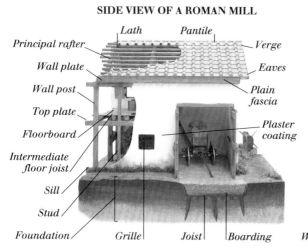

Lath
Pantile
Principal rafter
Verge
Wall plate
Eaves
Wall post
Plain fascia
Top plate
Floorboard
Plaster coating
Intermediate floor joist
Sill
Stud
Foundation
Grille
Joist
Boarding

FRONT VIEW OF A ROMAN MILL, 1ST CENTURY BC

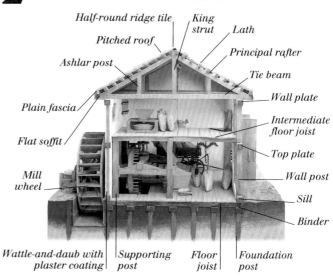

Half-round ridge tile
King strut
Lath
Pitched roof
Principal rafter
Ashlar post
Tie beam
Plain fascia
Wall plate
Flat soffit
Intermediate floor joist
Top plate
Mill wheel
Wall post
Sill
Binder
Wattle-and-daub with plaster coating
Supporting post
Floor joist
Foundation post

THE COLOSSEUM (FLAVIAN AMPHITHEATER), ROME, ITALY, 70-82

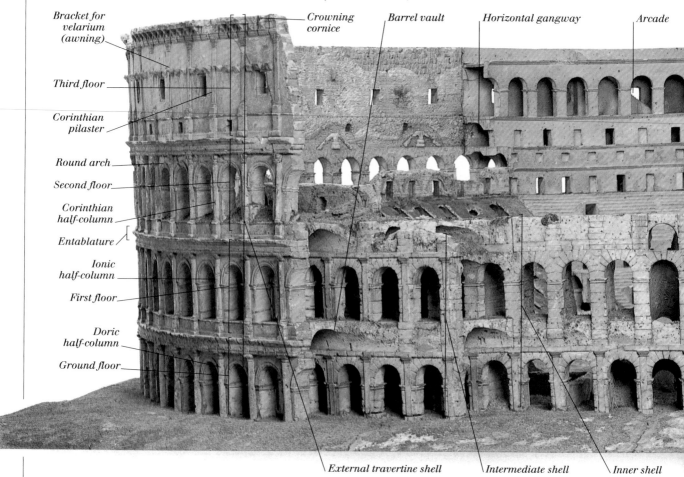

Bracket for velarium (awning)
Crowning cornice
Barrel vault
Horizontal gangway
Arcade
Third floor
Corinthian pilaster
Round arch
Second floor
Corinthian half-column
Entablature
Ionic half-column
First floor
Doric half-column
Ground floor
External travertine shell
Intermediate shell
Inner shell

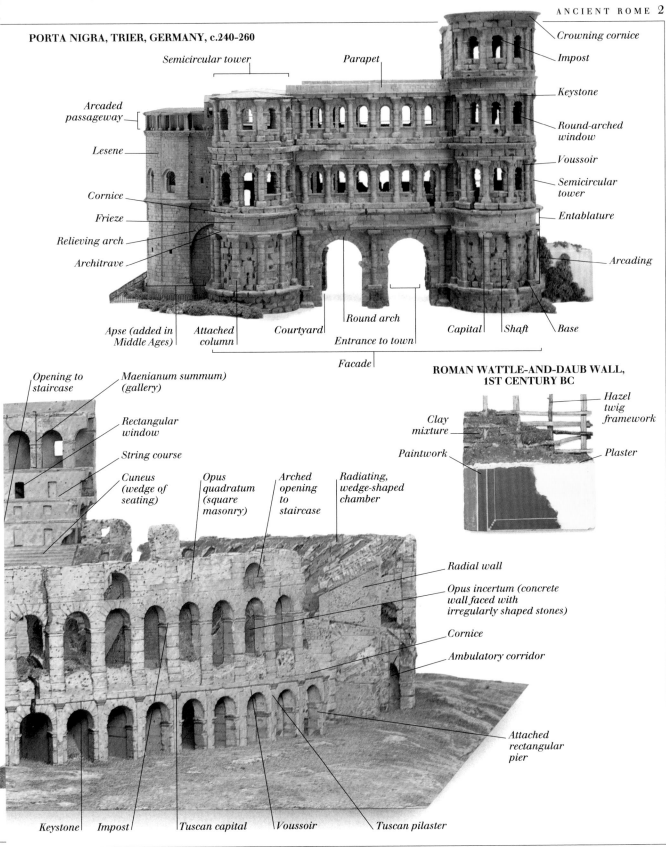

PORTA NIGRA, TRIER, GERMANY, c.240–260

Crowning cornice

Impost

Semicircular tower

Parapet

Keystone

Arcaded passageway

Round-arched window

Lesene

Voussoir

Semicircular tower

Cornice

Entablature

Frieze

Relieving arch

Architrave

Arcading

Apse (added in Middle Ages)

Attached column

Courtyard

Round arch

Entrance to town

Capital

Shaft

Base

Facade

ROMAN WATTLE-AND-DAUB WALL, 1ST CENTURY BC

Opening to staircase

Maenianum summum) (gallery)

Hazel twig framework

Rectangular window

Clay mixture

String course

Paintwork

Plaster

Cuneus (wedge of seating)

Opus quadratum (square masonry)

Arched opening to staircase

Radiating, wedge-shaped chamber

Radial wall

Opus incertum (concrete wall faced with irregularly shaped stones)

Cornice

Ambulatory corridor

Attached rectangular pier

Keystone

Impost

Tuscan capital

Voussoir

Tuscan pilaster

Gothic 2

SPIRAL STAIRCASE TO ORGAN, CHURCH OF ST. MACLOU, ROUEN, FRANCE, c.1519

CURVILINEAR (FLOWING) TRACERY FROM A BALUSTRADE, 14TH OR 15TH CENTURY

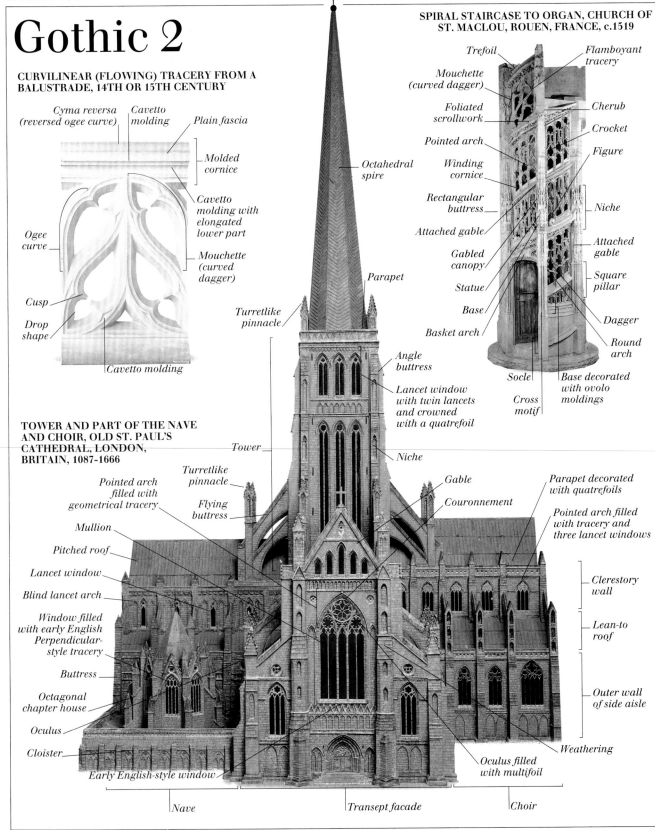

Cyma reversa (reversed ogee curve)

Cavetto molding

Plain fascia

Molded cornice

Cavetto molding with elongated lower part

Mouchette (curved dagger)

Ogee curve

Cusp

Drop shape

Cavetto molding

Trefoil

Mouchette (curved dagger)

Foliated scrollwork

Pointed arch

Winding cornice

Rectangular buttress

Attached gable

Gabled canopy

Statue

Base

Basket arch

Flamboyant tracery

Cherub

Crocket

Figure

Niche

Attached gable

Square pillar

Dagger

Round arch

Socle

Cross motif

Base decorated with ovolo moldings

Octahedral spire

Parapet

Turretlike pinnacle

Angle buttress

Lancet window with twin lancets and crowned with a quatrefoil

TOWER AND PART OF THE NAVE AND CHOIR, OLD ST. PAUL'S CATHEDRAL, LONDON, BRITAIN, 1087-1666

Tower

Niche

Pointed arch filled with geometrical tracery

Turretlike pinnacle

Flying buttress

Mullion

Pitched roof

Lancet window

Blind lancet arch

Window filled with early English Perpendicular- style tracery

Buttress

Octagonal chapter house

Oculus

Cloister

Early English-style window

Gable

Couronnement

Parapet decorated with quatrefoils

Pointed arch filled with tracery and three lancet windows

Clerestory wall

Lean-to roof

Outer wall of side aisle

Weathering

Oculus filled with multifoil

Nave

Transept facade

Choir

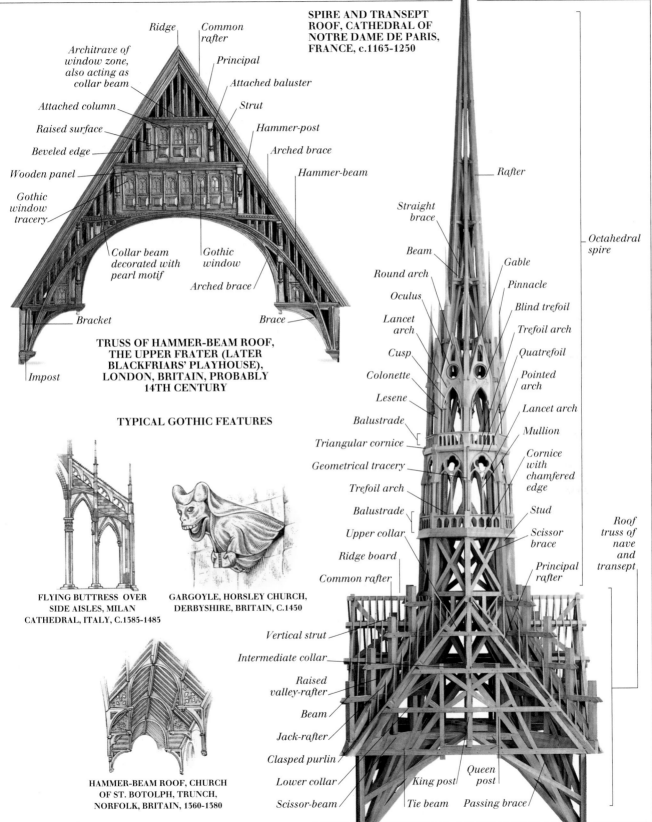

Ridge

Common rafter

SPIRE AND TRANSEPT ROOF, CATHEDRAL OF NOTRE DAME DE PARIS, FRANCE, c.1163-1250

Architrave of window zone, also acting as collar beam

Principal

Attached baluster

Attached column

Strut

Hammer-post

Raised surface

Arched brace

Beveled edge

Hammer-beam

Wooden panel

Rafter

Gothic window tracery

Straight brace

Collar beam decorated with pearl motif

Beam

Gable

Gothic window

Round arch

Pinnacle

Arched brace

Oculus

Blind trefoil

Brace

Lancet arch

Trefoil arch

TRUSS OF HAMMER-BEAM ROOF, THE UPPER FRATER (LATER BLACKFRIARS' PLAYHOUSE), LONDON, BRITAIN, PROBABLY 14TH CENTURY

Cusp

Quatrefoil

Colonette

Pointed arch

Bracket

Lesene

Lancet arch

Impost

Balustrade

Mullion

Octahedral spire

Triangular cornice

Geometrical tracery

Cornice with chamfered edge

TYPICAL GOTHIC FEATURES

Trefoil arch

Balustrade

Stud

Upper collar

Scissor brace

Ridge board

Principal rafter

Common rafter

FLYING BUTTRESS OVER SIDE AISLES, MILAN CATHEDRAL, ITALY, C.1385-1485

GARGOYLE, HORSLEY CHURCH, DERBYSHIRE, BRITAIN, C.1450

Vertical strut

Intermediate collar

Raised valley-rafter

Roof truss of nave and transept

Beam

Jack-rafter

Clasped purlin

Queen post

Lower collar

King post

HAMMER-BEAM ROOF, CHURCH OF ST. BOTOLPH, TRUNCH, NORFOLK, BRITAIN, 1360-1380

Scissor-beam

Tie beam

Passing brace

Renaissance 1

THE RENAISSANCE was a period in European history—lasting roughly from the 14th century to the mid-17th century—during which the arts and sciences underwent great changes. In architecture, these changes were marked by a return to the classical forms and proportions of ancient Roman buildings. The Renaissance originated in Italy, and the buildings most characteristic of its style can be found there, such as the Palazzo Strozzi shown here. Mannerism is a branch of the Renaissance style that distorts the classical forms; an example is the Laurentian Library staircase. As the Renaissance style spread to other European countries, many of its features were incorporated into the local architecture. For example, the Château de Montal in France (see pp. 476-477) incorporates aedicules (tabernacles).

FACADE ON TO PIAZZA, PALAZZO STROZZI

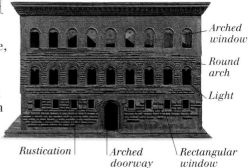

Crowning cornice

Arched window

Round arch

Light

Rustication

Arched doorway

Rectangular window

SIDE VIEW OF PALAZZO STROZZI, FLORENCE, ITALY, 1489 (BY G. DA SANGALLO, B. DA MAIANO, AND CRONACA)

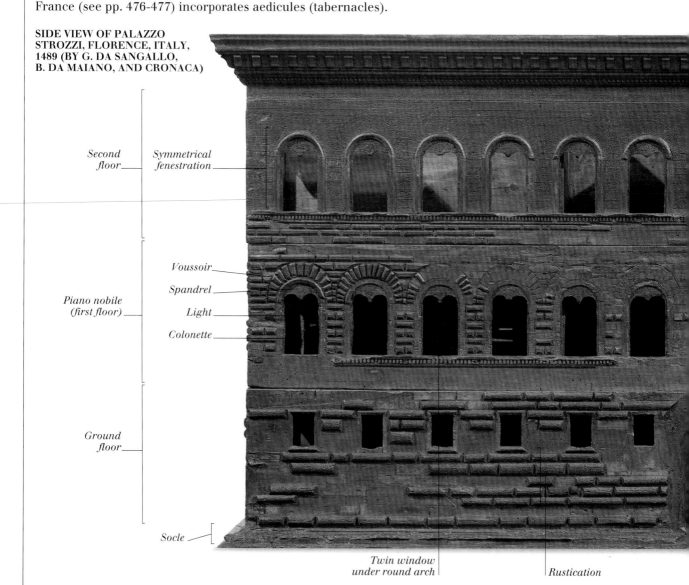

Second floor

Symmetrical fenestration

Piano nobile (first floor)

Voussoir

Spandrel

Light

Colonette

Ground floor

Socle

Twin window under round arch

Rustication

DETAILS FROM ITALIAN RENAISSANCE BUILDINGS

PANEL FROM DRUM OF DOME,
FLORENCE CATHEDRAL, 1420-1436

COFFERING IN DOME,
PAZZI CHAPEL,
FLORENCE, 1429-1461

STAIRCASE,
LAURENTIAN LIBRARY,
FLORENCE, 1559

PORTICO, VILLA ROTUNDA,
VICENZA, 1567-1569

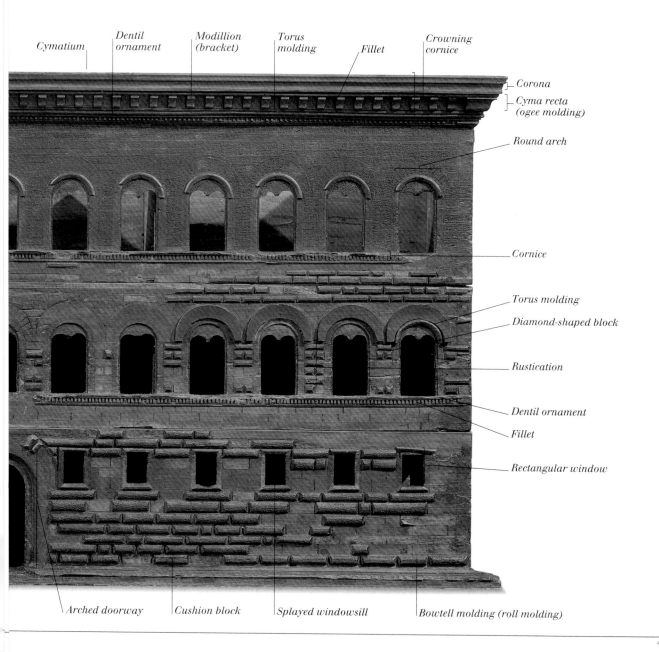

Cymatium

Dentil ornament

Modillion (bracket)

Torus molding

Fillet

Crowning cornice

Corona

Cyma recta (ogee molding)

Round arch

Cornice

Torus molding

Diamond-shaped block

Rustication

Dentil ornament

Fillet

Rectangular window

Arched doorway

Cushion block

Splayed windowsill

Bowtell molding (roll molding)

Baroque and neoclassical 2

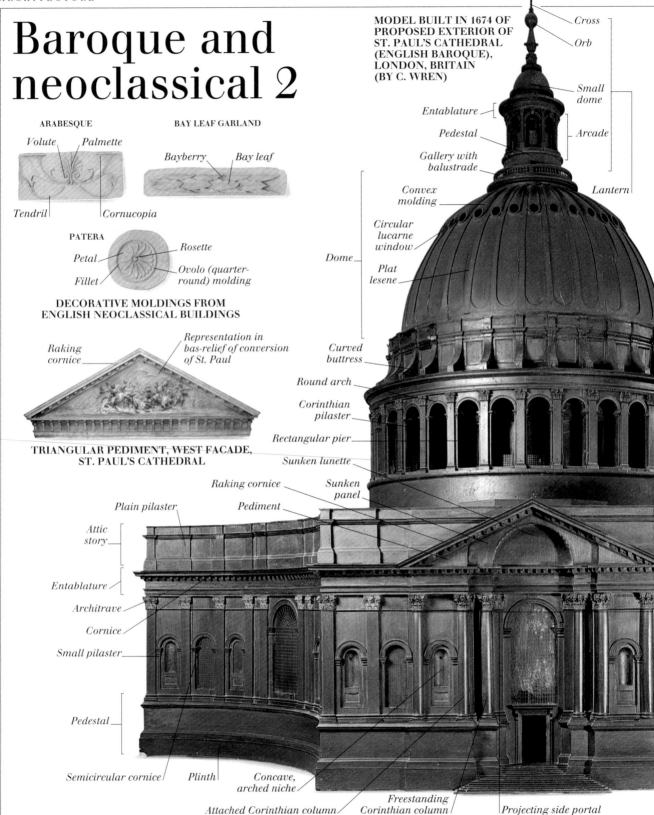

MODEL BUILT IN 1674 OF PROPOSED EXTERIOR OF ST. PAUL'S CATHEDRAL (ENGLISH BAROQUE), LONDON, BRITAIN (BY C. WREN)

Cross

Orb

Small dome

Entablature

Pedestal

Arcade

Gallery with balustrade

Lantern

Convex molding

Circular lucarne window

Dome

Plat lesene

Curved buttress

Round arch

Corinthian pilaster

Rectangular pier

Sunken lunette

ARABESQUE

Volute

Palmette

Tendril

Cornucopia

BAY LEAF GARLAND

Bayberry

Bay leaf

PATERA

Rosette

Petal

Ovolo (quarter-round) molding

Fillet

DECORATIVE MOLDINGS FROM ENGLISH NEOCLASSICAL BUILDINGS

Raking cornice

Representation in bas-relief of conversion of St. Paul

TRIANGULAR PEDIMENT, WEST FACADE, ST. PAUL'S CATHEDRAL

Plain pilaster

Raking cornice

Sunken panel

Pediment

Attic story

Entablature

Architrave

Cornice

Small pilaster

Pedestal

Semicircular cornice

Plinth

Concave, arched niche

Attached Corinthian column

Freestanding Corinthian column

Projecting side portal

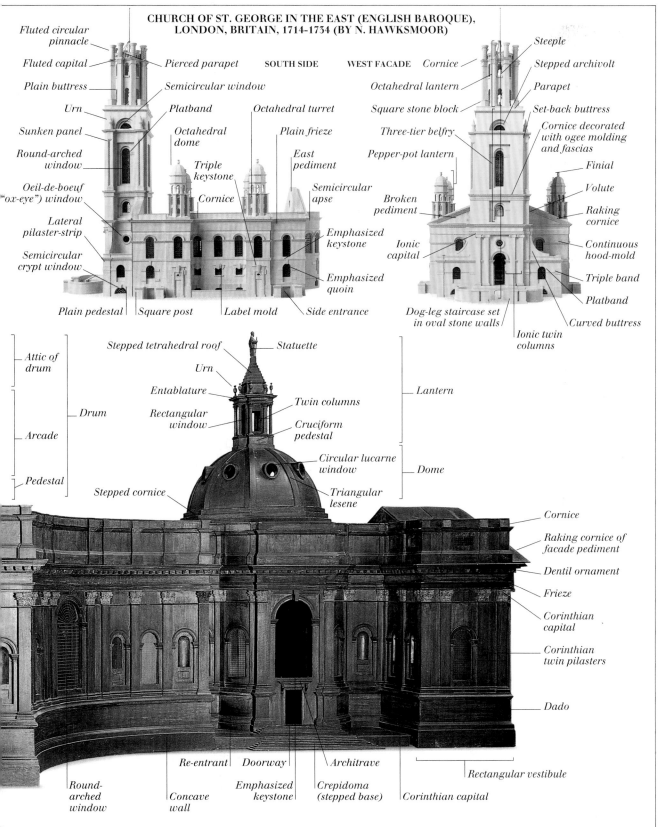

**CHURCH OF ST. GEORGE IN THE EAST (ENGLISH BAROQUE),
LONDON, BRITAIN, 1714-1734 (BY N. HAWKSMOOR)**

SOUTH SIDE   WEST FACADE

Fluted circular pinnacle

Fluted capital

Plain buttress

Urn

Sunken panel

Round-arched window

Oeil-de-boeuf ("ox-eye") window

Lateral pilaster-strip

Semicircular crypt window

Plain pedestal

Square post

Pierced parapet

Semicircular window

Platband

Octahedral dome

Triple keystone

Cornice

Label mold

Octahedral turret

Plain frieze

East pediment

Semicircular apse

Emphasized keystone

Emphasized quoin

Side entrance

Steeple

Cornice

Octahedral lantern

Square stone block

Three-tier belfry

Pepper-pot lantern

Broken pediment

Ionic capital

Dog-leg staircase set in oval stone walls

Ionic twin columns

Stepped archivolt

Parapet

Set-back buttress

Cornice decorated with ogee molding and fascias

Finial

Volute

Raking cornice

Continuous hood-mold

Triple band

Platband

Curved buttress

Attic of drum

Drum

Arcade

Pedestal

Stepped tetrahedral roof

Urn

Entablature

Rectangular window

Stepped cornice

Statuette

Twin columns

Cruciform pedestal

Circular lucarne window

Triangular lesene

Lantern

Dome

Cornice

Raking cornice of facade pediment

Dentil ornament

Frieze

Corinthian capital

Corinthian twin pilasters

Dado

Round-arched window

Concave wall

Re-entrant

Doorway

Emphasized keystone

Architrave

Crepidoma (stepped base)

Corinthian capital

Rectangular vestibule

Baroque and neoclassical 3

DETAILS FROM BAROQUE, NEOCLASSICAL, AND ROCOCO BUILDINGS

CORNER OF THE NEW STATE PAPER OFFICE (NEOCLASSICAL), LONDON, BRITAIN, 1830-1831 (BY J. SOANE)

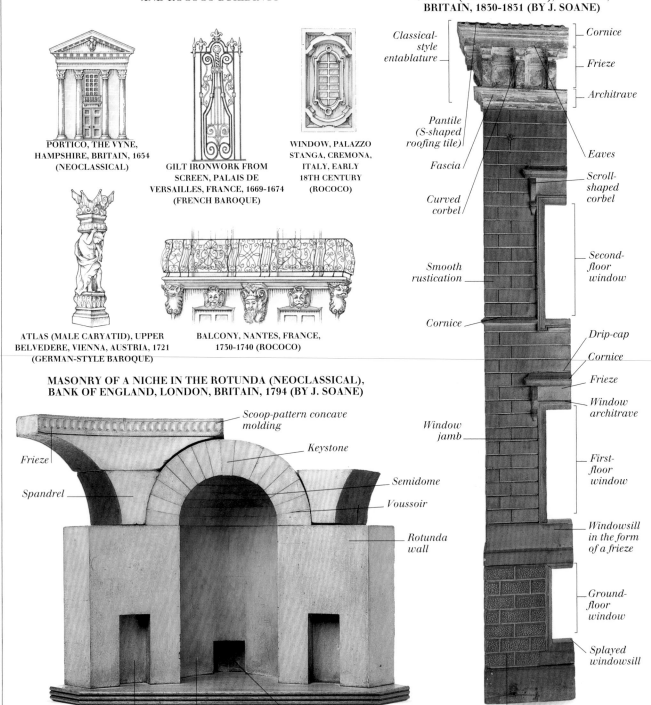

PORTICO, THE VYNE, HAMPSHIRE, BRITAIN, 1654 (NEOCLASSICAL)

GILT IRONWORK FROM SCREEN, PALAIS DE VERSAILLES, FRANCE, 1669-1674 (FRENCH BAROQUE)

WINDOW, PALAZZO STANGA, CREMONA, ITALY, EARLY 18TH CENTURY (ROCOCO)

ATLAS (MALE CARYATID), UPPER BELVEDERE, VIENNA, AUSTRIA, 1721 (GERMAN-STYLE BAROQUE)

BALCONY, NANTES, FRANCE, 1730-1740 (ROCOCO)

MASONRY OF A NICHE IN THE ROTUNDA (NEOCLASSICAL), BANK OF ENGLAND, LONDON, BRITAIN, 1794 (BY J. SOANE)

Classical-style entablature

Cornice

Frieze

Architrave

Pantile (S-shaped roofing tile)

Fascia

Curved corbel

Eaves

Scroll-shaped corbel

Smooth rustication

Second-floor window

Cornice

Drip-cap

Cornice

Frieze

Window architrave

First-floor window

Scoop-pattern concave molding

Keystone

Frieze

Semidome

Spandrel

Voussoir

Window jamb

Rotunda wall

Windowsill in the form of a frieze

Ground-floor window

Splayed windowsill

Flat, rectangular niche

Rounded niche

Flat, square niche

Vermiculated rustication

TYRINGHAM HOUSE (NEOCLASSICAL), BUCKINGHAMSHIRE, BRITAIN, 1793-1797 (BY J. SOANE)

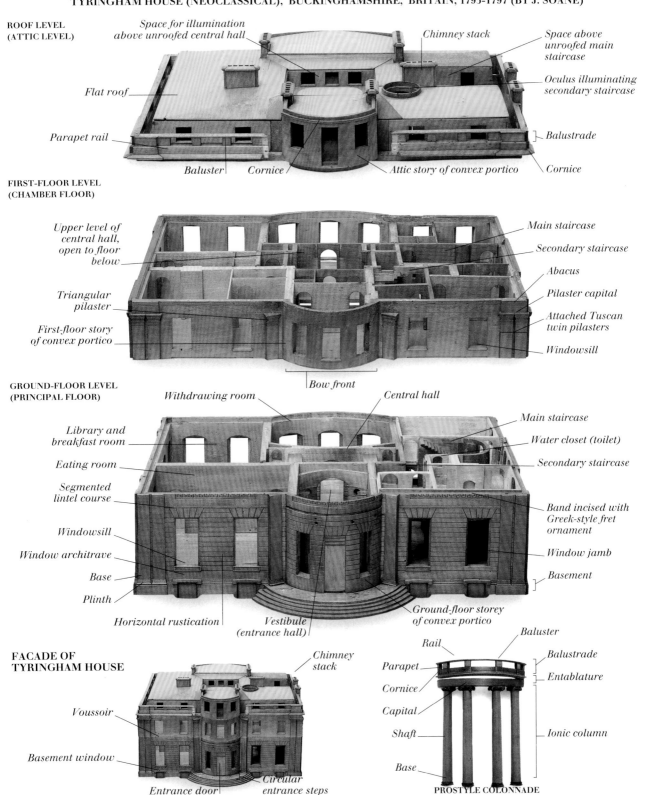

ROOF LEVEL (ATTIC LEVEL)

Space for illumination above unroofed central hall

Chimney stack

Space above unroofed main staircase

Oculus illuminating secondary staircase

Flat roof

Parapet rail

Balustrade

Cornice

Baluster

Cornice

Attic story of convex portico

FIRST-FLOOR LEVEL (CHAMBER FLOOR)

Upper level of central hall, open to floor below

Main staircase

Secondary staircase

Abacus

Pilaster capital

Triangular pilaster

Attached Tuscan twin pilasters

First-floor story of convex portico

Windowsill

Bow front

GROUND-FLOOR LEVEL (PRINCIPAL FLOOR)

Withdrawing room

Central hall

Library and breakfast room

Main staircase

Water closet (toilet)

Eating room

Secondary staircase

Segmented lintel course

Windowsill

Band incised with Greek-style fret ornament

Window architrave

Base

Window jamb

Plinth

Basement

Horizontal rustication

Vestibule (entrance hall)

Ground-floor storey of convex portico

FACADE OF TYRINGHAM HOUSE

Chimney stack

Voussoir

Basement window

Entrance door

Circular entrance steps

Rail

Baluster

Parapet

Balustrade

Cornice

Entablature

Capital

Shaft

Ionic column

Base

PROSTYLE COLONNADE

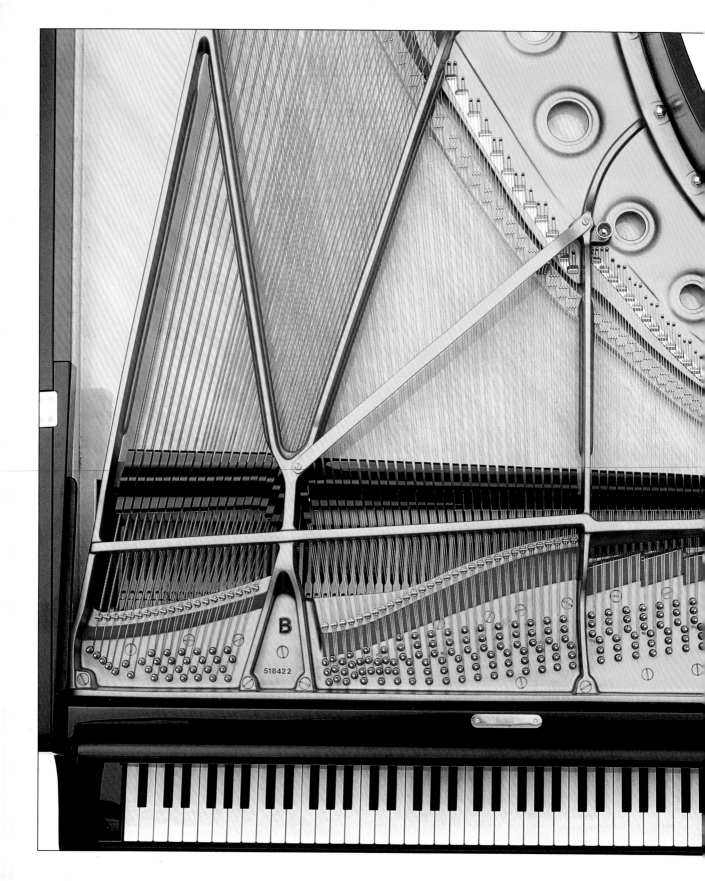

Music

Guitars

THE GUITAR IS A PLUCKED stringed instrument (see pp. 510-511). There are two types of guitar—acoustic and electric. Acoustic guitars have hollow bodies and six or twelve strings. Plucking or strumming the strings produces vibrations that are amplified by their hollow bodies. Electric guitars usually have solid bodies and six strings. Pick-ups placed under the strings convert vibrations into electronic signals that are magnified by an amplifier, and sent to a loudspeaker where they are converted into sounds (see pp. 520-521). Electric bass guitars are very similar in structure to electric guitars, and produce sound in the same way, but have four heavier-gage strings and play lower pitched notes.

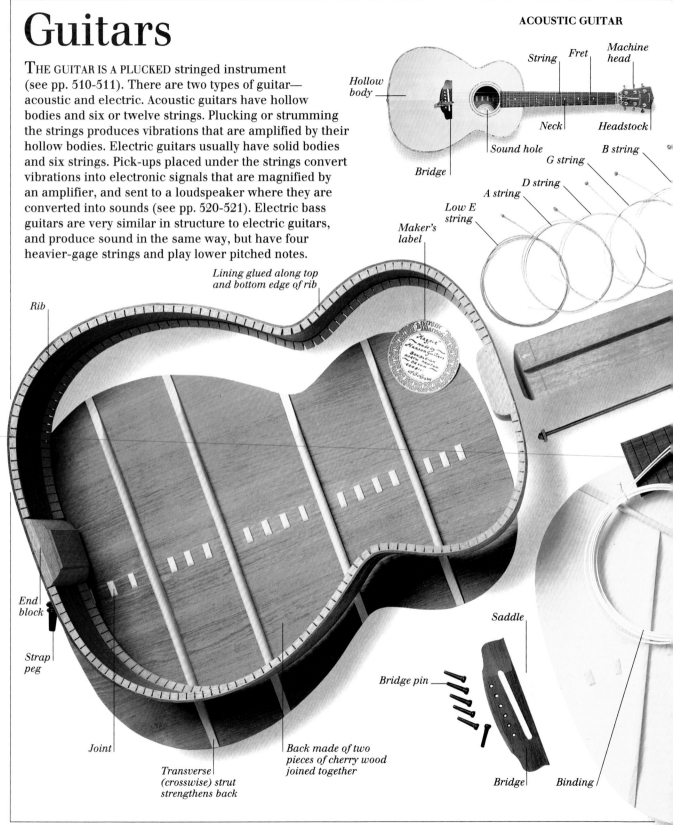

Hollow body

String   Fret   Machine head

Neck   Headstock

Sound hole   B string

G string

D string

A string

Low E string

Bridge

Maker's label

Rib

Lining glued along top and bottom edge of rib

End block

Strap peg

Joint

Transverse (crosswise) strut strengthens back

Back made of two pieces of cherry wood joined together

Saddle

Bridge pin

Bridge   Binding

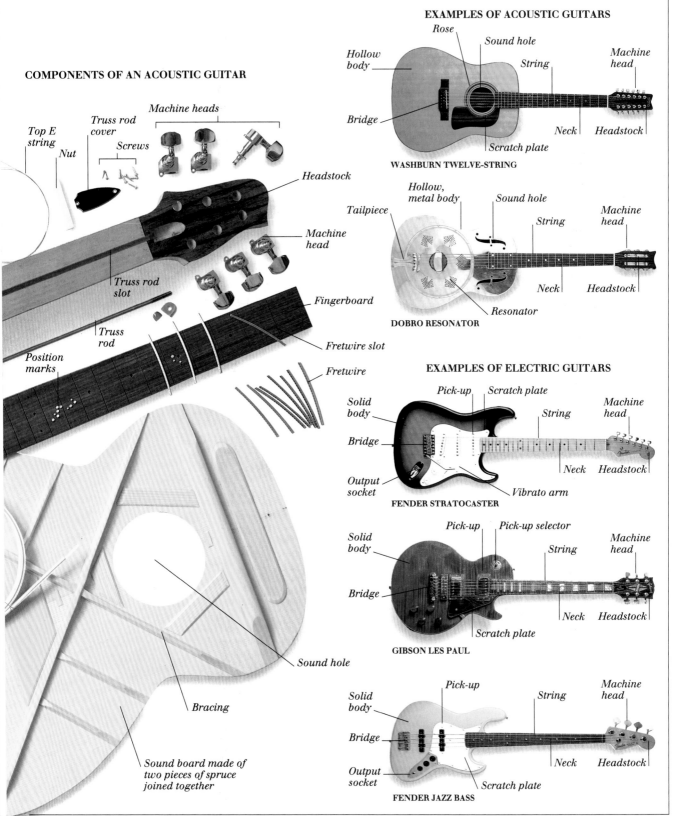

EXAMPLES OF ACOUSTIC GUITARS

Rose

Sound hole

Hollow body

String

Machine head

Bridge

Neck   Headstock

Scratch plate

WASHBURN TWELVE-STRING

COMPONENTS OF AN ACOUSTIC GUITAR

Machine heads

Truss rod cover

Top E string

Screws

Nut

Headstock

Machine head

Truss rod slot

Fingerboard

Truss rod

Fretwire slot

Position marks

Fretwire

Sound hole

Bracing

Sound board made of two pieces of spruce joined together

Hollow, metal body

Sound hole

Tailpiece

String

Machine head

Neck   Headstock

Resonator

DOBRO RESONATOR

EXAMPLES OF ELECTRIC GUITARS

Pick-up   Scratch plate

Solid body

String

Machine head

Bridge

Neck   Headstock

Output socket

Vibrato arm

FENDER STRATOCASTER

Pick-up   Pick-up selector

Solid body

String

Machine head

Bridge

Neck   Headstock

Scratch plate

GIBSON LES PAUL

Pick-up

Solid body

String

Machine head

Bridge

Neck   Headstock

Output socket

Scratch plate

FENDER JAZZ BASS

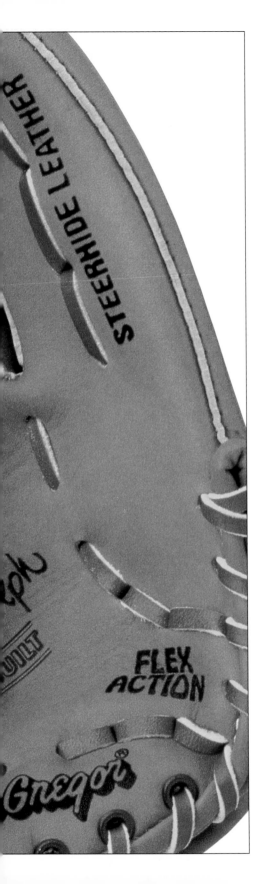

SPORTS

Soccer

GAMES INVOLVING KICKING A BALL have a long history and were recorded in China as early as 300 BC; in medieval Europe, street football was banned as a menace to the public; only in 1863 were the rules established, specifically banning carrying the ball for all players except the goalkeeper, and separating rugby from soccer. Soccer, also known as association football, is a team sport in which players attempt to score goals by passing and dribbling the ball down the field past opposing defenders, and kicking or heading the ball into the goal net, outwitting the defending goalkeeper or "goalie." Each team consists of ten outfield players (defenders, midfielders, and strikers) and a goalkeeper. Players from the opposing team may challenge the player in possession of the ball, but an illegal or foul tackle results in a penalty if a foul occurs inside the penalty area or a free kick if outside the penalty area. The round ball used in soccer is more easily controlled than the oval balls used in American, Canadian, and Australian rules football and in rugby. The result is a more "open" or flowing game which is played and watched by millions of people worldwide.

LINESMAN'S FLAG

Lightweight, brightly colored fabric

Handle with rubber grip

REFEREE'S EQUIPMENT

Red card

Yellow card

Referee's whistle

Stopwatch

FIELD MARKINGS

Halfway line

5 ft (1.5 m)

HALFWAY-LINE FLAG

Corner arc

CORNER FLAG

24 ft (7.3 m)

Goal line

GOAL

SOCCER FIELD

150–300 ft (46–91 m)

Goal line

Corner flag

Corner arc

Penalty area

Penalty mark

Referee

Halfway-line flag

Striker

Striker

Left midfielder

Central midfielder

Left back

Touch line

Central defender

Goal

Goalkeeper

Penalty arc

Linesman

Center circle

Center spot

Halfway line

Striker

Right midfielder

Right back

Central defender

Goal area

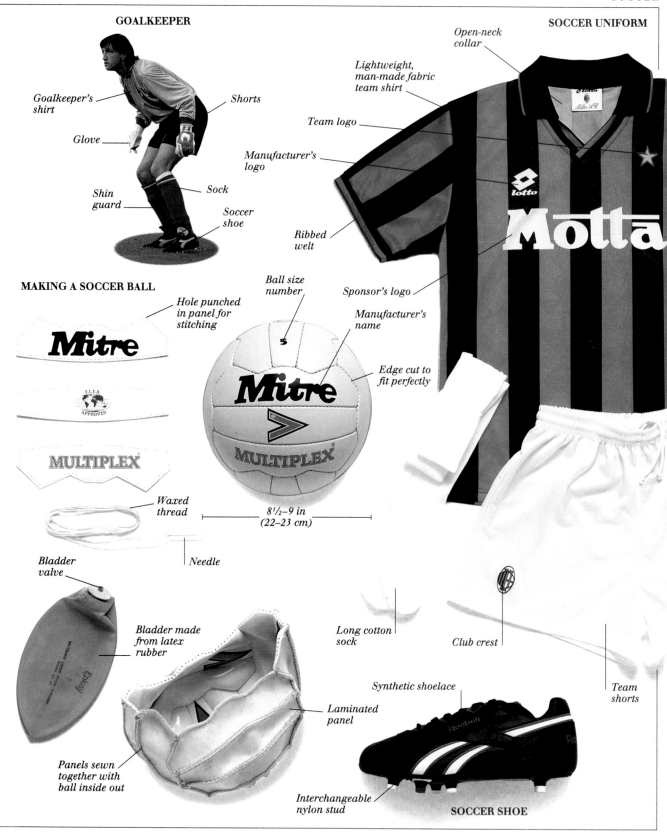

GOALKEEPER

Goalkeeper's shirt

Shorts

Glove

Shin guard

Sock

Soccer shoe

SOCCER UNIFORM

Open-neck collar

Lightweight, man-made fabric team shirt

Team logo

Manufacturer's logo

Ribbed welt

Sponsor's logo

MAKING A SOCCER BALL

Hole punched in panel for stitching

Ball size number

Manufacturer's name

Edge cut to fit perfectly

Waxed thread

8½–9 in (22–23 cm)

Needle

Bladder valve

Bladder made from latex rubber

Long cotton sock

Club crest

Team shorts

Synthetic shoelace

Laminated panel

Panels sewn together with ball inside out

Interchangeable nylon stud

SOCCER SHOE

525

Football

IN AMERICAN AND CANADIAN FOOTBALL, the object of the game is to get the ball across the opponent's goal line, either by passing or carrying it across (a touchdown), or by kicking it between their goalposts (a field goal). An American football team has 11 players on the field at a time, although up to 40 players can appear for each side in a single game. The agile offense tries to score points, and the heavy hitting defense holds back the opposition. When in possession of the ball, a team has four chances (downs), to move it at least ten yards up the field to make a first down. The opposition gains possession if they fail, or by tackling and intercepting the ball. Canadian football is played on a larger field, with 12 men on each side. A team has only three chances, instead of four, to achieve a first down. Otherwise, the game is very similar to American football. Helmets, face masks, and layers of body padding are worn by the players for protection.

AMERICAN FOOTBALL FIELD

Goalpost
End line
Inbound line
Goal line
Sideline
Players' bench
Referee
Umpire
Line judge
Back judge
End zone

160 ft 6 in
(49 m)

AMERICAN FOOTBALL PLAYING FORMATION

Right safety
Middle linebacker
Left safety
Right defensive tackle
Left defensive tackle
Right cornerback
Inside linebacker
Left cornerback
Outside linebacker
Right defensive end
Center
Left defensive end
Tight end
Split end
Left tackle
Right tackle
Right guard
Left guard
Quarterback
Left halfback
Right halfback
Fullback

30 ft
(9.2 m)

GOALPOST

CANADIAN FOOTBALL FIELD

Goalpost
Goal line
Players' bench
Referee
Umpire
Field judge
Yardsman
Head linesman
Yardsman
Sideline
End zone

195 ft
(59.5 m)

CANADIAN FOOTBALL PLAYING FORMATION

Right defensive back
Middle linebacker
Safety
Left defensive back
Left defensive tackle
Right cornerback
Left cornerback
Right outside linebacker
Left outside linebacker
Right defensive end
Left defensive end
Wide receiver
Right guard
Wide receiver
Right defensive tackle
Right tackle
Flanker
Running back
Left guard
Center
Left tackle
Quarterback
Fullback
Halfback

30 ft
(9.2 m)

GOALPOST

PLAYER

- Team logo
- Helmet
- Wrist pad
- Player's number
- Thigh pad
- Tie to shoulder pads
- Pants
- Studded shoe

PROTECTIVE EQUIPMENT

11 in (28 cm)

- Painted white ring
- Lace
- Brown pebbled leather

FOOTBALL

HELMET

- Non-breakable plastic
- Rubber-coated plastic
- Shock absorber

SHOULDER PAD

- Chest protector weight up to 5 lb 8 oz (2.5 kg)

RIB PADS

- Strap ties onto shoulder pad

UPPER ARM PAD

ELBOW PAD

FINGERLESS GLOVE

- Tail bone pad
- Foam-sponge filling

HIP PAD

- Rigid plastic covering

PANTS

- Screw-in stud
- Fold-over leather tongue

FOOTWEAR

THIGH PAD

KNEE PAD

REFEREE'S SIGNALS

- TIME OUT
- TOUCHDOWN OR FIELD GOAL
- PERSONAL FOUL
- OFFSIDE OR ENCROACHMENT
- HOLDING
- ILLEGAL MOTION
- FIRST DOWN
- PASS INTERFERENCE

Rugby

RUGBY IS PLAYED WITH AN OVAL BALL which may be carried, thrown, or kicked. There are two types of rugby. Rugby Union is an amateur game played by two teams of 15 players. Players can score points in two ways: by placing the ball behind the opponents' goal line (a try, scoring four points) or by kicking it over the crossbar of the opponent's goal (a conversion, scoring two points; a penalty kick, scoring three points; or a drop-kick, scoring three points). Rugby League developed from the Union game but is played by 13 players at amateur and professional levels. In League games, a try scores four points; a conversion scores two points; a drop goal scores three points, and a penalty kick scores two points. In both forms of the game, whenever a rule is broken, play is resumed with a scrum. In a scrum, each team's forwards bind together facing each other and fight for possession of the ball.

RUGBY UNION FIELD

Goal
Dead-ball line
Touch in-goal line
Goal line
Touch-line
5 m line
Referee
Scrum-half
Hooker
10 m line
Tight-head prop
Loose-head prop
Linesman
Flanker
Flanker
Lock forward
Lock forward
Center
Right wing
Left wing
Number 8
Center
Fly-half
Full back
In-goal area

225 ft (68 m) maximum

RUGBY UNION SCRUM

Loose-head prop
Hooker
Tight-head prop
Scrum-half
Crossbar
Flanker
Flanker
Lock forward
Lock forward
Number 8

18 ft (5.5 m)

Upright

Protective padding

9 ft 10 in (3 m)

RUGBY UNION GOALPOST

RUGBY LEAGUE SCRUM

Blind-side prop
Hooker
Open-side prop
Scrum-half
Second-row forward
Second-row forward
Loose forward

18 ft (5.5 m)

Upright
Crossbar
Protective padding

RUGBY LEAGUE GOALPOST

RUGBY LEAGUE FIELD

Goal
Dead-ball line
Touch in-goal
Touch in-goal line
Goal line
Touch-line
10 m line
Hooker
Referee
Open-side prop
Blind-side prop
Linesman
Linesman
Second-row forward
Second-row forward
Scrum-half
Loose forward
Stand-off half
Left wing
Center
Full back
Center
Right wing

225 ft (68 m) maximum

RUGBY SCORING AND SKILLS

GOAL

Goal line

TRY

PASS

PLACE KICK

FLYING TACKLE

Circular stud

RUGBY SHOE

Ankle support

RUGBY UNION PLAYER

Shirt in team color

Knee-high sock

Team shorts

Studded boot

RUGBY UNION BALL

Four-panel construction

Laminated leather panel covered with textured plastic

11–12 in (28–30 cm)

RUGBY LEAGUE BALL

Four-panel construction

Laminated leather panel covered with smooth plastic

11 in (28 cm)

RUGBY LEAGUE SHIRT

Team crest

Official logo of the British Rugby Football League

Three-quarter sleeve

RUGBY UNION SHIRT

Button-up collar

Team crest

Long sleeve

Team color

RUGBY SHIRTS

Basketball

BASKETBALL IS A BALL GAME for two teams of five players, originally devised in 1890 by James Naismath for the Y.M.C.A. in Springfield, Massachusetts. The object of the game is to take possession of the ball and score points by throwing the ball into the opposing team's basket. A player moves the ball up and down the court by bouncing it along the ground or "dribbling"; the ball may be passed between players by throwing, bouncing, or rolling. Players may not run with or kick the ball, although pivoting on one foot is allowed. The game begins with the referee throwing the ball into the air and a player from each team jumping up to try and "tip" the ball to a teammate. The length of the game and the number of periods played varies at different levels. There are amateur, professional, and international rules. No game ends in a draw. As many extra periods as necessary are played to break the tie. In addition to the five players on court, each team has up to seven substitutes, but players may only leave the court with the permission of the referee. Basketball is a noncontact sport and fouls on other players are penalized by a throw-in awarded against the offending team; a free throw at the basket is awarded when a player is fouled in the act of shooting. Basketball is a fast-moving game, requiring both physical and mental coordination. Skillful tactical play matters more than simple physical strength and the agility of the players makes the game an excellent spectator sport.

BASKETBALL SKILLS

CHEST PASS

DRIBBLE

OVERHEAD PASS

LAY-UP SHOT

JUMP SHOT

LONG PASS

INTERNATIONAL BASKETBALL COURT

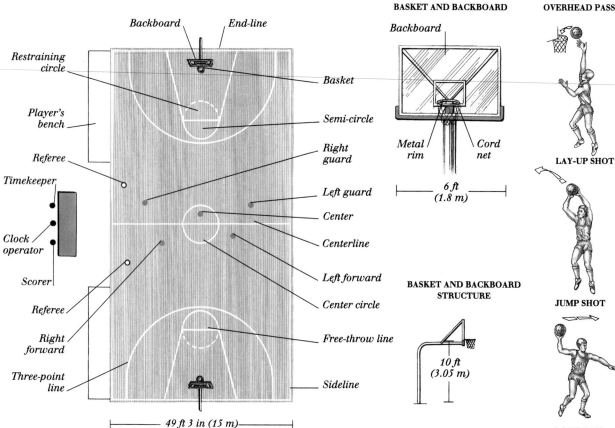

Backboard

End-line

Restraining circle

Player's bench

Referee

Timekeeper

Clock operator

Scorer

Referee

Right forward

Three-point line

Basket

Semi-circle

Right guard

Left guard

Center

Centerline

Left forward

Center circle

Free-throw line

Sideline

49 ft 3 in (15 m)

BASKET AND BACKBOARD

Backboard

Metal rim

Cord net

6 ft (1.8 m)

BASKET AND BACKBOARD STRUCTURE

10 ft (3.05 m)

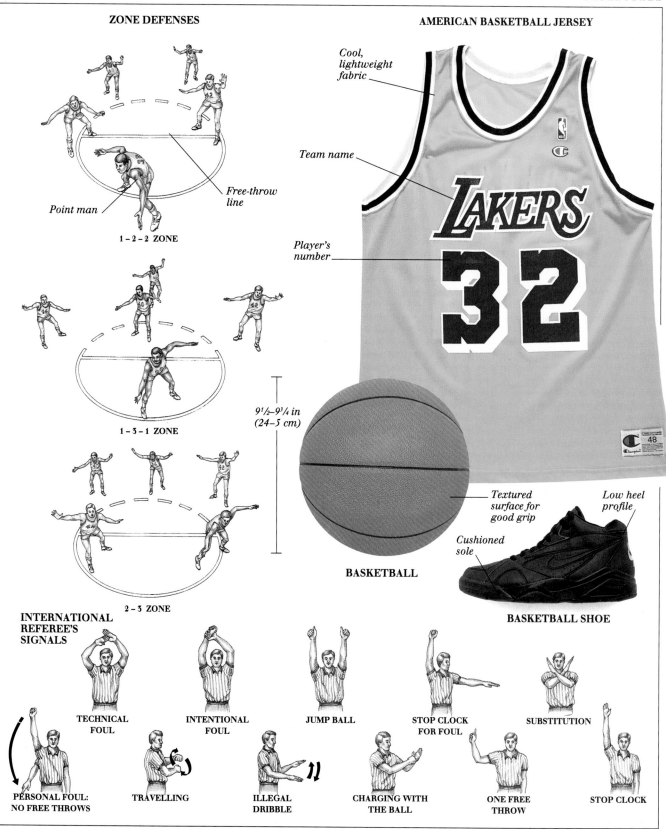

ZONE DEFENSES

AMERICAN BASKETBALL JERSEY

Cool, lightweight fabric

Team name

Player's number

Free-throw line

Point man

1 – 2 – 2 ZONE

1 – 3 – 1 ZONE

9¹⁄₂–9³⁄₄ in (24–5 cm)

2 – 3 ZONE

Textured surface for good grip

BASKETBALL

Low heel profile

Cushioned sole

BASKETBALL SHOE

INTERNATIONAL REFEREE'S SIGNALS

TECHNICAL FOUL

INTENTIONAL FOUL

JUMP BALL

STOP CLOCK FOR FOUL

SUBSTITUTION

PERSONAL FOUL: NO FREE THROWS

TRAVELLING

ILLEGAL DRIBBLE

CHARGING WITH THE BALL

ONE FREE THROW

STOP CLOCK

Volleyball, netball, and handball

VOLLEYBALL, NETBALL, AND HANDBALL are fast-moving team sports played with balls, usually on courts with a hard surface. In volleyball, the object of the game is to hit the ball over a net strung across the center of the court so that it touches the ground on the opponent's side. The team of six players can take three hits to direct the ball over the net, although the same player cannot hit the ball twice in a row. Players can hit the ball with their arms, hands or any other part of their upper body. Teams score points only while serving. The first team to score 15 points, with a two-point margin over their opponent, wins the game. Netball is similar to basketball (see pp. 532–533), but is played on a slightly larger court with seven players instead of five. A team moves the ball toward the goal by throwing, passing, and catching it with the aim of throwing the ball through the opponents' goal net. Players are confined by their playing position to specific areas of the court. Team handball is one of the world's fastest games. Each side has seven players. A team moves the ball by dribbling, passing, or bouncing it as they run. Players may stop, catch, throw, bounce, or strike the ball with any part of the body above the knees. Each team tries to score goals by directing the ball past the opposition's goalkeeper into the net, which is similar to a soccer goal net (see pp. 524–525).

VOLLEYBALL SHOTS

OVERHAND SERVE   SPIKE (SMASH)

UNDERHAND SERVE   FOREARM PASS (DIG)

VOLLEYBALL KIT

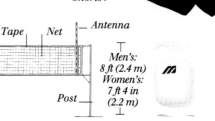

Team colors

Ribbed cuff

Cotton-knit jersey

Elastic waist

Leather covering

Elastic knit fabric

Shorts

VOLLEYBALL COURT

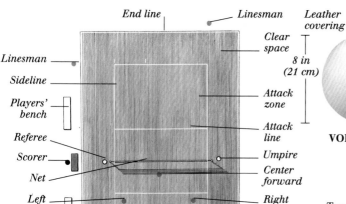

End line · Linesman

Linesman

Sideline

Players' bench

Referee

Scorer

Net

Left forward

Back zone

Left back

Linesman

Clear space

8 in (21 cm)

Attack zone

Attack line

Umpire

Center forward

Right forward

Center back

Linesman

Service area

Server

29 ft 6 in (9 m)

VOLLEYBALL

VOLLEYBALL NET

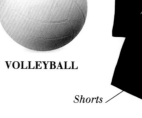

Tape · Net · Antenna

Men's: 8 ft (2.4 m) Women's: 7 ft 4 in (2.2 m)

Post

KNEE PADS

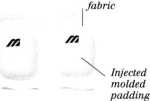

Injected molded padding

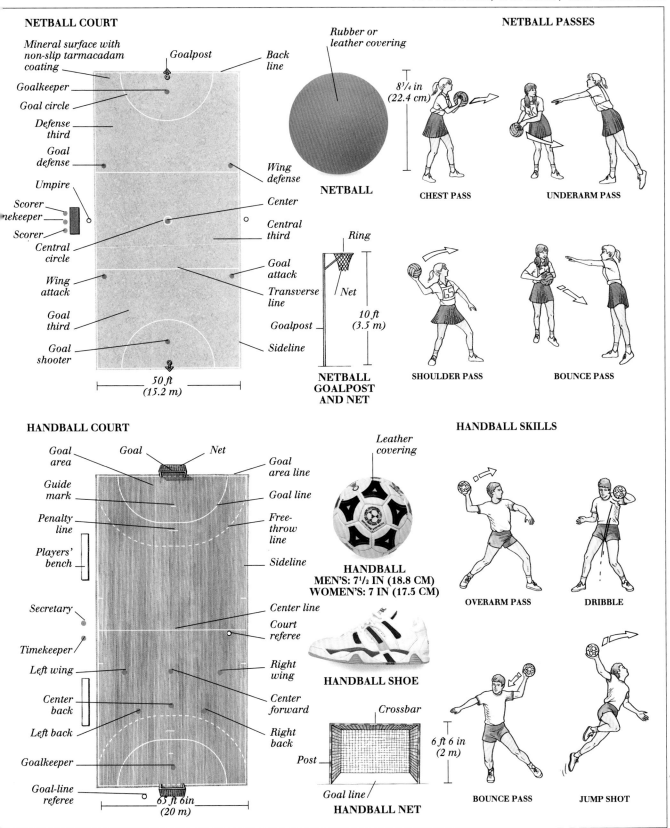

NETBALL COURT

Mineral surface with non-slip tarmacadam coating
Goalpost
Back line
Goalkeeper
Goal circle
Defense third
Goal defense
Wing defense
Umpire
Scorer
Timekeeper
Scorer
Center
Central third
Central circle
Goal attack
Wing attack
Transverse line
Goal third
Goal attack
Goal shooter
Sideline

50 ft (15.2 m)

NETBALL

Rubber or leather covering

8³/₄ in (22.4 cm)

NETBALL GOALPOST AND NET

Ring
Net
Goalpost

10 ft (3.5 m)

NETBALL PASSES

CHEST PASS
UNDERARM PASS
SHOULDER PASS
BOUNCE PASS

HANDBALL COURT

Goal area
Goal
Net
Goal area line
Guide mark
Goal line
Penalty line
Free-throw line
Players' bench
Sideline
Secretary
Center line
Court referee
Timekeeper
Left wing
Right wing
Center back
Center forward
Left back
Right back
Goalkeeper
Goal-line referee

65 ft 6in (20 m)

HANDBALL
MEN'S: 7¹/₂ IN (18.8 CM)
WOMEN'S: 7 IN (17.5 CM)

Leather covering

HANDBALL SHOE

HANDBALL NET

Crossbar
Post
Goal line

6 ft 6 in (2 m)

HANDBALL SKILLS

OVERARM PASS
DRIBBLE
BOUNCE PASS
JUMP SHOT

535

Baseball

BASEBALL IS A BALL GAME for two teams of nine players. The batter hits the ball thrown by the opposing team's pitcher, into the area between the foul lines. He then runs round all four fixed bases in order to score a run, touching or "tagging" each base in turn. The pitcher must throw the ball at a height between the batter's armpits and knees, a height which is called the strike zone. A ball pitched in this area that crosses over the home plate is called a "strike" and the batter has three strikes in which to try to hit the ball (otherwise he has "struck out"). The fielding team tries to get the batting team out by catching the ball before it bounces, tagging a player of the batting team who is running between bases with the ball, or by tagging a base before the player has reached it. Members of the batting team may stop safely at a base as long as it is not occupied by another member of their team. When the batter runs to first base, his teammate at first base must run onto second – this is called a force play. A game consists of nine innings and each team will bat once during an inning. When three members of the batting team are out, the teams swap roles. The team with the most runs wins the game.

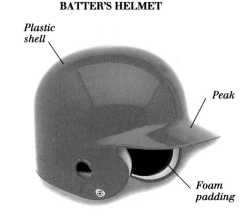

BATTER'S HELMET

Plastic shell

Peak

Foam padding

Wire coated in strong nylon

Plastic-coated foam padding

CATCHER'S MASK

BASEBALL FIELD

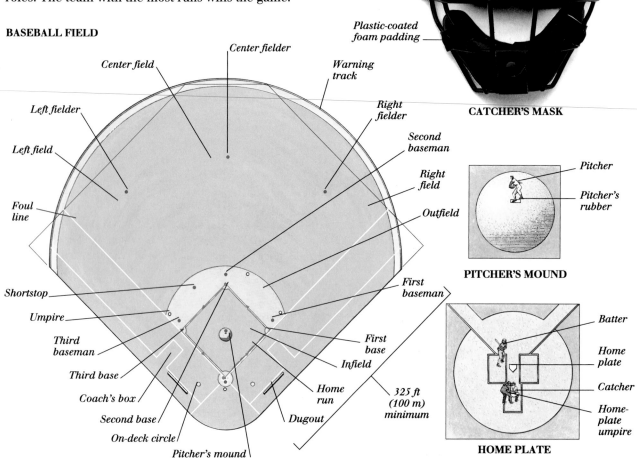

Center fielder

Center field

Warning track

Left fielder

Right fielder

Left field

Second baseman

Right field

Foul line

Outfield

Shortstop

First baseman

Umpire

First base

Third baseman

Infield

Third base

Coach's box

Home run

Second base

Dugout

On-deck circle

Pitcher's mound

325 ft (100 m) minimum

PITCHER'S MOUND

Pitcher

Pitcher's rubber

HOME PLATE

Batter

Home plate

Catcher

Home-plate umpire

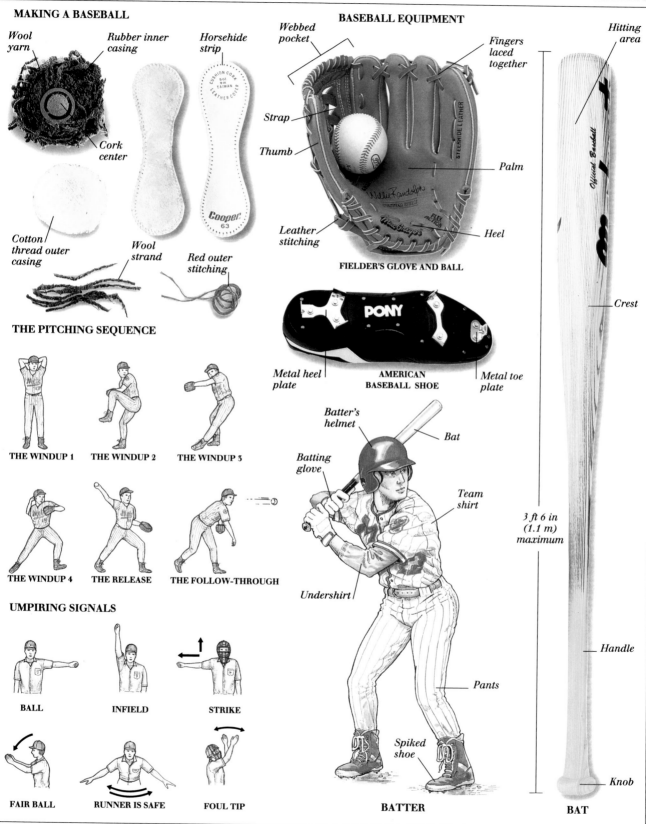

MAKING A BASEBALL

Wool yarn

Rubber inner casing

Horsehide strip

CUSHION CORK
5oz
9 in
TAIWAN
LEATHER COVER

Cooper
63

Cork center

Cotton thread outer casing

Wool strand

Red outer stitching

BASEBALL EQUIPMENT

Webbed pocket

Fingers laced together

Strap

Thumb

Palm

Leather stitching

Heel

FIELDER'S GLOVE AND BALL

PONY

Metal heel plate

AMERICAN BASEBALL SHOE

Metal toe plate

Hitting area

Official Baseball

Crest

THE PITCHING SEQUENCE

THE WINDUP 1

THE WINDUP 2

THE WINDUP 3

THE WINDUP 4

THE RELEASE

THE FOLLOW-THROUGH

UMPIRING SIGNALS

BALL

INFIELD

STRIKE

FAIR BALL

RUNNER IS SAFE

FOUL TIP

Batter's helmet

Bat

Batting glove

Team shirt

Undershirt

Pants

Spiked shoe

BATTER

3 ft 6 in (1.1 m) maximum

Handle

Knob

BAT

Cricket

CRICKET IS A BALL GAME PLAYED by two teams of eleven players on a pitch with two sets of three stumps (wickets). The bowler bowls the ball down the pitch to the batsman of the opposing team, who must defend the wicket in front of which he stands. The object of the game is to score as many runs as possible. Runs can be scored individually by running the length of the playing strip, or by hitting a ball which lands outside the boundary (six), or which lands inside the boundary but bounces or rolls outside (four); the opposing team will bowl and field, attempting to dismiss the batsmen. A batsman can be dismissed in one of several ways: by the bowler hitting the wicket with the ball ("bowled"); by a fielder catching the ball hit by the batsman before it touches the ground ("caught"); by the wicket-keeper or another fielder breaking the wicket while the batsman is attempting a run and is therefore out of his ground ("stumped" or "run out"); by the batsman breaking the wicket with his own bat or body ("hit wicket"); by a part of the batsman's body being hit by a ball that would otherwise have hit the wicket ("leg before wicket" ["lbw"]). A match consists of one or two innings and each innings ends when the tenth batsman of the batting team is out, when a certain number of overs (a series of six balls bowled) have been played, or when the captain of the batting team "declares" ending the innings voluntarily.

POSSIBLE FIELD POSITIONS FOR AN AWAY SWING BOWLER TO A RIGHT-HANDED BATSMAN (IN RED) AND OTHER FIELD POSITIONS

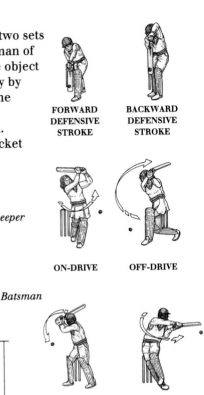

CRICKET PITCH

Wicket-keeper

Batsman

Wicket

Bowling crease

66 ft (20 m)

Bowler

Umpire | Non-striking batsman

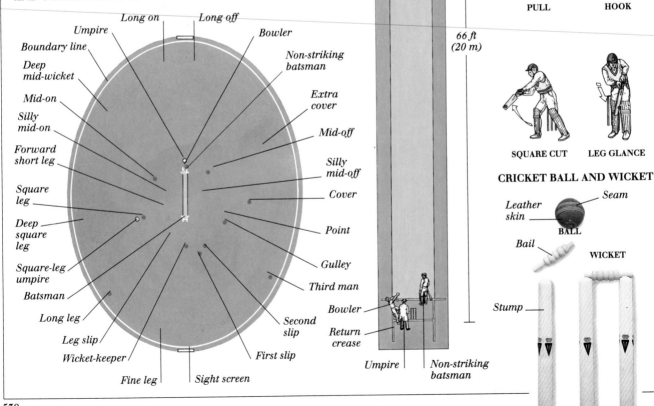

Long on   Long off

Umpire

Boundary line

Deep mid-wicket

Mid-on

Silly mid-on

Forward short leg

Square leg

Deep square leg

Square-leg umpire

Batsman

Long leg

Leg slip

Wicket-keeper

Fine leg   Sight screen

Bowler

Non-striking batsman

Extra cover

Mid-off

Silly mid-off

Cover

Point

Gulley

Third man

Bowler

Return crease

Second slip

First slip

CRICKET STROKES

FORWARD DEFENSIVE STROKE   BACKWARD DEFENSIVE STROKE

ON-DRIVE   OFF-DRIVE

PULL   HOOK

SQUARE CUT   LEG GLANCE

CRICKET BALL AND WICKET

Leather skin   Seam

BALL

Bail

WICKET

Stump

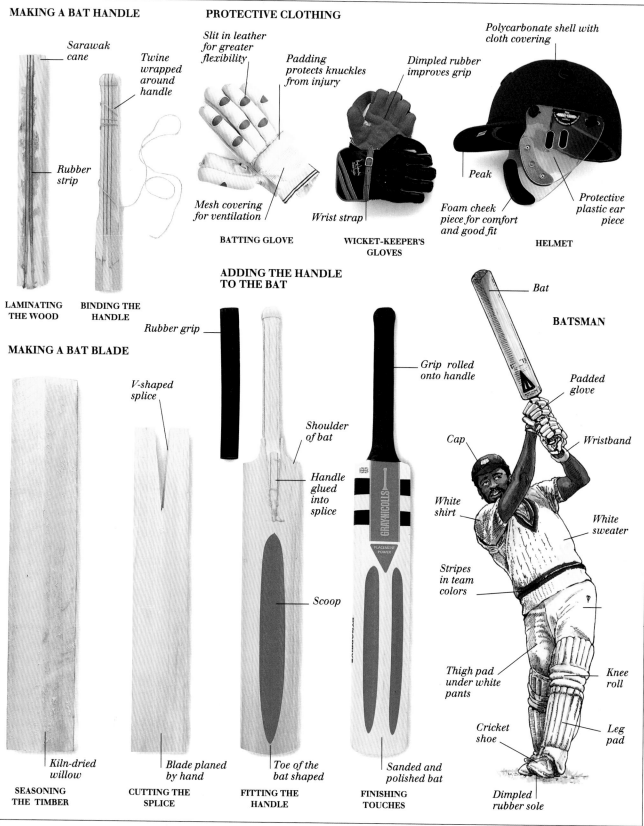

MAKING A BAT HANDLE

Sarawak cane

Twine wrapped around handle

Rubber strip

LAMINATING THE WOOD

BINDING THE HANDLE

PROTECTIVE CLOTHING

Slit in leather for greater flexibility

Padding protects knuckles from injury

Dimpled rubber improves grip

Polycarbonate shell with cloth covering

Mesh covering for ventilation

Wrist strap

Peak

Foam cheek piece for comfort and good fit

Protective plastic ear piece

BATTING GLOVE

WICKET-KEEPER'S GLOVES

HELMET

MAKING A BAT BLADE

ADDING THE HANDLE TO THE BAT

Rubber grip

Grip rolled onto handle

Shoulder of bat

Handle glued into splice

Scoop

V-shaped splice

Kiln-dried willow

Blade planed by hand

Toe of the bat shaped

Sanded and polished bat

SEASONING THE TIMBER

CUTTING THE SPLICE

FITTING THE HANDLE

FINISHING TOUCHES

BATSMAN

Bat

Padded glove

Cap

Wristband

White shirt

White sweater

Stripes in team colors

Thigh pad under white pants

Knee roll

Cricket shoe

Leg pad

Dimpled rubber sole

539

Field hockey, lacrosse, and hurling

ALL OVER THE WORLD, TEAM GAMES have evolved which require that a ball be struck or carried, and tossed at the end of a stick. Early forms of these games include hurling, shinty, bandy, and pelota. Field hockey is played by men and women: two teams of eleven players try to gain and keep possession of the ball and score goals by using the hockey stick to propel the ball into their opponents' goal net. Skills such as passing, pushing, or hitting the ball by slapping or lifting it in a flicking movement, and shooting at the goal are crucial. Field hockey is played indoors and outdoors on grass or synthetic fields. Lacrosse is played internationally as a 12-a-side game for women and as 10-a-side game for men. The women's field has no absolute boundaries but the men's has clearly defined sidelines and end lines. The ball is kept in play by being carried, thrown or batted with the crosse, and rolled or kicked in any direction. In men's and women's lacrosse, play can continue behind the marked goal areas. Similar skills are required in hurling – a Gaelic field game played on the same pitch as Gaelic football (see pp. 528–529), using the same goalposts and net. In hurling, the ball may be struck with or carried on the hurley and, when off the ground, may be struck with the hand or kicked. Goals (three points) are scored when the ball passes between the posts and under the crossbar; one point is scored when the ball passes between the posts and over the crossbar.

GOALKEEPER'S EQUIPMENT

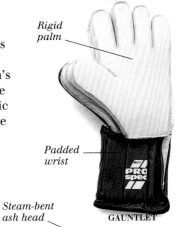

Face mask

Hard shell

Air vent

HELMET

Strap

Rigid palm

Padded wrist

GAUNTLET

FIELD HOCKEY STICK AND BALL

STICK

Handle

Tape

Steam-bent ash head

Blade

Stitched seam

2³⁄₄–3 in (7–7.5 cm)

Slazenger FLEXI

3 ft (91 cm)

BALL

FIELD HOCKEY FIELD

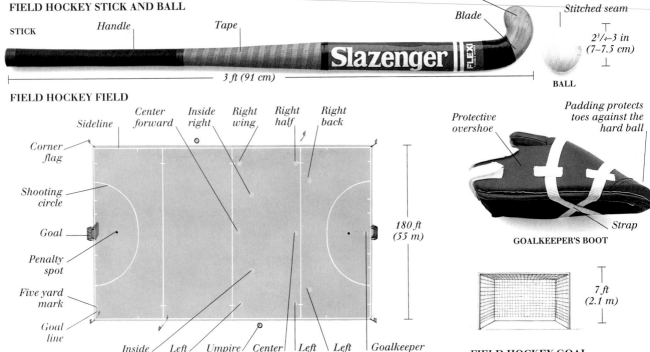

Sideline

Center forward

Inside right

Right wing

Right half

Right back

Corner flag

Shooting circle

Goal

Penalty spot

Five yard mark

Goal line

Inside left

Left wing

Umpire

Center half

Left half

Left back

Goalkeeper

180 ft (55 m)

Protective overshoe

Padding protects toes against the hard ball

Strap

GOALKEEPER'S BOOT

7 ft (2.1 m)

FIELD HOCKEY GOAL

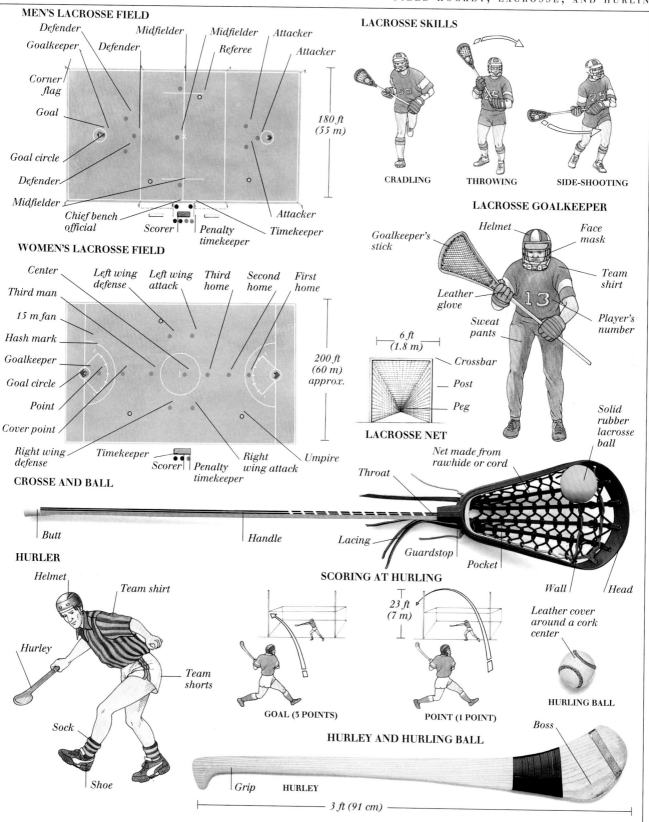

MEN'S LACROSSE FIELD

Defender
Goalkeeper
Defender
Midfielder
Midfielder
Referee
Attacker
Attacker

Corner flag
Goal
Goal circle
Defender
Midfielder
Chief bench official
Scorer
Penalty timekeeper
Attacker
Timekeeper

180 ft (55 m)

WOMEN'S LACROSSE FIELD

Center
Third man
15 m fan
Hash mark
Goalkeeper
Goal circle
Point
Cover point
Right wing defense

Left wing defense
Left wing attack
Third home
Second home
First home

Timekeeper
Scorer
Penalty timekeeper
Right wing attack
Umpire

200 ft (60 m) approx.

CROSSE AND BALL

Butt
Handle
Lacing
Throat
Guardstop
Pocket

Net made from rawhide or cord
Wall
Head

LACROSSE SKILLS

CRADLING
THROWING
SIDE-SHOOTING

LACROSSE GOALKEEPER

Goalkeeper's stick
Leather glove
Sweat pants
Helmet
Face mask
Team shirt
Player's number
Solid rubber lacrosse ball

6 ft (1.8 m)
Crossbar
Post
Peg

LACROSSE NET

HURLER

Helmet
Team shirt
Hurley
Team shorts
Sock
Shoe

SCORING AT HURLING

23 ft (7 m)

GOAL (3 POINTS)
POINT (1 POINT)

Leather cover around a cork center

HURLING BALL

Boss

HURLEY AND HURLING BALL

Grip
HURLEY
3 ft (91 cm)

Track and field

THE SPORTS that make up athletics are divided into two main groups: track events – which include sprinting, middle, and long distance running, relay running, hurdling, and walking – and field events which require jumping and throwing skills. Contests designed to test the speed, strength, agility, and stamina of athletes were held by the ancient Greeks over 4,000 years ago. However, the abolition of the Olympic Games in 393 AD meant that track and field events were neglected until the revival of large-scale competitions in the mid-nineteenth century. Modern stadiums offer areas reserved for the long jump, triple jump, and pole vault usually situated outside the running track. The javelin, shot, hammer, and discus are thrown within the track area. Most athletes specialize in one or two events but, in the heptathlon, women compete in seven events, held over two days: 200 m and 800 m races, 100 m hurdles, javelin, shot put, high jump, and long jump. In the decathlon, men compete in ten events over two days: 100 m, 400 m, and 1,500 m races, 110 m hurdles, javelin, discus, shot put, pole vault, high jump, and long jump.

FIELD EVENT EQUIPMENT

Steel wire

Head

Body

Swivel

Metal rim

Center weight

Hammer handle

DISCUS
MEN'S: 4 LB 7 OZ (2 KG)
WOMEN'S: 2 LB 3 OZ (1 KG)

HAMMER 16 LB (7 KG)

Rubber coating

Shot pellet filling

5 in (12.7 cm)

4 in (10 cm)

MEN'S SHOT 16 LB (7 KG)

WOMEN'S SHOT 8 LB 12 OZ (4 KG)

JAVELIN   *Cord grip*   *Shaft*   *Tip*

Men: 8 ft 6 in (2.6 m)
Women: 7 ft 6 in (2.3 m)

TRACK AND FIELD

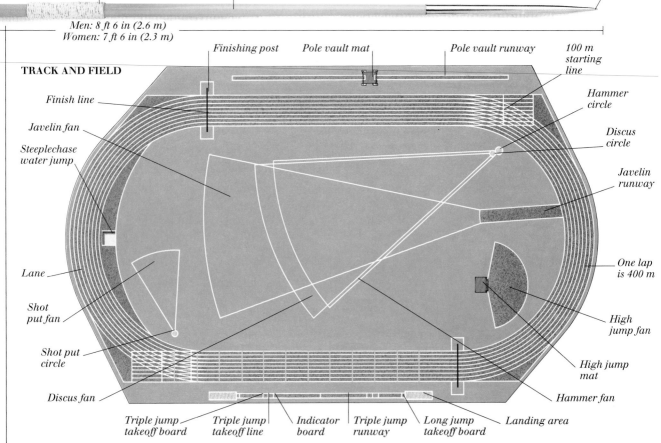

Finishing post · Pole vault mat · Pole vault runway · 100 m starting line

Finish line · Hammer circle · Javelin fan · Discus circle · Steeplechase water jump · Javelin runway · Lane · One lap is 400 m · Shot put fan · High jump fan · Shot put circle · High jump mat · Discus fan · Hammer fan

Triple jump takeoff board · Triple jump takeoff line · Indicator board · Triple jump runway · Long jump takeoff board · Landing area

RELAY BATONS

Hollow
plastic
tube

TYPES OF SHOE

Lightweight
construction

Spiked sole

TRACK SHOE

Air "pumping" device
for comfort and fit

Reflective
side strip

Wedge
heel

Air-cushioned
sole

RUNNING SHOE

DISCUS THROW

Swing

Shift

Twist

Release

SHOT PUT

Crouch

Shift

Release

Thrust

HAMMER THROW

Swing

Entry

Lift

Release

JAVELIN THROW

Withdrawal
stride

Halfturn

Step

Drive
forward

Release

LONG JUMP

Takeoff

Flight

Hitch kick

Stretch

Landing

Takeoff
board

TRIPLE JUMP

Takeoff

Hop

Skip

Jump

Takeoff
board

Land on foot
used for takeoff

Land on
opposite foot

HIGH JUMP

Drive

Arch

Takeoff

Approach

Landing

POLE VAULT

Handstand

Push-pull

Release

Rock-back

Hang

Takeoff

Plant

Landing

Racket sports

PROTECTIVE
EYEWEAR

THE OBJECT OF ALL RACKET SPORTS is to make shots the opponent cannot return. Games are played by two players (singles) or four players (doubles). Racket shape and size is tailored to each sport, but all rackets are constructed of wood, plastic, aluminum, or high-performance materials such as fiberglass and carbon graphite. Racket strings are usually synthetic, although natural gut is still used. Tennis is played on a court divided by a low net. Opposing players serve alternate games. At least six games must be won to gain a set, and two or sometimes three sets are needed to win a match. Tennis courts may be concrete, grass, clay, or synthetic, each surface requiring a different style of play. Badminton is an indoor sport that is played with light, flexible rackets and a birdie on a court with a high net. Players can score points only on their serve. The first to reach 15 points (11 points for women's singles) wins the game. Two games are needed to win a match. Squash and racketball are both played in enclosed courts. One player hits the ball against the front wall, and the other tries to return it before it bounces on the floor more than once. Squash rackets have smaller, rounder heads and stiffer frames than badminton rackets. International courts are wider than those in the U.S., where a much harder ball is used. Squash games are played to nine points (international) or 15 points (U.S.). In racketball, players use a ball that is larger and bouncier than a squash ball. The racketball racket is thick and sturdy, with a large head, short handle, and a strap that loops around the wrist. Points can be won only when serving, and the first player to reach 21 points wins.

TENNIS RACKET

Synthetic string

Frame

Head

Logo

Throat

Grip

Butt

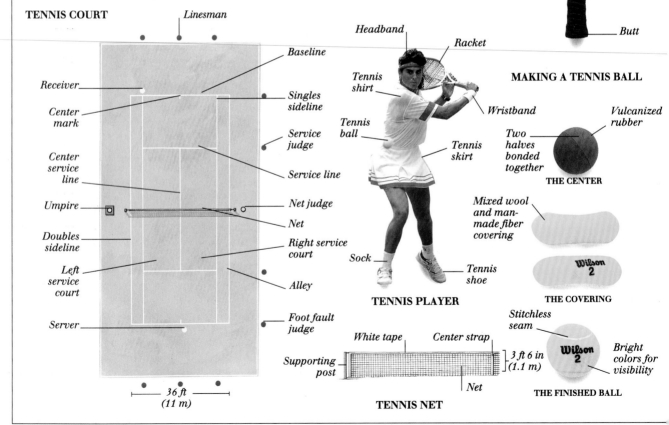

TENNIS COURT

Linesman

Receiver

Center mark

Center service line

Umpire

Doubles sideline

Left service court

Server

Baseline

Singles sideline

Service judge

Service line

Net judge

Net

Right service court

Alley

Foot fault judge

36 ft
(11 m)

Headband

Racket

Tennis shirt

Tennis ball

Wristband

Tennis skirt

Sock

Tennis shoe

TENNIS PLAYER

MAKING A TENNIS BALL

Vulcanized rubber

Two halves bonded together

THE CENTER

Mixed wool and man-made fiber covering

THE COVERING

Stitchless seam

Wilson 2

Bright colors for visibility

THE FINISHED BALL

White tape

Center strap

3 ft 6 in
(1.1 m)

Supporting post

Net

TENNIS NET

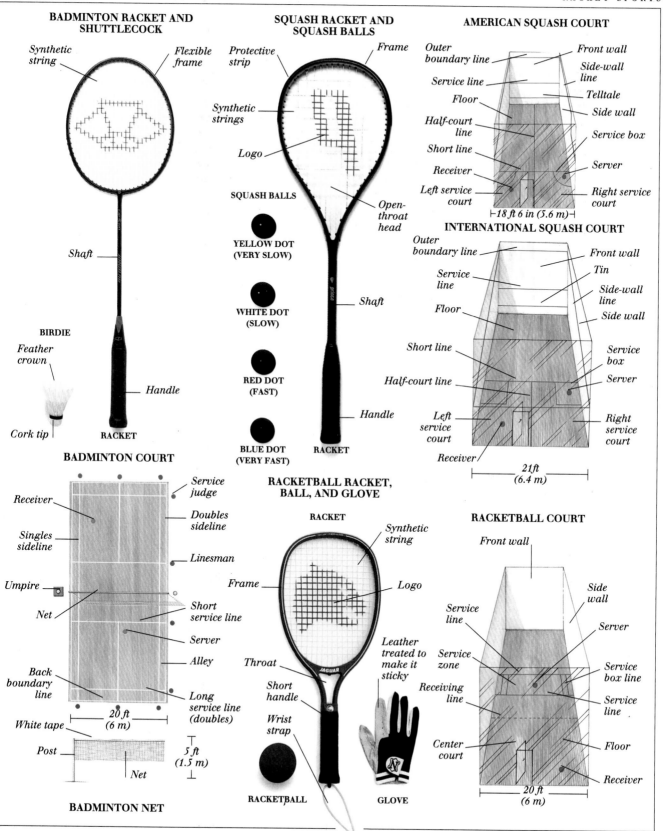

BADMINTON RACKET AND SHUTTLECOCK

Synthetic string

Flexible frame

Shaft

Handle

BIRDIE

Feather crown

Cork tip

RACKET

BADMINTON COURT

Service judge

Receiver

Doubles sideline

Singles sideline

Linesman

Umpire

Net

Short service line

Server

Alley

Back boundary line

Long service line (doubles)

20 ft (6 m)

White tape

Post

Net

5 ft (1.5 m)

BADMINTON NET

SQUASH RACKET AND SQUASH BALLS

Protective strip

Frame

Synthetic strings

Logo

Open-throat head

Shaft

Handle

RACKET

SQUASH BALLS

YELLOW DOT (VERY SLOW)

WHITE DOT (SLOW)

RED DOT (FAST)

BLUE DOT (VERY FAST)

RACKETBALL RACKET, BALL, AND GLOVE

RACKET

Synthetic string

Frame

Logo

Leather treated to make it sticky

Throat

Short handle

Wrist strap

RACKETBALL

GLOVE

AMERICAN SQUASH COURT

Outer boundary line

Front wall

Service line

Side-wall line

Floor

Telltale

Half-court line

Side wall

Short line

Service box

Receiver

Server

Left service court

Right service court

18 ft 6 in (5.6 m)

INTERNATIONAL SQUASH COURT

Outer boundary line

Service line

Front wall

Tin

Floor

Side-wall line

Side wall

Short line

Half-court line

Service box

Server

Left service court

Right service court

Receiver

21 ft (6.4 m)

RACKETBALL COURT

Front wall

Side wall

Service line

Server

Service zone

Service box line

Receiving line

Service line

Center court

Floor

Receiver

20 ft (6 m)

545

Golf

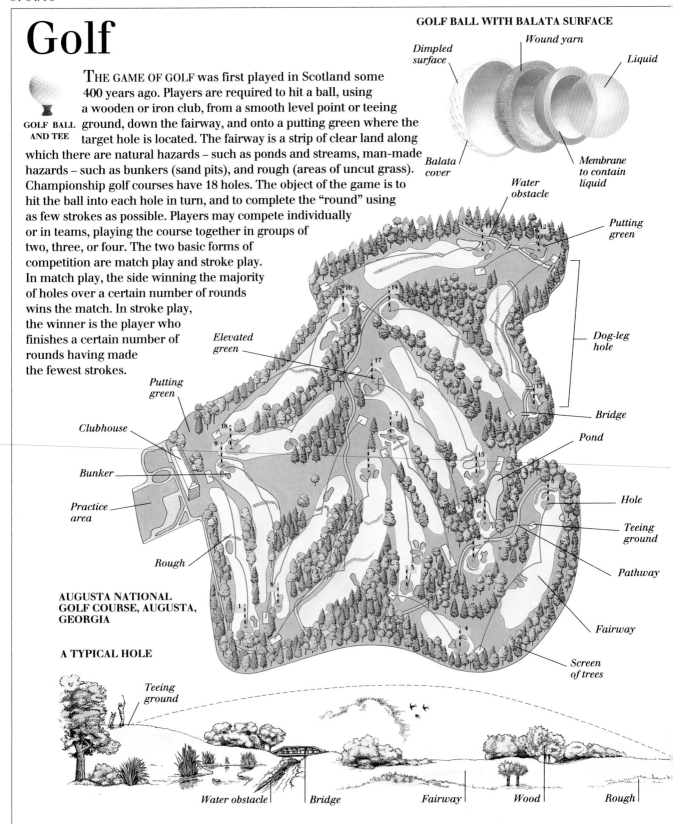

GOLF BALL AND TEE

THE GAME OF GOLF was first played in Scotland some 400 years ago. Players are required to hit a ball, using a wooden or iron club, from a smooth level point or teeing ground, down the fairway, and onto a putting green where the target hole is located. The fairway is a strip of clear land along which there are natural hazards – such as ponds and streams, man-made hazards – such as bunkers (sand pits), and rough (areas of uncut grass). Championship golf courses have 18 holes. The object of the game is to hit the ball into each hole in turn, and to complete the "round" using as few strokes as possible. Players may compete individually or in teams, playing the course together in groups of two, three, or four. The two basic forms of competition are match play and stroke play. In match play, the side winning the majority of holes over a certain number of rounds wins the match. In stroke play, the winner is the player who finishes a certain number of rounds having made the fewest strokes.

Dimpled surface

Wound yarn

Liquid

Balata cover

Membrane to contain liquid

Water obstacle

Putting green

Dog-leg hole

Bridge

Elevated green

Putting green

Pond

Clubhouse

Bunker

Hole

Practice area

Teeing ground

Rough

Pathway

AUGUSTA NATIONAL GOLF COURSE, AUGUSTA, GEORGIA

Fairway

Screen of trees

A TYPICAL HOLE

Teeing ground

Water obstacle

Bridge

Fairway

Wood

Rough

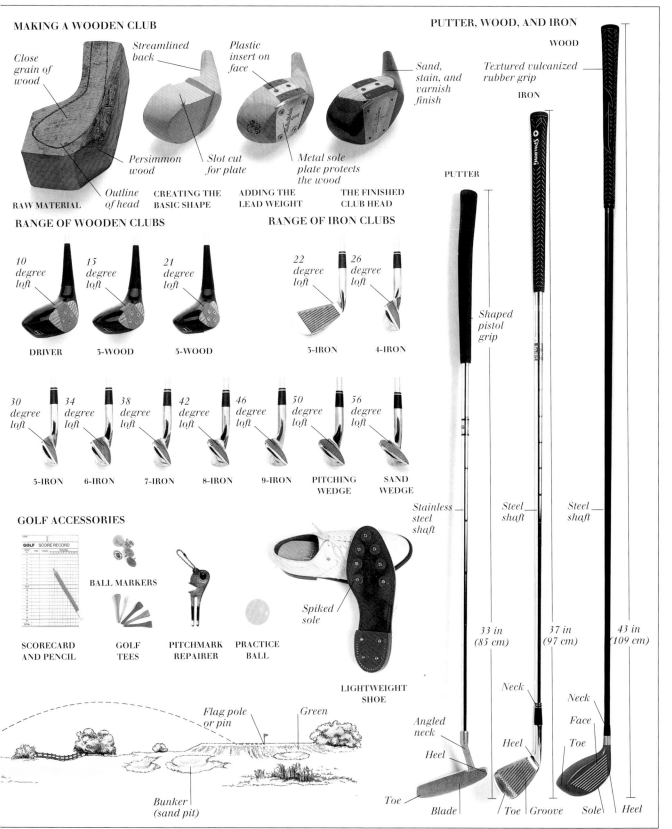

MAKING A WOODEN CLUB

Close grain of wood

Streamlined back

Plastic insert on face

Sand, stain, and varnish finish

Persimmon wood

Slot cut for plate

Metal sole plate protects the wood

Outline of head

RAW MATERIAL

CREATING THE BASIC SHAPE

ADDING THE LEAD WEIGHT

THE FINISHED CLUB HEAD

RANGE OF WOODEN CLUBS

10 degree loft

15 degree loft

21 degree loft

DRIVER

3-WOOD

5-WOOD

RANGE OF IRON CLUBS

22 degree loft

26 degree loft

3-IRON

4-IRON

30 degree loft

34 degree loft

38 degree loft

42 degree loft

46 degree loft

50 degree loft

56 degree loft

5-IRON

6-IRON

7-IRON

8-IRON

9-IRON

PITCHING WEDGE

SAND WEDGE

GOLF ACCESSORIES

SCORECARD AND PENCIL

BALL MARKERS

GOLF TEES

PITCHMARK REPAIRER

PRACTICE BALL

Spiked sole

LIGHTWEIGHT SHOE

Flag pole or pin

Green

Bunker (sand pit)

PUTTER, WOOD, AND IRON

WOOD

Textured vulcanized rubber grip

IRON

PUTTER

Shaped pistol grip

Stainless steel shaft

Steel shaft

Steel shaft

33 in (85 cm)

37 in (97 cm)

43 in (109 cm)

Neck

Neck

Angled neck

Face

Heel

Heel

Toe

Toe

Toe

Groove

Sole

Heel

Blade

Archery and shooting

TARGET SHOOTING AND ARCHERY EVOLVED as practice for hunting and battle skills. Modern bows, although designed according to the principles of early hunting bows, use laminates, fiberglass, dacron, and carbon, and are equipped with sights and stabilizers. Competitors in target archery shoot over distances of 100 ft (30 m), 165 ft (50 m), 230 ft (70 m), and 300 ft (90 m) for men, and 100 ft (30 m), 165 ft (50 m), 200 ft (60 m), and 230 ft (70 m) for women. The closer the shot is to the center of the target, the higher the score. The individual scores are added up, and the archer with the highest total wins the competition. Crossbows are used in match competitions over 33 ft (10 m), and 100 ft (30 m). Rifle shooting is divided into three categories: smallbore, bigbore, and air rifle. Contests take place over a variety of distances and further subdivisions are based on the type of shooting position used; prone, kneeling, or standing. The Olympic biathlon combines cross-country skiing and rifle shooting over a course of approximately 12½ miles (20 km). Additional magazines of ammunition are carried in the butt of the rifles. Bigbore rifles fitted with a telescopic sight can be used for hunting and running game target shooting. Pistol shooting events, using rapid-fire pistols, target pistols, and air pistols, take place over 33 ft (10 m), 82 ft (25 m), and 165 ft (50 m) distances. In rapid-fire pistol shooting, a total of 60 shots are fired from a distance of 82 ft (25 m).

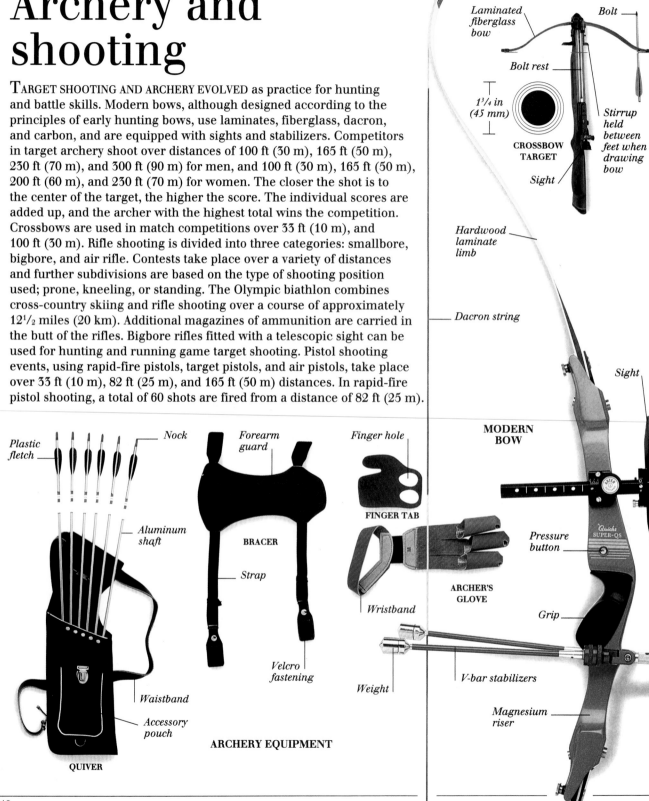

CROSSBOW AND BOLT

Laminated fiberglass bow

Bolt

Bolt rest

1¾ in (45 mm)

CROSSBOW TARGET

Stirrup held between feet when drawing bow

Sight

Hardwood laminate limb

Dacron string

Sight

MODERN BOW

Plastic fletch

Nock

Forearm guard

Finger hole

Aluminum shaft

BRACER

Strap

FINGER TAB

ARCHER'S GLOVE

Pressure button

Wristband

Grip

Velcro fastening

Weight

V-bar stabilizers

Waistband

Accessory pouch

ARCHERY EQUIPMENT

Magnesium riser

QUIVER

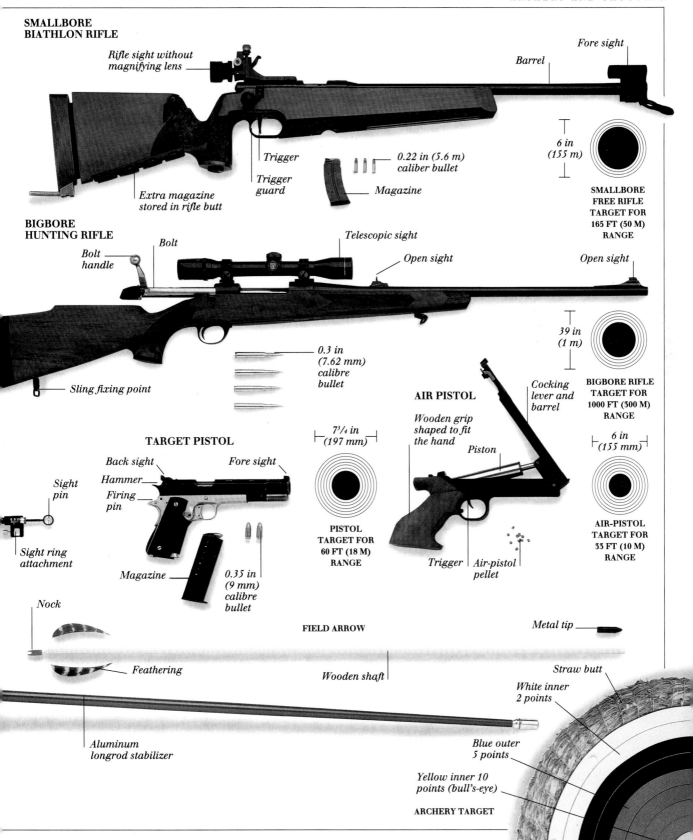

**SMALLBORE
BIATHLON RIFLE**

*Rifle sight without
magnifying lens*

Fore sight

Barrel

Trigger

*0.22 in (5.6 m)
caliber bullet*

*Trigger
guard*

Magazine

*Extra magazine
stored in rifle butt*

6 in
(155 m)

**SMALLBORE
FREE RIFLE
TARGET FOR
165 FT (50 M)
RANGE**

**BIGBORE
HUNTING RIFLE**

Bolt

Telescopic sight

*Bolt
handle*

Open sight

Open sight

*0.3 in
(7.62 mm)
calibre
bullet*

Sling fixing point

39 in
(1 m)

**BIGBORE RIFLE
TARGET FOR
1000 FT (300 M)
RANGE**

*Cocking
lever and
barrel*

AIR PISTOL

*Wooden grip
shaped to fit
the hand*

Piston

6 in
(155 mm)

**AIR-PISTOL
TARGET FOR
33 FT (10 M)
RANGE**

TARGET PISTOL

Back sight

Fore sight

7³/₄ in
(197 mm)

*Sight
pin*

Hammer

*Firing
pin*

*Sight ring
attachment*

**PISTOL
TARGET FOR
60 FT (18 M)
RANGE**

Trigger

*Air-pistol
pellet*

Magazine

*0.35 in
(9 mm)
calibre
bullet*

Nock

FIELD ARROW

Metal tip

Feathering

Wooden shaft

Straw butt

*White inner
2 points*

*Aluminum
longrod stabilizer*

*Blue outer
5 points*

*Yellow inner 10
points (bull's-eye)*

ARCHERY TARGET

Ice hockey

ICE HOCKEY IS PLAYED by two teams of six players on an ice rink, with a goal net at each end. The object of this fast, and often dangerous, game is to hit a frozen rubber puck into the opposing team's net with an ice hockey stick. The game begins when the referee drops the puck between the sticks of two players from opposing teams, who face off. The rink is divided into three areas: defending, neutral, and attacking zones. Players may move with the puck and pass it to one another along the ice, but the puck should not travel more than two zones across the rink markings. A goal is scored when the puck entirely crosses the goal-line between the posts and under the crossbar of the goal. A team may field up to 20 players although only six players are allowed on the ice at one time; substitutions occur frequently. Each game consists of three periods of 20 minutes, divided by breaks of 15 minutes.

GOALKEEPER

Helmet

Face mask

Throat protector

Team shirt

Butt end

Catch glove

Pants

Blocking pad

Goalkeeper's pad

Blade

Skate

Blade

Goalkeeper's stick

Heel

ICE HOCKEY RINK

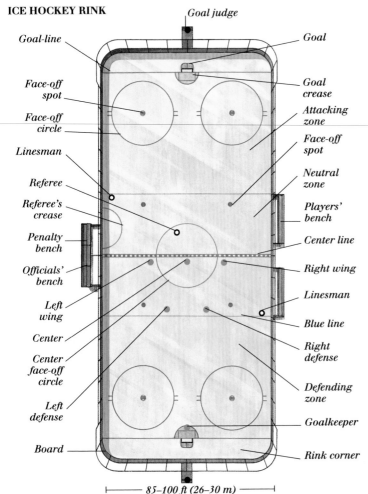

Goal judge

Goal-line

Goal

Face-off spot

Goal crease

Face-off circle

Attacking zone

Face-off spot

Linesman

Neutral zone

Referee

Referee's crease

Players' bench

Penalty bench

Center line

Officials' bench

Right wing

Left wing

Linesman

Center

Blue line

Center face-off circle

Right defense

Left defense

Defending zone

Board

Goalkeeper

Rink corner

├── 85–100 ft (26–30 m) ──┤

THE FACE OFF

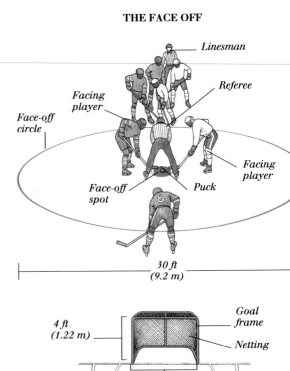

Linesman

Facing player

Referee

Face-off circle

Facing player

Face-off spot

Puck

├── 30 ft (9.2 m) ──┤

4 ft (1.22 m)

Goal frame

Netting

Goal crease

6 ft (1.83 m)

ICE HOCKEY GOAL

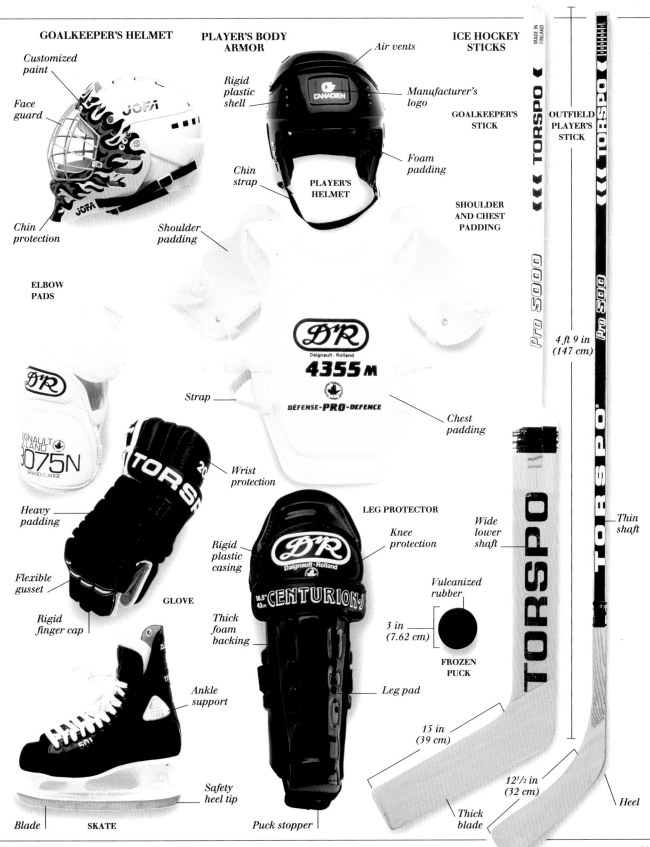

GOALKEEPER'S HELMET

Customized paint

Face guard

JOFA

Chin protection

JOFA

PLAYER'S BODY ARMOR

Air vents

Rigid plastic shell

CANADIEN

Manufacturer's logo

Chin strap

Foam padding

PLAYER'S HELMET

Shoulder padding

ICE HOCKEY STICKS

MADE IN FINLAND

TORSPO

GOALKEEPER'S STICK

Pro 5000

OUTFIELD PLAYER'S STICK

TORSPO

SHOULDER AND CHEST PADDING

Pro 5000

4 ft 9 in (147 cm)

ELBOW PADS

DAIGNAULT ROLLAND

3075N

GRAND/LARGE

Heavy padding

Flexible gusset

Rigid finger cap

TORSPO

20

GLOVE

DR

Daignault · Rolland

4355 M

DÉFENSE-**PRO**-DEFENCE

Strap

Chest padding

Wrist protection

LEG PROTECTOR

Rigid plastic casing

DR

Daignault · Rolland

16.5" 43cm

CENTURION J

Knee protection

Thick foam backing

Leg pad

Wide lower shaft

TORSPO

Vulcanized rubber

3 in (7.62 cm)

FROZEN PUCK

Thin shaft

TORSPO

Ankle support

501

TITAN

501

15 in (39 cm)

Safety heel tip

Blade

SKATE

Puck stopper

Thick blade

12½ in (32 cm)

Heel

551

Alpine skiing

COMPETITIVE ALPINE SKIING is divided into four disciplines: downhill, slalom, giant slalom, and super-giant slalom (Super-G). Each one tests different skills. In downhill skiing, competitors race down a slope marked out by control flags, known as "gates," and are timed on a single run only. Competitors wear crash helmets, one-piece Lycra suits, and long skis with flattened tips to minimize air resistance. Slalom and giant slalom skiers negotiate a twisting course requiring balance, agility, and quick reactions. Courses are defined by pairs of gates. Racers must pass through each pair of gates to complete the course successfully. Competitors are timed on two runs over different courses, and the skier who completes the courses in the shortest time wins. The equipment and protective guards used by slalom skiers are shown opposite. In Super-G races, competitors ski a single run that combines the technical challenge of slalom with the speed of downhill. The course requires skiers to complete medium-to-long radius turns at high speed, and contain up to two jumps. Clothing is the same as for downhill, but slightly shorter skis are used.

DOWNHILL SKIER

Ski goggles
Helmet
One-piece lycra ski suit
Wrist strap
Ski pole
Basket
Ski boot
Safety binding
Ski glove
Tail

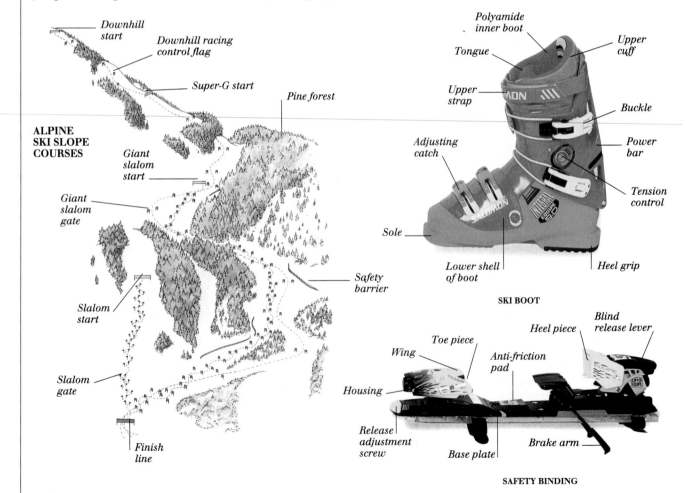

ALPINE SKI SLOPE COURSES

Downhill start
Downhill racing control flag
Super-G start
Pine forest
Giant slalom start
Giant slalom gate
Slalom start
Slalom gate
Finish line
Safety barrier

Polyamide inner boot
Tongue
Upper strap
Adjusting catch
Sole
Lower shell of boot
Upper cuff
Buckle
Power bar
Tension control
Heel grip

SKI BOOT

Toe piece
Wing
Housing
Release adjustment screw
Anti-friction pad
Base plate
Heel piece
Blind release lever
Brake arm

SAFETY BINDING

SLALOM CLOTHING AND EQUIPMENT

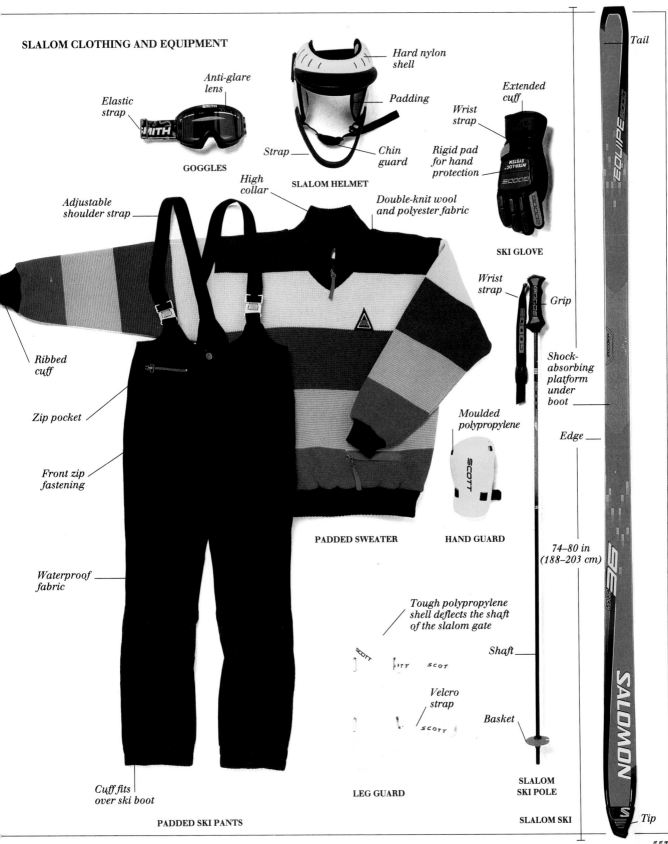

GOGGLES
- Elastic strap
- Anti-glare lens

SLALOM HELMET
- Hard nylon shell
- Padding
- Strap
- Chin guard

SKI GLOVE
- Extended cuff
- Wrist strap
- Rigid pad for hand protection

PADDED SWEATER
- High collar
- Double-knit wool and polyester fabric

HAND GUARD
- Moulded polypropylene

PADDED SKI PANTS
- Adjustable shoulder strap
- Ribbed cuff
- Zip pocket
- Front zip fastening
- Waterproof fabric
- Cuff fits over ski boot

LEG GUARD
- Tough polypropylene shell deflects the shaft of the slalom gate
- Velcro strap

SLALOM SKI POLE
- Wrist strap
- Grip
- Shaft
- Basket

SLALOM SKI
- Tail
- Shock-absorbing platform under boot
- Edge
- 74–80 in (188–203 cm)
- Tip

553

Equestrian sports

EQUESTRIAN SPORTS HAVE TAKEN place throughout the world for centuries: events involving mounted horses were recorded in the Olympic Games of 642 BC. Show jumping, however, is a much more recent innovation, and the first competitions were held at the beginning of the 1900s. In this sport, horse and rider must negotiate a course of variable, unfixed obstacles, making as few mistakes as possible. Show-jumping fences consist of wooden stands, known as standards or wings, that support planks or poles. Parts of the fence are designed to collapse on impact, preventing injury to the horse and rider. Judges penalize competitors for errors, such as knocking down obstacles, refusing jumps, or deviating from the course. Depending on the type of competition, the rider with the fewest faults, most points, or fastest time wins. There are two basic forms of horse racing – flat races and races with jumps, such as steeplechase or hurdle races. Thoroughbred horses are used in this sport, because they have great strength and stamina and can achieve speeds of up to 40 mph (65 kph). Jockeys wear silks – caps and jackets designed in distinctive colors and patterns which help identify the horses. In harness racing, the horse is driven from a light, two-wheeled carriage called a sulky. Horses are trained to trot and to pace, and different races are held for each of these types of gait. In pacing races, the horses wear hobbles to prevent them from breaking into a trot or gallop. Breeds such as the Standard-bred and the French Trotter have been developed especially for this sport.

SHOW-JUMPING SADDLE

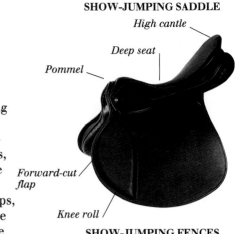

High cantle
Deep seat
Pommel
Forward-cut flap
Knee roll

SHOW-JUMPING FENCES

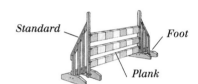

Standard
Foot
Plank

UPRIGHT PLANKS

Standard
Foot
Pole

UPRIGHT POLES

Back pole
Standard
Foot
Pole

TRIPLE BAR (STAIRCASE)

Standard
Pole
Foot

HOG'S-BACK

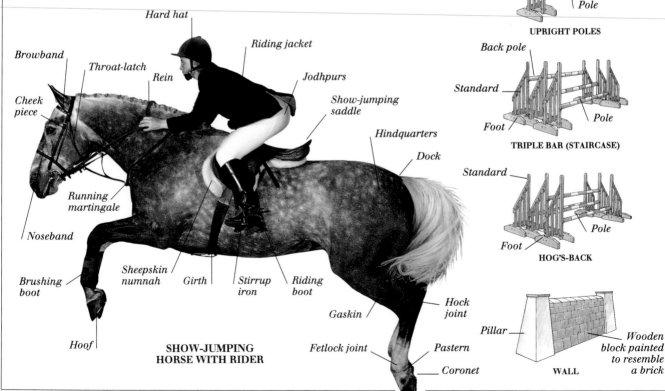

Hard hat
Browband
Throat-latch
Rein
Riding jacket
Jodhpurs
Cheek piece
Show-jumping saddle
Hindquarters
Dock
Running martingale
Noseband
Brushing boot
Sheepskin numnah
Girth
Stirrup iron
Riding boot
Hock joint
Gaskin
Hoof
Fetlock joint
Pastern
Coronet

SHOW-JUMPING HORSE WITH RIDER

Pillar
Wooden block painted to resemble a brick

WALL

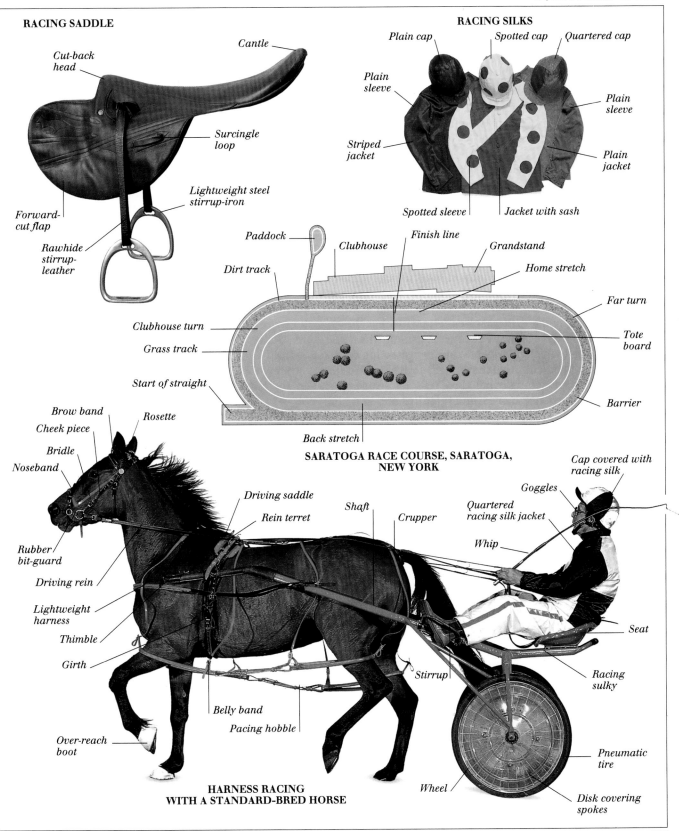

RACING SADDLE

Cut-back head

Cantle

Surcingle loop

Lightweight steel stirrup-iron

Forward-cut flap

Rawhide stirrup-leather

RACING SILKS

Plain cap

Spotted cap

Quartered cap

Plain sleeve

Plain sleeve

Striped jacket

Plain jacket

Spotted sleeve

Jacket with sash

Paddock

Finish line

Clubhouse

Grandstand

Dirt track

Home stretch

Clubhouse turn

Far turn

Grass track

Tote board

Start of straight

Barrier

Back stretch

SARATOGA RACE COURSE, SARATOGA, NEW YORK

Brow band

Rosette

Cheek piece

Bridle

Noseband

Driving saddle

Shaft

Cap covered with racing silk

Rein terret

Crupper

Goggles

Quartered racing silk jacket

Whip

Rubber bit-guard

Driving rein

Lightweight harness

Thimble

Seat

Girth

Stirrup

Racing sulky

Belly band

Over-reach boot

Pacing hobble

Pneumatic tire

Wheel

Disk covering spokes

HARNESS RACING WITH A STANDARD-BRED HORSE

Swimming and diving

SWIMMING GOGGLES

SWIMMING WAS INCLUDED in the first modern Olympic Games in 1896 and diving events were added in 1904. Swimming is both an individual and a team sport and races take place over a predetermined distance in one of the four major categories of stroke – freestyle (usually front crawl), butterfly, breaststroke, and backstroke. Competition pools are clearly marked for racing and anti-turbulence lane lines are used to separate the swimmers and help keep the water calm. The first team or individual to finish the race is the winner. Competitive diving is divided into men's and women's springboard and platform (highboard) events. There are six official groups of dives: forward dives, backward dives, armstand dives, twist dives, reverse dives, and inward dives. Competitors perform a set number of dives and after each one a panel of judges awards marks according to the quality of execution and the degree of difficulty.

STYLES OF DIVES

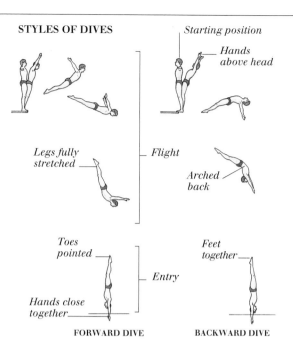

Starting position

Hands above head

Legs fully stretched

Flight

Arched back

Toes pointed

Entry

Feet together

Hands close together

FORWARD DIVE

BACKWARD DIVE

SWIMWEAR

Latex rubber molds to shape of head

CAPS

Rubber-covered wire

NOSE CLIP

Molded rubber

EARPLUG

High neckline

Man-made stretch fabric

Drawstring

High-cut leg

Strong seam

SWIMSUIT

TRUNKS

SWIMMING POOL

Swimmer

Lane number

Starting block

Chief timekeeper

Lane timekeeper

Placing judge

End wall

Starter

Recorder

Side wall

Backstroke marker 49 ft (15 m) from end of pool

Anti-turbulence lane line

Referee

Stroke judge

Backstroke turn indicator 16 ft (5 m) from end of pool

Bottom line

Turning judge

Turning wall

Lane

75 ft 6 in
(23 m)

558

Perfectly steady armstand

Arms and legs align throughout flight and entry

ARMSTAND DIVE

Arms spread wide apart

Body and legs straighten for flight and entry

TWIST DIVE

Height of dive

Pike position

Shoulders fall backward for vertical entry

REVERSE PIKE DIVE

Pike position

Hands touch toes

Feet lift up for straight entry

INWARD PIKE DIVE

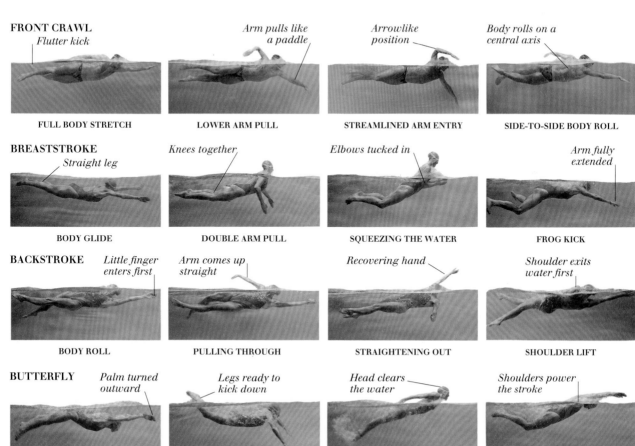

FRONT CRAWL
Flutter kick

Arm pulls like a paddle

Arrowlike position

Body rolls on a central axis

FULL BODY STRETCH **LOWER ARM PULL** **STREAMLINED ARM ENTRY** **SIDE-TO-SIDE BODY ROLL**

BREASTSTROKE
Straight leg

Knees together

Elbows tucked in

Arm fully extended

BODY GLIDE **DOUBLE ARM PULL** **SQUEEZING THE WATER** **FROG KICK**

BACKSTROKE *Little finger enters first*

Arm comes up straight

Recovering hand

Shoulder exits water first

BODY ROLL **PULLING THROUGH** **STRAIGHTENING OUT** **SHOULDER LIFT**

BUTTERFLY *Palm turned outward*

Legs ready to kick down

Head clears the water

Shoulders power the stroke

CATCHING THE WATER **DOUBLE ARM PULL** **KICKING DOWN** **WHOLE BODY UNDULATION**

Kayaking, rowing, and sailing

WATERBORNE SPORTS are as varied as the crafts used. There are two disciplines in rowing; sweep rowing, in which each rower has one oar, and sculling, in which rowers use two oars. There are a number of different Olympic and competitive rowing events for both men and women. The number of rowers and weight classes vary. Some rowing events use a coxswain; a steersman who does not row but directs the crew. Kayaks are used in straight sprint and slalom races. Slalom races take place over a course consisting of 20 to 25 gates, including at least six upstream gates. In yacht racing, competitors must complete prescribed courses, organized by the race committees, in the shortest possible time, using sail power only. Olympic events include classes for keel boats, dinghies, catamarans, and windsurfers.

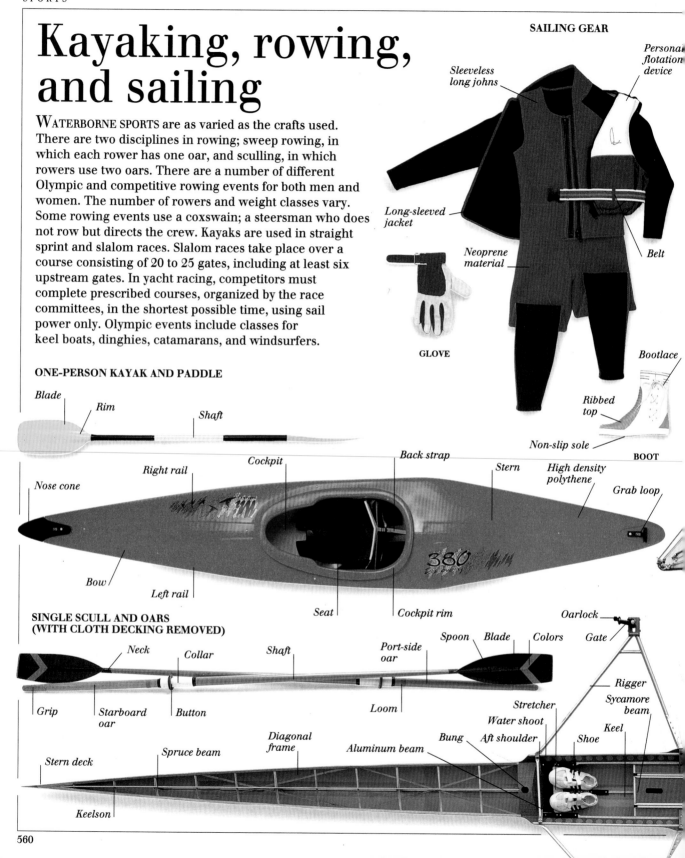

SAILING GEAR

Sleeveless long johns

Personal flotation device

Long-sleeved jacket

Neoprene material

Belt

GLOVE

Bootlace

Ribbed top

Non-slip sole

BOOT

ONE-PERSON KAYAK AND PADDLE

Blade

Rim

Shaft

Nose cone

Right rail

Cockpit

Back strap

Stern

High density polythene

Grab loop

Bow

Left rail

Seat

Cockpit rim

SINGLE SCULL AND OARS (WITH CLOTH DECKING REMOVED)

Neck

Collar

Shaft

Port-side oar

Spoon

Blade

Colors

Oarlock

Gate

Grip

Starboard oar

Button

Loom

Rigger

Stretcher

Sycamore beam

Water shoot

Keel

Bung

Aft shoulder

Shoe

Stern deck

Spruce beam

Diagonal frame

Aluminum beam

Keelson

560

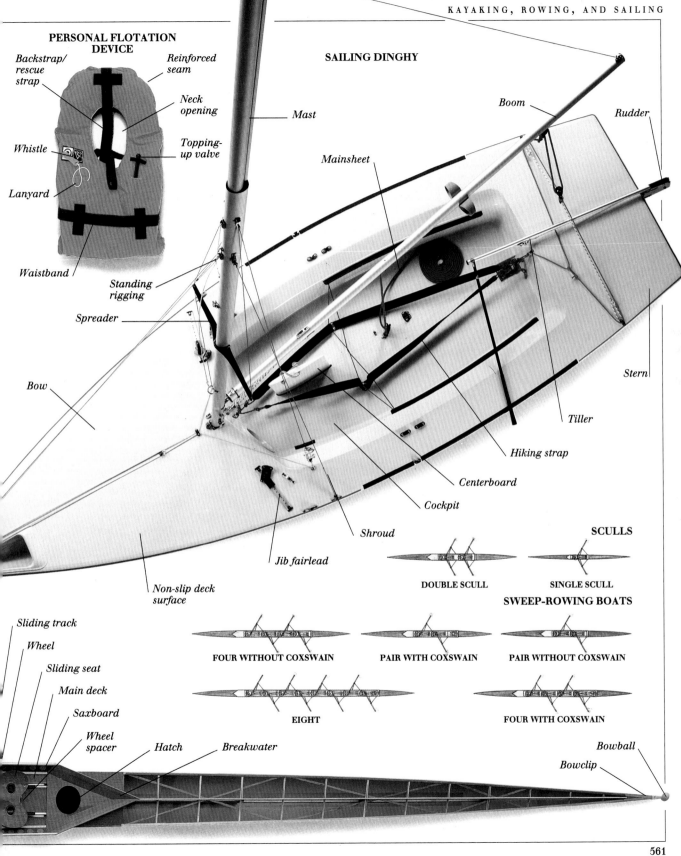

PERSONAL FLOTATION DEVICE

Backstrap/ rescue strap

Reinforced seam

Neck opening

Whistle

Topping-up valve

Lanyard

Waistband

SAILING DINGHY

Boom

Rudder

Mast

Mainsheet

Standing rigging

Spreader

Bow

Stern

Tiller

Hiking strap

Centerboard

Cockpit

Shroud

Jib fairlead

Non-slip deck surface

SCULLS

DOUBLE SCULL

SINGLE SCULL

SWEEP-ROWING BOATS

Sliding track

Wheel

Sliding seat

Main deck

Saxboard

Wheel spacer

Hatch

Breakwater

FOUR WITHOUT COXSWAIN

PAIR WITH COXSWAIN

PAIR WITHOUT COXSWAIN

EIGHT

FOUR WITH COXSWAIN

Bowball

Bowclip

561

Angling

ANGLING MEANS FISHING WITH A ROD, reel, line, and lure. There are several different types of angling: freshwater coarse angling, for members of the carp family and pike; freshwater game angling, for salmon and trout; and sea angling, for sea fish such as flatfish, bass, and mackerel. Anglers use a variety of methods of catching fish. These include bait fishing, in which bait (food to allure the fish) is placed on a hook and cast into the water; fly fishing, in which a natural or artificial fly is used to lure the fish; and spinning, in which a lure that looks like a small fish revolves as it is pulled through the water. The angler uses the rod, reel, and line to cast the lure over the water. The reel controls the line as it spills off the spool and as it is wound back. Weights may be fixed to the line so that it will sink. Swivels are attached to prevent the line from twisting. When a fish bites, the hook must become embedded in its mouth and remain there while the catch is reeled in.

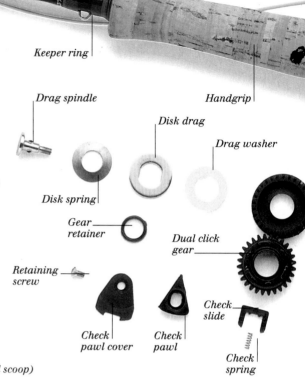

BUTT SECTION

Keeper ring

Drag spindle

Handgrip

Disk drag

Drag washer

Disk spring

Gear retainer

Dual click gear

Retaining screw

Check slide

Check pawl cover

Check pawl

Check spring

REELS

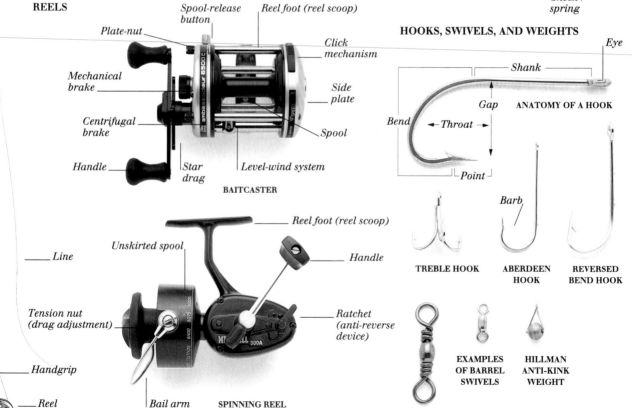

Plate-nut

Spool-release button

Reel foot (reel scoop)

Click mechanism

Mechanical brake

Side plate

Centrifugal brake

Spool

Handle

Star drag

Level-wind system

BAITCASTER

Line

Unskirted spool

Reel foot (reel scoop)

Handle

Tension nut (drag adjustment)

Ratchet (anti-reverse device)

Handgrip

Reel

Bail arm

SPINNING REEL

HOOKS, SWIVELS, AND WEIGHTS

Eye

Shank

Gap

ANATOMY OF A HOOK

Bend

Throat

Point

Barb

TREBLE HOOK

ABERDEEN HOOK

REVERSED BEND HOOK

EXAMPLES OF BARREL SWIVELS

HILLMAN ANTI-KINK WEIGHT

FLY ROD AND REEL

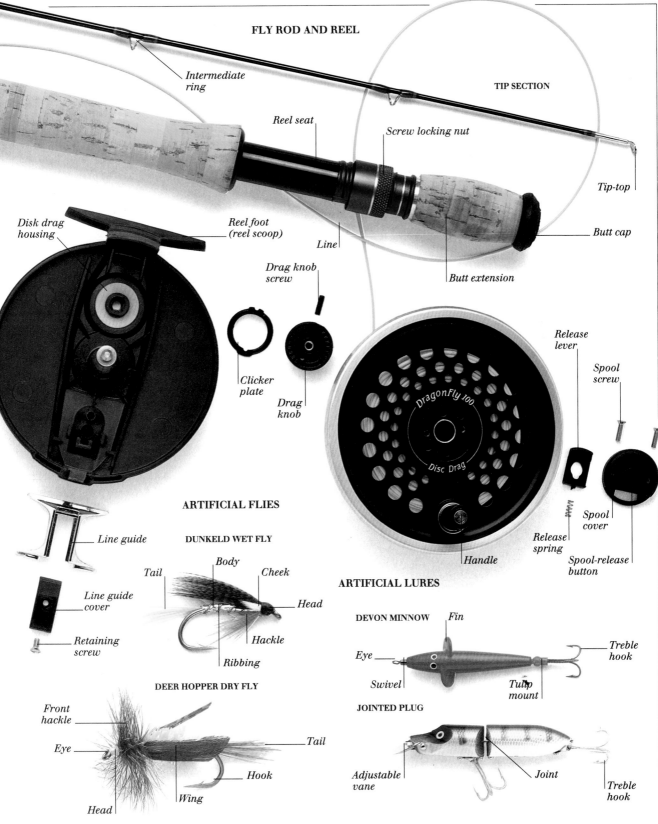

Intermediate ring

TIP SECTION

Reel seat

Screw locking nut

Tip-top

Butt cap

Disk drag housing

Reel foot (reel scoop)

Line

Butt extension

Drag knob screw

Release lever

Spool screw

Clicker plate

Drag knob

Line guide

ARTIFICIAL FLIES

DUNKELD WET FLY

Release spring

Spool cover

Spool-release button

Handle

Tail

Body

Cheek

Head

ARTIFICIAL LURES

Line guide cover

Retaining screw

Hackle

Ribbing

DEER HOPPER DRY FLY

DEVON MINNOW

Fin

Eye

Treble hook

Swivel

Tulip mount

Front hackle

Eye

Tail

Head

Wing

Hook

JOINTED PLUG

Adjustable vane

Joint

Treble hook

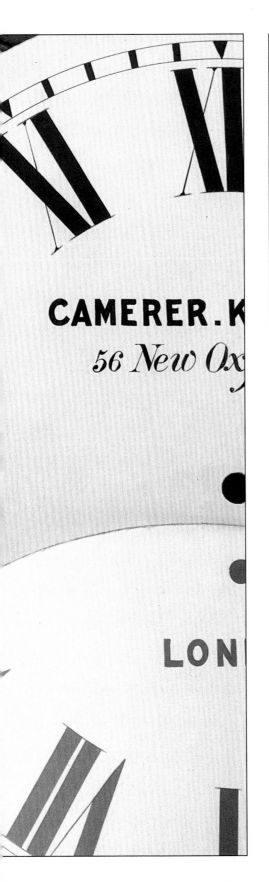

EVERYDAY THINGS

Drills

THE ELECTRICALLY POWERED MOTOR OF A POWER DRILL, cooled by a fan, turns a shaft at high speed. The shaft connects, in turn, to a system of gears that rotates a chuck even faster. Clamped by the chuck, a sharp drill bit cuts out the hole, and at the same time the bit's screw-shaped grooves channel the waste out of the hole. For drilling hard materials, many power drills have a hammer mechanism; when this is operated a ratchet in the gearcase causes the chuck and bit to pound in and out as they drill. A hand drill, although slower and less forceful than a power drill, is easier to control. For cutting wide holes, carpenters often prefer a brace-and-bit. This acts like a lever: the bowed handle of the brace moves a larger distance than the bit, turning the bit with extra force.

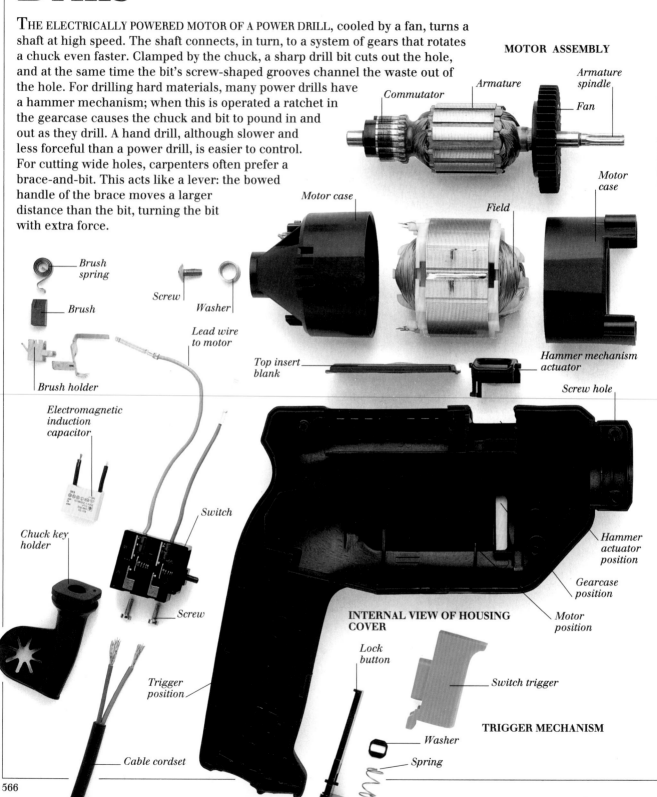

MOTOR ASSEMBLY

Armature spindle

Armature

Commutator

Fan

Motor case

Motor case

Field

Motor case

Brush spring

Screw

Washer

Brush

Lead wire to motor

Brush holder

Hammer mechanism actuator

Top insert blank

Screw hole

Electromagnetic induction capacitor

Switch

Chuck key holder

Hammer actuator position

Gearcase position

Screw

Motor position

INTERNAL VIEW OF HOUSING COVER

Trigger position

Lock button

Switch trigger

TRIGGER MECHANISM

Washer

Cable cordset

Spring

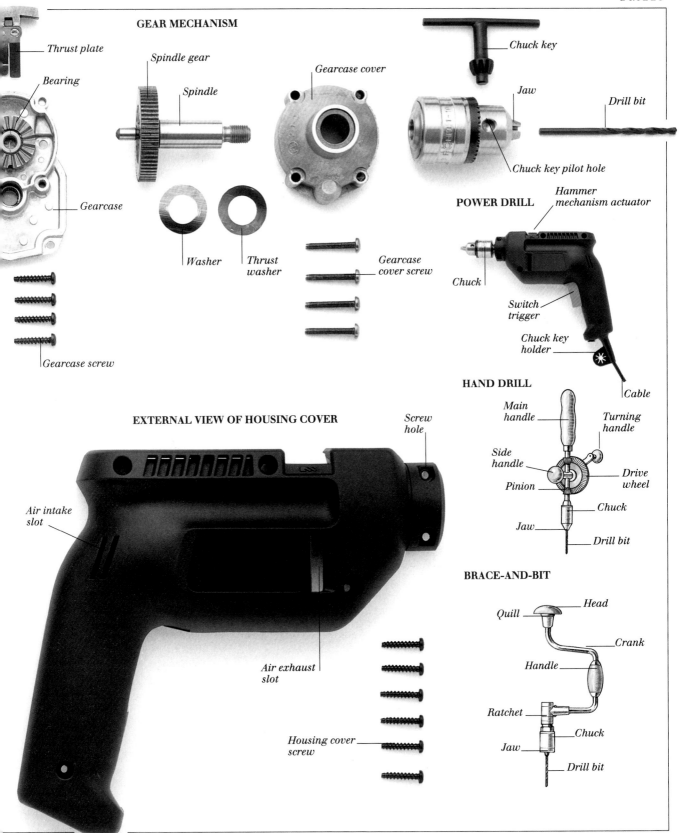

GEAR MECHANISM

Thrust plate

Bearing

Gearcase

Gearcase screw

Spindle gear

Spindle

Washer

Thrust washer

Gearcase cover

Gearcase cover screw

Chuck key

Jaw

Chuck key pilot hole

Drill bit

POWER DRILL

Hammer mechanism actuator

Chuck

Switch trigger

Chuck key holder

Cable

HAND DRILL

Main handle

Turning handle

Side handle

Pinion

Drive wheel

Chuck

Jaw

Drill bit

EXTERNAL VIEW OF HOUSING COVER

Screw hole

Air intake slot

Air exhaust slot

Housing cover screw

BRACE-AND-BIT

Quill

Head

Crank

Handle

Ratchet

Chuck

Jaw

Drill bit

Shoes

WELL MADE SHOES PROTECT THE FEET and are also comfortable and long lasting. The best shoemakers use a wood or plastic mold, called a last, which matches the shape of the customer's foot. The different parts of a shoe are stitched and glued together around the last; rivets and nails are used only in the heel, which is built up from layers of leather and rubber. The steel shank gives support to the arch of the foot and, with the seat lift, helps the wearer maintain posture. The layers of the sole give strength, while the soft insole cushions the foot. The leather welt sewn between the leather uppers and the sole ensures a strong join.

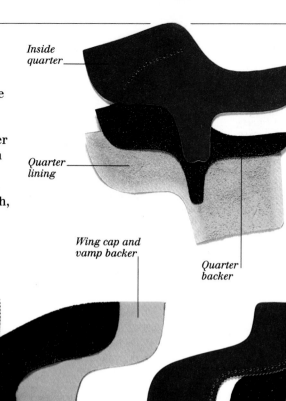

Inside quarter

Quarter lining

Wing cap and vamp backer

Quarter backer

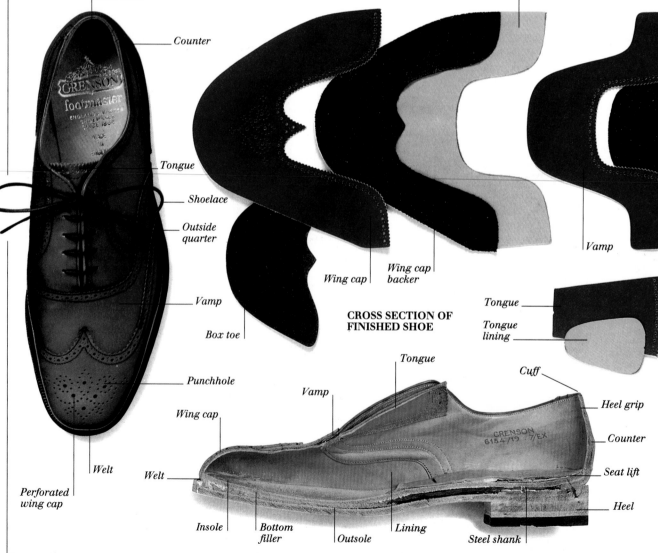

Inner sock

Counter

Tongue

Shoelace

Outside quarter

Vamp

Box toe

Punchhole

Welt

Perforated wing cap

Wing cap

Wing cap backer

CROSS SECTION OF FINISHED SHOE

Vamp

Tongue

Tongue lining

Vamp

Tongue

Cuff

Heel grip

Counter

Seat lift

Heel

Wing cap

Welt

Insole

Bottom filler

Outsole

Lining

Steel shank

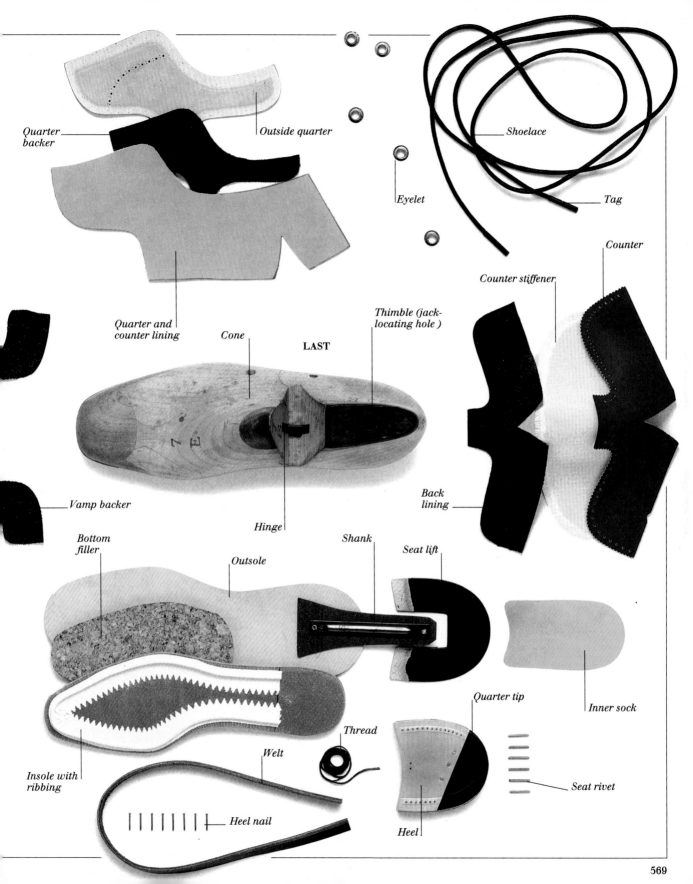

Quarter backer

Outside quarter

Shoelace

Eyelet

Tag

Counter

Counter stiffener

Quarter and counter lining

Cone

LAST

Thimble (jack-locating hole)

Back lining

Vamp backer

Hinge

Bottom filler

Outsole

Shank

Seat lift

Quarter tip

Inner sock

Insole with ribbing

Welt

Thread

Heel nail

Heel

Seat rivet

Clock

MECHANICAL CLOCKS HAVE TWO essential elements: a mainspring and a pendulum. When the clock is wound with the key, the mainspring is tightened. As the mainspring unwinds, it turns the gears, which move the minute and hour hands at different speeds around the face of the clock. The pendulum ensures that the hands move at a regular pace. At the top of the pendulum are two hooks called pallets. As the pendulum swings, the pallets allow the escape wheel to turn slowly and evenly.

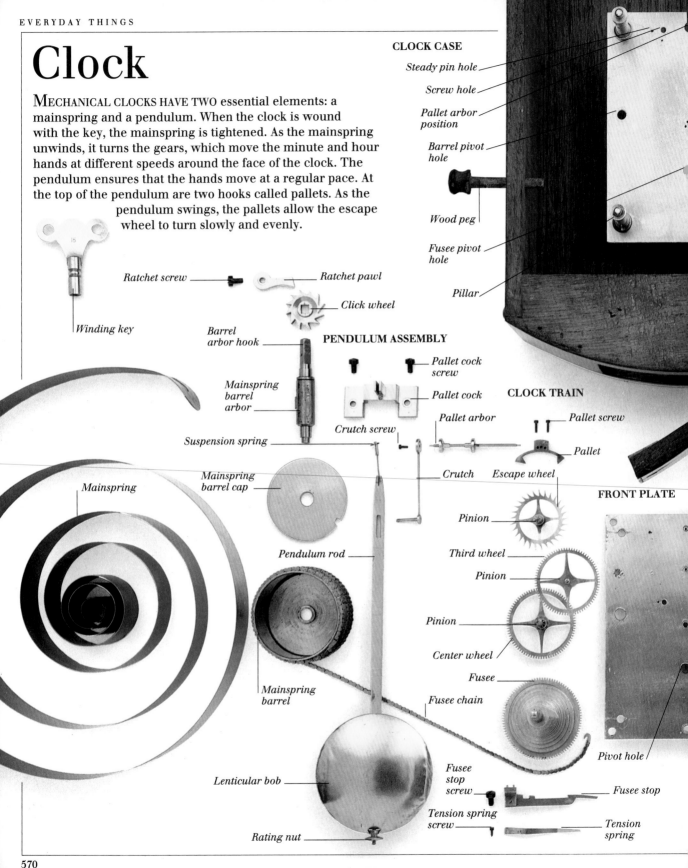

CLOCK CASE

Steady pin hole

Screw hole

Pallet arbor position

Barrel pivot hole

Wood peg

Fusee pivot hole

Pillar

Winding key

Ratchet screw

Ratchet pawl

Click wheel

Barrel arbor hook

PENDULUM ASSEMBLY

Pallet cock screw

Pallet cock

CLOCK TRAIN

Mainspring barrel arbor

Pallet arbor

Pallet screw

Suspension spring

Crutch screw

Pallet

Crutch

Escape wheel

Mainspring

Mainspring barrel cap

Pinion

FRONT PLATE

Third wheel

Pinion

Pendulum rod

Pinion

Center wheel

Mainspring barrel

Fusee

Fusee chain

Lenticular bob

Pivot hole

Fusee stop screw

Fusee stop

Tension spring screw

Tension spring

Rating nut

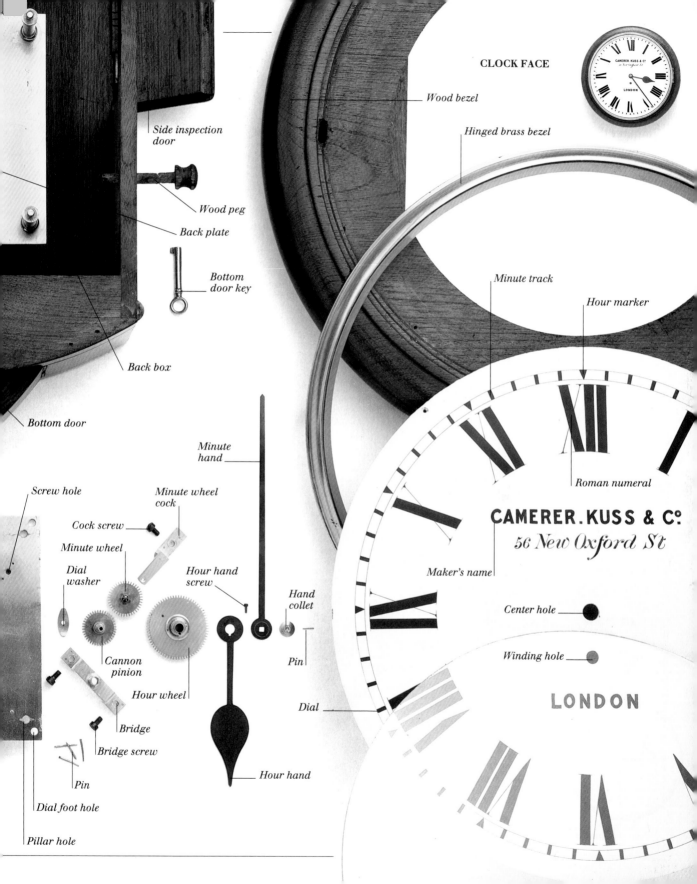

Side inspection door

Wood peg

Back plate

Bottom door key

Back box

Bottom door

CLOCK FACE

Wood bezel

Hinged brass bezel

Minute track

Hour marker

Roman numeral

CAMERER. KUSS & C°.
56 New Oxford St

Maker's name

Center hole

Winding hole

LONDON

Screw hole

Minute wheel cock

Cock screw

Minute wheel

Dial washer

Minute hand

Hour hand screw

Hand collet

Cannon pinion

Hour wheel

Pin

Bridge

Bridge screw

Pin

Dial foot hole

Pillar hole

Hour hand

Dial

Mini television

MINIATURIZED TELEVISION SETS are small enough to be held in the hand while being watched. A signal sent by a broadcast transmitter is picked up by the television antenna and passed to an electron gun at the back of the television set. In response to the signal this gun produces an electron beam that is passed through a deflection yoke. The yoke contains magnets and coils that cause the beam to scan across the screen in a series of lines. The screen is coated with phosphor, which glows when hit by the beam. As the beam scans the screen, its strength is varied so that the phosphor glows with different intensities in different parts of the screen. A continuous sequence of 25 black-and-white pictures per second appears on the screen so rapidly that the illusion of a moving picture is created.

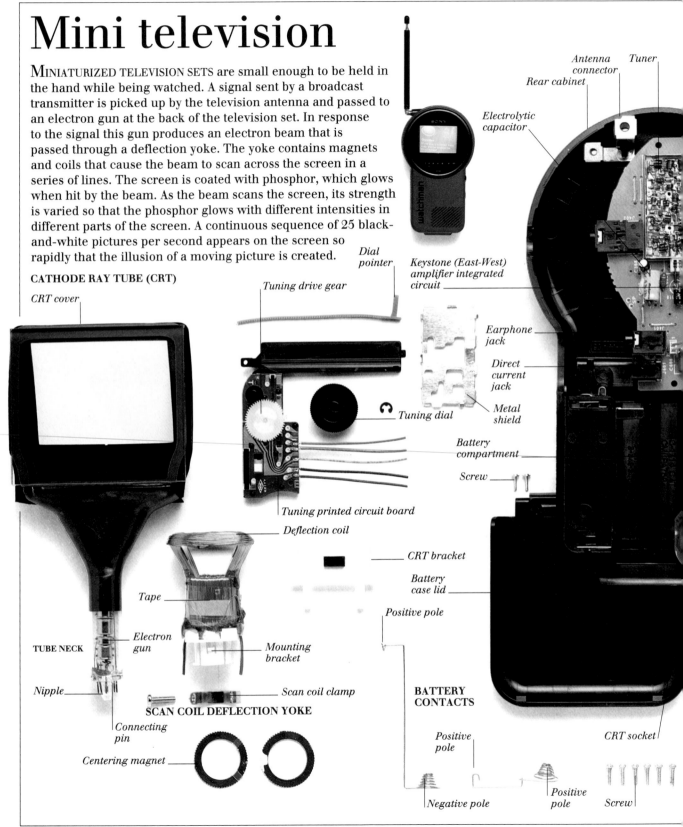

CATHODE RAY TUBE (CRT)

CRT cover

Dial pointer

Tuning drive gear

Antenna connector

Tuner

Rear cabinet

Electrolytic capacitor

Keystone (East-West) amplifier integrated circuit

Earphone jack

Direct current jack

Metal shield

Tuning dial

Battery compartment

Screw

Tuning printed circuit board

Deflection coil

CRT bracket

Battery case lid

Positive pole

Tape

Electron gun

Mounting bracket

Scan coil clamp

BATTERY CONTACTS

CRT socket

TUBE NECK

Nipple

SCAN COIL DEFLECTION YOKE

Connecting pin

Centering magnet

Positive pole

Negative pole

Positive pole

Screw

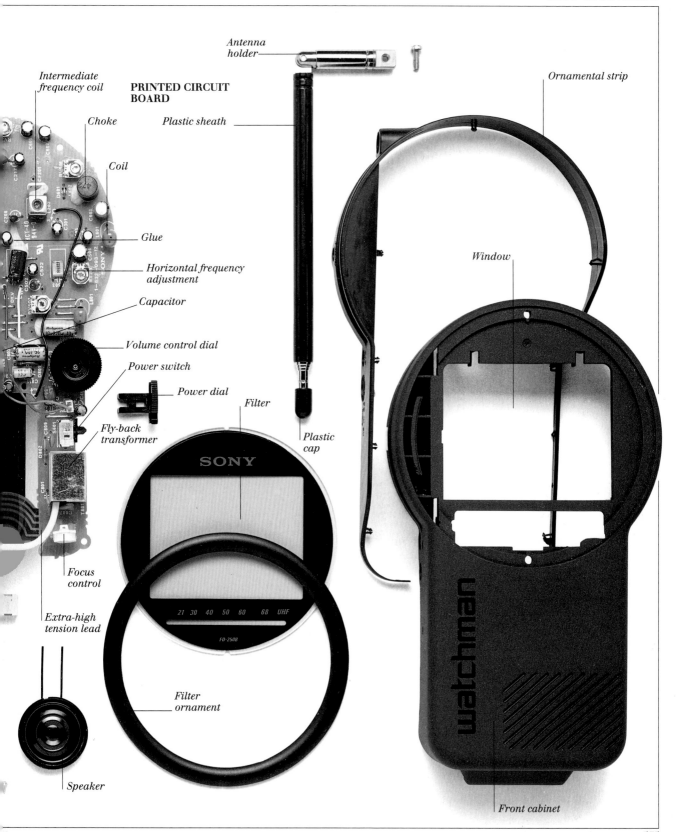

Antenna holder

Intermediate frequency coil

PRINTED CIRCUIT BOARD

Choke

Plastic sheath

Coil

Glue

Horizontal frequency adjustment

Capacitor

Volume control dial

Power switch

Power dial

Fly-back transformer

Filter

Plastic cap

Focus control

Extra-high tension lead

Filter ornament

Speaker

Ornamental strip

Window

SONY

21 30 40 50 60 68 UHF

FD-250B

watchman

Front cabinet

Chair

A TRADITIONALLY MADE DINING CHAIR, such as the Regency-style carver shown here, is held together, not by nails or bolts, but by snugly fitting joints, screws, dowels, and glue. Its curved arms and top splats, as well as its tapering legs, are cut from seasoned—that is, dried—mahogany. Mortice slots in the back legs receive the tenon tongues of the top and bottom splats; angled grooves at the top of the back legs, called rebates, take the curved arm rail. Though the various joints are so tight-fitting that they could produce a solid frame on their own, screws and glue are used to give the joints added strength. The comfortable, upholstered seat pad shown here consists of a patterned cover, calico lining, and foam padding that has been treated for fire safety; it is supported by webbing stretched across a wood frame.

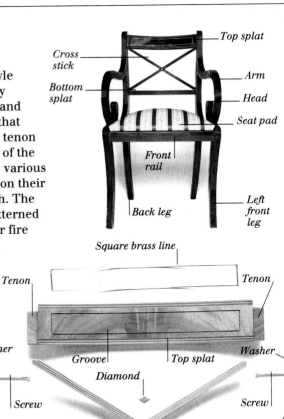

Cross stick
Top splat
Arm
Head
Seat pad
Bottom splat
Front rail
Back leg
Left front leg

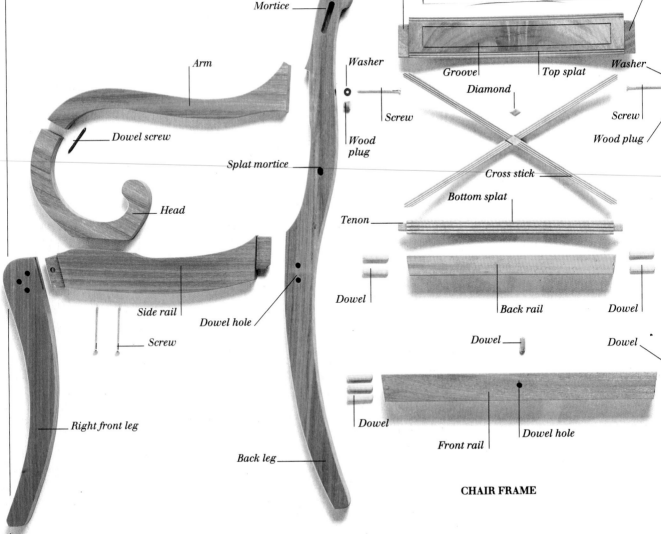

Mortice
Square brass line
Tenon
Tenon
Arm
Washer
Groove
Top splat
Washer
Dowel screw
Screw
Diamond
Screw
Splat mortice
Wood plug
Wood plug
Head
Cross stick
Bottom splat
Tenon
Side rail
Dowel
Back rail
Dowel
Screw
Dowel hole
Dowel
Dowel
Right front leg
Front rail
Dowel hole
Back leg
Dowel

CHAIR FRAME

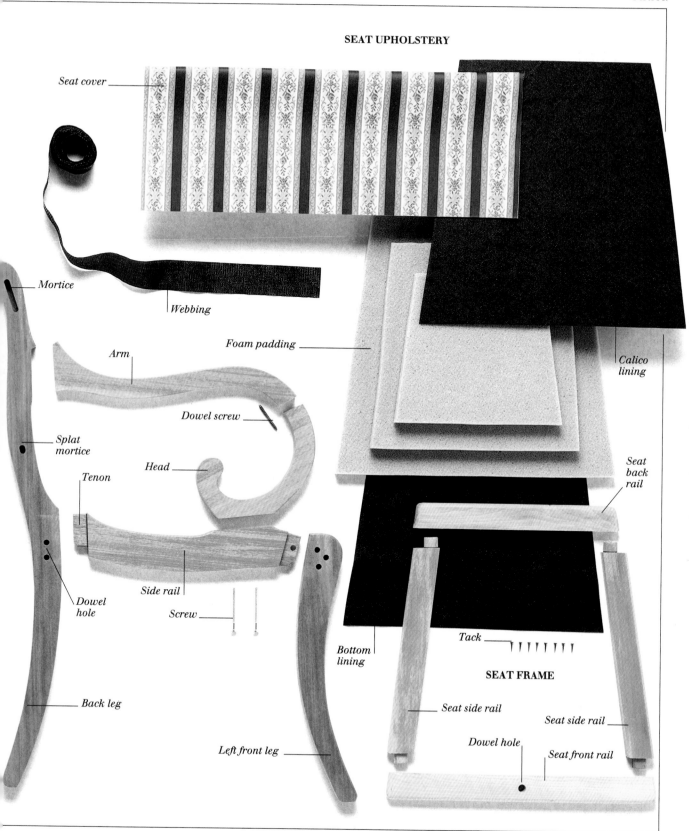

SEAT UPHOLSTERY

Seat cover

Mortice

Webbing

Arm

Foam padding

Dowel screw

Splat mortice

Tenon

Head

Calico lining

Seat back rail

Dowel hole

Side rail

Screw

Bottom lining

Tack

SEAT FRAME

Back leg

Seat side rail

Left front leg

Dowel hole

Seat side rail

Seat front rail

Toaster

MOST ELECTRIC TOASTERS NOT ONLY GRILL slices of bread, they also pop them up when ready. While the slices rest on a spring-loaded rack, electric heating elements toast the bread. At the same time, a bimetallic strip heats and expands. One of the two metals in this strip expands more quickly than the other, causing the strip to curve. As it bends, it completes an electrical circuit and activates an electromagnet. The magnet attracts a catch, releasing the spring that holds the rack down in the toaster. The elements switch off, and the toasted slices pop up.

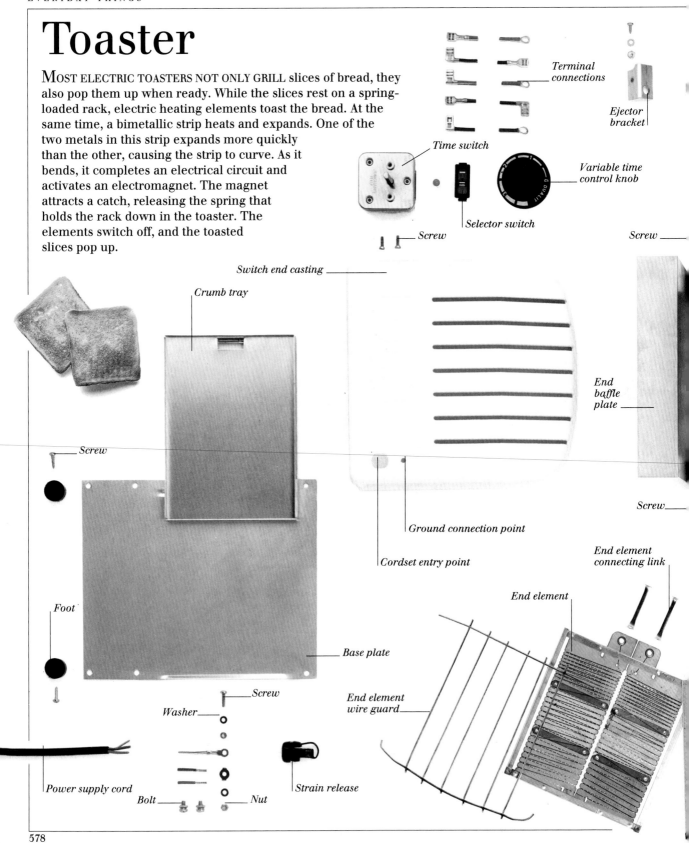

Terminal connections

Ejector bracket

Time switch

Variable time control knob

Selector switch

Screw

Screw

Switch end casting

Crumb tray

End baffle plate

Screw

Ground connection point

Screw

Cordset entry point

End element connecting link

End element

Foot

Base plate

End element wire guard

Screw

Washer

Power supply cord

Strain release

Bolt

Nut

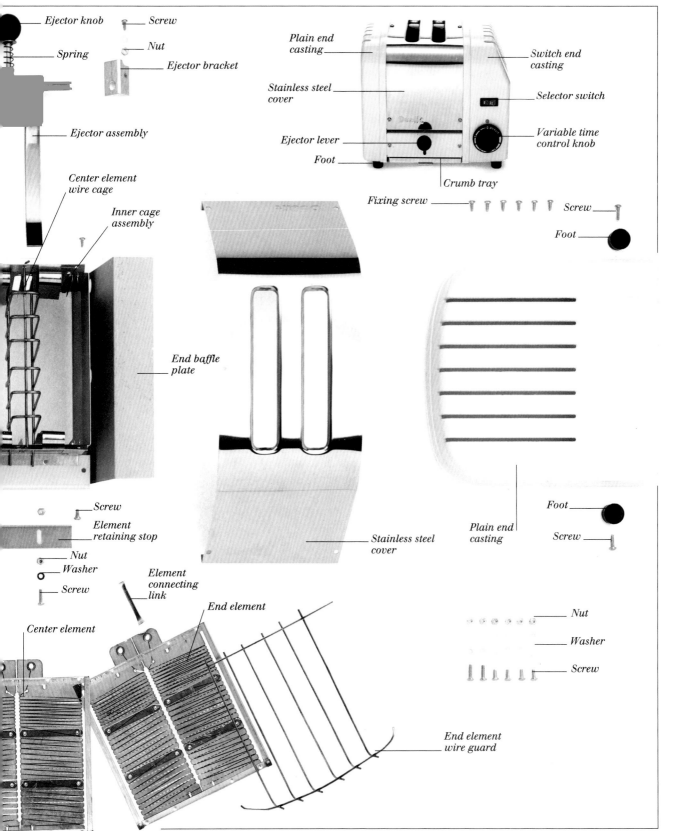

Ejector knob

Screw

Spring

Nut

Ejector bracket

Ejector assembly

Center element
wire cage

Inner cage
assembly

Plain end
casting

Switch end
casting

Stainless steel
cover

Selector switch

Ejector lever

Variable time
control knob

Foot

Crumb tray

Fixing screw

Screw

Foot

End baffle
plate

Screw

Element
retaining stop

Nut

Washer

Screw

Element
connecting
link

End element

Center element

Stainless steel
cover

Plain end
casting

Foot

Screw

Nut

Washer

Screw

End element
wire guard

Lawnmower

THE SHARP BLADES OF A LAWNMOWER—whether driven by electrical, gasoline, or human power—shave grass close to the ground. The gasoline-powered type shown here has a small engine that is electrically ignited by a battery and spark plug. This engine rotates a horizontal blade at the base of the lawnmower, which then slices the grass against a fixed blade. A grass bag at the back of the machine collects the cuttings. As the engine rotates the blades, it also turns the rear wheels, moving the lawnmower forward. Gears ensure that the horizontal blade spins faster than the wheels so that all of the grass is cut neatly before the lawnmower moves on.

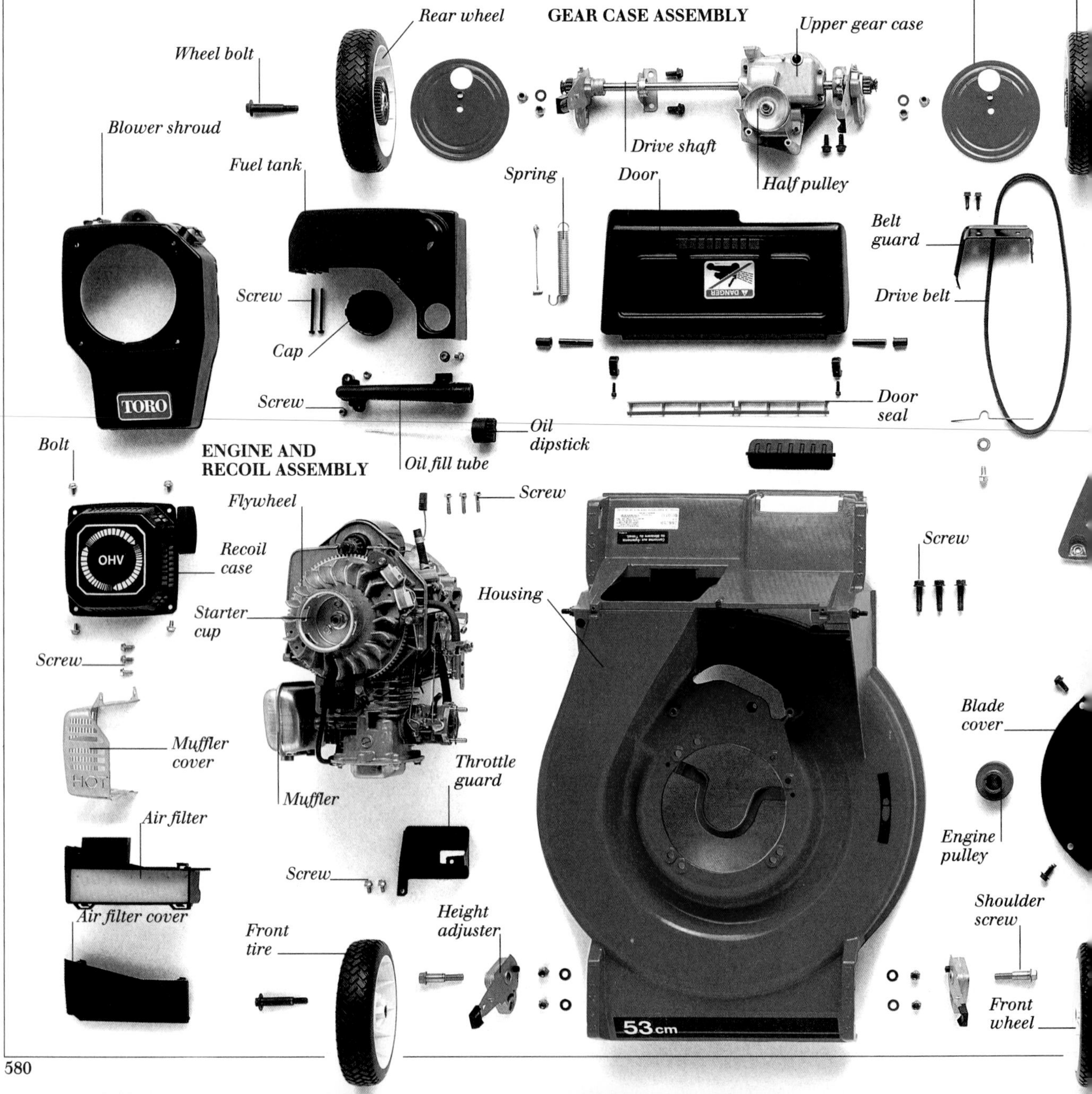

Rear tire

Wheel cover

Rear wheel

GEAR CASE ASSEMBLY

Upper gear case

Wheel bolt

Blower shroud

Drive shaft

Fuel tank

Spring

Door

Half pulley

Belt guard

Screw

Drive belt

Cap

Screw

Door seal

Oil dipstick

Bolt

ENGINE AND RECOIL ASSEMBLY

Oil fill tube

TORO

Screw

Flywheel

Screw

Screw

Recoil case

Housing

Starter cup

Screw

Blade cover

Muffler cover

Throttle guard

Engine pulley

Air filter

Muffler

Screw

Air filter cover

Screw

Shoulder screw

Front tire

Height adjuster

Front wheel

53cm

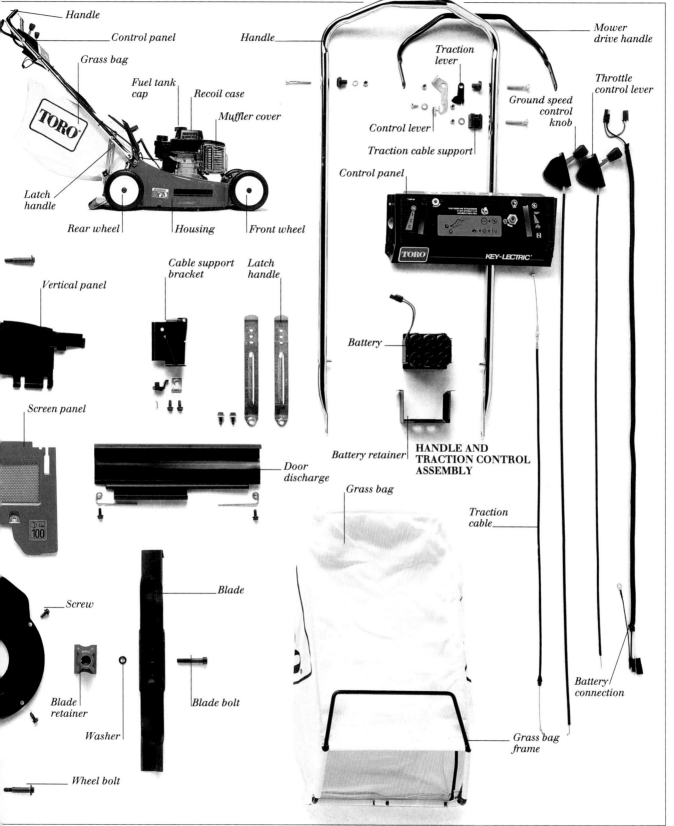

Handle

Control panel

Grass bag

Fuel tank cap

Recoil case

Muffler cover

Latch handle

Rear wheel

Housing

Front wheel

Handle

Traction lever

Mower drive handle

Control lever

Traction cable support

Throttle control lever

Ground speed control knob

Control panel

Battery

Battery retainer

HANDLE AND TRACTION CONTROL ASSEMBLY

Vertical panel

Cable support bracket

Latch handle

Screen panel

Door discharge

Grass bag

Traction cable

Screw

Blade

Blade retainer

Washer

Blade bolt

Battery connection

Wheel bolt

Grass bag frame

Saddle

THE FIRST HORSEBACK RIDERS HAD NO SADDLES; they sat bareback, clinging to the animal's mane. Next came a simple cloth saddle. The leather saddle, which was invented about 2,000 years ago by the warriors of the Asian steppes, revolutionized horseback riding. On this saddle, horsemen could gallop toward the enemy, fire arrows in all directions, and stay on their horses. Modern saddles are of two main types. The Western saddle is a heavy, working saddle used mainly by ranch hands in the United States. It has a metal horn at the front for securing a lasso and a high cantle at the back to keep the rider on the horse. The English saddle is much lighter. Designed for sport, it allows the horse to gallop fast. Its drawback is that it provides less stability; to stay on the horse, the rider must grip the animal with the knees.

ENGLISH SADDLE

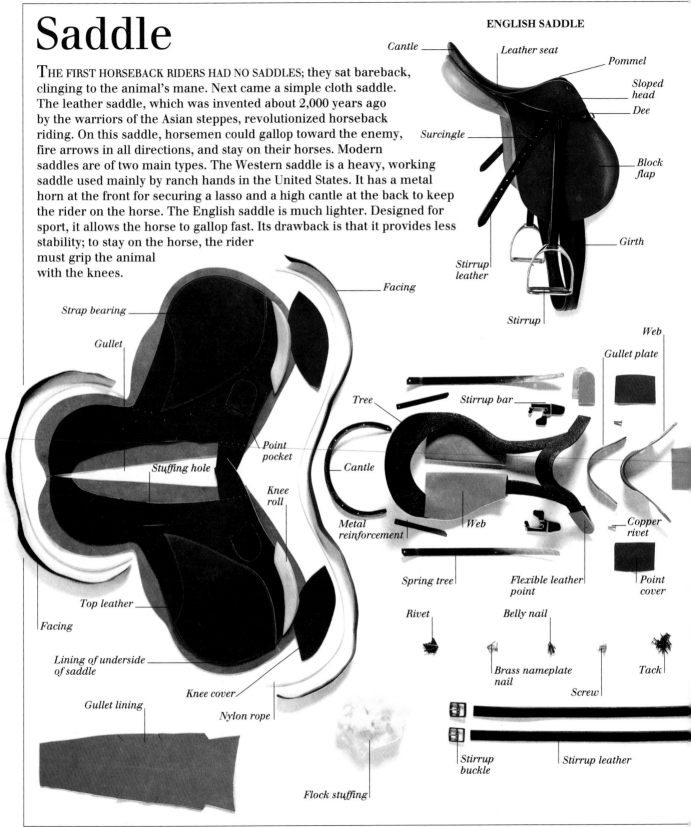

Cantle

Leather seat

Pommel

Sloped head

Dee

Surcingle

Block flap

Girth

Stirrup leather

Stirrup

Facing

Strap bearing

Gullet

Web

Gullet plate

Tree

Stirrup bar

Point pocket

Stuffing hole

Cantle

Knee roll

Metal reinforcement

Web

Copper rivet

Top leather

Spring tree

Flexible leather point

Point cover

Facing

Lining of underside of saddle

Rivet

Belly nail

Knee cover

Brass nameplate nail

Screw

Tack

Gullet lining

Nylon rope

Stirrup buckle

Stirrup leather

Flock stuffing

SHAPED GIRTH

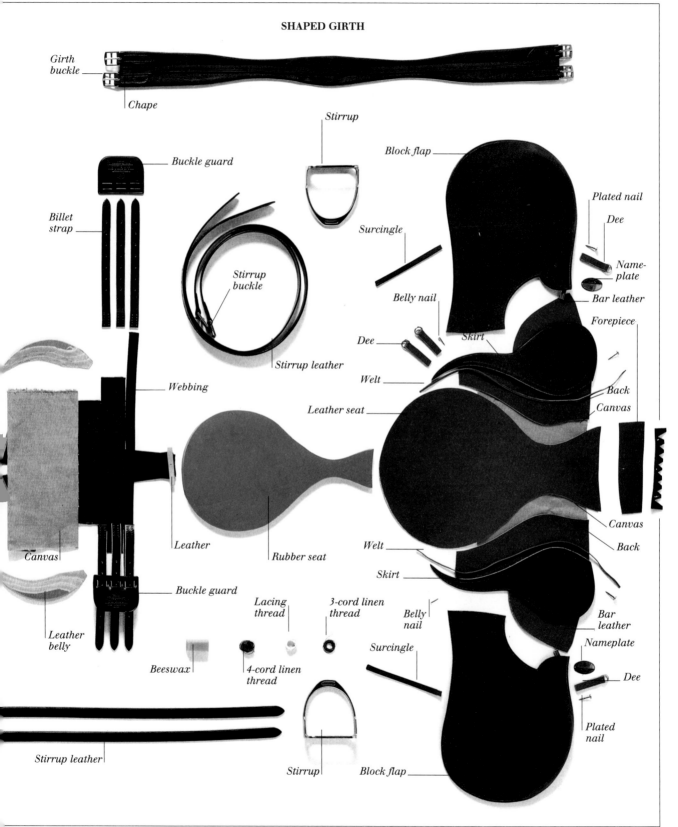

Girth buckle

Chape

Stirrup

Block flap

Buckle guard

Plated nail

Dee

Billet strap

Surcingle

Name-plate

Stirrup buckle

Belly nail

Bar leather

Dee

Forepiece

Skirt

Webbing

Welt

Back

Canvas

Leather seat

Leather

Canvas

Rubber seat

Back

Canvas

Welt

Buckle guard

Skirt

Leather belly

Lacing thread

3-cord linen thread

Belly nail

Bar leather

Beeswax

4-cord linen thread

Surcingle

Nameplate

Dee

Stirrup leather

Stirrup

Block flap

Plated nail

CD-ROM

A CD-ROM IS A TYPE OF COMPACT DISC (CD) that can be used to produce images on a computer screen. ROM stands for Read Only Memory, which means that the digitally recorded data registered in pits on the surface of the disc is fixed and cannot be altered or replaced. The CD is loaded into the CD-ROM player, where the data on the spinning disc is read by a laser. CD-ROMs are different from vinyl records in that they are not read along a spiral groove, from outer circumference to inner edge: instead each image or piece of information has a coordinate on the disc, which is located by the laser. Information picked up by the laser is relayed to the computer, where it is translated into the text and images that appear on screen. The information is relayed through a SCSI (Small Computer System Interface), which processes the electronic impulses between the disc drive and the computer system. The user can move around the program by clicking on different parts of the screen with a mouse (a hand-held tool with a clicking button whose movement on its pad is mimicked by an icon on the screen). The image in the viewing area (see opposite) can be changed by clicking on the active scrolling button: this moves a rectangular panel down the scrolling figure in the navigational panel. Clicking on active text will provide a new screen with more information, either in the form of text and diagrams, or as narrated animated sequences.

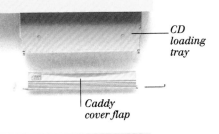

CD-ROM drive

CD loading tray

Caddy cover flap

Front bezel

Push button

CD-ROM CASING

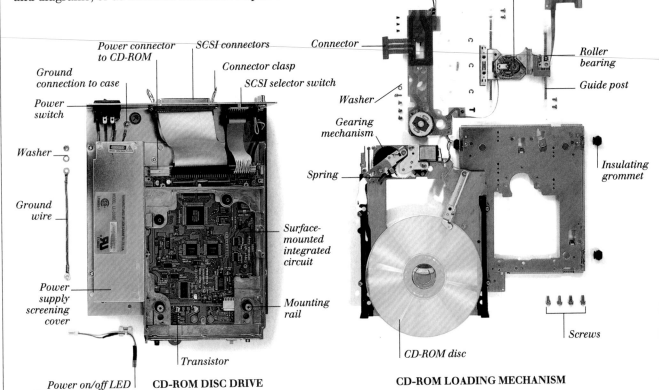

Power connector to CD-ROM

SCSI connectors

Connector clasp

SCSI selector switch

Ground connection to case

Power switch

Washer

Ground wire

Power supply screening cover

Surface-mounted integrated circuit

Mounting rail

Transistor

Power on/off LED (Light Emitting Diode)

CD-ROM DISC DRIVE

CD-ROM drive motor

Connector

Washer

Gearing mechanism

Spring

Laser

Film strip connector

Roller bearing

Guide post

Insulating grommet

Screws

CD-ROM disc

CD-ROM LOADING MECHANISM

CONTENTS PAGE

THE ULTIMATE HUMAN BODY

BODY MACHINE	BODY ORGANS	BODY SYSTEMS

Disc

External speaker

Keyboard

Display monitor

Dorling Kindersley
MULTIMEDIA

Mouse

CD-ROM PLAYER

COMPUTER HARDWARE

Mouse pad

**SCREEN FROM A
CD-ROM PROGRAM**

Navigational panel

Help button

Index button

Back button

Pronunciation button on/off

Options button

Navigational figures

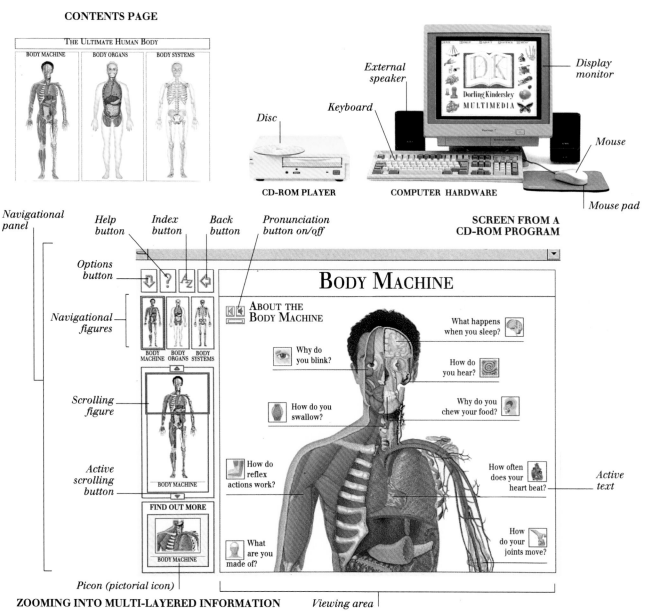

BODY MACHINE | BODY ORGANS | BODY SYSTEMS

BODY MACHINE

ABOUT THE
BODY MACHINE

Why do you blink?

What happens when you sleep?

How do you hear?

How do you swallow?

Why do you chew your food?

Scrolling figure

BODY MACHINE

How do reflex actions work?

How often does your heart beat?

Active text

Active scrolling button

FIND OUT MORE

BODY MACHINE

What are you made of?

How do your joints move?

Picon (pictorial icon)

ZOOMING INTO MULTI-LAYERED INFORMATION

Viewing area

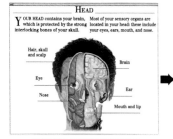

HEAD

YOUR HEAD contains your brain, which is protected by the strong interlocking bones of your skull. Most of your sensory organs are located in your head: these include your eyes, ears, mouth, and nose.

Hair, skull and scalp

Brain

Eye

Ear

Nose

Mouth and lip

**INITIAL SCREEN UNDER
BODY ORGANS MENU**

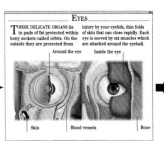

EYES

THESE DELICATE ORGANS lie in pads of fat protected within bony sockets called orbits. On the outside they are protected from injury by your eyelids, thin folds of skin that can close rapidly. Each eye is moved by six muscles which are attached around the eyeball.

Around the eye

Inside the eye

Skin

Blood vessels

Bone

**CLICKING ON "EYES" LABEL
PRODUCES MORE INFORMATION**

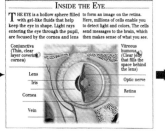

INSIDE THE EYE

THE EYE is a hollow sphere filled with gel-like fluids that help keep the eye in shape. Light rays entering the eye through the pupil, are focused by the cornea and lens to form an image on the retina. Here, millions of cells enable you to detect light and colors, The cells send messages to the brain, which then makes sense of what you see.

Conjunctiva (Thin, clear layer covering cornea)

Vitreous humous (Clear jelly that fills the space behind the lens)

Lens

Optic nerve

Iris

Retina

Cornea

Vein

**EACH LABEL PRODUCES A
FURTHER SCREEN**

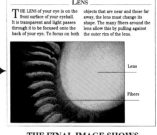

LENS

THE LENS of your eye is on the front surface of your eyeball. It is transparent and light passes through it to be focused onto the back of your eye. To focus on both objects that are near and those far away, the lens must change its shape. The many fibers around the lens allow this by pulling against the outer rim of the lens.

Lens

Fibers

**THE FINAL IMAGE SHOWS
MICROSCOPIC DETAIL**

Books

THOUGH THE PROCESS OF BOOKBINDING today is usually mechanized, some books are still bound by hand. The pages of a book are printed on large sheets of paper called sections, or signatures. When folded, sections usually make 8, 16, or 32 pages. To assemble a hand-bound hardback book, the binder first places the folded sections in the correct order within the endpapers. Next, he or she sews the sections together along the spine edge using strong thread and then pastes them with glue for extra strength. After trimming the pages, the binder puts the book in a press and hammers the spine to shape it. The binder then glues one or more linings on the spine. The cover, or case, comes last. To make this, the bookbinder sticks cover boards to the endpapers, front and back, and then covers them with cloth or leather.

HALF-BOUND BOOK

Corner piece
Spine
Fore edge
Tail
Marbleized paper

LEATHER-BOUND BOOK

Joint
Leather cover
Rib
Spine
Tail
Ribbon
Gold tooling

HALF-BOUND BOOK

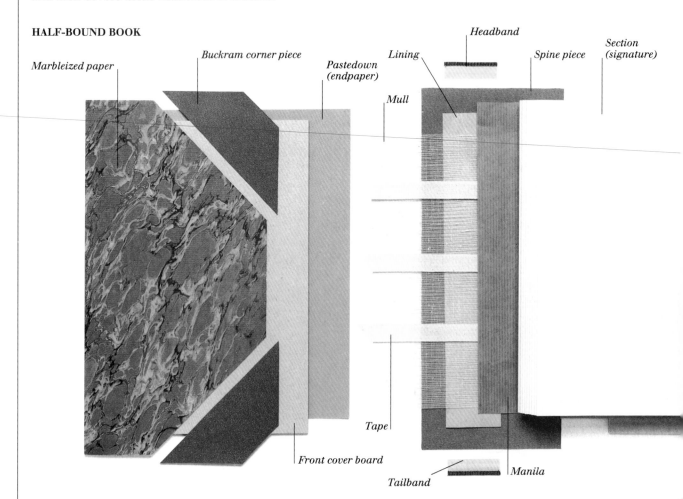

Marbleized paper
Buckram corner piece
Pastedown (endpaper)
Mull
Lining
Headband
Spine piece
Section (signature)
Tape
Front cover board
Tailband
Manila

LEATHER-BOUND BOOK

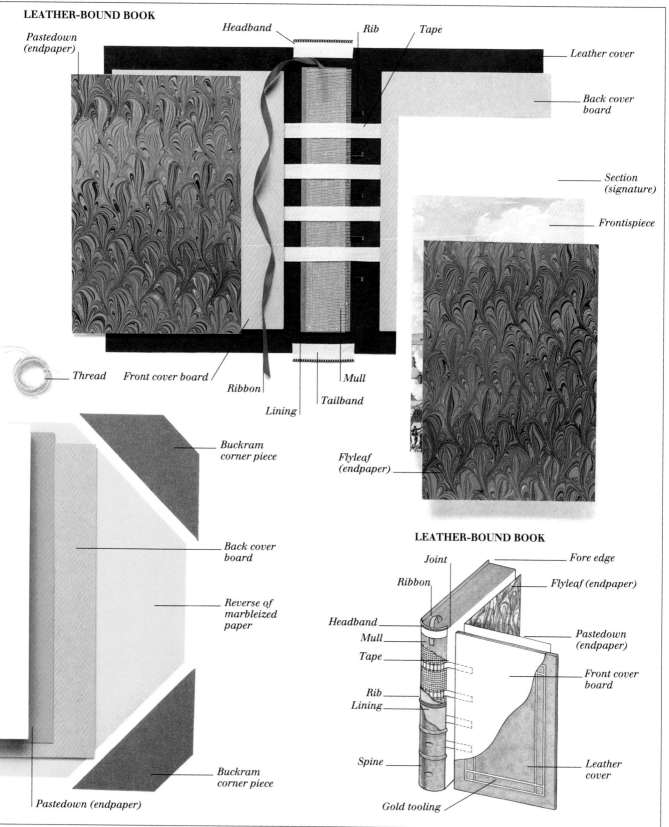

Pastedown (endpaper)

Headband

Rib

Tape

Leather cover

Back cover board

Section (signature)

Frontispiece

Thread

Front cover board

Ribbon

Lining

Mull

Tailband

Flyleaf (endpaper)

Buckram corner piece

Back cover board

Reverse of marbleized paper

Pastedown (endpaper)

LEATHER-BOUND BOOK

Joint

Ribbon

Headband

Mull

Tape

Rib

Lining

Spine

Fore edge

Flyleaf (endpaper)

Pastedown (endpaper)

Front cover board

Leather cover

Gold tooling

Buckram corner piece

Camera

A CAMERA IS AN INSTRUMENT used for recording images on photographic film. It consists of a light-tight box with a shutter, a lens containing a diaphragm, and a viewing system. When the shutter is released, the film is exposed to light from the subject that is being photographed. Adjusting the shutter speed alters the time for which the film is exposed to light. The diaphragm, by altering the aperture of the lens, controls the intensity of light entering the camera. The total amount of light entering the camera is called the exposure. The lens focuses the light onto the film. When there is insufficient light to produce an adequate image, a flashgun may be used to give extra light.

FRONT VIEW OF CAMERA

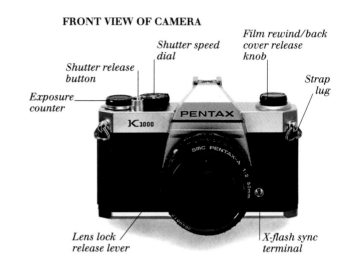

Shutter release button
Shutter speed dial
Film rewind/back cover release knob
Strap lug
Exposure counter
Lens lock release lever
X-flash sync terminal

FRONT BOARD ASSEMBLY

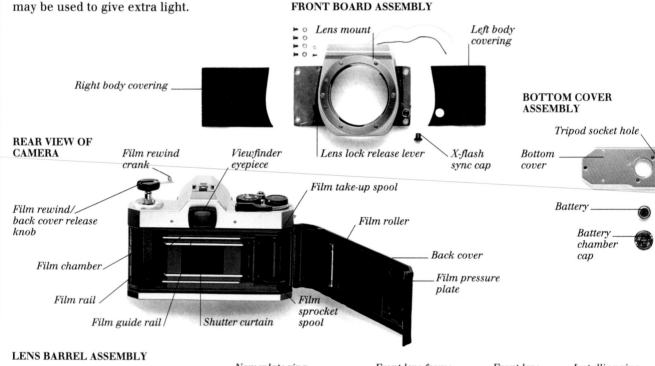

Lens mount
Left body covering
Right body covering
Lens lock release lever
X-flash sync cap

BOTTOM COVER ASSEMBLY

Tripod socket hole
Bottom cover
Battery
Battery chamber cap

REAR VIEW OF CAMERA

Film rewind crank
Viewfinder eyepiece
Film take-up spool
Film rewind/back cover release knob
Film roller
Film chamber
Back cover
Film rail
Film pressure plate
Film guide rail
Film sprocket spool
Shutter curtain

LENS BARREL ASSEMBLY

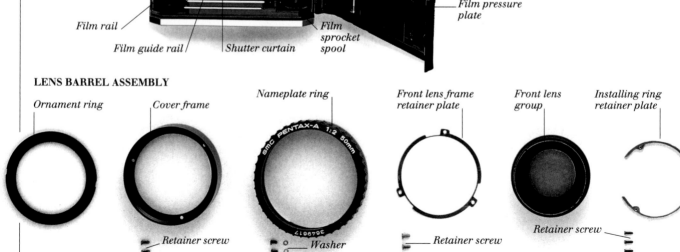

Ornament ring
Cover frame
Nameplate ring
Front lens frame retainer plate
Front lens group
Installing ring retainer plate
Retainer screw
Washer
Retainer screw
Retainer screw
Retainer screw

TOP COVER ASSEMBLY

Counter dial cover · *Exposure counter dial* · *Counter dial housing* · *Wind lever install spring* · *Film wind lever* · *Wind lever collar* · *Shutter dial knob spring* · *Speed dial knob* · *Film speed indicator* · *Shutter speed dial* · *Retainer screw* · *Top cover* · *X-contact* · *Hot shoe* · *Rewind shaft* · *Film rewind/ back cover release knob*

Retainer screw · *Washer* · *Window* · *Prism retainer spring* · *Prism retainer plate* · *Shutter release button* · *Shutter speed index* · *Pentaprism* · *Cover frame* · *Retainer screw* · *Rewind shaft bushing* · *Film rewind crank*

MAIN BODY

Strap lug · *Viewfinder eyepiece* · *Hole for film rewind button* · *Retainer screw*

TOP VIEW OF CAMERA

Focusing ring · *Aperture/distance index* · *Subject distance scale* · *Depth-of-field guide* · *Lens alignment node* · *Aperture auto-lock button* · *Lens lock release lever* · *Shutter release button* · *Shutter cocked indicator* · *Exposure counter* · *Film rewind crank* · *Film rewind/back cover release knob* · *Hot shoe* · *X-contact* · *Shutter speed index* · *Film speed indicator* · *Shutter speed dial* · *Film wind lever*

Supporter ring retainer plate · *Supporter ring* · *Diaphragm blade* · *Installing ring* · *Main barrel assembly* · *Rear lens group* · *Opening and closing plate*

589

Appendix: useful data

UNITS OF MEASUREMENT

U.S. unit	Equivalent
Length	
1 foot (ft)	12 inches (in)
1 yard (yd)	3 feet
1 rod (rd)	5.5 yards
1 mile (mi)	1,760 yards
Mass	
1 dram (dr)	27.344 grains (gr)
1 ounce (oz)	16 drams
1 pound (lb)	16 ounces
1 hundredweight (cwt) (long)	112 pounds
1 hundredweight (cwt) (short)	100 pounds
1 ton (long)	2,240 pounds
1 ton (short)	2,000 pounds
Area	
1 square foot (ft²)	144 square inches (in²)
1 square yard (yd²)	9 square feet
1 acre	4,840 square yards
1 square mile	640 acres
Volume	
1 cubic foot	1,728 cubic inches
1 cubic yard	27 cubic feet
Capacity (liquid and dry measures)	
1 fluidram (fl dr)	60 minims (min)
1 fluid ounce (fl oz)	8 fluidrams
1 gill (gi)	4 fluid ounces
1 pint (pt)	4 gills
1 quart (qt)	2 pints
1 gallon (gal)	4 quarts
1 peck (pk)	2 gallons
1 bushel (bu)	4 pecks

Metric unit	Equivalent
Length	
1 centimeter (cm)	10 millimeters (mm)
1 meter (m)	100 centimeters
1 kilometer (km)	1,000 meters
Mass	
1 kilogram (kg)	1,000 grams (g)
1 tonne (t)	1,000 kilograms
Area	
1 square centimeter (cm²)	100 square millimeters (mm²)
1 square meter (m²)	10,000 square centimeters
1 hectare	10,000 square meters
1 square kilometer (km²)	1,000,000 square meters
Volume	
1 cubic centimeter (cc)	1 milliliter (ml)
1 liter (l)	1,000 milliliters
1 cubic meter (m³)	1,000 liters
Capacity (liquid and dry measures)	
1 centiliter (cl)	10 milliliters (ml)
1 deciliter (dl)	10 centiliters
1 liter (l)	10 deciliters
1 decaliter (dal)	10 liters
1 hectoliter (hi)	10 decaliters
1 kiloliter (kl)	10 hectoliters

TEMPERATURE SCALES

To convert from Celsius (C) to Fahrenheit (F): $F = (C \times 9 \div 5) + 32$
To convert from Fahrenheit to Celsius: $C = (F - 32) \times 5 \div 9$
To convert from Celsius to Kelvin (K): $K = C + 273$
To convert from Kelvin to Celsius: $C = K - 273$

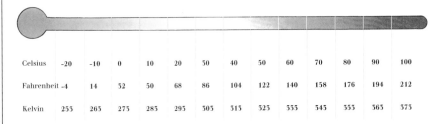

Celsius	-20	-10	0	10	20	30	40	50	60	70	80	90	100
Fahrenheit	-4	14	32	50	68	86	104	122	140	158	176	194	212
Kelvin	255	263	273	283	293	303	313	323	333	343	353	363	373

AREAS AND VOLUMES

CIRCLE
Circumference = $2 \times \pi \times r$
Area = $\pi \times r^2$
($\pi = 3.1416$)

Radius r
Diameter
$d = 2 \times r$

TRIANGLE
Perimeter = $a + b + c$
Area = $\frac{1}{2} \times b \times h$

Height h
Sides a, b, c

RECTANGLE
Perimeter = $2 \times (a + b)$
Area = $a \times b$

Sides a, b

CYLINDER
Surface area = $2 \times \pi \times r \times h$
(excluding ends)
Volume = $\pi \times r^2 \times h$

Height h
Radius r

CONE
Surface area = $\pi \times r \times l$ (excluding base)
Volume = $\frac{1}{3} \times \pi \times r^2 \times l$

Height h
Radius r
Side l

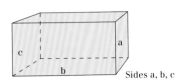

RECTANGULAR BLOCK
Surface area = $2 \times (a \times b + b \times c + a \times c)$
Volume = $a \times b \times c$

Sides a, b, c

U.S. – METRIC CONVERSIONS

To convert	Into	Multiply by
Length		
Inches	centimeters	2.5400
Feet	meters	0.3048
Miles	kilometers	1.6090
Yards	meters	0.9144
Mass		
Ounces	grams	28.3500
Pounds	kilograms	0.4536
Long tons	tonnes	1.0160
Short tons	tonnes	0.9070
Area		
Square inches	square centimeters	6.4520
Square feet	square meters	0.0929
Acres	hectares	0.4047
Square miles	square kilometers	2.5900
Square yards	square meters	0.8361
Volume		
Cubic inches	cubic centimeters	16.3900
Cubic feet	cubic meters	0.0283
Capacity		
Pints (liquid)	liters	0.4730
Gallons (liquid)	liters	3.7850

METRIC – U.S. CONVERSIONS

To convert	Into	Multiply by
Length		
Centimeters	inches	0.3937
Meters	feet	3.2810
Kilometers	miles	0.6214
Meters	yards	1.0940
Mass		
Grams	ounces	0.0352
Kilograms	pounds	2.2050
Tonnes	long tons	0.9843
Tonnes	short tons	1.1025
Area		
Square centimeters	square inches	0.1550
Square meters	square feet	10.7600
Hectares	acres	2.4710
Square kilometers	square miles	0.3861
Square meters	square yards	1.1960
Volume		
Cubic centimeters	cubic inches	0.0610
Cubic meters	cubic feet	35.3100
Capacity		
Liters	pints (liquid)	2.1142
Liters	gallons (liquid)	0.2642

NUMBER SYSTEMS

Roman	Arabic
I	1
II	2
III	3
IV	4
V	5
VI	6
VII	7
VIII	8
IX	9
X	10
XI	11
XII	12
XIII	13
XIV	14
XV	15
XX	20
XXI	21
XXX	30
XL	40
L	50
LX	60
LXX	70
LXXX	80
XC	90
C	100
CI	101
CC	200
CCC	300
CD	400
D	500
DC	600
DCC	700
DCCC	800
CM	900
M	1,000
MM	2,000

PHYSICS SYMBOLS

Symbol	Meaning
α	alpha particle
β	beta ray
γ	gamma ray; photon
ϵ	electromotive force
η	efficiency; viscosity
λ	wavelength
μ	micro-; permeability
ν	frequency; neutrino
ρ	density; resistivity
σ	conductivity
c	velocity of light
e	electronic charge

MATHEMATICS SYMBOLS

Symbol	Meaning
$+$	plus
$-$	minus
$\pm$	plus-or-minus
$\times$	multiplied by
$\div$	divided by
$=$	equals
$>$	is greater than
$<$	is less than
$\geq$	is greater than or equal to
$\leq$	is less than or equal to
$\%$	per cent
$\sqrt{}$	root
π	pi (3.1416)
$\circ$	degree
∞	infinity
$\approx$	is approximately equal to
$\angle$	angle

CHEMISTRY SYMBOLS

Symbol	Meaning
$+$	plus; together with
$-$	single bond
$\cdot$	single bond; single unpaired electron; two separate parts or compounds regarded as loosely joined
$=$	double bond
$\equiv$	triple bond
R	group
X	halogen atom
Z	atomic number

BIOLOGY SYMBOLS

Symbol	Meaning
$\circ$	female individual (used in inheritance charts)
$\square$	male individual (used in inheritance charts)
$\female$	female
$\male$	male
$\times$	crossed with; hybrid
$+$	wild type
F_1	offspring of the first generation
F_2	offspring of the second generation

POWERS OF TEN USED WITH SCIENTIFIC UNITS

Factor	Name	Prefix	Symbol
10^{18}	quintillion	exa-	E
10^{15}	quadrillion	peta-	P
10^{12}	trillion	tera-	T
10^{9}	billion	giga-	G
10^{6}	million	mega-	M
10^{3}	thousand	kilo-	k
10^{2}	hundred	hecto-	h
10^{1}	ten	deca-	da
10^{-1}	one tenth	deci-	d
10^{-2}	one hundredth	centi-	c
10^{-3}	one thousandth	milli-	m
10^{-6}	one millionth	micro-	μ
10^{-9}	one billionth	nano-	n
10^{-12}	one trillionth	pico-	p
10^{-15}	one quadrillionth	femto-	f
10^{-18}	one quintillionth	atto-	a

Index

602

632

Acknowledgments

Dorling Kindersley would like to thank (in order of sections):

**The Universe
(consultant editors – Sue Becklake, Gevorkyan Tatyana Alekseyevna):**
John Becklake; the Memorial Museum of Cosmonautics, Moscow; The Cosmos Pavilion, Moscow; The United States Space and Rocket Center, Alabama; Broadhurst, Clarkson and Fuller Ltd; Susannah Massey

**Prehistoric Earth
(consultant editors – William Lindsay, Martyn Bramwell, Dr. Ralph E. Molnar, David Lambert):**
Dr. Monty Reid, Andrew Neuman, and the staff of the Royal Tyrrell Museum of Palaeontology, Drumheller, Alberta; Dr. Angela Milner and the staff of the Department of Palaeontology, the Natural History Museum, London; Professor W. Ziegler and the staff, in particular Michael Loderstaedt, of the Naturmuseum Senckenburg, Frankfurt; Dr. Alexander Liebau, Axel Hunghrebüller, Reiner Schoch, and the staff of the Institut und Museum für Geologie und Paläontologie der Universität, Tübingen; Rupert Wild of the Institut für Paläontologie, Staatliches Museum für Naturkunde, Stuttgart; Dr. Scheiber of the Stadtmuseum, Nördlingen; Professor Dr. Dietrich Herm of Staatssammlung für Paläontologie und Historische Geologie, München; Dr. Michael Keith-Lucas of the Department of Botany, University of Reading; Richard Walker; American Museum of Natural History, New York

**Plants
(consultant editor – Richard Walker):**
Diana Miller; Lawrie Springate; Karen Sidwell; Chris Thody; Michelle End; Susan Barnes and Chris Jones of the EMU Unit of the Natural History Museum, London; Jenny Evans of Kew Gardens, London; Kate Biggs of the Royal Horticultural Society Gardens, Wisley, Surrey; Spike Walker of Microworld Services; Neil Fletcher; John Bryant of Bedgebury Pinetum, Kent; Dean Franklin

**Animals
(consultant editor – Richard Walker):**
David Manning's Animal Ark; Intellectual Animals; Howletts Zoo, Canterbury; John Dunlop; Alexander O'Donnell; Sue Evans of the Royal Veterinary College, London; Dr. Geoff Potts and Fred Frettsome of the Marine Biological Association of the United Kingdom, Plymouth; Jeremy Adams of the Booth Museum of Natural History, Brighton; Derek Telling of the Department of Anatomy, University of Bristol; the Natural History Museum, London; Andy Highfield of the Tortoise Trust; Brian Harris of the Aquarium, London Zoo; the Invertebrate Department, London Zoo; Dr. Harold McClure of the Yerkes Regional Primate Research Center, Emory University, Atlanta, Georgia; Nielson Lausen of the Harvard Medical School, New England Regional Primates Research Center, Southborough, Massachusetts; Dr. Paul Hopwood of the Department of Veterinary Anatomy, University of Sydney; Dean Franklin

**The Human Body
(consultant editors – Dr. Frances Williams, Dr. Fiona Payne, Richard Cummins FRCS):**
Derek Edwards and Dr Martin Collins, British School of Osteopathy; Dr. M.C.E. Hutchinson of the Department of Anatomy, United Medical and Dental Schools of Guy's and St. Thomas' Hospitals, London. Models – Barry O'Rorke (Bodyline Agency) and Pauline Swaine (MOT Model Agency)

**Geology, Geography, and Meteorology
(consultant editor – Martyn Bramwell):**
Dr. John Nudds of the Manchester Museum, Manchester; Dr. Alan Wooley and Dr. Andrew Clark of the Natural History Museum, London; Graham Bartlett of the National Meteorological Library and Archive, Bracknell; Tony Drake of BP Exploration, Uxbridge; Jane Davies of the Royal Society of Chemistry, Cambridge; Dr. Tony Waltham of Nottingham Trent University, Nottingham; staff of the Smithsonian Institute, Washington; staff of the United States Geological Survey, Washington; staff of the National Geographic Society, Washington; staff of Edward Lawrence Associates (Export Ltd), Midhurst; John Farndon; David Lambert

**Rail and Road
Rail (consultant editor – John Coiley)**
Michael Ashworth of the London Transport Museum

***Road* (consultant editors – David Burgess-Wise, Hugo Wilson)**
The National Motor Museum, Beaulieu; Alf Newell of Renault UK Ltd; David Suter of Cheltenham Cutaway Exhibits Ltd; Francesca Riccini of the Science Museum, London. Signore Amadelli of the Museo dell' Automobile Carlo Biscaretti di Ruffia; Paul Bolton of the Mazda MCL Group; Duncan Bradford of Reg Mills Wire Wheels; John and Leslie Brewster of Autocavan; David Burgess-Wise; Trevor Cass of Garrett Turbo Service; John Corbett of The Patrick Collection; Gary Crumpler of Williams Grand Prix Engineering Ltd; Mollie Easterbrooke and Duncan Gough of Overland Ltd; Arthur Fairley of the Vauxhall Motor Co; Paul Foulkes-Halbard of Filching Manor Motor Museum; Frank Gilbert of I. Wilkinson and Son Ltd; Paolo Gratton of Gratton Museum; Colvin Gunn of Gunn and Son; Judy Hogg of Ecurie Bertelli; Milton Holman of Dream Cars; Ian Matthews of IMAT Electronics; Eric Neal of Jaguar Cars Ltd; Paul Niblett, Keith Davidson, Mark Reumel, and David Woolf of Michelin Tyre plc; Doug Nye; Kevin O'Keefe of O'Keefe Cars; Seat UK; Roger Smith; Jim Stirling of Ironbridge Gorge Museum, Staffordshire; Jon Taylor; Doug Thompson; Martyn Watkins of Ford Motor Co Ltd; John Cattermole, Customer Services Manager, at London Northern Buses; F. W. Evans Cycles Ltd; Trek UK Ltd (Bicycle); Sam Grimmer

**Physics and Chemistry
(consultant editor – Jack Challoner)**

**Sea and Air
Sea (consultant editors – Geoff Hales and Harvey B. Loomis):**
David Spence, Gillian Hutchinson, David Topliss, Simon Stephens, Robert Baldwin, Jonathan Betts, all of the National Maritime Museum, London; Ian Friel; Simon Turnage of Captain O.M. Watts of London Ltd; Davey and Co Ltd, Great Dunmow; Avon Inflatables Ltd, Llanelli; Musto Ltd, Benfleet; Peter Martin of Spencer Rigging Ltd, Southampton; Peter Rowson of Ratseys Sailmakers, Southampton; Swiftech Ltd, Wallingford; Colin Scattergood of the Barrow Boat Co Ltd, Colchester; Professor J.S. Morrison of the Trireme Trust, Cambridge; The Cutty Sark Maritime Trust; Adrian Daniels of Kelvin Hughes Marine Instruments, London; Arthur Credland of Hull City Council Museums and Art Galleries; The Hull Maritime Society; Gerald Clark; Peter Fitzgerald of the Science Museum, London; Alec Michael of HMB Subwork Ltd, Great Yarmouth, and Ray Ward of the OSEL Group, Great Yarmouth; Richard Bird of UWI, Weybridge; Walker Marine Instruments, Birmingham; The International Sailing Craft Association; The Exeter Maritime Museum; Jane Wilson of the Trinity Lighthouse Co, London; The Imperial War Museum Collections; Thorn Security Ltd; Michael Bach

***Air* (consultant editor – Bill Gunston):**
Aeromega Helicopters, Stapleford; Aero Shopping, London; Avionics Mobile Services Ltd, Watford; Roy Barber and John Chapman of the RAF Museum, Hendon; Mitch Barnes Aviation, London; Mike Beach; British Caledonian Flight Training Ltd; Fred Coates of Helitech (Luton) Ltd; Michael Cuttell and CSE Aviation Ltd, Oxford; Dowty Aerospace Landing Gear, Gloucester; Guy Hartcup of the Airship Association; Anthony Hooley, Chris Walsh, and David Cord of British Aerospace Regional Aircraft Ltd; Ken Huntley of Mid-West Aero Engines Ltd; Imperial War Museum, Duxford; The London Gliding Club, Dunstable; Musée des Ballons, Calvados; Noel Penny Turbines Ltd; Andy Pavey of Aviation Scotland Ltd; Tony Pavey of Thermal Aircraft Developments, London; the Commanding Officer and personnel of RAF St Athan; the Commanding Officer and personnel of RAF Wittering; The Science Museum, London; Ross Sharp of the Science Museum, Wroughton; The Shuttleworth Collection; Skysport Engineering; Mike Smith; Solar Wings Ltd, Marlborough; Julian Temple of Brooklands Museum Trust Ltd; Kelvin Wilson of Flying Start

**Architecture
(consultant editor – Alexandra Kennedy):**
Stephen Cutler for advice and text; Gavin Morgan of the Museum of London, London; Chris Zeuner of the Weald and Downland Museum, Singleton, Sussex; Alan Hills and James Putnam of the British Museum, London; Dr. Simon Penn and Michael Thomas of the Avoncroft Museum of Buildings, Bromsgrove,

Worcestershire; Christina Scull of Sir John Soane's Museum, London; Paul Kennedy and John Williamson of the London Door Co, London; Lou Davis of The Original Box Sash Window Co, Windsor; Goddard and Gibbs Studios Ltd, London, for access to stained glass windows; The Royal Courts of Justice, Strand, London; Charles Brooking and Peter Dalton for access to the doors and windows in the Charles Brooking Collection, University of Greenwich, Dartford, Kent; Clare O'Brien of the Shakespeare Globe Trust, Shakespeare's Globe Museum, Bear Gardens, Southwark, London; Ken Teague of the Horniman Museum, London; Canon Haliburton, Mike Payton, Ken Stones, and Anthony Webb of St. Paul's Cathedral, London; Roy Spring of Salisbury Cathedral; Reverend Gillean Craig of the Church of St. George in the East, London; the Science Museum, London; Dr. Neil Bingham; Lin Kennedy of Historic Royal Palaces; Katy Harris of Sir Norman Foster and Partners; Production Design, Thames Television plc, London, for supplying models; Dominique Reynier of Le Centre Georges Pompidou, Paris; Denis Roche of Le Musée National des Monuments Français, Paris; Franck Gioria and students of Les Compagnons du Devoir, Paris, for access to construction models; Frank Folliot of Le Musée Carnavalet, Paris; Dr Martina Harms of Hessische Landesmuseums, Darmstadt; Jefferson Chapman of the University of Tennessee, Knoxville, for access to the model of the Hypostyle Hall, Temple of Amon-Re; staff of the Palazzo Strozzi, Florence; staff of the Sydney Opera House, Sydney; staff of the Empire State Building, New York; Nick Jackson; Ann Terrell

The Visual Arts
(consultant editor – Pip Seymour):
Rosemary Simmons; Michael Taylor of Paupers Press, London; Tessa Hunkin and Emma Biggs of Mosaic Workshop, London; John Tiranti, Jonathan Lyons of Alec Tiranti Ltd, London; Chris Hough; Dr. Ashok Roy; Satwinder Sehmi of Alphabet Soup, London; Phillip Poole of Cornelissens, London; George Weil and Sons Ltd, London; The National Gallery, London; Chris Webster of the Tate Gallery, London; China Art Cultural Centre, London; London Graphic Centre, London; A.P. Fitzpatrick, London; Flowers Graphics, London; Intaglio Printmaker, London; Falkiner Papers, London; Edgar Udny and Co, London; John Green

Music
(consultant editor – Susan Sturrock):
Boosey and Hawkes Music Publishers Ltd, London, for permission to reproduce extract from The Prodigal Son by Arthur Sullivan; The Bass and Drum Cellar, London; Empire Drums and Percussion, London; Argents (part of World of Music), London; Bill Lewington Ltd, London; Frobenius organ at Kingston Parish Church, Kingston-upon-Thames, Surrey; Yamaha-Kemble Music (UK) Ltd, Tilbrook, Milton Keynes; Yamaha Atelier, London; Akai (UK) Ltd, Hounslow, Middlesex; Casio Electronics Co Ltd, London; Roland (UK) Ltd, Fleet, Hampshire; Richard Schulman

Sports
The Sports Council Information Centre, London; The British Olympic Games Committee; Brian Crennell of Black's Leisure Group (First Sport); Lillywhites of Piccadilly, London; Mitre Sports International Ltd, Huddersfield; David Bloomfield of the Football Association; Denver Athletics Ltd, Norfolk; Greg Everest and Keith Birley of the British League of Australian Rules Football; Peter McNally of the Gaelic Athletic Association; Rex King of the Rugby Football Union, Twickenham; Neil Tunnicliffe of the Rugby Football League, Leeds; Wayne Patterson of the Basketball Hall of Fame, Springfield, Connecticut; Brian Coleman of the English Basketball Association; All American Imports, Northampton; George Bulman of the English Volleyball Association; Julie Longdon of Mizuno Mallory (UK) Ltd; Juliet Stanford of the All-England Netball Association; Jeff Rowland of the British Handball Association; Cally Melin of Adidas UK Ltd; Patrick Donnely of the Baseball Hall of Fame, Cooperstown, New York; Ian Lepage and Stephen Barlow of the Hockey Association, Milton Keynes; Alison Taylor and Anita Mason of the All England Women's Lacrosse Association, Birmingham; David Shuttleworth of the English Lacrosse Union; Les Barnett and Jock Bentley of the British Athletic Federation Ltd, Birmingham; Mike Gilks of the Badminton Association of England; Gurinder Purewall for advice on archery; Chris McCartney of the US Archery Association; Geoff Doe of the National Smallbore Rifle Association, Bisley, Surrey, for information and reference material on shooting; Fagan Sports Goods Distributors, Surrey; Konrad Bartelski for advice on skiing; The British Ski Federation, Edinburgh; Mike Barnett of Snow and Rock of London; Sally Spurway of Mast-Co. Ltd, Reading; Sarah Morgan for advice on equestrian sports; Steve Brown and the New York Racing Association Inc, New York; Danrho of London; Alan Skipp and James Chambers of the Amateur Fencing Association, London; Carla Richards of the US Fencing Association; Hamilton Bland and John Dryer of the Amateur Swimming Association, Loughborough; Cotswold Camping Ltd, London; Tim Spalton of Glyn Locke (Racing Shells) Ltd, Chalgrove; Terry Friel of the US Rowing Association; House of Hardy; Leeda Fishing Tackle

Everyday Things
City Clocks (Clocks); Christopher Cullen of Babber Electronics; Sony UK Ltd (Mini-television); Black and Decker Ltd (Drills); British Footwear Manufacturing Federation; Grenson Shoes Ltd (Shoes); The Folio Society; R S Bookbinders (Books); Pentax UK Ltd (Camera); F E Murdin of the Decorative Lighting Association; Habitat (Lamp); Chingford Reproductions Ltd (Chair); Dualit Ltd (Toaster); J B Dove; Toro Wheelhorse UK Ltd (Lawnmower); WandH Gidden Ltd (Saddle)

PHOTOGRAPHY:
M. Alexander; Peter Anderson; Charles Brooks; Jane Burton; Peter Chadwick; Simon Clay; John Coiley; Andy Crawford; Geoff Dann; Philip Dowell; John Downs; Mike Dunning; Torla Evans; David Exton; Robert and Anthony Fretwell of Fretwell Photography Ltd.; Philip Gatward; Anna Hodgson; Gary Kevin; J. Heseltine; Cyril Laubscher; John Lepine; Lynton Gardiner (American Museum of Natural History, New York); Steve Gorton; Michelangelo Gratton; Judith Harrington; Peter Hayman; Anna Hodgson; Colin Keates; Gary Kevin; Dave King; Bob Langrish; Brian D.Morgan; Nick Nicholls; Nick Parfitt; Tim Parmenter and Colin Keates (Natural History Museum, London); Tim Ridley; Dave Rudkin; Philippe Sebert; James Stevenson; Clive Streeter; Harry Taylor; Matthew Ward; Jerry Young

PHOTOGRAPHIC ASSISTANCE:
Kevin Zak; Gary Ombler

ILLUSTRATORS:
Julian Baum; Rick Blakeley; Kuo Kang Chen; Karen Cochrane; Simone End; Ian Fleming; Roy Flooks; Mark Franklin; David Gardner; Will Giles; Mick Gillah; David Hopkins; Selwyn Hutchinson; Mei Lim; Linden Artists; Nick Loates; Chris Lyon; Kathleen McDougall; Coral Mula; Sandra Pond; Dave Pugh; Colin Rose; Graham Rosewarne; John Temperton; John Woodcock; Chris Woolmer

MODEL MAKERS:
Roby Braun; David Donkin; Morrison Frederick; Gordon Models; John Holmes; Graham High and Jeremy Hunt of Centaur Studios; Richard Kemp; Kelvin Thatcher; Paul Wilkinson

ADDITIONAL DESIGN ASSISTANCE:
Stefan Morris; Ulysses Santos; Suchada Smith

ADDITIONAL EDITORIAL ASSISTANCE:
Helen Castle; Colette Connolly; Camela Decaire; Nick Harris; Andrea Horth; Stewart McEwen; Damien Moore; Melanie Tham;

INDEX: Kay Wright

Picture credits:

Action Plus 530tc; Anglo Australian Telescope Board 11cl, 11cra, 11cbl, 12tr, 12bc, 13tl, 13bl, 14tl, 16b, 17tc, 17bl, 22tl/D.Malin 16tl, 26tr, 27tl; Austin Brown and the Aviation Picture Library 426tl; Baptistery, Florence/Alison Harris 453r; Biophoto Associates 217ca, 217cra, 228cbc, 228cbc 230tr; Paul Brierley 311bra; British Aerospace/Anthony Hooley 412tl, 415tl; British Aerospace (Commercial Aircraft) Ltd 416tl; by permission of the British Library 432tl; British Museum 459tl, 459tr, 460tr, 460tc, 460tb, 489b; BP Exploration 299; Duncan Brown 25tl; Frank Lloyd Wright, American, 1867-1959, Model of Midway Gardens, 1914, executed by Richard Tickner, mixed media, 1987, 41.9 x 81.3 x 76.2, 1989.48. view 1. Photography courtesy of the Art Intitute of Chicago 495t; J.A. Coiley 331cr; Bruce Coleman Ltd/Andy Price 272tl; Courtesy of the Board of Trustees of the Victoria and Albert Museum, London 454-455b; European Passenger Services 329tl; ESA /PLV 11bl; French Railways 329c; Geoscience Features 311cla; Robert Harding Picture Library 62tl; Michael Holford /British Museum 372bl, Michael Holford 374tr; Hutchison Picture Library 60cl; The Image Bank/Edward Bower 306tr; Jet Propulsion Laboratory 11cbr; 30bc; 31bc; 31bcr; 38tl; 42crb; 44cb; 44cbr; 44bc; 44br; 46tl; 46cr; 46cb; 46bc; 46br; 50tl; 50cra; 50cl; 50c; 50cr; 50br; KeyMed Ltd 248bl, 249bl, 249bcl; Department of Prints and Drawings, Uffizi, Florence/Philip Gatward 431tc/Uffizi, Florence/Philip Gatward 453tl; Dr. D.N. Landon (Institute of Neurology) 228bl,br; Life Science Images/Ron Boardman 244bl, 244br; The Lund Observatory 15bc; Brian Morrison 329tl, 329tr;

© The Henry Moore Foundation 455tl, 455tr; Musée d'Orsay, Paris/Philippe Sebert 437tc, 441tc; Musée du Louvre, Paris/Philippe Sebert 453tl, 453r; NASA/AUI 13tr; NASA/JPL 11 cbr, 11br, 30tl, 30bl, 30br, 30bc, 31bc, 31bcr, 31bl, 34cr, 38tl, 40tl, 40cr, 42cr, 44tl, 44cb, 44cbr, 44bc, 44br, 44cr, 46crb, 46tl, 46cr, 46cb, 46bc, 46br, 48tl, 48cra, 48bca, 48bc, 48br, 50tl, 50bc, 50bc, 50cbr, 50br, 50cr, 52cr; National Maritime Museum 373br, 392-393b; National Medical Slide Bank 217cr; Nature Photographers/Paul Sterry 286tl; Newage International 317bl; Oxford Scientific Films/Breck P. Kent 166tl; Planet Earth 274tr; Quadrant 326tr; Margaret Robinson 332tl, 453br; Giotto The Expulsion of the Merchants from the Temple Scala 435tc, 435bl, 435br; Science Photo Library 10bl, 13tr, 28tr, 214bcr, 214bl, 236tr/Michael Abbey 225tc/Agema Infrared Systems 318tl/AGFA 220tl/Biophoto Associates: 217crb/Dr. Jeremy Burgess/Science Photo Library 132tr; Dr. Jeremy Burgess 235bcl/CNRI 214tl, 214cl, 214c, 214cr, 214bl, 214clb, 214crb, 214blc, 214br, 217cb, 235bcr, 238tl, 249bcr, 253tr, 253cra, 256tl; Science Photo library /Earth Satellite Corporation 288cl, 293br/Dr. Brian Eyden 228cbr/Professor C. Ferlaud 245bl/Vaughan Fleming 311tl/Simon Fraser/U.S. Dept.of Energy 214bcl, 266tl/Eric Grave 217br/Hale Observatories 32br/Max Planck Institute for Radio Astronomy 15tl/Jan Hinsch 225tc/Jodrell Bank 11 tr, 13c /Manfred Kage 217c, 235br, 237br/Dr. William C. Keel 13br/Keith Kent 316tl/Russ Lappa 310bra/Astrid & Hans-Freider Michler 217tr/Dennis Milon 52bl/NASA 11cla, 12tl, 15tr, 30c, 31br, 32tl, 35tl, 36tl, 36cl, 36cr, 36bc, 42br, 42tr, 44tl 52tl, 291tr, 300tl/National Optical Astro Observatory 52tr/NIBSC 253crb/

Novosti Press Agency 42bc/Omikron 244bc/ David Parker 63bl, 304-305, 308br/Philippe Plailly 308tl, Roussel-UCLAF/CNRI 217tc/Rev Ronald Royer 32cr/Royal Observatory, Edinburgh/D Malin 11 tl, 11cr,12c, 16cl, 16cr, 17br/ David Scharf 235bl/Dr. Kaus Schiller 248bcl, 248bcr, 248br/Secchi-Lecaque/Roussel-UCLAF/CNRI 253br/H. Sochurek 214cb/ Stammers/Thompson 230tl/Sheila Terry 234tl/ US Department of Energy 310bc/US Geological Survey/Science Photo Library 8-9, 30bcr, 42tl, 42bl/Tom Van Sant/Geosphere Project, Santa Monica/Science Photo Library 273tr, 281tr, 296tr, 297tl/Dr. Christopher B. Williams/(Saint Marks Hospital)249br; Oxford Scientific Films/ Animals Animals/Breck P. Kent 167tl; Pratt & Whitney Canada 418-419b, 419t; Science Museum 306bl, 306bcl, 306 bcr, 324t, 326-327b, 330tr, 331ct, 331 cb; Sporting Pictures 524tl, 544cr; Tony Stone Worldwide 280tl; David Bomberg St. Pauls and River 1945/Dinora Davies-Rees/Tate Gallery 431bc; David Hockney A Bigger Splash 1967/ © David Hockney/Tate Gallery 443tc; J.M.W. Turner The Burning of the Houses of Parliament Tate Gallery 439tc; Vision 26tr, 27c; Jerry Young 306tl; Dr. Robert Youngson 241cr; Zefa 217bc/ Janicek 276tl/H. Sochurek 210tl, 250tl, 254tl,/ G. Steenmans 292tl

(t=top, b=bottom, a=above, l-left, r=right, c=center)

Every effort has been made to trace the copyright holders. Dorling Kindersley apologises for any unintentional omissions and would be pleased, in any such cases, to add an acknowledgment in future editions.

Some pages in this book previously appeared in the *Visual Dictionary* series published by Dorling Kindersley. Contributors to this series include:

Project Art Editors:
Duncan Brown, Ross George, Nicola Liddiard, Andrew Nash, Clare Shedden, Bryn Walls

Designers:
Lesley Betts, Paul Calver, Simone End, Ellen Woodward

Additional design assistance:
Sandra Archer, Christina Betts, Alexandra Brown, Nick Jackson, Susan Knight

Project Editors:
Fiona Courtney-Thompson, Paul Docherty, Tim Fraser, Stephanie Jackson, Mary Lindsay

Editorial Assistant:
Emily Hill

Additional editorial assistance:
Susan Bosanko, Edward Bunting, Candace Burch, Deirdre Clark, Jeanette Cossar, Danièle Guitton, Jacqui Hand, David Harding, Nicholas Jackson, Edwina Johnson, David Lambert, Gail Lawther, David Learmount, Paul Jackson, Christine Murdock, Bob Ogden, Cathy Rubinstein, Louise Tucker, Dr. Robert Youngson

Picture Researchers:
Vere Dodds, Danièle Guitton, Anna Lord, Catherine O'Rourke, Christine Rista, Sandra Schneider, Vanessa Smith, Clive Webster

Series Editor:
Martyn Page

Series Art Editor:
Paul Wilkinson

Managing Art Editors
Philip Gilderdale, Steve Knowlden

Art Director
Chez Picthall

Managing Editor
Ruth Midgley

Production:
Jayne Simpson